MECHANICAL RADIATION

INTERNATIONAL SERIES IN PURE AND APPLIED PHYSICS

Leonard I. Schiff, *Consulting Editor*

The late F. K. Richtmyer was Consulting Editor of the series from its inception in 1929 to his death in 1939. Lee A. DuBridge was Consulting Editor from 1939 to 1946; and G. P. Harnwell from 1947 to 1954.

MECHANICAL RADIATION

ROBERT BRUCE LINDSAY

Hazard Professor of Physics
Brown University

McGRAW-HILL BOOK COMPANY, INC.

New York   Toronto   London

1960

MECHANICAL RADIATION

THE MAPLE PRESS COMPANY, YORK, PA.

37894

PREFACE

Wave propagation is a fascinating branch of physical science, and its importance is certainly not lessened by the fact that it cuts across so many boundaries of the conventional specialized disciplines. This is being recognized to an increasing extent in colleges and universities through the introduction of unified courses in radiation physics in place of the previously standardized courses in optics, acoustics, and electromagnetic radiation. From a pedagogical point of view, much may be said in favor of introducing the subject with mechanical radiation, since here the student grasps most directly what is meant by a wave. The first purpose of this book is therefore to provide such an introduction to wave motion for advanced undergraduate and first-year graduate students, using mechanical radiation as the principal vehicle but laying stress on those aspects which are common to all kinds of wave propagation.

The second aim of the book is the presentation, in integrated form, of mechanical radiation in the broad sense. This does not mean that the author has prepared simply another text on acoustics, a subject which has now become so highly diversified that it is impossible to do justice to all its aspects with any degree of analytical thoroughness in a single book. Rather, the endeavor has been to bring together a unified treatment of the most significant radiation aspects of acoustics and thus to emphasize what is in some danger of being overlooked, namely, the enduring position of this subject as a branch of modern fundamental physics. In this connection, mention may be made of the introduction of such topics, for example, as elastic radiation in bounded solids, absorption and dispersion in fluids, large-amplitude waves, magnetohydrodynamics, mechanical wave filtration in both its macroscopic and microscopic aspects, as well as the relation between elastic wave radiation and other properties of matter, with stress on the significance of this new tool in chemical physics.

As a text, the book should be suitable for students who have had substantial intermediate college courses in mechanics and electricity and magnetism, together with mathematics through the elements of partial differential equations. There is enough material in the first three chapters to serve for a one-semester course in general radiation physics, with selected illustrative material from the rest of the book or from other sources, such as optics, at the pleasure of the teacher. For a thorough understanding of both parts, a year course is indicated. Though the principal stress throughout is theoretical and there are no lengthy descriptions of experimental methods or results, the author has tried not to let the mathematical analysis dominate the physical meaning of the results.

To assist students using the book as a text, as well as those readers who expect to turn to it for reference, cross referencing has been freely used. At the same time, key ideas are frequently recapitulated, so that, in general, it should not be necessary for the reader to master the whole book up to any given point in order to pursue successfully the part of the remainder which interests him. A set of problems at the end of the book provides a useful test of the reader's understanding, as well as further illustrations of the fundamental principles developed in the text.

The author acknowledges gratefully the help received from numerous discussions about radiation physics with students and colleagues. He also expresses deep appreciation for the inspiration received from the perusal of the scientific papers and books of the many investigators who have contributed so notably to this field. He wishes particularly to acknowledge the assistance of his wife, Rachel T. Lindsay, in the preparation of the index of this book.

Robert Bruce Lindsay

CONTENTS

CHAPTER 1

ELEMENTS OF WAVE MOTION

1.1. Introduction. The Meaning of a Wave

A wave is a disturbance moving through a medium. Examples of wave motion are so numerous both in everyday life and in scientific laboratories that the study of its characteristics forms a fascinating chapter in physical science, cutting across, as it does, the boundaries separating the various domains into which physics has been for a long time more or less artificially divided. Since every disturbance in a medium involves energy, wave propagation implies the transfer of energy through space and is indeed one of the most important ways in which this takes place.

The standard illustration of wave motion is provided by disturbances on the surface of a liquid like water. Everyone has observed the ripples produced when a stone is dropped into originally still water. The disturbance produced at the point of impact, that is, the splash, does not stay there but moves outward in all directions in the form of a circular hump or deformation of the water surface. Careful observation reveals that the motion is not that of a restricted amount of water moving horizontally across the surface in the manner of a collection of water spiders but, rather, is that of the change in shape of the surface brought about by the fall of the stone. Since the change in shape itself involves the motion of the water particles near the surface, we have really to deal with the transfer of the result of this particle motion from one part of the surface to another. This transfer constitutes the surface water wave, whether it is the ripple produced by a splash or the long ocean roller which can lift an ocean liner in its path.

Phenomenologically an even more common example of wave motion is produced every time the reader opens his mouth and utters a sound. The disturbance in the surrounding air does not remain localized at the mouth but spreads out in all directions, eventually perhaps encountering an ear or other sound-detecting device. This is a sound, or acoustical, wave. To be sure, it is not so immediately obvious that the wave motion represented by sound transmission in air is somehow analogous to the motion of a surface disturbance in water, and it clearly takes more careful observation and analysis to convince one that it is so.   At the moment an impartial critic would be willing to regard it as no more than plausible. However, as we shall see, the wave theory of sound has proved to be a highly successful physical theory.

More sophisticated by far are the illustrations of wave propagation supplied by light and electromagnetic waves in general, though here again the plausibility of a wave explanation of these phenomena is inherent in their observed properties.   We attain the present height of sophistication in the "matter" and "probability" waves of quantum mechanics, in its attempt to give a rational explanation of the constitution of matter. It is clear that the nature of the "disturbance" whose motion describes the propagation of light must be expected to be rather different from that in water waves and sound waves.

What does the study of wave propagation entail?   If the disturbances in question are mechanical, they present the usual kinematical features, such as displacement, velocity, and acceleration.   More important in some respects is the relation between the direction of the disturbance and that of the wave itself; we speak of transverse waves (e.g., light) and longitudinal waves (e.g., sound in air).   A disturbance propagated in one direction (along a straight line) is spoken of as a plane wave.   More commonly we encounter waves spreading out in all directions from a single point or straight-line source.   These we refer to, respectively, as spherical and cylindrical waves.   The spreading of waves introduces properties like scattering and diffraction, and the combination of wave systems from various sources can lead to interference.   A more simple property arises when a wave encounters a boundary separating two media with different properties (i.e., differing wave velocity, as in the case of air and water). Part of the disturbance is reflected, or turned back, into the medium where it originated, and part is refracted, or changed in direction, on penetrating the second medium.   Waves need not be associated with periodically recurring disturbances, as is illustrated by the solitary wave that constitutes the tidal bore in a narrow inlet.   But periodic waves are of such importance that they demand principal attention; hence we must consider the concepts of frequency and wavelength and their connection with other characteristic behavior of waves.

As has already been suggested, waves carry energy through various media and hence involve dynamical considerations. Some of this energy always gets dissipated into heat on the way, and we must therefore consider absorption.   The dynamical properties of waves evidently imply a direct connection with the internal constitution of the wave-bearing medium.   Hence wave propagation often provides a convenient tool for the exploration of properties of matter.

In this book we shall be particularly concerned with *mechanical radiation*, that is, with wave motion arising from disturbances associated with the mutual motion of parts of material media. It will be worthwhile in the first three chapters to discuss some fundamental properties of wave motion in general.

1.2. Mathematical Representation of a Wave

To introduce an analytical representation of wave motion we begin with the simple case of a wave propagated in one direction, say along the x axis of a rectangular coordinate system. Actually this is not the simplest example of wave motion as we find it in experience; we have already observed that a wave resulting from a localized disturbance tends to spread out in many directions. However, as is usually the case in

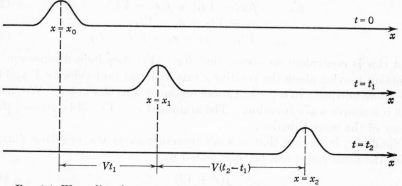

FIG. 1.1. Wave disturbance progressing with velocity V in the x direction.

physical problems, the most commonly observed physical phenomena are not those which lend themselves most directly to mathematical analysis. Hence we idealize in order to get started with a minimum of complexity.

It is necessary to find a mathematical expression for a disturbance moving along the x axis. The disturbance itself will be represented by an appropriate function of x, say $f(x)$, which for each value of x gives the magnitude of the disturbance from equilibrium at that point. The analytical representation of the wave will then be a function of x and the time t, which at $t = 0$ reduces to $f(x)$ but at any other time corresponds to another function of x, having indeed the same form as $f(x)$ but displaced from the neighborhood of the original disturbance by a distance proportional to t. What we seek to do, in other words, is to provide a symbolic functional representation of the situation depicted in Fig. 1.1. On the top, the hump represents the disturbance at $t = 0$; its mathematical representation is $f(x)$. Next we have the situation at the later time $t = t_1$. The hump, *maintaining its shape*, has moved to the right; if its velocity of motion is constant and equal to V, the distance between corresponding points is Vt_1, as indicated in the figure. At the still later time t_2, the hump has moved to the right a farther distance $V(t_2 - t_1)$ in the time interval $t_2 - t_1$.

By inspection, we see that the appropriate function of x and t to represent this state of affairs is the single-valued function

$$f(x - Vt) \tag{1}$$

This reduces indeed to $f(x)$ at $t = 0$ and takes on the forms $f(x - Vt_1)$ and $f(x - Vt_2)$ at times t_1 and t_2, respectively. These are all different functions of x. But if we recall that the value of a single-valued function is always the same if the argument is the same and if we denote the values of x for which the hump has its maximum at $t = 0$, t_1, and t_2, respectively, by x_0, x_1, and x_2, we see that

$$f(x_0) = f(x_1 - Vt_1) = f(x_2 - Vt_2) \tag{2}$$

if
$$x_0 = x_1 - Vt_1 = x_2 - Vt_2$$

or
$$x_1 - x_0 = Vt_1 \qquad x_2 - x_1 = V(t_2 - t_1) \tag{3}$$

But this is equivalent to saying that $f(x - Vt)$ does indeed represent a function moving along the positive x axis with constant velocity V and is therefore adequate to represent wave motion of this character. We shall call it a simple wave function. The argument $x - Vt$ will be termed the *phase* of the wave function.

Similarly, it follows that a wave traveling along the negative x axis with the same speed will be represented by

$$f(x + Vt) \tag{4}$$

We have discussed here an arbitrary disturbance. It can correspond physically to one of many different types, examples of which have already been mentioned in Sec. 1.1. These will be treated in detail in this book. It is necessary to emphasize again that the analytical representation just given is highly idealized. In actual practice we must describe disturbances which change their magnitude, and in some cases even their form, as they move through the medium. An illustration of a change in magnitude is provided by a sound wave in air in which the maximum pressure change from equilibrium decreases as the wave progresses; in this case we say that the wave is *attenuated*. An example of a change in form is the change in the shape of a water wave as it approaches a shelving beach. It is clear that in neither case can we represent what happens by a simple function of x and t like (1)† or (4). Moreover, it is unusual

---

† In this book the equations are numbered consecutively in each section without reference to the section number. When a given equation is referred to in the text of its own section, it is given as listed. When an equation in one section is referred to in the text of another, the section number always precedes the equation number. Thus, for example, (1.2-3) refers to Eq. (3) in Sec. 1.2.

to find in experience a simple wave moving in one direction. Actual disturbances produced in media tend to move in many directions at the same time; even in the simple case of a string, a deformation produced at one point by a flick will move in both directions along the string. Hence we must expect to find that real wave motion is complicated. Nevertheless it is sensible to begin our story with the simplest possible type of wave representation in the hope that a good many important properties of waves can be described thereby. It is indeed fortunate that in a great many cases only relatively simple modifications of (1) will be necessary to provide a more precise expression of actual wave motion.

A solitary disturbance moving through a medium, as pictured in Fig. 1.1, is sometimes referred to as a *pulse*. Modern instrumentation has made it possible to produce with comparative ease both sound and radio pulses of arbitrary shape, as well as successions of such pulses with arbitrary repetition rate. The practical applications of sonar in underwater sound detection and radar in airplane detection come to mind in this connection. We shall examine in detail the properties of special types of pulses in Chap. 3. The continuous wave train commonly encountered in elementary treatments of sound and light involves the additional idea of periodicity, which, as we have already noted, is not inherent in the wave concept itself.

It is clear that the wave velocity V, so far introduced as a purely kinematic quantity, is an important property. The simplest observation indicates that it depends markedly on the type of wave and the medium through which it travels. Waves on the surface of water may travel only a few meters per second, whereas sound waves in air under standard conditions travel at 330 m/sec and in water at 1,500 m/sec. Compressional waves in a solid bar may travel at as high a rate as 5,000 m/sec and seismic waves in the earth's crust at even higher velocities. Light and other electromagnetic radiation in free space has the velocity 3×10^8 m/sec, which indeed, according to the theory of relativity, represents the maximum possible velocity for the transmission of energy in any form in our universe.

In our further discussion, the term *wave velocity* shall always mean the velocity relative to a medium which is itself stationary with respect to a primary inertial reference system. Of course, in the case of waves in a *material* medium the effective velocity of the wave in the inertial system depends on the velocity of the medium itself. Propagation in such moving media can be very important in practice—for example, in sound transmitted through the atmosphere when winds are blowing. The situation with respect to light and electromagnetic radiation in general is more complicated, for it has proved impossible to detect a change in the velocity of light connected with any presumptive motion of the light-bearing medium, the so-called ether. This is, of course, closely associated with the theory of relativity.[1]

Since the wave velocity depends on the medium, it will change from point to point in a nonhomogeneous medium, and we may expect this to complicate the mathematical representation of the propagation considerably. A practical illustration is provided by the transmission of sound through the atmosphere when a temperature gradient is present. Sound travels faster in warm air than in cool air. The result, as one might expect, is a *refraction* of the sound analogous to the refraction of light in passing from one medium to another in which the velocity is different. Here again we postpone more careful consideration to Chap. 2.

Another important property of a wave is the *amplitude*, that is, the maximum deviation from equilibrium involved in the disturbance. This may be an actual displacement in space; a pressure, density, or temperature change; or, in electromagnetic waves, a change in the electric or magnetic field intensity. The dimensions of the amplitude will vary accordingly.

1.3. Waves in Three Dimensions.   Wavefront and Normal

For the sake of simplicity we introduced the mathematical representation of wave motion through a one-dimensional model. One of the most obvious features of waves, however, is their tendency to spread in all directions from the source of a disturbance. It is now necessary to see how such a spreading wave can be treated analytically.

Suppose a disturbance spreads uniformly from a point source in a three-dimensional[2] homogeneous medium. To represent it we need a function of t and r, the distance from the source to any point in the medium. From the analogy of (1.2-1) it appears that this function should be of the form

$$f(r - Vt) \tag{1}$$

in which V is the velocity of the diverging three-dimensional wave and the phase is now $r - Vt$. This seems formally satisfactory, but a little reflection shows that it cannot be physically correct. If indeed, in the case of a three-dimensional wave spreading from a point source, the *actual* disturbance found at a given instant t at all points on a sphere of radius r about the source were to propagate itself unchanged, so as to

<hr />

[1] R. B. Lindsay and H. Margenau, "Foundations of Physics," pp. 319ff., John Wiley & Sons, Inc., New York, 1936. Reprinted by Dover Publications, New York, 1957.

[2] We pass over here what might be thought to be the simpler case of a two-dimensional wave on a water surface or a membrane. This introduces problems which are better postponed to Chap. 5.

have the same value at a subsequent instant t' at all points on a larger sphere of radius r', we should have to admit that in the process of propagation the total disturbance in the medium had increased. Kinematically this might be possible, but physically it violates our intuition. (This problem obviously does not arise in the one-dimensional case.) It is hard to see how, by itself, in the process of spreading, more disturbance can be produced from less; rather it seems plausible that the amplitude at each point must decrease as the wave diverges, so that some appropriate measure of the total disturbance remains constant.[1] Hence, to represent properly a three-dimensional wave diverging from a point source, the expression (1) must be multiplied by an appropriate function of r. What this function is can be determined only by a more elaborate study. In Sec. 3.5 it is shown that, if the measure of the disturbance is the pressure or density change in a homogeneous, compressible fluid medium associated with the passage of a compressional elastic wave (i.e., a sound wave), the appropriate three-dimensional wave function is

$$\frac{1}{r} f(r - Vt) \tag{2}$$

This brings out the essential dependence of wave amplitude for a spreading wave on distance from the source. For obvious reasons we shall refer to (2) as a spreading *spherical* wave. If the point source is located at the origin of a system of rectangular coordinates, we can express (2) in the form

$$\frac{1}{\sqrt{x^2 + y^2 + z^2}} f(\sqrt{x^2 + y^2 + z^2} - Vt) \tag{3}$$

It may be remarked that the appearance of the r in the denominator of (2) satisfies the intuitive demand that the amplitude of the spreading spherical wave shall *decrease* as the disturbance moves outward from the source. It turns out, however, that the precise rate of decrease can be ascertained only by a careful study of the mechanism by which the wave progresses. In other words, we must not limit outselves to the kinematical aspects of wave motion but must examine it from the dynamical point of view.

However, there are a few more kinematical considerations of value which should be introduced here. The first is the concept of *wavefront*. In the spreading spherical wave just considered, the disturbance at given instant t_0 has the value

$$\frac{1}{r_0} f(r_0 - Vt_0)$$

[1] This is closely connected with the problem of energy transfer in a wave (see Sec. 1.10).

at *all* points of the *sphere* of radius r_0 about the source as center. This surface, at all points of which at the same instant the phase of the disturbance has the same value, is called the *wavefront*. We may look upon the propagation of the wave as the motion of the wavefront with velocity V through the medium. For a spherical diverging wave the wavefront has the particularly simple form of a sphere, but wavefronts may be distorted by the presence of obstacles in the medium, and we must not conclude that their progress is a simple kinematical affair in all cases (see Sec. 2.1).

There is indeed another particularly simple type of wavefront besides the spherical. If the wave propagation takes place in a three-dimensional medium but is restricted to one direction, the disturbance at a given instant will be the same at all points of a *plane* perpendicular to this direction. The wavefront is then a plane, and we call the wave a plane wave.

For plane and spherical waves we may write a progressive wave function for three-dimensional propagation in the form

$$g[\varphi(x,y,z)]f[\varphi(x,y,z) - Vt] \tag{4}$$

where f and g are arbitrary, though well-behaved, mathematical functions. For at any arbitrary instant $t = t_0$, the argument of the f function is constant over the surface

$$\varphi(x,y,z) = Vt_0 + C \tag{5}$$

where C is an arbitrary constant. Hence the f function itself will be constant over this surface. The same will be true of the g function, which, as the notation indicates, depends on x, y, z only through $\varphi(x,y,z)$. The surface (5) is then the wavefront. For a spherical wave

$$\varphi(x,y,z) = \sqrt{x^2 + y^2 + z^2} \tag{6}$$

and (5) reduces to a sphere. For a general plane wave

$$\varphi(x,y,z) = \alpha x + \beta y + \gamma z \tag{7}$$

where α, β, γ are three arbitrary constants. Equation (5) is then the equation of a plane, and indeed the direction cosines of the normal to the plane are

$$\frac{\alpha}{D} \qquad \frac{\beta}{D} \qquad \frac{\gamma}{D} \tag{8}$$

respectively, where $D = \sqrt{\alpha^2 + \beta^2 + \gamma^2}$. We have already considered the special case (Sec. 1.2) in which $\alpha = 1$, $\beta = 0$, and $\gamma = 0$ and the propagation takes place in a plane wave in which the wavefronts are always perpendicular to the x axis.

The fact that the propagation can be described in terms of moving wavefronts can be seen at once from (5) for the special case of a plane wave; for the *same* value of the argument will be realized at times $t = t_0$ and $t = t_1$ ($>t_0$) on the two planes

$$\alpha x + \beta y + \gamma z - Vt_0 = C$$
$$\alpha x + \beta y + \gamma z - Vt_1 = C \tag{9}$$

But from analytical geometry the perpendicular distance between these two planes is (assuming $\alpha^2 + \beta^2 + \gamma^2 = 1$, that is, α, β, γ are already normalized to the direction cosines of the normal)

$$V(t_1 - t_0)$$

which is precisely the distance traveled by the plane wave in the time interval $t_1 - t_0$.

For many purposes the normal to the wavefront, or the *wave normal*, as it is usually called, is a useful concept, since it gives the direction of propagation at any point. We shall meet it again in Sec. 1.12 when we discuss wave motion in terms of *rays*.

1.4. Harmonic Waves

We have already emphasized that there is nothing essentially periodic about the idea of wave motion. Nevertheless, whenever waves are propagated in a bounded medium, as, for example, sound waves in an organ pipe, the resultant disturbance at any point will be periodic in time, because of the reflections (Sec. 2.1) at the boundaries. Hence periodic waves are important. Moreover, many wave sources produce disturbances varying periodically with time, thus leading to periodic waves. Such disturbances have long had a fascination for the human race, as have periodic phenomena in general, largely because of the well-known rhythms in common experience (day and night, the tides, phases of the moon, etc.). The possibility of representing a single pulse, as mentioned in Sec. 1.2, as a sum of periodic waves also suggests that the study of such waves introduces valuable simplicity into the whole subject of wave propagation.

The simplest type of periodic function is the simple harmonic. A simple harmonic progressive wave, or harmonic wave (for short), is one in which the disturbance at any point in space varies sinusoidally (i.e., as cosine or sine) with the time and at any instant of time varies sinusoidally in space. The corresponding wave function for one-dimensional wave motion in the positive x direction can therefore be written in the form

$$f(x - Vt) = A \cos(\omega t - kx) \tag{1}$$

where ω and k are constants.

Inspection shows that the formulation in (1) satisfies the conditions just laid down. At any point on the x axis, say x_0, the function varies periodically with the time with a period equal to $2\pi/\omega$, as is evident from the properties of the cosine. This is called the *period* of the wave and is denoted by the symbol T. Its reciprocal, $\omega/2\pi$, is the *frequency* of the wave, for which we shall use the symbol ν. Frequency is expressed in cycles per second, though often the "per second" is omitted, particularly after kilocycles and megacycles. The term *angular frequency* is assigned to ω.

At any instant of time, say $t = t_0$, the function (1) varies periodically with x, with a spatial period equal to $2\pi/k$. To distinguish this

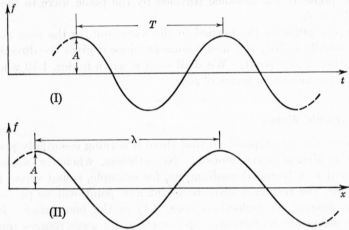

FIG. 1.2. (I) Moving picture of a harmonic wave disturbance at $x = x_0$ as a function of time. (II) Snapshot of a harmonic wave disturbance at $t = t_0$ as a function of x.

from the temporal period just defined, it is customary to refer to $2\pi/k$ as the *wavelength* of the harmonic wave and to denote it by λ. The physical significance of T and λ is exhibited in Fig. 1.2, in which we have plotted in I the harmonic wave function f as a function of t at some value of x, say x_0. It is, of course, a cosine curve with the epoch, or initial-phase value, $-kx_0$. The time interval between successive maxima is the period T (more generally this is the interval between any two points on the curve differing in phase by 2π). The curve may be thought of as a moving picture of the disturbance taken at x_0. In II we have plotted the function f as a function of x at some value of t, say t_0. It is a cosine curve with the initial-phase value ωt_0. The space interval between successive maxima (or any two points differing in phase by 2π) is the wavelength λ. This curve may be looked at as a snapshot of the whole disturbance along the x axis at the instant t_0. In both curves A is the amplitude, or maximum value, of the function and hence of the disturbance being represented.

It still remains to be shown under what conditions the argument $\omega t - kx$ has the form $x - Vt$ (multiplied by a constant) demanded in order that f may be a simple wave function. Disregarding sign (the cosine function is *even*, in any case), we see that we must have

$$\frac{\omega}{k} = V \tag{2}$$

or, in terms of frequency and wavelength,

$$\nu\lambda = V \tag{3}$$

an alternative form of which is

$$\lambda = VT \tag{4}$$

These simple expressions connecting frequency (or period) with velocity and wavelength are fundamental for harmonic waves of all kinds. Long wavelengths correspond to low frequencies, and vice versa.

For many purposes it is useful to replace (1) by the more general form

$$e^{i(\omega t - kx)} = \cos(\omega t - kx) + i\sin(\omega t - kx) \tag{5}$$

where $i = \sqrt{-1}$. Either the real or imaginary part of this expression can represent a harmonic wave. Indeed

$$\cos(\omega t - kx) = \sin\left(\omega t - kx + \frac{\pi}{2}\right) \tag{6}$$

and the two harmonic wave functions differ only in phase by $\pi/2$. Obviously nothing prevents us from representing a harmonic wave progressing in the positive x direction by

$$e^{i(kx - \omega t)}$$

and in fact some authors[1] prefer to use the time factor consistently in the form $e^{-i\omega t}$. We shall continue the practice indicated in (5). The use of j in place of i, that is, $e^{j\omega t}$, is common in engineering treatises.

From the discussion in Sec. 1.3 it follows that the general expression (in complex form) for a harmonic *plane* wave proceeding in the direction with direction cosines α, β, γ is

$$A e^{i[\omega t - k(\alpha x + \beta y + \gamma z)]} \tag{7}$$

The corresponding expression for a harmonic spherical wave diverging from the origin is

$$\frac{A}{r} e^{i(\omega t - kr)} \tag{8}$$

---

[1] P. M. Morse, "Vibration and Sound," 2d ed., pp. 10f., McGraw-Hill Book Company, Inc., New York, 1948.

Frequency is the key concept for harmonic waves, since in a medium at rest it remains the same independently of any change in properties from place to place, whereas the wavelength changes with the velocity. (For the case of moving media, see Sec. 10.3.) Hence a word about the range of frequencies commonly encountered in wave-propagation problems may not be out of place. In mechanical radiation we may deal with frequencies as low as a fraction of a cycle per second, as, for example, in surface waves on water. Harmonic sound waves with frequency below about 15 cycles/sec at normal amplitude are inaudible (*infrasonic*). At the other extreme, sound waves of frequency greater than around 18,000 cycles/sec (18 kc) are also inaudible to most persons at normal amplitude. These are called *ultrasonic* waves. Audible sound forms only a small part of the physically interesting sound spectrum. Ultrasonic frequencies up to 10^9 cycles/sec have been produced and studied. Hypersound waves with frequencies up to 10^{13} cycles/sec have been detected in liquids by their scattering effect on light but have not been produced by regular vibratory methods.

In visible light, the red end of the spectrum corresponds to a frequency of approximately 4×10^{14} cycles/sec, whereas at the violet end the figure becomes about 8×10^{14} cycles/sec. The shortest ultraviolet radiation detected optically has a frequency of about 4×10^{16} cycles/sec. Still shorter are the X rays, which have frequencies running down to 3×10^{18} cycles/sec. At the other end of the scale, the infrared radiation produced optically has frequencies going down to about 10^{12} cycles/sec. Radio waves overlap this region somewhat and have been produced at frequencies as high as 1.5×10^{14} cycles/sec. For these there is strictly no lower limit, though in practice frequencies below 15 kc are rarely used.

1.5. Superposition of Harmonic Waves. Stationary Waves

Anyone who has observed the complicated wave pattern produced when a stone is dropped into the water near the shore of a lake or into a pool of relatively small dimensions will recognize that the harmonic progressive wave defined in the previous section is a considerable idealization. It is, however, plausible to assume that complicated wave patterns result from the superposition or addition of simple wave trains. Indeed, some well-known wave phenomena immediately emerge from this assumption. The simplest case, that is, the addition of two harmonic waves progressing in the same direction and characterized by the same frequency, velocity, and initial phases but having different amplitudes, possesses little physical interest. The only effect is to produce a single wave with amplitude equal to the sum of the amplitudes of the two waves separately.

A more interesting example is provided by the superposition of two harmonic waves with the same velocity but different angular frequencies ω_1 and ω_2. For simplicity, let us first suppose that the amplitudes are each equal to unity, so that we have for the composite wave function

$$f = \cos(\omega_1 t - k_1 x) + \cos(\omega_2 t - k_2 x) \tag{1}$$

which can be rewritten in the form

$$f = \cos \omega_1 \left(t - \frac{x}{V} \right) + \cos \omega_2 \left(t - \frac{x}{V} \right) \tag{2}$$

By means of a well-known trigonometric identity, (2) can at once be put into the form

$$f = 2 \cos \frac{1}{2} \left[(\omega_1 + \omega_2) \left(t - \frac{x}{V} \right) \right] \cos \frac{1}{2} \left[(\omega_1 - \omega_2) \left(t - \frac{x}{V} \right) \right] \tag{3}$$

What physical result would we expect to follow from this? The first factor on the right represents a wave progressing in the x direction with

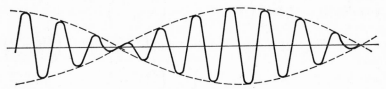

Fig. 1.3. Modulated sinusoidal wave.

velocity V and with frequency equal to the arithmetical average of the frequencies of the individual waves, whereas the second factor is a similar wave with frequency equal to half the difference of the individual frequencies. Let us suppose that the frequencies ω_1 and ω_2 are rather close together, that is,

$$\omega_1 = \omega_2 + \epsilon \tag{4}$$

where ϵ is small compared with ω_2. Then f has the form

$$f = 2 \cos \frac{\epsilon}{2} \left(t - \frac{x}{V} \right) \cos \left[\left(\omega_2 + \frac{\epsilon}{2} \right) \left(t - \frac{x}{V} \right) \right] \tag{5}$$

where we have interchanged the terms. The composite wave function now acts like a harmonic progressive wave with frequency $\omega_2 + \epsilon/2$ (very close to ω_2 or ω_1) with an amplitude $2 \cos[(\epsilon/2)(t - x/V)]$ which varies *slowly* with the time at any one place with angular frequency $\epsilon/2$. If we were to plot f as a function of t for a given x, the result would look like Fig. 1.3. The wave of angular frequency $(\omega_1 + \omega_2)/2$ is said to be *modulated* in amplitude (often expressed as *amplitude-modulated*) with angular frequency $(\omega_1 - \omega_2)/2$.

The well-known phenomenon of *beats* in acoustics is a good illustration of amplitude modulation. In amplitude-modulated radio, a relatively high frequency carrier wave is modulated in amplitude when it is combined with the lower-frequency electromagnetic wave produced by the audible sound whose transmission is desired.

The amplitudes of the component waves whose superposition is desired need not be restricted to the same value. Consider

$$f = A_1 \cos (\omega_1 t - k_1 x) + A_2 \cos (\omega_2 t - k_2 x) \tag{6}$$

We write

$$\cos (\omega_1 t - k_1 x) = \cos \left[\left(\frac{\omega_1 + \omega_2}{2} \right) t - \left(\frac{k_1 + k_2}{2} \right) x - \theta \right]$$

$$\cos (\omega_2 t - k_2 x) = \cos \left[\left(\frac{\omega_1 + \omega_2}{2} \right) t - \left(\frac{k_1 + k_2}{2} \right) x + \theta \right] \tag{7}$$

where

$$\theta = \left(\frac{\omega_2 - \omega_1}{2} \right) t - \left(\frac{k_2 - k_1}{2} \right) x \tag{8}$$

Then we may write

$$f = (A_1 + A_2) \cos \theta \cos \left[\left(\frac{\omega_1 + \omega_2}{2} \right) t - \left(\frac{k_1 + k_2}{2} \right) x \right]$$

$$+ (A_1 - A_2) \sin \theta \sin \left[\left(\frac{\omega_1 + \omega_2}{2} \right) t - \left(\frac{k_1 + k_2}{2} \right) x \right]$$

or

$$f = B \cos \left[\left(\frac{\omega_1 + \omega_2}{2} \right) t - \left(\frac{k_1 + k_2}{2} \right) x + \delta \right] \tag{9}$$

if

$$B^2 = (A_1 + A_2)^2 \cos^2 \theta + (A_1 - A_2)^2 \sin^2 \theta \tag{10}$$

and

$$\tan \delta = \frac{(A_1 - A_2) \tan \theta}{A_1 + A_2} \tag{11}$$

If we again assume that $\omega_2 - \omega_1$ is small compared with either ω_1 or ω_2, we can look upon the result of superposition as a harmonic progressive wave with angular frequency $(\omega_1 + \omega_2)/2$ but with variable amplitude B and variable phase δ, both varying harmonically with time at given place with angular frequency $(\omega_2 - \omega_1)/2$. The amplitude reaches its one extreme value, $A_1 + A_2$, for $\cos \theta = 1$ and its other extreme value, $A_1 - A_2$, for $\cos \theta = 0$. The modulation is evident.

In the preceding discussion we considered the superposition of harmonic progressive waves without regard to their origin. But now let us consider another example. If a harmonic wave traveling in a linear medium strikes an obstacle, there immediately arises a reflected wave traveling in the opposite direction. This clearly will superpose on the original wave. If the medium is finite in both directions, this process will take place over and over again. We now investigate the pattern that results.

At any point in the finite linear medium through which harmonic waves are being propagated the resultant disturbance is made up of two kinds of waves: (1) those which after reflection are traveling to the right and (2) those which after reflection are traveling to the left. All these waves will have the same frequency and velocity but will differ in phase because of the different distances they have traveled. However, we can always absorb phase differences in a complex amplitude, by using the complex notation (1.4-5), with the result that the composite disturbance can be represented in the form

$$f = A e^{i(\omega t - kx)} + B e^{i(\omega t + kx)} \tag{12}$$

in which A and B are now to be treated as complex quantities.

We must introduce some boundary conditions. Let us suppose that the ends of the finite medium, taken for simplicity at $x = 0$ and $x = l$, are kept rigidly fixed, so that the resultant disturbance is zero there. It therefore follows from (12) that

$$\begin{aligned} A + B &= 0 \\ A e^{-ikl} + B e^{ikl} &= 0 \end{aligned} \tag{13}$$

since the conditions in question must hold for all values of t. The two equations (13) at once lead to

$$\sin kl = 0 \tag{14}$$

or

$$kl = n\pi \tag{15}$$

where n is an integer. The imposition of the boundary conditions thus has the interesting consequence that it is impossible to have individual harmonic waves of *all* frequencies propagated in the *finite* linear medium. Actually the allowed frequencies are those satisfying (15), namely,

$$\nu_n = \frac{nV}{2l} \tag{16}$$

These are called the characteristic, or normal-mode, frequencies of the finite linear medium for harmonic waves. The lowest frequency (for $n = 1$) is the *fundamental*, or first harmonic; the rest (for $n = 2, 3, 4, \ldots$) are the higher *harmonics* ($n = 2$ corresponding to the second harmonic, etc.).

Corresponding to the harmonic frequencies (16) are the wavelengths

$$\lambda_n = \frac{2l}{n} \tag{17}$$

Associated with each characteristic frequency there is an expression for f which represents the state of disturbance of the medium as a function of space and time. Thus for ν_n we have

$$f_n = A_n [e^{i(\omega_n t - k_n x)} - e^{i(\omega_n t + k_n x)}] \tag{18}$$

It is here necessary to treat A_n as complex. If we let

$$A_n = a_n + ib_n$$

and take the real part of f, which is, of course, the only physically meaningful expression, we have

$$f_{nr} = (a_n \sin \omega_n t + b_n \cos \omega_n t) \sin \frac{n\pi x}{l} \qquad (19)$$

where, naturally, $\omega_n = 2\pi\nu_n$. This may also be written

$$f_{nr} = C_n \sin (\omega_n t + \alpha_n) \sin \frac{n\pi x}{l} \qquad (20)$$

where $C_n = \sqrt{a_n{}^2 + b_n{}^2}$ and $\tan \alpha_n = b_n/a_n$. The quantities a_n and b_n will in any actual case depend on the initial conditions (see Sec. 3.1). It is clear that f_n is no longer a *propagated* disturbance and therefore does not correspond to a wave in the usual sense. It is still, however, a function of space and time and, in particular, varies harmonically with x for given t, and conversely. The term *stationary* or *standing* wave is associated with this state of affairs. In a standing wave, in contradistinction to a progressive wave, there are certain points at which the disturbance vanishes for all t. Inspection of (19) shows that this takes place for

$$x = \frac{n'l}{n} \qquad (21)$$

in which n' is also integral or zero and less than or equal to n. These places of zero disturbance are called *nodes*. The two ends of the finite vibrating medium are, of course, nodes by definition [since this assumption provided the boundary conditions (13)] for all harmonics. The number of interior nodes is always equal to one less than the order of the harmonic. Comparison of λ_n in (17) and the nodal values of x in (21) leads to the important result that the distance between successive nodes is always equal to a half wavelength of the standing wave. This is of value in the measurement of wave velocity.

Midway between successive nodes is a point at which the disturbance reaches the maximum value C_n at time intervals equal, of course, to the period $T_n = 2l/nV = 2\pi/\omega_n$. Points of this kind are called *antinodes*, or *loops*. The distances of these points from the origin end of the linear medium are

$$x = \frac{2n' + 1}{2} \frac{l}{n} \qquad (22)$$

where n' is integral or zero and equal to or less than $(2n - 1)/2$.

It is also possible to have stationary waves in a three-dimensional bounded medium. Thus in a rectangular parallelepiped with one corner placed at the origin of a rectangular coordinate system, with its sides along the x, y, and z axes, respectively, and equal to a, b, c, respectively, if the wave disturbance in question vanishes for all t over all surfaces, it can be shown (see Sec. 1.8) that the resultant plane wave inside the box has the stationary pattern

$$f_n = (a_n \sin \omega_n t + b_n \cos \omega_n t) \sin \frac{n_1 \pi x}{a} \sin \frac{n_2 \pi y}{b} \sin \frac{n_3 \pi z}{c} \qquad (23)$$

where n_1, n_2, n_3 are integers and

$$\omega_n{}^2 = \pi^2 V^2 \left(\frac{n_1{}^2}{a^2} + \frac{n_2{}^2}{b^2} + \frac{n_3{}^2}{c^2} \right) \qquad (24)$$

In place of nodes we now have nodal planes over which the disturbance is zero at all times. This problem has application to sound waves in rooms and is discussed in detail in Chap. 11 (see also the general discussion of harmonic analysis in Sec. 3.1).

1.6. Modulation of Waves

In Sec. 1.5 we pointed out how the superposition of two harmonic progressive waves of differing frequency leads to a resultant harmonic wave with frequency equal to the arithmetical mean of the two individual frequencies and amplitude which at any one place varies harmonically with the time with frequency equal to half the difference between the individual frequencies. We called this an amplitude-modulation effect.

It is possible by proper instrumentation in the production of a harmonic wave to secure an amplitude modulation of any desired character. Such a wave could be simpler than that due to direct superposition. For example, one can produce a harmonic wave progressing in the x direction and having the form

$$f = (A_0 + A_1 \cos \omega_m t) \cos (\omega t - kx) \qquad (1)$$

where the wave frequency is $\omega/2\pi$ and the amplitude is the harmonically varying function

$$A = A_0 + A_1 \cos \omega_m t \qquad (2)$$

in which $\omega_m/2\pi$ is the modulating frequency. The amplitude at any particular place varies between $A_0 + A_1$ and $A_0 - A_1$. Another way of looking at this phenomenon is to write

$$f = A_0 \cos (\omega t - kx)$$
$$+ \frac{A_1}{2} \{ \cos [(\omega + \omega_m)t - kx] + \cos [(\omega - \omega_m)t - kx] \} \qquad (3)$$

Here the disturbance appears as the superposition of a progressive harmonic wave of frequency $\omega/2\pi$ and *constant* amplitude, as well as two waves of frequencies $(\omega + \omega_m)/2\pi$ and $(\omega - \omega_m)/2\pi$, respectively, both with *constant* amplitude $A_1/2$. The effect of the modulation is thus to introduce the *combination* tones of sum and difference frequencies, respectively. We thus establish again a connection with the considerations of the previous section.

Other types of modulation are possible. For example, one can allow the frequency of a harmonic wave to vary harmonically with the time. Here we encounter some difficulty in writing the expression for the wave function in the form $\cos(\omega t - kx)$, since there must be a different k corresponding to each value of ω. In order to avoid the necessity for indicating this, we find it most convenient to fix attention on the modulation in time at some fixed place, say $x = 0$. This does not affect the physical meaning. Hence we shall consider

$$f = A \cos(\omega_0 + \omega_1 \cos \omega_m t)t \tag{4}$$

Here the frequency of the disturbance oscillates between the limits $(\omega_0 + \omega_1)/2\pi$ and $(\omega_0 - \omega_1)/2\pi$ with modulating frequency $\omega_m/2\pi$. This is called *frequency modulation*. To see what is involved physically, we may simplify by assuming that $\omega_1 \ll \omega_0$ and that t is confined to such an interval that $\omega_1 t \ll 1$. The trigonometric expansion of (4) then yields to this approximation

$$\frac{f}{A} = \cos \omega_0 t - \omega_1 t \cos \omega_m t \sin \omega_0 t \tag{5}$$

Writing $\omega_1 t \approx \sin \omega_1 t$, it is readily seen that f consists of $A \cos \omega_0 t$ superposed on four other harmonic functions of angular frequencies $\omega_0 \pm \omega_1 \pm \omega_m$, the latter each having amplitude equal to $A/4$. More careful examination by more powerful methods shows that there are actually present other components with angular frequencies $\omega_0 \pm \omega_1 \pm n\omega_m$, where n is any integer. The amplitudes of the components, or *sidebands*, as they are technically termed, decrease considerably with increasing n.

Actually (4) does not quite represent the type of frequency modulation currently employed by radio engineers.[1] They start rather with

$$f = A \cos \phi(t) \tag{6}$$

where
$$\phi = \int \omega(t)\, dt \tag{7}$$

and $\omega(t)$ is the time-dependent equivalent angular frequency. Thus, if, for example,

[1] T. S. Gray, "Applied Electronics," 2d ed., p. 763, John Wiley & Sons, Inc., New York, 1954.

$$\omega(t) = \omega_0 + a_m \cos \omega_m t \tag{8}$$

$$f = A \cos \left(\omega_0 t + \frac{a_m \sin \omega_m t}{\omega_m}\right) \tag{9}$$

which by expansion becomes

$$\frac{f}{A} = \cos \omega_0 t \cos \frac{a_m \sin \omega_m t}{\omega_m} - \sin \omega_0 t \sin \frac{a_m \sin \omega_m t}{\omega_m} \tag{10}$$

If
$$\left| \frac{a_m \sin \omega_m t}{\omega_m} \right| \ll 1$$

$$\frac{f}{A} = \cos \omega_0 t + \frac{a_m}{2\omega_m} [\cos (\omega_0 + \omega_m)t - \cos (\omega_0 - \omega_m)t] \tag{11}$$

with results similar to those already presented. In general, however, we must introduce

$$\cos \frac{a_m \sin \omega_m t}{\omega_m} = J_0 \left(\frac{a_m}{\omega_m}\right) + 2J_2 \left(\frac{a_m}{\omega_m}\right) \cos 2\omega_m t$$

$$+ 2J_4 \left(\frac{a_m}{\omega_m}\right) \cos 4\omega_m t + \cdots$$

$$\sin \frac{a_m \sin \omega_m t}{\omega_m} = 2J_1 \left(\frac{a_m}{\omega_m}\right) \sin \omega_m t + 2J_3 \left(\frac{a_m}{\omega_m}\right) \sin 3\omega_m t + \cdots \tag{12}$$

where the J's are the Bessel functions of the first kind and various orders.[1]

Another possible type of modulation makes use of periodic variation of the *phase* of the wave. Consider

$$f = A \cos (\omega t + \epsilon) \tag{13}$$
where
$$\epsilon = a_0 + a_1 \cos \omega_m t \tag{14}$$

Here the initial phase, or epoch, ϵ varies harmonically between the values $a_0 + a_1$ and $a_0 - a_1$, with angular frequency ω_m. If we expand as follows:

$$f = \cos (\omega t + a_0) \cos (a_1 \cos \omega_m t) - \sin (\omega t + a_0) \sin (a_1 \cos \omega_m t) \tag{15}$$

and consider $a_1 \cos \omega_m t \ll 1$, we can approximate

$$f = \cos (\omega t + a_0) - a_1 \cos \omega_m t \sin (\omega t + a_0) \tag{16}$$

Trigonometric treatment of the second term on the right reveals the presence in the phase-modulated disturbance of harmonic components with angular frequencies $\omega \pm \omega_m$ and amplitude $A a_1/2$ superposed on the original wave of frequency ω and amplitude A. The existence and importance of sidebands is thus evident in all varieties of modulation.

[1] F. S. Woods, "Advanced Calculus," p. 281, Ginn & Company, Boston, 1934.

1.7. The Wave Equation. Waves of Various Types

So far in this chapter we have considered the kinematics of wave motion based on the mathematical functions that describe it. To proceed, it is now necessary to examine the differential equation satisfied by wave functions, since this will enable us ultimately to introduce some dynamical properties. In particular we wish to ascertain what the wave velocity depends on.

We begin with the simplest case of the one-dimensional wave [Eq. (1.2-1)], for which

$$f = f(x - Vt) \tag{1}$$

If we differentiate this function partially with respect to x and t, respectively, we obtain

$$\frac{\partial f}{\partial x} = f' \tag{2}$$

and

$$\frac{\partial f}{\partial t} = -Vf' \tag{3}$$

where

$$f' = f'(x - Vt) = \frac{df(x - Vt)}{d(x - Vt)} \tag{4}$$

It follows from (2) and (3) that

$$V = -\frac{\partial f/\partial t}{\partial f/\partial x} \tag{5}$$

This holds, of course, for a wave proceeding in the positive x direction. For a wave in the negative x direction,

$$V = \frac{\partial f/\partial t}{\partial f/\partial x} \tag{6}$$

It is clear that a first-order partial differential equation will not uniquely define the wave velocity independently of direction. Moreover, we recall from mechanics the fact that dynamical equations are second-order equations. Hence we proceed to carry out a second differentiation with respect to each variable and get

$$V^2 = \frac{\partial^2 f/\partial t^2}{\partial^2 f/\partial x^2} \tag{7}$$

This result is general and independent of direction; as a differential equation, it is satisfied by both $f(x - Vt)$ and $f(x + Vt)$.

Equation (7) is called the differential wave equation for one-dimensional waves represented by wave functions of the form $f(x \pm Vt)$. It is therefore the simplest one-dimensional wave equation, though we shall see later that as a differential equation it is inadequate to represent many important kinds of waves encountered in nature—for example, attenuated waves, flexural waves in rods, and compressional waves of large amplitude.   Fortunately it can serve as a basis, albeit in idealized fashion, for the discussion of many important wave properties, and the modifications necessary to provide a more realistic picture are rather closely related to it.   It will pay at this point to make a few comments on its possible physical significance.

If the function f denotes an actual physical displacement of a particle of a material medium when it is disturbed from its equilibrium condition, the numerator in (7) is an acceleration and hence, from a dynamical point of view, is equivalent to a resultant force per unit mass.   On the other hand, $\partial f/\partial x$ denotes a fractional deformation of the medium, or what is called a *strain*, and $\partial^2 f/\partial x^2$ represents the space rate of change of the strain.   The ratio on the right-hand side of (7) is then a measure of the force per unit mass needed to bring about unit rate of change of strain in the medium.   A homogeneous medium for which the ratio is constant is said to be *elastic*.   In this case the velocity V is the square root of the ratio of an elastic constant to an inertial term (usually the density). We can show this very simply for a linear medium.

Let us take the special example of a long, thin elastic solid rod of cross-sectional area S.   If we consider an element of the rod of length dx, the tension force at the left-hand end is SX, where X is the tensile stress, or stretching force per unit area.   The corresponding tension force at the right-hand end is $SX + (S\ \partial X/\partial x)\ dx$.   Hence the *net* tension force on the element is

$$S\,\frac{\partial X}{\partial x}\,dx$$

Since the rod is elastic, Hooke's law is obeyed, and

$$X = Y\,\frac{\partial f}{\partial x} \tag{8}$$

where Y is Young's modulus.   Newton's second law applied to the motion of the element yields

$$SY\,\frac{\partial^2 f}{\partial x^2}\,dx = S\rho\ddot{f}\,dx \tag{9}$$

in which ρ is the mean density of the medium and the dot notation indicates partial differentiation with respect to the time, that is, $\dot{f} = \partial f/\partial t$, $\ddot{f} = \partial^2 f/\partial t^2$, ...   We shall follow this throughout the book.   Equation (9) reduces to (7) with

$$V = \sqrt{\frac{Y}{\rho}} \tag{10}$$

We have here presented a case in which the simple one-dimensional wave equation results from a straightforward dynamical analysis of the deformation of a medium. Many physically similar but mathematically more complicated cases are discussed further on in the book.

We now wish to write an equation similar to (7) for the case of waves in three dimensions. From Sec. 1.3 the general expression for a plane wave function in three dimensions is

$$f = f(\alpha x + \beta y + \gamma z \pm Vt) \tag{11}$$

where α, β, γ are the direction cosines of the normal to the wavefront, and hence

$$\alpha^2 + \beta^2 + \gamma^2 = 1 \tag{12}$$

To find the differential equation satisfied by (11), we differentiate twice with respect to x, y, z, and t, respectively, and utilize (12). The result is

$$\frac{\partial^2 f}{\partial x^2} + \frac{\partial^2 f}{\partial y^2} + \frac{\partial^2 f}{\partial z^2} = \frac{\ddot{f}}{V^2} \tag{13}$$

This is more commonly written

$$\nabla^2 f = \frac{\ddot{f}}{V^2} \tag{14}$$

where ∇^2 is the differential operator (the Laplacian)

$$\nabla^2 \equiv \frac{\partial^2}{\partial x^2} + \frac{\partial^2}{\partial y^2} + \frac{\partial^2}{\partial z^2}$$

Equation (13) is commonly called the differential equation of wave motion for three-dimensional media. Once again we note its idealized character, corresponding as it does to solutions of the form (11), which relate to disturbances moving without change of size or shape. It will be noted that we have set it up with the use of a plane wave function and its generality might therefore come into question. However, we shall later see that it can serve to represent spherical and even other types of spreading waves as well, though we must be careful not to assume that f in that case can represent any arbitrary measure of the disturbance. Section 3.5 may be consulted for a discussion of this matter. In the meantime we can learn a great deal about wave properties by confining our attention to plane waves.

It is worthwhile here to comment on certain general properties of (14). It is, of course, a partial differential equation, in that the wave function f depends on the space coordinates x, y, z as well as on the time t. The general solution of such an equation involves arbitrary functions, as indeed would be surmised from the foregoing considerations. This corresponds physically to the fact that waves come in truly infinite variety, and reducing them to a limited number of specific types is either

a matter of convenience or a necessity dictated by the boundary conditions imposed on the wave-bearing medium. We have already noticed
(Sec. 1.4) how boundedness in the medium introduces temporal periodicity into wave motion and hence reduces the arbitrariness of the wave
solution.

Another important mathematical characteristic of the wave equation
is its *linearity*. All its terms are of the first degree in the derivatives
which enter. As a result, if $f_1, f_2, f_3, \ldots, f_n$ are individually solutions
of the equation,

$$a_1f_1 + a_2f_2 + \cdots + a_nf_n \tag{15}$$

where $a_1, a_2, \ldots, a_n$ are arbitrary constants, is also a solution. Solutions of the wave equation are thus said to obey a principle of *superposition*. We have already used this in Sec. 1.5, where we discussed the
superposition of harmonic waves. It is important to recognize that this
property is not shared by the equation representing waves of finite
amplitude. This equation is discussed in Chap. 9.

The nature of the wave function f also calls for comment. As has
already been indicated, great variety must be expected here, corresponding to waves of all kinds. Two important classifications of wave functions are *scalars* and *vectors*. A scalar wave function has magnitude
only—for example, excess density or velocity potential in the case of compressional waves in a fluid. On the other hand, a vector wave function
consists essentially of a set of three scalar functions of position and time
which transform the way the rectangular coordinates of a point transform under rotation of axes. Though we may continue to write (14)
formally as a single equation in this case [usually putting f in boldface
type ($\mathbf{f}$) to indicate its vector character] actually the equation is mathematically equivalent to three scalar equations in the rectangular components[1] of f. An example of a vector wave function is the displacement
from equilibrium at a point in an elastic medium. Another illustration is
the electric field intensity in free space.

We have already commented in Sec. 1.1 on the distinction between
longitudinal and *transverse* waves. This is also reflected in the nature of
the wave function. If the wave function is a vector and its direction is
always parallel to the direction of propagation of the wave, we speak of a
longitudinal wave function. If, on the other hand, the direction of the
wave-function vector is always at right angles to the direction of propagation, the wave is termed transverse. An important example of a longitudinal wave function is the displacement from equilibrium of the fluid

---

[1] This does not mean, of course, that the rectangular components are necessarily
independent. In general there are relations connecting them (see, for example,
Sec. 6.3).

particles in the propagation of a plane compressional wave in the fluid (e.g., a sound wave in air). On the other hand, in the propagation of plane electromagnetic waves (including visible light) the electric and magnetic vector wave functions are always transverse.

Somewhat more general is the distinction between irrotational and solenoidal vector wave functions. It will be recalled from vector analysis[1] that a vector whose *curl* is zero is called an *irrotational* vector, whereas one whose *divergence* is zero is termed *solenoidal*. If a velocity potential exists in fluid flow, the fluid velocity is the gradient of the potential. In this case the curl of the velocity is identically zero, and the velocity is an irrotational vector. It turns out that this situation prevails in sound propagation in an ideal fluid, and hence such sound waves are called irrotational. This is indeed associated with the longitudinal character of plane sound waves in a fluid. In a solid, as we shall see, things are more complicated, since one can have both compressional and shear waves. The former are irrotational and the latter solenoidal. As might be expected, the electric and magnetic vector wave functions in electromagnetic wave propagation in free space are solenoidal.

These general properties of wave functions are set down here for reference. They will, of course, be discussed in detail in the subsequent chapters in connection with special types of wave propagation.

1.8. Solution of the Wave Equation by Separation of Variables

Though we have introduced the wave equations in one dimension (1.7-7) and in three dimensions (1.7-14) in purely mathematical fashion as partial differential equations satisfied by certain types of wave functions, we shall see that these equations arise normally as a result of a variety of well-known physical situations. The problem of their solution in numerous special cases will arise, and it is advantageous to discuss here a standard method which is often helpful. This utilizes the so-called "separation of variables" and will serve to emphasize the great variety of possible solutions available. In employing it to find solutions of (1.7-14), we let f be a product of functions, each of which depends on one variable only. Thus we try

$$f = X(x)Y(y)Z(z)T(t) \tag{1}$$

where, at first, X, Y, Z, and T are arbitrary functions. We seek to find the conditions they must satisfy in order that (1) shall satisfy (1.7-14). If we substitute into (1.7-14), the result is, after a little simplification,

---

[1] Leigh Page, "Introduction to Theoretical Physics," 2d ed., p. 29, D. Van Nostrand Company, Inc., Princeton, N.J., 1935.

$$\frac{1}{X}\frac{d^2X}{dx^2} + \frac{1}{Y}\frac{d^2Y}{dy^2} + \frac{1}{Z}\frac{d^2Z}{dz^2} = \frac{1}{V^2T}\frac{d^2T}{dt^2} \qquad (2)$$

Now the expression on the right is a function of t alone. The only way it can be identically equal to the left-hand side, which is a function of x, y, z alone, is for both sides to be equal to the same constant. For convenience let us call this constant $-k^2$ (k real). It is a quantity with the dimensions of the reciprocal of the square of a length. The equation for T then becomes the second-order ordinary differential equation

$$\frac{d^2T}{dt^2} = -V^2k^2T \qquad (3)$$

with the general solution

$$T = Ae^{iVkt} + Be^{-iVkt} \qquad (4)$$

where A and B are arbitrary complex constants. It is clear that this does not exhaust the possibilities, since the constant to which both sides of (2) are set equal need not be negative as just assumed. We then have from (2)

$$\frac{1}{Y}\frac{d^2Y}{dy^2} + \frac{1}{Z}\frac{d^2Z}{dz^2} = -k^2 - \frac{1}{X}\frac{d^2X}{dx^2} \qquad (5)$$

Using the same technique as before, we see that both sides must be equal to the same constant, which we call $-k^2 + k_1^2$ (k_1 real). This means that

$$\frac{d^2X}{dx^2} + k_1^2X = 0 \qquad (6)$$

Similarly, we introduce two other positive constants k_2^2 and k_3^2 such that

$$\frac{d^2Y}{dy^2} + k_2^2Y = 0 \qquad \frac{d^2Z}{dz^2} + k_3^2Z = 0 \qquad (7)$$

where, of course, we must have the relation

$$k_1^2 + k_2^2 + k_3^2 = k^2 \qquad (8)$$

The solutions of the second-order linear equations for X, Y, and Z are, respectively,

$$\begin{aligned} X &= A_1e^{-ik_1x} + B_1e^{ik_1x} \\ Y &= A_2e^{-ik_2y} + B_2e^{ik_2y} \\ Z &= A_3e^{-ik_3z} + B_3e^{ik_3z} \end{aligned} \qquad (9)$$

where the A's and B's are arbitrary constants. The number of possible solutions of the wave equation (1.7-14) in the form (1) is thus very large. But it is interesting to observe that a plane harmonic progressive wave is one of these. Thus in (9) let $B_1 = B_2 = B_3 = 0$ and assume that

$$k_1 = k\alpha \qquad k_2 = k\beta \qquad k_3 = k\gamma \tag{10}$$

where
$$\alpha^2 + \beta^2 + \gamma^2 = 1 \tag{11}$$

Also assume in (4) that $B = 0$. Then (1) takes the form

$$f = Ce^{i[kVt - k(\alpha x + \beta y + \gamma z)]} \tag{12}$$

which is in precisely the form (1.4-7) with $kV = \omega$ and α, β, γ as the direction cosines of the normal to the advancing plane wavefront.

As we have noted, nothing prevents us from assuming that k in the foregoing analysis is pure imaginary. In this case f in (12) is not a harmonic wave. In the special case where $k = ik'$ (k' positive) and $\alpha = 1, \beta = \gamma = 0$, we then have

$$f = Ce^{k'(x - Vt)} \tag{13}$$

The initial shape of the disturbance represented here is $Ce^{k'x}$. As time goes on, this moves along the x axis with velocity V, so that at any given x, the disturbance becomes progressively smaller in value; there is no periodicity to the wave.[1] It is clear, of course, that the method of separation of variables always leads to wave disturbances which are exponential in the time and hence either harmonic (imaginary exponent) or hyperbolic (real exponent) in character.

Of course it is also possible that k may be neither real nor pure imaginary but, rather, complex, and in Sec. 1.10 we shall see that useful results may be obtained from this last assumption.

Going back to (9) and assuming $k_1, k_2,$ and k_3 real, we can readily handle the case in which the disturbance is restricted to a rectangular box with sides a_1, a_2, a_3, respectively, and one corner placed at the origin of the coordinate system. Then X, Y, Z must vanish for all time everywhere on the sides of the box, leading to the six equations

$$A_j + B_j = 0 \qquad A_je^{-ik_ja_j} + B_je^{ik_ja_j} = 0 \tag{14}$$

where $j = 1, 2, 3$. These have the solution $k_ja_j = n_j\pi$, where n_j is any integer. This gives, from (9),

$$k^2 = \pi^2\left(\frac{n_1^2}{a_1^2} + \frac{n_2^2}{a_2^2} + \frac{n_3^2}{a_3^2}\right)$$

or the possible frequencies of the harmonic waves which can satisfy the imposed conditions as

$$\omega_n^2 = \pi^2 V^2\left(\frac{n_1^2}{a_1^2} + \frac{n_2^2}{a_2^2} + \frac{n_3^2}{a_3^2}\right) \tag{15}$$

---

[1] Of course k' might be negative. The reader should plot this case also.

where n_1, n_2, n_3 are *any* three integers (positive or negative). The disturbance then takes the possible forms

$$f_n = (C_n e^{i\omega_n t} + C'_n e^{-i\omega_n t}) \sin \frac{n_1 \pi x}{a_1} \sin \frac{n_2 \pi y}{a_2} \sin \frac{n_3 \pi z}{a_3} \qquad (16)$$

which corresponds to the stationary wave solutions already mentioned at the end of Sec. 1.5. The characteristic, or normal-mode, frequencies are given (in angular form) by (15). Separation of variables thus leads rather simply to this result.

The method of separation of variables is, of course, not restricted to rectangular coordinates. It is often advantageous to express the three-dimensional wave equation (1.7-14) in terms of spherical or cylindrical coordinates and the method works equally well for them, as we shall see in Sec. 3.6. On the other hand, the method has the limitation that it does not lead to solutions which immediately express in unmistakable fashion the physical meaning of wave propagation; in a certain sense it is better adapted to the case in which the solutions are subject to boundary conditions, leading to stationary waves. In Appendix A we present a general solution of the three-dimensional wave equation which brings out more categorically its ability to represent propagation.

1.9. Damped Harmonic Waves. Spatial and Temporal Attenuation and Dispersion

The ideal harmonic wave discussed in the preceding sections is rarely realized in practice, since in addition to any decrease in the amplitude of the disturbance due to spherical or cylindrical spreading, every wave-bearing medium exacts an additional toll of dissipation. The part played by viscosity in the case of compressional waves in a fluid medium at once comes to mind as an illustration. There are many other wave-dissipating or -absorbing mechanisms which will be studied in detail in the later chapters (see Chap. 12). Here we wish to introduce some formal considerations about damped waves, confining our attention entirely to waves that are otherwise harmonic. Moreover, for the sake of simplicity we shall stick to plane waves in the x direction. Thus we shall assume a solution of the wave equation (1.7-7) in the form

$$f = Fe^{i(\omega t - kx)} \qquad (1)$$

If this is to be a solution, we know that we must have

$$k^2 V^2 = \omega^2 \qquad (2)$$

where V, if a real quantity, is, as previously, the wave velocity. It is the velocity of advance of the wavefront (Sec. 1.3) and is often referred to as the *phase velocity*, since the phase of the wave [i.e., the argument of the exponential in (1)] also moves with this velocity. Now, though the phase velocity must clearly be represented by a real quantity, there is no mathematical reason why V in (2) should be real. Let us see whether we can extract some useful result by assuming that V is complex, that is,

$$V = V_r + iV_i \qquad (3)$$

in which V_r and V_i are the real and imaginary parts, respectively. If ω is real, k must also be complex. We write

$$k = k_r - i\alpha \qquad (4)$$

But in this case f becomes

$$f = Fe^{-\alpha x}e^{i(\omega t - k_r x)} \qquad (5)$$

Equation (5) represents a plane harmonic wave in the positive x direction with amplitude decreasing exponentially with distance and is an immediate mathematical consequence of the complex character of V. The attenuation coefficient is α, which measures the reciprocal of the distance in which (at any instant of time) the amplitude is decreased in the ratio 1 to e. The phase velocity of the wave V_p is now given by

$$V_p = \frac{\omega}{k_r} \qquad (6)$$

We are dealing here with what may be called a *spatially* attenuated wave. The values of α and k_r (and hence V_p) may be determined in terms of V_r and V_i by substitution from (3) and (4) into (2), yielding

$$(k_r{}^2 - \alpha^2 - 2ik_r\alpha)(V_r{}^2 - V_i{}^2 + 2iV_rV_i) = \omega^2 \qquad (7)$$

By expanding and equating the real and imaginary parts on the two sides, we obtain two equations of the second degree, each involving k_r and α. By the elimination of k_r between these two expressions we arrive at a biquadratic equation for α which, when solved, yields for the real solution

$$\alpha = \frac{\omega V_i}{V_r{}^2 + V_i{}^2} = \frac{\omega V_i}{|V|^2} \qquad (8)$$

Similar treatment for k_r gives

$$k_r = \frac{\omega V_r}{V_r{}^2 + V_i{}^2} = \frac{\omega V_r}{|V|^2} \qquad (9)$$

The absorption, or attenuation, coefficient thus is proportional to the imaginary part of the complex wave velocity, and the wave parameter k_r is proportional to the real part of V (with the same coefficient of proportionality). From (6) we conclude that the phase velocity V_p becomes

$$V_p = \frac{|V|^2}{V_r} \tag{10}$$

If $|V|^2/V_r$ is independent of frequency, the medium through which the sound passes is said to be nondispersive. On the other hand, if this quantity does depend on the frequency, as is the case with most mechanisms which render the velocity V complex, V_p varies with frequency, and the medium is said to be *dispersive*. We can write (10) in the form

$$V_p = V_r \left(1 + \frac{V_i^2}{V_r^2} \right) \tag{11}$$

whence it appears that, if $V_i \ll V_r$, the change in phase velocity due to the imaginary component of V is a second-order effect. On the other hand, the absorption can still be a first-order effect, as is clear from (8). In Chaps. 9 and 12 we shall discuss actual mechanisms whose effect is most simply described by assuming a complex velocity.

From a formal standpoint nothing prevents us from replacing the assumption that k is complex in (2) for V complex by the assumption that ω is complex and k is real. But if we set

$$\omega = \omega_r + i\omega_i \tag{12}$$

the result for the disturbance is

$$f = Fe^{-\omega_i t}e^{i(\omega_r t - kx)} \tag{13}$$

This also corresponds to a damped harmonic wave with frequency $\omega_r/2\pi$, but the damping takes place in *time* rather than in *space;* we may call it *temporally* damped, and the temporal attenuation coefficient is ω_i. It represents the reciprocal of the time during which the amplitude of the disturbance at any particular place is reduced in the ratio 1 to e.

Using techniques similar to those employed in the previous case, we have

$$k^2(V_r^2 - V_i^2 + 2iV_rV_i) = \omega_r^2 - \omega_i^2 + 2i\omega_r\omega_i \tag{14}$$

Once again, equating real and imaginary parts gives

$$\begin{aligned} \omega_r^2 - \omega_i^2 &= k^2(V_r^2 - V_i^2) \\ 2\omega_r\omega_i &= 2k^2V_rV_i \end{aligned} \tag{15}$$

The solution of the associated biquadratics for ω_i and ω_r, respectively, leads to

$$\omega_i = kV_i \qquad \omega_r = kV_r \tag{16}$$

The temporal attenuation, or damping, coefficient is proportional to the imaginary part of the complex velocity, and the effective frequency ω_r of the corresponding damped harmonic motion is proportional to the real part of the complex velocity, the coefficients of proportionality in each case being equal to k. The actual phase velocity now becomes

$$V_p = \frac{\omega_r}{k} = V_r \tag{17}$$

It is of some interest to observe that this differs from the phase velocity (11) for the case of spatial attenuation, though the two approach the same value as $V_i/V_r \to 0$.

Physically we should expect that spatial attenuation would be of particular significance for progressive harmonic waves, whereas temporal attenuation would apply more appropriately to a standing wave or finite wave train.

The association of absorption and dispersion with a complex wave velocity may appear somewhat mysterious. Actually, as we shall see later in a detailed study of absorption mechanisms, this is a formal mathematical device and not necessary for the theory, though it is often very convenient.

It must be emphasized that neither (5) nor (13) satisfies the simple one-dimensional wave equation (1.7-7) for real V. If we wish a wave equation containing nothing but real quantities and yielding a solution corresponding to an attenuated wave, it is clear that its form must differ from (1.7-7). The task of finding such an equation involves the study of the physical mechanism responsible for the attenuation. This is taken up in Secs. 9.11 and 12.1.

1.10. Energy Propagation in Waves

In order to produce in a medium a disturbance which proceeds to propagate itself as a wave, energy in some form must be communicated to the medium. When the disturbance travels through the medium, this energy may be thought of as being transmitted by the wave. Hence energy propagation is an important concomitant of wave motion. We present here a few general considerations as an introduction to the more elaborate treatment of the succeeding chapters.

It will be simplest to consider the disturbance as a deformation of an elastic medium, and we shall further suppose it to be characterized by relative motion of parts of the medium in a single direction, taken along the x axis. The wave will then be called a one-dimensional *dilatational* wave. Here f denotes the displacement of the particle of the medium at x from its original equilibrium position and $\dot{f}$ the corresponding displacement velocity. The displacement at $x + dx$ then becomes

$$f + \frac{\partial f}{\partial x} dx$$

and hence the change in displacement per unit length is

$$\frac{\partial f}{\partial x} \tag{1}$$

which is called the linear *strain* (Sec. 1.7). Clearly, if $\partial f/\partial x$ is positive, the medium is being *stretched* in the x direction, whereas if $\partial f/\partial x$ is negative, the medium is being *squeezed*, or compressed, in the x direction. Now, if the medium is elastic, the tensile stress X, or force per unit area needed to produce this strain, is proportional to the strain (Hooke's law), and hence

$$X = Y \frac{\partial f}{\partial x} \tag{2}$$

where Y appears as a modulus of elasticity (in this case the stretch modulus).

From elementary mechanics the product of the stress X and the displacement velocity $\dot{f}$ at any point gives the rate at which energy is being communicated per unit area of wavefront to the medium by the wave at this point. This is indeed the *power* per unit area represented by the propagation of the wave. We thus write for this quantity

$$P = Y\dot{f}\frac{\partial f}{\partial x} \tag{3}$$

This quantity varies in both time and space. For a harmonic progressive wave of the form

$$f = Ae^{i(\omega t - kx)} \tag{4}$$

we can form P by finding the real parts of $\dot{f}$ and $\partial f/\partial x$ and multiplying them. Note that the use of the complex notation does not permit us to multiply complex quantities (in general the real part of the product of two complex numbers is not the same as the product of the real parts; it is the latter which alone has physical significance). We shall therefore write

$$f = A \cos(\omega t - kx) \tag{5}$$
whence
$$\dot{f} = -A\omega \sin(\omega t - kx) \tag{6}$$
and
$$\frac{\partial f}{\partial x} = Ak \sin(\omega t - kx) \tag{7}$$
Then
$$P = -\frac{YA^2\omega^2}{V} \sin^2(\omega t - kx) \tag{8}$$

since $k = \omega/V$, where V is the phase velocity of the wave, as defined and discussed in the previous section. The significance of the negative sign in (8) lies in the fact that, when the strain is positive, f is negative and vice versa. Physically this means that, when the medium is being squeezed, energy is flowing into it from another part of the medium which is expanding. We are primarily interested in the magnitude of the power and hence shall ignore the minus sign.

The dependence of P on both x and t through $\sin^2 (\omega t - kx)$ renders its practical value dubious. However, if we take an average over time at any particular place, we find the average flow of power per unit area of wavefront at that place. Thus, denoting time average by placing a bar over the letter, we can write

$$\bar{P} = \frac{1}{2} \frac{YA^2\omega^2}{V} \tag{9}$$

since the time average of $\sin^2 (\omega t - kx)$ is

$$\overline{\sin^2 (\omega t - kx)} = \frac{1}{T} \int_0^T \sin^2 (\omega t - kx) \, dt \to \frac{1}{2} \tag{10}$$

as the interval T over which the average is taken (not the period of the wave!) increases indefinitely. Note that, although we have taken the average over time, $\bar{P}$ is independent of both x and t. The average flow of power per unit area in the wave can serve as a good representation of the *intensity* I of the wave, and so we shall set

$$I = \bar{P} \tag{11}$$

In the cgs system I is measured in ergs/sec-cm². In the mks system I appears in watts/sec-m². The dependence on the square of the displacement amplitude and the square of the frequency is worthy of note. It is also of importance to observe that I can be expressed in terms of the maximum stress $X_{\max}$. Since

$$X_{\max} = \frac{YA\omega}{V}$$

it follows that

$$I = \frac{1}{2} \frac{V}{Y} X_{m\,x}^2 \tag{12}$$

The intensity for a dilatational wave of the kind under discussion is thus proportional to the square of the excess stress. If the medium is a solid, X is a tensile stress; if it is a fluid, X is more appropriately looked upon as a pressure.

Though the illustration we have presented is a special one, the energy and intensity considerations are rather general. Thus we shall always find it possible to express the power per unit area for any mechanical wave as proportional to the product of the *time* derivative of a quantity representing the deformation with the *space* derivative of the same quantity. One can even press this analogy into the domain of electromagnetic radiation.

The wave intensity has another interesting aspect. Since it expresses the average power transmission per unit area of wavefront in the wave, it should also be possible to represent it as the product of the wave velocity and the average total energy per unit volume in the portion of the medium being traversed by the wave. This energy per unit volume is appropriately referred to as the energy density; we shall denote its time average by $\bar{w}$ and write

$$\bar{P} = I = \bar{w}V \tag{13}$$

where V is the wave velocity. From (12) we have, therefore,

$$\bar{w} = \frac{1}{2}\frac{X_{max}^2}{Y} \tag{14}$$

From elementary physical considerations the average total energy density should be the sum of the average kinetic energy density and the average potential energy density. But the former is simply

$$\bar{w}_K = \tfrac{1}{2}\rho\overline{\dot{f}^2} \tag{15}$$

where ρ is the density of the medium. Using (6), we can write

$$\bar{w}_K = \tfrac{1}{4}\rho A^2\omega^2 \tag{16}$$

It therefore follows that, if we denote the average potential energy density by $\bar{w}_P$, we have

$$\bar{w}_P = \bar{w} - \bar{w}_K = \frac{1}{4}\frac{A^2\omega^2}{V^2}(2Y - \rho V^2) \tag{17}$$

For an elastic wave of the kind under consideration we showed in Sec. 1.7 that the velocity

$$V = \sqrt{\frac{Y}{\rho}} \tag{18}$$

Hence in this case

$$\bar{w}_P = \frac{1}{4}\rho A^2\omega^2 = \frac{1}{4}\frac{YA^2\omega^2}{V} = \bar{w}_K = \frac{\bar{w}}{2} \tag{19}$$

Thus, on the average, the energy density is equally divided between kinetic and potential. It must be emphasized that we have shown this only for a plane harmonic progressive dilatational wave. Further investigation is necessary before we may safely generalize.

So far we have discussed the intensity of a progressive wave from the dynamical point of view, relating it to the average flow of energy. For practical purposes there is considerable advantage in a notation which enables us to compare the intensities of two different waves in a simple fashion. If the waves have intensities I_1 and I_2, respectively, we shall agree to say that they differ in intensity level by δ db (decibels), where

$$\delta = 10 \log_{10} \frac{I_2}{I_1} \qquad (20)$$

Thus for a ratio of intensities of 2 to 1 the decibel interval is 3.01, or approximately 3. This notation is now widely used throughout acoustics and, indeed, communication physics generally.

Let us return for a moment to the averaging process used in defining intensity. The reader may object that this is a somewhat arbitrary affair since nothing is really said about the time T over which the time average is taken, save that it must be long enough. Actually it is clear from the previous discussion that different times of averaging, particularly if short compared with the period of the harmonic wave, will lead to different intensities. All measuring devices require finite time for the registration of the quantity being measured, and an intensity meter is no exception. Hence they are essentially time-averaging devices. An intensity meter which averages over a time that is short compared with one period of a wave will therefore indicate the actual time fluctuations of the intensity, whereas a meter which averages over a time that is long compared with the period will essentially smooth out the fluctuations and yield a result comparable with that given in (9). In comparing the results of wave-propagation theory with experiment, one must therefore take into account the nature of the measuring device. The ear, for example, hears a fluctuating intensity if two harmonic sounds of frequencies very close to each other are produced simultaneously.

The discussion of energy flow in waves in the preceding paragraphs has been confined to plane waves. This restriction is for convenience only and serves to bring out the essential ideas. We shall deal in greater detail with other types of waves in subsequent sections (e.g., Sec. 9.3), but it is worthwhile noting that we can easily make an important comment about energy transfer in spherical waves (Sec. 1.3 and Appendix A). If the point source of a spreading spherical wave emits energy at a constant average rate, since the area of a sphere of radius r about this point as center is $4\pi r^2$, it must necessarily follow that the average rate of flow of energy across any spherical surface of radius r varies inversely as the square of r. Hence the intensity of a spherical wave diverging from a point source varies inversely as the square of the distance from the source.

So far in our discussion of energy propagation we have neglected the effect of damping. From (19) it follows that, if the amplitude A of the wave decreases with distance x [see (1.9-5)], the average energy density $\bar{w}$ will also decrease as the wave progresses, and this will be a measure of the energy loss through damping, or absorption. We may write

$$\bar{w} = \bar{w}_0 e^{-2\alpha x} \tag{21}$$

where α is the spatial absorption coefficient, as defined in Sec. 1.9, and $\bar{w}_0$ is the average energy density at some chosen reference place. The fractional rate of change of $\bar{w}$ with x is

$$\frac{1}{\bar{w}}\frac{d\bar{w}}{dx} = -2\alpha \tag{22}$$

and hence the fractional loss in average energy density in one wavelength is numerically

$$2\alpha\lambda = -\frac{\lambda}{\bar{w}}\frac{d\bar{w}}{dx} \tag{23}$$

Note that we get the same result if we form

$$-\frac{\bar{w}_\lambda - \bar{w}_0}{\bar{w}}$$

where $\bar{w}_\lambda$ is the average energy density after traversing one wavelength and $\bar{w}$ is the mean average energy density in the space interval of one wavelength. We may therefore treat $2\alpha\lambda$ as a measure of the average energy loss due to damping per unit volume in one wavelength.

In the previous section we introduced temporal, as well as spatial, damping. In this case we can equally well write

$$\bar{w} = \bar{w}_0 e^{-2\omega_i t} \tag{24}$$

Then
$$2\omega_i T = \frac{T}{\bar{w}}\frac{d\bar{w}}{dt} \tag{25}$$

represents the fractional loss in average energy density in one *period* of the wave, where T is here the period. Hence $2\omega_i T$ is a measure of the average energy loss due to damping per unit volume in one period. What is the relation of $2\alpha\lambda$ and $2\omega_i T$? We suspect that

$$2\alpha\lambda = 2\omega_i T \tag{26}$$

and this indeed turns out to be the case, as use of the analysis in Sec. 1.9 shows. This provides an interesting relation between the spatial and temporal attenuation coefficients. It should again be emphasized that these results are independent of the precise mechanism of attenuation, provided that the amplitude of the wave decays exponentially.

Our discussion in this section has been so far subject to another limitation, namely, to *progressive* waves. What can we say of the energy density and intensity in *stationary* waves? Let us recall (1.5-20) and the expression for a harmonic stationary wave disturbance on the x axis for a bounded linear medium of length l:

$$f_n = C_n \sin (\omega_n t + \alpha_n) \sin \frac{n\pi x}{l} \tag{27}$$

where the integer n defines the stationary mode in question. We shall assume that the disturbance is dilatational so that we can use the notation developed earlier in this section. Since the wave does not travel, the intuitive notion of a flow of energy would not appear to apply. We can, however, discuss the kinetic and potential energy density. Instead of calculating the averages at once, let us get first the time-dependent quantities. From (15) we can write

$$w_{K,n} = \frac{1}{2} \rho \dot{f_n}^2 = \frac{1}{2} \rho C_n{}^2 \omega_n{}^2 \sin^2 \frac{n\pi x}{l} \cos^2 (\omega_n t + \alpha_n) \tag{28}$$

The potential energy density is always a more troublesome quantity. Earlier in this section we obtained it by a kind of subterfuge. Here we shall proceed more directly. The potential energy associated with the deformation of an element of the medium having extension Δx in the x direction and volume $S \Delta x$, where S is the area of cross section normal to the x axis, is the work done by the variable stress force SX as the element has its length changed from $(\Delta x)_1$ to $(\Delta x)_2$. We can write this, denoting potential energy by W_P,

$$W_P = S \int_{(\Delta x)_1}^{(\Delta x)_2} X \, d(\Delta x) \tag{29}$$

Now since $\partial f / \partial x$ is the linear strain, by definition

$$d(\Delta x) = d\left(\frac{\partial f}{\partial x}\right) \Delta x \tag{30}$$

whereas from (2)

$$X = Y \frac{\partial f}{\partial x}$$

Hence (29) becomes

$$W_P = YS \, \Delta x \int_0^{\partial f/\partial x} \frac{\partial f}{\partial x} d\left(\frac{\partial f}{\partial x}\right)$$
$$= \frac{YS \, \Delta x}{2} \left(\frac{\partial f}{\partial x}\right)^2 \tag{31}$$

Therefore the potential energy density is

$$w_P = \frac{W_P}{S \, \Delta x} = \frac{Y}{2} \left(\frac{\partial f}{\partial x}\right)^2 \tag{32}$$

Comparison shows that $\bar{w}_P$ calculated from (32) agrees with (19) for the case of a progressive wave. Let us therefore use it for the stationary wave. Using (27), we obtain

$$w_{P,n} = \frac{Y n^2 \pi^2 C_n^2}{2l^2} \cos^2 \frac{n\pi x}{l} \sin^2 (\omega_n t + \alpha_n) \tag{33}$$

If once more we assume (18), we see that

$$\frac{n^2 \pi^2 Y}{l^2} = \rho \omega_n^2$$

and hence

$$w = w_{K,n} + w_{P,n} = \frac{n^2 \pi^2 Y}{2l^2} C_n^2 \left[\sin^2 \frac{n\pi x}{l} \cos^2 (\omega_n t + \alpha_n) \right.$$
$$\left. + \cos^2 \frac{n\pi x}{l} \sin^2 (\omega_n t + \alpha_n) \right] \tag{34}$$

is the total energy density for the nth vibrational mode. It is clear that if we form the *space-time* average we get

$$\bar{\bar{w}} = \frac{n^2 \pi^2 Y C_n^2}{4l^2} = \frac{\rho \omega_n^2 C_n^2}{4} \tag{35}$$

where we use the double bar to indicate the space average of the time average. This gives us the *average* total energy density in the nth mode. It is of interest to observe that at a node in a stationary wave, at which $\sin (n\pi x/l) = 0$ [see (1.5-21, 22)], $w_{K,n}$ is identically zero, whereas at an antinode, or loop, for which $\cos (n\pi x/l) = 0$, $w_{P,n}$ vanishes identically. On the other hand, the potential energy density reaches its maximum amplitude at a node, whereas the kinetic energy density attains its maximum amplitude at a loop.

The dependence of the average total energy density on frequency and amplitude for the mode in question should be compared with the corresponding situation for progressive waves [Eq. (19)].

Suppose, instead of only one mode, all modes are considered to be present. The total disturbance [from (27)] then is

$$f = \sum_{n=1}^{\infty} C_n \sin \frac{n\pi x}{l} \sin (\omega_n t + \alpha_n) \tag{36}$$

For the kinetic energy density we now get

$$w_K = \tfrac{1}{2} \rho \Sigma \dot{f}_n^2$$
$$= \tfrac{1}{2} \rho \left(\sum_{n=1}^{\infty} \dot{f}_n^2 + 2 \sum_{r \neq s=1}^{\infty} \dot{f}_r \dot{f}_s \right) \tag{37}$$

The result is complicated, but it can be simplified if we proceed to a time average.   Over a sufficiently long time

$$\overline{f_r f_s} = 0 \tag{38}$$

and in this case

$$\bar{w}_K = \frac{1}{4} \rho \sum_{n=1}^{\infty} \omega_n{}^2 C_n{}^2 \sin^2 \frac{n\pi x}{l} \tag{39}$$

If we go further to a space average over the complete length of the medium, the result is

$$\bar{\bar{w}}_K = \tfrac{1}{8}\rho\Sigma\omega_n{}^2 C_n{}^2 \tag{40}$$

The space-time average of the kinetic energy density for the motion of the medium in all modes thus turns out to be the sum of the average kinetic energy densities for the various modes.   Similarly, we have for the potential energy density average over both space and time

$$\bar{\bar{w}}_P = \tfrac{1}{8}\rho\Sigma\omega_n{}^2 C_n{}^2 = \bar{\bar{w}}_K \tag{41}$$

and
$$\bar{\bar{w}} = \tfrac{1}{4}\rho\Sigma\omega_n{}^2 C_n{}^2 \tag{42}$$

which should be compared with (35).   The importance of the condition (38) should not be overlooked.   It demands an averaging time T having the property

$$T \gg \frac{2l}{V}$$

since in this case

$$T \gg \frac{2l}{V(r - s)} \quad \text{and} \quad T \gg \frac{2l}{V(r + s)}$$

Under these conditions the result of the averaging process applied to $\Sigma f_n{}^2$ in (37) is also guaranteed to be that presented in (39).   If the condition is not fulfilled, the cross-product terms in (37) play a role, and $\bar{w}_K$ becomes a fluctuating function of the time.

The question now arises, To what extent are we allowed to speak of an intensity of radiation in the case of stationary waves?   Referring to (1.5-12), we see that, in the simplest case of stationary waves in a one-dimensional medium arising by the imposition of the boundary conditions, the disturbance shall vanish at the two ends of the confined medium; the relation between the amplitudes of the two sets of harmonic waves moving in the plus and minus x directions, respectively, is $A = -B$. We may therefore think of the positive traveling wave as conveying energy on the average from left to right and the negative traveling wave as conveying energy on the average from right to left.   The two average rates of flow per unit area will be equal and opposite, and hence the intensity as previously defined will be zero.   It is questionable, however, whether this has any useful physical meaning, since any displacement-measuring instrument placed at any point in a stationary wave except a node will certainly indicate that something is happening there and any stress-measuring instrument placed at any point except a loop will also indicate that something is happening there.   Consequently the energy density would appear to be a more meaningful quantity than intensity in the case of stationary waves.   As a matter of fact, we shall later have occasion to examine standing waves under conditions in which energy is being fed into the medium from one end and reflected with possible decrease of amplitude at the other.   The lack of symmetry in the boundary conditions at the two ends will then mean that A is no longer equal to $-B$ in (1.5-12), but rather

$$A = Be^\gamma \tag{43}$$

where γ is, in general, complex.   In this case, the average flow of energy in the plus and minus directions need not be equal, and there *can* be a net nonvanishing intensity in the usual meaning of the word.   Even here, however, it is likely that the total energy density will have more meaning.

1.11. Variational Method and the Wave Equation

The discussion of energy flow in wave propagation in the preceding section suggests the use of an energy method for deriving the wave equation.   It will be recalled that the equations of motion of a dynamical system of particles can be obtained from Hamilton's principle.[1]   It is possible to apply the same technique to a continuous distribution of matter.

Let us suppose that we have a function

$$L\left(f_s, \frac{\partial f_s}{\partial q_r}, q_r\right) \tag{1}$$

of a set of variables $f_1, f_2, \ldots, f_s, \ldots$, which in turn are functions of independent variables $q_1, q_2, \ldots, q_r, \ldots$.   The function L also depends on the derivatives $\partial f_s/\partial q_r$, and perhaps on the variables q_r themselves.   It is well established in the calculus of variations[2] that the condition that the integral

$$\int_{a_1}^{b_1} \cdots \int_{a_n}^{b_n} L\, dq_1 \cdots dq_n \tag{2}$$

shall have a stationary value with respect to all possible values for which

[1] R. B. Lindsay, "Concepts and Methods of Theoretical Physics," pp. 131ff., D. Van Nostrand Company, Inc., Princeton, N.J., 1951.

[2] P. M. Morse and H. Feshbach, "Methods of Theoretical Physics," pp. 275ff., McGraw-Hill Book Company, Inc., New York, 1953.

the variables $q_1, \ldots, q_n$ have the same end points (i.e., for all integrations the a's and b's remain the same) is the existence of the set of partial differential equations

$$\sum_{r=1}^{n} \frac{\partial}{\partial q_r} \left[\frac{\partial L}{\partial(\partial f_s/\partial q_r)} \right] - \frac{\partial L}{\partial f_s} = 0 \tag{3}$$

There is one equation for each value of s. These are the so-called Euler equations of the variation problem involved in the establishment of the stationary value. In the special case of a dynamical system of particles, there is only one q, namely, the time parameter t. The functions f are the dynamical coordinates—for example, the displacements corresponding to the various degrees of freedom of the system. The function L in this case is, of course, the ordinary Lagrangian of classical particle mechanics, that is, the difference between the kinetic and potential energies.

For a continuous distribution of matter the function L in the integral becomes the Lagrangian density, or the difference between the kinetic energy density and the potential energy density. Thus for the simple case of a finite continuous linear system, like the linear elastic one described in the earlier sections of this chapter, there are two q's, namely, the independent space variable x and the time t. The Lagrangian density is then

$$L = \frac{1}{2} \rho \dot{f}^2 - \frac{1}{2} Y \left(\frac{\partial f}{\partial x} \right)^2 \tag{4}$$

and the integral (1) becomes

$$\int_{t_a}^{t_b} \int_0^l L \, dx \, dt \tag{5}$$

Equations (3) immediately apply and reduce to the single equation (there is only one f)

$$\frac{\partial}{\partial x} \left[\frac{\partial L}{\partial(\partial f/\partial x)} \right] + \frac{\partial}{\partial t} \left[\frac{\partial L}{\partial(\partial f/\partial t)} \right] - \frac{\partial L}{\partial f} = 0 \tag{6}$$

Since $\partial L/\partial f = 0$, the above reduces to

$$\frac{\partial}{\partial x} \left(-Y \frac{\partial f}{\partial x} \right) + \frac{\partial}{\partial t} \left(\rho \frac{\partial f}{\partial t} \right) = 0$$

or the wave equation for the linear elastic medium subject to a longitudinal disturbance governed by Young's modulus, namely,

$$\frac{\partial^2 f}{\partial t^2} = \frac{Y}{\rho} \frac{\partial^2 f}{\partial x^2} \tag{7}$$

Knowledge of the kinetic and potential energy densities enables us to employ this variational method to set up the wave equation for mechanical waves in any material medium. We give a more elaborate example in Sec. 7.4.

1.12. Waves and Rays. The Eikonal Equation. Geometrical Radiation Theory

In Sec. 1.3 we commented on the significance of the concept of wavefront and emphasized that wave propagation in three-dimensional media can be considered from the standpoint of the motion of these surfaces of constant disturbance in magnitude and phase. This is a problem in geometry which can often be simplified by constructing the curves which are normal at every point to the wavefronts; such curves are known as *rays*. The problem we now consider is the conditions under which it is allowable to talk about wavefront motion in terms of rays.

Let us return to the general idealized equation of wave motion in three dimensions [Eq. (1.7-13)] and rewrite it

$$\ddot{f} = V^2 \nabla^2 f \tag{1}$$

We shall generalize indeed to a certain extent by not assuming that V is necessarily a constant; it may be a function of x, y, z. We try the following harmonic solution:

$$f = A(x,y,z)e^{i[\omega t - k\psi(x,y,z)]} \tag{2}$$

This is in more general form than the harmonic waves hitherto considered, since we now contemplate an amplitude A which may vary in space and replace the space part of the phase by $k\psi$, where ψ is a real function of position having the physical dimensions of length. It is here assumed that k has the dimensions of reciprocal length and is physically analogous to the wave parameter k introduced in Sec. 1.4. The quantity ω is still an angular frequency. We have already encountered a general wave expression of the form (2), namely, (1.3-4), which we showed could describe plane and spherical waves. We must not conclude that waves of arbitrary wavefront can be successfully put in the form (2). For example, cylindrical waves are considerably more complicated. However, even these can be rather well approximated by (2) at distances from the source of the radiation very large compared with the wavelength, and the same is true of all types of wavefronts we are likely to encounter in practice. The expressions for A and ψ for plane and spherical waves are given in (1.4-7) and (1.4-8), respectively.

At the instant t, the phase of the wave in (2) has the constant value

$$v = f\lambda = 2\pi f\left(\frac{1}{2\pi}\right) = \frac{\omega}{k}$$

ωt_0 at all points of the surface whose equation is

$$\psi(x,y,x) = \frac{\omega}{k}(t - t_0) = V_0 t - V_0 t_0 \qquad (3)$$

This is accordingly the equation at time t of the wavefront carrying the phase value ωt_0. Let us find the conditions which A and ψ must satisfy in order that (2) shall be a solution of the wave equation (1). Substituting and making use of standard vector notation for the gradient and the Laplacian, we finally arrive at

$$\nabla^2 A - 2ik\nabla A \cdot \nabla\psi - ikA\nabla^2\psi - k^2 A|\nabla\psi|^2 + \frac{\omega^2}{V^2}A = 0 \qquad (4)$$

Since the real and imaginary parts of the left-hand side must be zero identically, we obtain two equations to be satisfied by A and ψ:

$$\frac{\nabla^2 A}{A} - k^2|\nabla\psi|^2 + \frac{\omega^2}{V^2} = 0 \qquad (5)$$

$$2\nabla A \cdot \nabla\psi + A\nabla^2\psi = 0 \qquad (6)$$

The special case of a plane harmonic wave of constant amplitude, for which

$$\psi = \alpha x + \beta y + \gamma z$$

clearly satisfies (5) and (6), since then $\nabla A \cdot \nabla\psi = 0$, $\nabla^2 A = 0$,

$$|\nabla\psi|^2 = \alpha^2 + \beta^2 + \gamma^2 = 1 \qquad \text{and} \qquad \nabla^2\psi = 0$$

The only requirement is $k = \omega/V$, which is, of course, familiar from our discussion of plane harmonic waves in Sec. 1.4. We now wish to proceed with greater generality, but since (5) and (6) are rather formidable, we must submit to some approximations. Let us assume that

$$\frac{\nabla^2 A}{A} \ll k^2|\nabla\psi|^2 \qquad \text{as well as} \qquad \frac{\omega^2}{V^2} \qquad (7)$$

and $\qquad k^2 A|\nabla\psi|^2 \gg 2k\nabla\psi \cdot \nabla A \qquad \text{as well as} \qquad kA\nabla^2\psi \qquad (8)$

The physical significance of these approximations will be looked into presently. If we grant them, it appears that (5) reduces to

$$|\nabla\psi|^2 = \frac{\omega^2}{k^2 V^2} \qquad (9)$$

and (6) becomes an identity to the order of the terms retained in (5). We recall that V need not be constant; that is, the wave velocity may vary from place to place. Let us write

$$V = V(x,y,z) \qquad (10)$$

and set $\qquad\qquad V_0 = \frac{\omega}{k} \qquad (11)$

Equation (9) then takes the form of the first-order partial differential equation

$$\left(\frac{\partial\psi}{\partial x}\right)^2 + \left(\frac{\partial\psi}{\partial y}\right)^2 + \left(\frac{\partial\psi}{\partial z}\right)^2 = \frac{V_0^2}{[V(x,y,z)]^2} \tag{12}$$

This equation is known as the *eikonal* equation and $\psi(x,y,z)$ as the eikonal. It is customary to set

$$\frac{V_0}{V} = n \tag{13}$$

and call n the index of refraction of the medium. If V is actually independent of position, n is a constant, and the eikonal equation assumes a relatively simple form, whose solution yields the equation of the wavefronts, as in (3). Since the equation is a partial differential equation, its solutions are diverse, and boundary conditions must be applied to pick out the appropriate one in any given case.

Before studying (12) in detail, we shall investigate the nature of approximations (7) and (8), which led to it. First we recall that

$$\sqrt{\left(\frac{\partial\psi}{\partial x}\right)^2 + \left(\frac{\partial\psi}{\partial y}\right)^2 + \left(\frac{\partial\psi}{\partial z}\right)^2} = |\nabla\psi|$$

measures the rate of change of ψ in the direction of the normal to the wavefront surface given by (3); that is,

$$|\nabla\psi| = \frac{d\psi}{dl} \tag{14}$$

where dl is the increment of distance along the normal and $d\psi$ is the change in ψ over this distance. But now, from (12),

$$|\nabla\psi| = \frac{V_0}{V} \tag{15}$$

We conclude from (14) and (15) that

$$\frac{d\psi}{dl} = \frac{V_0}{V}$$

We can also write

$$\frac{d\psi}{dl} = \frac{d\psi}{dt} \bigg/ \frac{dl}{dt} \tag{16}$$

Here, from (3), $d\psi/dt = \omega/k = V_0$, and

$$\frac{dl}{dt} = V_p \tag{17}$$

or the velocity with which a given phase value propagates itself along the normal to the wavefront. Comparison between (15) and (16) shows that

$$V = V_p \tag{18}$$

We now go back to the inequality (8), which takes the form

$$\nabla^2\psi \ll \frac{\omega V_0}{V^2} \tag{19}$$

We now reflect that $\nabla^2\psi \equiv \nabla \cdot \nabla\psi$ and write

$$\nabla\psi = \mathbf{l}_1 |\nabla\psi| \tag{20}$$

where $\mathbf{l}_1$ is the unit normal to the wavefront, or

$$\mathbf{l}_1 = \mathbf{i}\alpha + \mathbf{j}\beta + \mathbf{k}\gamma \tag{21}$$

where α, β, γ are the direction cosines of the unit normal. From differential geometry[1] we know that for the surface $\psi(x,y,z) = $ const, the direction cosines of the normal are

$$\alpha = \frac{\partial\psi/\partial x}{|\nabla\psi|} \qquad \beta = \frac{\partial\psi/\partial y}{|\nabla\psi|} \qquad \gamma = \frac{\partial\psi/\partial z}{|\nabla\psi|} \tag{22}$$

Hence we can write

$$\begin{aligned}
\nabla \cdot \nabla\psi &= \nabla \cdot (\mathbf{i}\alpha|\nabla\psi| + \mathbf{j}\beta|\nabla\psi| + \mathbf{k}\gamma|\nabla\psi|) \\
&= \frac{\partial}{\partial x}(\alpha|\nabla\psi|) + \frac{\partial}{\partial y}(\beta|\nabla\psi|) + \frac{\partial}{\partial z}(\gamma|\nabla\psi|) \\
&= |\nabla\psi|\nabla \cdot \mathbf{l}_1 + \frac{d|\nabla\psi|}{dl}
\end{aligned} \tag{23}$$

where we have utilized the fact that

$$\alpha = \frac{dx}{dl} \qquad \beta = \frac{dy}{dl} \qquad \gamma = \frac{dz}{dl} \tag{24}$$

since dx is the projection of dl on the x axis, etc., as well as

$$\frac{\partial\alpha}{\partial x} + \frac{\partial\beta}{\partial y} + \frac{\partial\gamma}{\partial z} = \nabla \cdot \mathbf{l}_1 \tag{25}$$

The inequality (19) now becomes

$$\frac{V_0}{V}\nabla \cdot \mathbf{l}_1 + \frac{d}{dl}\left(\frac{V_0}{V}\right) \ll \frac{\omega V_0}{V^2} \tag{26}$$

The only way to ensure this is to have

$$\lambda\nabla \cdot \mathbf{l}_1 \ll 1 \tag{27}$$

and

$$\frac{d\lambda}{dl} \ll 1 \tag{28}$$

[1] R. S. Burington and C. C. Torrance, "Higher Mathematics with Applications to Science and Engineering," p. 695, McGraw-Hill Book Company, Inc., New York, 1939.

where λ is the wavelength of the wave ($\lambda = V/\nu$). The inequality (27) demands, in effect, that the change in the direction cosines α, β, γ over a distance of one wavelength shall be negligible compared with unity. This means that, in order for the phase advance of the wave in space to be calculable from the eikonal equation, the wavefront normal must not curve too rapidly. The inequality (28) imposes the further restriction that the change in wavelength (due to change in velocity V) over a distance of the order of one wavelength is a negligible fraction of the wavelength itself. Finally, of course, there is the additional condition (7). Use of an argument similar to the one already employed shows that this means that the change in the amplitude A over a single wavelength must be small compared with A itself.

We now pause to consider some simple special cases of the eikonal equation (12). We have already noted that the plane wavefront for which $\psi = \alpha x + \beta y + \gamma z$ satisfies the equation. If

$$\psi = \sqrt{x^2 + y^2 + z^2}$$

we also get a solution, which clearly corresponds to a spherical wave. In this case, to be sure, it is only by assuming $A = A_0/\sqrt{x^2 + y^2 + z^2}$, where A_0 is constant, that we can satisfy (5) and (6) exactly.

It is now in order to examine the ray paths which are normal to the wavefronts. A particular ray can be drawn by constructing the normal trajectory which passes through a particular point on an arbitrarily chosen wavefront. But we can actually determine the differential equations of a family of normal trajectories in the following fashion. Indeed, we can write (20) in the form

$$\nabla\psi = n\mathbf{l}_1 = n(\mathbf{i}\alpha + \mathbf{j}\beta + \mathbf{k}\gamma)$$

where $n = V_0/V$ is the index of refraction. It follows identically that

$$\nabla \times \nabla\psi = 0$$

and hence that

$$\frac{\partial(\alpha n)}{\partial y} = \frac{\partial(\beta n)}{\partial x} \qquad \frac{\partial(\beta n)}{\partial z} = \frac{\partial(\gamma n)}{\partial y} \qquad \frac{\partial(\alpha n)}{\partial z} = \frac{\partial(\gamma n)}{\partial x}$$

We therefore have

$$\frac{d(\alpha n)}{dl} = \mathbf{l}_1 \cdot \nabla(\alpha n) = \frac{\partial n}{\partial x}$$

$$\frac{d(\beta n)}{dl} = \mathbf{l}_1 \cdot \nabla(\beta n) = \frac{\partial n}{\partial y} \qquad (29)$$

$$\frac{d(\gamma n)}{dl} = \mathbf{l}_1 \cdot \nabla(\gamma n) = \frac{\partial n}{\partial z}$$

The three equations (29), when solved, yield α, β, γ as functions of x, y, z, once n is given in terms of the coordinates. Hence they are the differential equations of the rays. As an example, let us suppose n is a constant (constant phase velocity throughout the medium). Then α, β, γ are also constants, and the rays, or normal trajectories, are parallel straight lines.

In Chap. 10, where we discuss sound propagation in the atmosphere and in the sea, we give illustrations of the geometrical treatment of radiation. Thus, for example, we show that, in a stratified medium in which the wave velocity varies only normally to the layers, the rays are plane curves in planes normal to the layers and that their curvature obeys a law like Snell's law of refraction in optics. As a more specific example of the same general situation, if the velocity depends linearly on distance normal to the layers, the rays are circular arcs. The case of a moving medium with a variable index of refraction is also handled in Chap. 10.

An interesting point emerges here: Can one profitably discuss the intensity or energy propagation of waves in terms of the ray picture? A plausibility consideration pointing in the direction of this possibility is already at hand in the case of plane and spherical waves. For the former the rays are parallel straight lines, and we know that the intensity remains constant if we neglect the dissipation due to absorption by the medium. On the other hand, for diverging spherical waves the rays are nonparallel straight lines radiating from the source of the radiation. In this case (Secs. 1.10 and 9.3), as we go away from the source, the intensity decreases proportionally to the inverse square of the distance, that is, in the inverse ratio of the areas subtended by a given solid angle at distance r and unit distance from the source, the diverging of rays thus appearing to be connected with decrease in intensity. Similarly, we should expect the converging of rays to be associated with increase in intensity. Consequently, if in any case we can plot a ray pattern in a radiation field, we can follow the *variation* in intensity from one part of the field to another by the changing divergence or convergence of the ray paths.

There is a fascinating problem in general theoretical physics connected with the eikonal equation (12) which ought to be mentioned here. In the transformation theory of mechanics[1] the Hamilton-Jacobi equation for a single particle of mass m moving in a field of force characterized by a potential energy function $\varphi(x,y,z)$ is

$$\left(\frac{\partial S}{\partial x}\right)^2 + \left(\frac{\partial S}{\partial y}\right)^2 + \left(\frac{\partial S}{\partial z}\right)^2 = 2m[E - \varphi(x,y,z)] \tag{30}$$

where S is the so-called "transformation function" and E is the total

---

[1] Lindsay, "Concepts and Methods of Theoretical Physics," chap. 9.

energy. S as a complete integral of (30) is a function of x, y, z, and E and of constants α_1, α_2, α_3, of which the first is additive only. As soon as this integral is found, the path of the particle and the motion along the path in time follow from the equations

$$\frac{\partial S}{\partial E} = t + \beta_1 \qquad \frac{\partial S}{\partial \alpha_2} = \beta_2 \qquad \frac{\partial S}{\partial \alpha_3} = \beta_3 \qquad (31)$$

where β_1, β_2, and β_3 are constants depending on the initial conditions. In other words, the solution of the complete dynamical problem is inherent in (31). The mathematical similarity between (30) and (12) is very striking. We could make them the same if we were to interpret the spatial phase function ψ as proportional to a transformation function S and were to take the index of refraction of the medium n as given by

$$[n(x,y,z)]^2 = \frac{2m[E - \varphi(x,y,z)]}{M_0{}^2} \qquad (32)$$

where M_0 is a constant having the dimensions of mass times velocity. It would therefore appear to be possible to treat the wave propagation of radiation [under the conditions, of course, when (12) holds] in terms of the motion of a particle for which (12) is essentially the Hamilton-Jacobi equation. In this case, then, wave motion becomes explicable in terms of particle motion. On the other hand, we could treat the Hamilton-Jacobi equation for the motion of a particle as equivalent to the eikonal equation for a radiation field and explain the motion of a particle in terms of wave motion. Then, indeed, we might expect that when, in the particle motion, the potential energy $\varphi(x,y,z)$ varied very rapidly from place to place—in particular, suffered a large fractional change over a distance of the dimensions of the particle itself—we should no longer be justified in describing its motion by an eikonal or Hamilton-Jacobi equation but would be forced to go back and employ the wave equation for which the eikonal was just a first approximation. This is the basic idea of De Broglie's *wave mechanics*,[1] so useful in the study of electrons and the other elementary particles of atomic physics.

[1] L. De Broglie, "Wave Mechanics," Macmillan & Co., Ltd., London, 1930.

CHAPTER 2

SOME GENERAL PROPERTIES OF PROGRESSIVE WAVES

2.1. Reflection and Refraction

We observed in Sec. 1.1 that, when a wave progressing through a medium encounters a surface separating this medium from another of different properties, reflection and refraction in general take place. We now desire to establish the simple geometrical principles governing these phenomena.

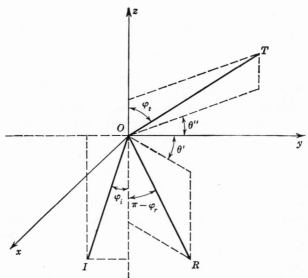

FIG. 2.1. Reflection and refraction of a plane wave at a plane interface.

We shall discuss the oblique incidence of a plane wave traveling in a medium of density ρ_1 in which the wave velocity is V_1 on the plane boundary separating this medium from another of density ρ_2 in which the wave velocity is V_2. For convenience, in Fig. 2.1 we take the boundary surface as the xy plane and let medium 1 be below the plane and medium 2 above it. There is no loss in generality in allowing the incident plane wavefront to be perpendicular to the zy plane, so that its normal IO passing through the origin O lies *in* the zy plane, which is therefore usually called the plane of incidence. If we assume that the normal extended makes the angle φ_i with the z axis, its direction cosines are 0, $\sin \varphi_i$, $\cos \varphi_i$, respectively.

To proceed as generally as possible, let us assume that the normal to the reflected wavefront OR (called for short the reflected wave normal) forms with the z axis a plane whose angle with the yz plane we call θ'. Similarly, the transmitted wave normal OT determines with the z axis a plane making the angle θ'' with the yz plane. The reflected wave normal is assumed to make the angle φ_r with the positive z axis, and the corresponding angle between the transmitted wave normal and the z axis is φ_t. The situation is depicted graphically in Fig. 2.1.

Since the incident disturbance is a plane wave, we can write the measure of the corresponding disturbance (e.g., displacement) in the form [see (1.3-4)]

$$\xi_i = g_i(\alpha_i x + \beta_i y + \gamma_i z)f\left(\frac{\alpha_i x + \beta_i y + \gamma_i z}{V_1} - t\right) \tag{1}$$

in which α_i, β_i, γ_i are the direction cosines of the normal to the wavefront. From what has been said above

$$\alpha_i = 0 \qquad \beta_i = \sin \varphi_i \qquad \gamma_i = \cos \varphi_i \tag{2}$$

for the incident wave contemplated in Fig. 2.1. Similarly, the reflected disturbance can be written in the form

$$\xi_r = g_r(\alpha_r x + \beta_r y + \gamma_r z)f\left(\frac{\alpha_r x + \beta_r y + \gamma_r z}{V_1} - t\right) \tag{3}$$

with $\qquad \alpha_r = \sin \varphi_r \sin \theta' \qquad \beta_r = \sin \varphi_r \cos \theta' \qquad \gamma_r = \cos \varphi_r \tag{4}$

Finally, the transmitted disturbance is

$$\xi_t = g_t(\alpha_t x + \beta_t y + \gamma_t z)f\left(\frac{\alpha_t x + \beta_t y + \gamma_t z}{V_2} - t\right) \tag{5}$$

with $\qquad \alpha_t = -\sin \varphi_t \sin \theta'' \qquad \beta_t = \sin \varphi_t \cos \theta'' \qquad \gamma_t = \cos \varphi_t \tag{6}$

It will be noted that in writing the reflected and transmitted waves we have assumed that the amplitude function g can change on reflection and transmission. On the other hand, we have assumed that the phase function f must remain the same. The reason is the necessity for satisfying certain boundary conditions on the interface $z = 0$ for all x, y, and t. This would be impossible if the f functions were different, no matter what the precise form of the boundary condition is. This presupposes, to be sure, that the boundary conditions are linear and homogeneous in character, which appears to be demanded by the physics of the situation.

But it is also clear that, in order to satisfy any set of boundary conditions identically everywhere on the interface at all times, the phases (or arguments of the phase functions) must be equal for all three waves. This leads to the equations

$$\frac{\sin \varphi_i}{V_1} = \frac{\sin \varphi_r \cos \theta'}{V_1} = \frac{\sin \varphi_t \cos \theta''}{V_2} \tag{7}$$

and
$$\frac{\sin \varphi_r \sin \theta'}{V_1} = -\frac{\sin \varphi_t \sin \theta''}{V_2} = 0 \tag{8}$$

From (8) it follows that, since, in general, $\sin \varphi_r$ and $\sin \varphi_t$ are different from zero,

$$\sin \theta' = \sin \theta'' = 0 \tag{9}$$

and θ' and θ'' are either zero or π. But the value of π for either is inconsistent with (7). Hence we must choose

$$\theta' = \theta'' = 0 \tag{10}$$

Equation (7) then yields (if we recall the definition of φ_r and note that the reflected wave normal must lie on the same side of the xy plane as the incident wave normal)

$$\varphi_i = \pi - \varphi_r \tag{11}$$

and
$$\frac{\sin \varphi_i}{V_1} = \frac{\sin \varphi_t}{V_2} \tag{12}$$

The laws of the reflection and refraction of a plane wavefront at a plane interface are contained in the three preceding equations. Equation (10) says that the reflected and transmitted wave normals lie in the plane of incidence. Equation (11) says that the *angle of incidence* φ_i is equal to the *angle of reflection* $\pi - \varphi_r$. Finally, (12) is the well-known Snell *law of refraction*. It is important to realize that these laws follow from the necessity of satisfying boundary conditions at the interface but are independent of the precise nature of the conditions. There are, of course, many ways of deriving them. The reader will recall the standard elementary method employing Huygens' principle. This poses difficulties which will be examined in Sec. 2.4.

It is instructive to note the bearing of the eikonal equation (1.12-12) and the theory of rays on the laws of reflection and refraction. The differential equations of the family of rays in a medium in which the index of refraction is $n(x,y,z)$ are given by (1.12-29). Let us specialize to the case in which n is a function of z only. It will then be convenient, without loss of generality, to confine our attention to the rays in the xz plane. If θ is now the angle which the tangent to the ray makes with the x axis, we have

$$\alpha = \cos \theta \qquad \gamma = \sin \theta \qquad (13)$$

and (1.12-29) become

$$\frac{d(n \cos \theta)}{dl} = 0 \qquad (14)$$

$$\frac{d(n \sin \theta)}{dl} = \frac{dn}{dz} \qquad (15)$$

Now (14) says that $n \cos \theta$ is constant along a particular ray. Recalling the definition of n as V_0/V, we can write this as

$$\frac{\cos \theta}{V} = \frac{\cos \theta''}{V'} \qquad (16)$$

where θ and θ' are the angles corresponding to the wave velocities V and V', respectively. But (16) is the generalized form of Snell's law for the case of a continuously refracting medium in which the velocity varies continuously from point to point. We thus see that the ray analysis based on the eikonal equation leads at once to the general law for the bending of rays, of which Snell's law for refraction at the discontinuous interface separating two different media is a special case. Details of ray analysis in a variable medium are presented in Sec. 2.2.

Another possible way of looking at the problem of the reflection and refraction of radiation is provided by Fermat's principle of least time. According to this, a wave disturbance always proceeds from one point to another of any medium, whether homogeneous or not, or whether or not discontinuous boundaries are encountered, in such a way that the time of transit is a minimum as compared with all possible alternative methods of transmission.[1]

If we interpret this in terms of the ray theory of wave propagation, it means that the actual ray must always be such that the time along it is a minimum as compared with all alternative possible rays connecting the same two points. We can deduce this principle from the connection between the eikonal equation (1.12-12) and the Hamilton-Jacobi equation (1.12-30) for the motion of a material particle in a force field. It will be recalled that the two equations have the same mathematical form and become identical if we identify the spatial phase function $\psi(x,y,z)$ in the eikonal equation with the transformation function $S(x,y,z)$ in the Hamil-

---

[1] This is the way in which Fermat phrased it. Actually, the more correct statement is that the time of transit has a *stationary* value compared with its values for all possible alternative paths connecting the two points. Thus it behaves like the slope of the tangent to a curve at a minimum or maximum point or at a point of inflection. In most practical cases the actual path corresponds to minimum time.

ton-Jacobi equation divided by a constant M_0 of the dimensions of mass times velocity [see (1.12-32)]. At the same time we must have

$$n(x,y,z) = \frac{\sqrt{2m[E - \varphi(x,y,z)]}}{M_0} \qquad (17)$$

We may thus say that the transmission of a wave from one point to another in a nonhomogeneous medium characterized by index of refraction $n(x,y,z)$, in so far as it can be treated by means of rays, is equivalent to the motion of a material particle of mass m and total energy E in a field of force given by the potential energy $\varphi(x,y,z)$. But we know that the motion of the particle proceeds in accordance with the principle of least action, so that for the actual path between two points A and B the integral

$$\int_A^B \sqrt{2m[E - \varphi(x,y,z)]}\, ds \qquad (18)$$

has a stationary value compared with its values for all possible alternative paths connecting A and B for which the same total energy E is involved. Consequently we conclude that the actual ray in the case of wave-ray transmission from A to B is that for which

$$\int_A^B \frac{ds}{V} \qquad (19)$$

has a stationary value compared with all possible alternative rays connecting A and B for which the radiation quantity corresponding to the energy of the analogous material particle remains the same. Leaving aside for a moment the significance of this last point, we see that the integral (19) is the total time of transit from A to B if ds measures elementary distance along a ray. Hence we have Fermat's principle, though we are left with the problem of deciding what it is for radiation that corresponds to the energy of the particle in the analogy on which the demonstration depends. In the case of light the quantum theory supplies the answer: it is the product of Planck's constant h and the frequency. We have thus to suppose that the frequency of the radiation remains constant as the medium is traversed, independently of its homogeneity. This assumption appears well substantiated. The case of elastic radiation, if treated analogously, would appear to demand the introduction of a quantum of such radiation energy. This has actually been provided by the assumption of the existence of the so-called *phonon* (see Sec. 12.10).

We can now apply Fermat's principle to deduce the laws of reflection and refraction. In Fig. 2.2, A denotes a source of radiation, and MM' is the trace of a plane boundary separating two media, in the upper of which the wave velocity is V_1 and in the lower V_2. Assuming that we can treat the radiation leaving A as in the form of rays, we desire to find the ray from A which, when reflected at MM', arrives at the point B, it being assumed for simplicity that B lies in the plane which A forms with MM'. First we draw AO and OB in such a way that

The angle $AON =$ the angle NOB

Then we extend BO to C where AC is perpendicular to MM'. We wish to show that the path AOB is traversed in shorter time than any other path, such as $AO'B$, joining A and B after reflection at the boundary. (Note that we initially assume all the alternative rays to lie in the plane

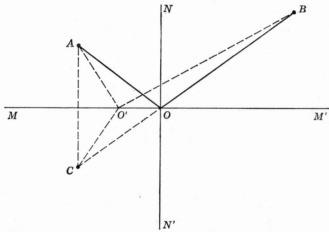

FIG. 2.2. Reflection at a plane interface by Fermat's principle.

passing through MM' and containing A and B.) From the geometry of the figure, $AO = OC$, and $AO' = O'C$. Now from the properties of the triangle

$$CO' + O'B > COB$$

Hence
$$AO' + O'B > AO + OB$$

which means that the path AOB is indeed the shortest one that meets the conditions. But since the velocity is the same along all paths above MM', it is also the path traversed in minimum time. To make the demonstration cogent we really have to compare the time along AOB with that along $AO'B$ when O' is at any point of the boundary interface and not specialized in the plane AOB. However, the reader is asked to make the same kind of construction as that used above and to show that, no matter where O' lies in the boundary surface, the total path length of the reflected ray from A to B is greater than AOB. Hence we can conclude that the reflected ray lies in the same plane as the incident ray and that the angle of reflection ($\angle NOB$) equals the angle of incidence ($\angle AON$).

In Fig. 2.3 we consider the case of transmission from point A at perpendicular distance h_1 above the boundary plane to point B at perpendicular distance h_2 below it. The normal to the plane is denoted by NPN', and we assume that the plane containing A and B is the plane MNM' normal to the boundary plane and intersecting it in MPM'. The normal projection of A on the boundary plane is O and that of B is Q. The distance OQ is taken as l. The problem is to construct the path of the rays from A to B so as to satisfy Fermat's principle. It is assumed

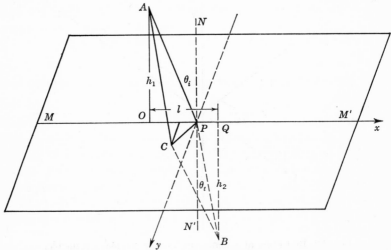

Fig. 2.3. Refraction at a plane interface by Fermat's principle.

that in each medium the ray will be a straight line, since everywhere in the top medium the wave velocity has the constant value V_1 and everywhere in the bottom medium the value V_2. Let us arbitrarily suppose that the proper ray in the top medium is AC, where the coordinates of C in a system of rectangular axes with origin at O are x, y. Then CB is the transmitted ray. Fermat's principle now requires that we minimize the expression

$$\frac{AC}{V_1} + \frac{CB}{V_2} = \frac{\sqrt{x^2 + y^2 + h_1{}^2}}{V_1} + \frac{\sqrt{(l-x)^2 + y^2 + h_2{}^2}}{V_2}$$

with respect to changes in both x and y. The necessary conditions for the minimum are obtained by differentiating with respect to y and x, respectively, and placing the results equal to zero. Thus

$$\frac{y}{V_1 \sqrt{x^2 + y^2 + h_1{}^2}} + \frac{y}{V_2 \sqrt{(l - x)^2 + y^2 + h_2{}^2}} = 0 \qquad (20)$$

$$\frac{x}{V_1 \sqrt{x^2 + y^2 + h_1{}^2}} - \frac{l - x}{V_2 \sqrt{(l - x)^2 + y^2 + h_2{}^2}} = 0 \qquad (21)$$

Equation (20) yields

$$y = 0$$

which means that the rays AC and CB lie in the same plane. Using $y = 0$ in (21) yields ultimately

$$\frac{\sin \theta_i}{\sin \theta_t} = \frac{V_1}{V_2} \qquad (22)$$

where θ_i is the angle of incidence ($\angle APN$) and θ_t the angle of refraction ($\angle BPN'$). This is Snell's law of refraction and completes the deduction of the laws of reflection and refraction by Fermat's principle.

2.2. Ray Theory of Transmission through a Medium of Variable Index of Refraction

In numerous cases it is adequate to discuss by means of ray analysis the transmission of radiation through a nonhomogeneous medium in which the velocity (and hence the index of refraction) varies with position. The conditions governing the existence of the eikonal equation (1.12-12) must of course be observed, but these will be satisfied if we are dealing with variations in velocity which are small in a distance of the order of a wavelength for harmonic waves. Ray analysis may therefore in general be expected to work best for relatively short wavelengths.

Instead of using the differential ray equations (1.12-29) we can profitably start with the eikonal equation itself and the associated analysis in Sec. 1.12. For simplicity, we confine our attention to a stratified medium in which the index of refraction n is a function of one variable only, say z. We then examine the rays in the xz plane, so that ψ is a function of x and z only and $\partial \psi / \partial y = 0$. The eikonal equation (1.12-12) then becomes, with V_0/V written as $n(z)$,

$$\left(\frac{\partial \psi}{\partial x}\right)^2 + \left(\frac{\partial \psi}{\partial z}\right)^2 = [n(z)]^2 \qquad (1)$$

A complete integral of this equation may be obtained by a method of separation of variables of a different kind[1] from that employed in Sec.

---

[1] For the general theory of first-order partial differential equations and their so-called complete integrals or primitives, see R. S. Burington and C. C. Torrance, "Higher Mathematics with Applications to Science and Engineering," pp. 326ff., McGraw-Hill Book Company, Inc., New York, 1939.

1.8.   Let us suppose that ψ can be written as the sum of a function of x alone and a function of z alone.   Thus

$$\psi = \psi_1(x) + \psi_2(z) \tag{2}$$

whence substitution into (1) yields

$$\left(\frac{d\psi_1}{dx}\right)^2 = [n(z)]^2 - \left(\frac{d\psi_2}{dz}\right)^2 \tag{3}$$

Since the left-hand side of (3) is a function of x alone and the right-hand side is a function of z, the only way to satisfy the equation is to put each side equal to a constant, say, C_1^2.   Thus

$$\psi_1 = C_1 x$$

and $$\psi_2 = \int \sqrt{[n(z)]^2 - C_1^2}\, dz + C_2$$

The complete integral is then

$$\psi(x,z) = C_1 x + \int \sqrt{[n(z)]^2 - C_1^2}\, dz + C_2 \tag{4}$$

We can now use this solution to obtain the differential equation of the family of rays in the xz plane, as follows.   From (1.12-15, 22) we see that the direction cosines of the ray, α and γ, are given by (note here that $\beta = 0$)

$$\alpha = \cos\theta = \frac{\partial\psi}{\partial x}\bigg/ n \qquad \gamma = \sin\theta = \frac{\partial\psi}{\partial z}\bigg/ n \tag{5}$$

where θ is the angle which the tangent to the ray at any point makes with the x axis.   If the equation of the ray is written in the form

$$z = f(x) \tag{6}$$

it is clear that

$$\frac{dz}{dx} = \tan\theta = \frac{\partial\psi}{\partial z}\bigg/ \frac{\partial\psi}{\partial x} \tag{7}$$

Therefore, from (4), we have

$$\frac{dz}{dx} = \sqrt{\frac{[n(z)]^2}{C_1^2} - 1} \tag{8}$$

Integrating yields

$$x = \int_0^z \frac{dz}{\sqrt{[n(z)]^2/C_1^2 - 1}} + x_0 \tag{9}$$

as the equation of the family of rays in the xz plane.

As an illustration, let us examine the case in which n is of the form

$$n = \frac{1}{1 + az} \tag{10}$$

where a is a constant parameter. If we introduce the transformation

$$1 + az = \frac{\sin \theta}{C_1} \tag{11}$$

(9) takes the form

$$x - x_0 = \frac{1}{C_1 a} \int_{\arcsin C_1}^{\arcsin C_1(1+az)} \sin \theta \, d\theta$$

or the resulting x, z relation becomes

$$\left[x - \left(x_0 - \frac{\sqrt{1 - C_1^2}}{C_1 a} \right) \right]^2 + \left(z + \frac{1}{a} \right)^2 = \frac{1}{C_1^2 a^2} \tag{12}$$

which is the equation of a circle in the xz plane with center at

$$\left(x_0 - \frac{\sqrt{1 - C_1^2}}{C_1 a}, \; -\frac{1}{a} \right)$$

and with radius $1/C_1 a$.

The situation is depicted in Fig. 2.4. If $a > 0$, the rays are arcs of circles that in the quadrant for which $x > 0$, $z > 0$ are concave upward

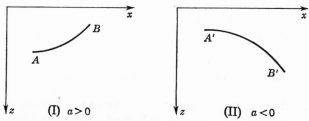

FIG. 2.4. Rays in a medium of variable index of refraction. (I) $a > 0$; (II) $a < 0$.

(AB in I), whereas for $a < 0$, the rays are arcs of circles that in the same quadrant are concave downward for sufficiently small z ($A'B'$ in II). The situation in II will of course be reversed if the z coordinate of A' is greater than $-1/a$. These results can be checked qualitatively by drawing wavefronts in any direction from A or A' and taking account of the variation of wave velocity with z. These conclusions are useful in the study of the propagation of sound in the atmosphere and in the sea (see Chap. 10).

2.3. Elementary Theory of Diffraction and Interference

The diffraction of waves, which we have already commented on in Sec. 1.1, is, in its simplest terms, the capacity for wave radiation to bend around the corners of obstacles. This means that no obstacle in the path of an advancing wave can ever cast a sharp shadow. It will be instructive to begin our study with a simple example, namely, the passage of radiation through a circular orifice in a screen which is otherwise opaque.

Figure 2.5 shows in perspective the orifice of radius R and center O in the plane screen S. It is assumed that a plane harmonic wave is incident on the screen from the left, with its wavefront parallel to the plane of the screen, and passes through the hole to the right. Our task is to study the nature of the disturbance produced by the wave at points to the right of the screen. We shall first consider the effect at P, where OP $(= r)$ is the normal to the hole through its center. It is plausible to

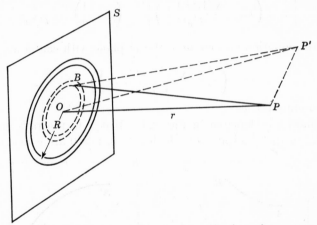

FIG. 2.5. Diffraction through a circular orifice in a plane screen.

assume that the resultant effect at P will be due to the superposition of the effects produced separately by each small portion of the wavefront in the hole. We imagine the construction about O as a center of an annular ring of such mean radius OB that the difference between PB and PO is much smaller than a half wavelength of the radiation in question. We then proceed to construct a whole series of circles about O so that the areas of the annular rings thus formed all have the same area. This will be achieved if the radii increase in the ratio of the square roots of the integers. We further suppose that the effect of each annular ring at P is due to two causes: (1) its area and (2) its distance from P. The larger the area, the greater the magnitude of the effect; the greater the distance, the smaller the intensity in the ratio of the inverse square of the distance. Finally, the phase at P will also depend on the distance.

The total effect at P can be most simply represented by a vector diagram (see Fig. 2.6) in which the magnitude of the disturbance produced by each annular ring is represented by the length of a vector and the phase difference in the disturbances is indicated by the angles made by the various vectors with each other. The situation is best represented graphically in rather approximate fashion. In the figure we have laid off the vector $\mathbf{a}_1$ from Q to A_1 on an arbitrarily chosen x axis to represent the amplitude of the disturbance due to the first annular ring about O in the center of the opening in Fig. 2.5. (Strictly, this is a circle with O as center and radius much smaller than a half wavelength.) The magnitude of $\mathbf{a}_1$ represents the magnitude of the wave disturbance produced at P by the wavefront region in question. The effect of the next annular region is represented by the vector $\mathbf{a}_2$ from A_1 to A_2. This is somewhat smaller in magnitude than $\mathbf{a}_1$ and, moreover, makes the angle θ_1 with the

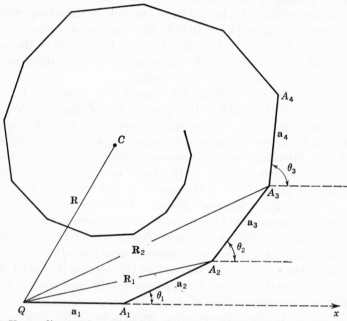

Fig. 2.6. Vector diagram for computing magnitude of diffracted disturbance at a point.

x axis. The former characteristic reflects the fact that the annular region in question is somewhat farther from P and hence must be expected to contribute a smaller disturbance; the latter implies that the second disturbance is somewhat out of phase with the first, since it takes longer to reach P than the first. When we superpose the disturbances, we therefore get $\mathbf{R}_1$ as the sum of $\mathbf{a}_1$ and $\mathbf{a}_2$. Proceeding in this way, we find that the successive annular rings produce individual disturbances $\mathbf{a}_3$, $\mathbf{a}_4$— with corresponding resultant disturbances $\mathbf{R}_2$, $\mathbf{R}_3$. The latter grow in magnitude until we reach that $\mathbf{a}$ for which the angle θ is equal to π. This implies that the last component disturbance is due to an annular ring which is a half wavelength farther from P than is O. If this annular ring has an outside circumference just coinciding with the hole, the radiation passing through the hole will produce a maximum effect at P. However, if the hole is larger than this, continuation of the above process will produce R vectors which gradually *decrease* in magnitude (see Fig. 2.6) to a minimum when $\theta = 2\pi$, corresponding to a phase difference of a whole wavelength.[1]

It is unnecessary to labor the point further to see that the disturbance at P passes through a series of maxima and minima as the number of annular rings in the hole increases, the corresponding vectors in Fig. 2.6 forming effectively a spiral, so that the resultant disturbance approaches a limiting value given by R, the vector from Q to the limit point C of the spiral. If the radius of the hole is very large compared with the wavelength of the radiation, the limiting disturbance will be very nearly produced. On the other hand, if the hole is of the order of magnitude of the wavelength, the disturbance at P will differ markedly in intensity with small changes in its radius.

The question now arises, What will happen if we consider a point P' in the plane through P parallel to the screen S but off the axis OP? Here the situation is more complicated, since we no longer have the symmetry presented by P and can therefore not use annular rings as effective sources in the hole. However, by an argument similar to that just presented, we can see qualitatively that, as P' moves away from P, the intensity of the radiation falls off, but in the process passes through a succession of steadily decreasing maxima and minima. Another way of putting this is to say that P is surrounded by a series of diffraction rings which gradually grow weaker in intensity as the radii increase, until the intensity falls effectively to zero at a sufficiently large distance from P.

Even from the qualitative treatment of this section it is clear that we cannot discuss the diffraction of waves successfully unless we assume the possibility of the superposition of waves reaching a given point from different sources. In the corresponding problem in optics such waves are said to *interfere* with each other, and there are many illustrations of the interference of light waves—for example, the famous Young experiment on the interference of light reaching a given screen after emerging from two slits. All waves show this property, and we have indeed already encountered examples in Chap. 1. Thus the production of standing waves in extended media (Sec. 1.5) is an illustration of interference; at certain points the superposition of the waves in various directions takes place in such a fashion as to produce a large amplitude (i.e., the loops), and this is called *constructive* interference. At other points (the nodes) the resultant disturbance vanishes, and the interference is termed

---

[1] All this is approximate to the extent that it ignores edge effects. For an account of the diffraction of light, see F. A. Jenkins and H. E. White, "Fundamentals of Optics," 2d ed., pp. 279ff., McGraw-Hill Book Company, Inc., New York, 1950.

destructive. Certain types of wave modulation (Sec. 1.6) leading to beats and similar phenomena provide other examples of interference.

Any situation in which waves can reach a given point after having traversed different paths from the same source provides a particularly good illustration of interference. Numerous examples are encountered in practice. Thus, when a source of sound radiates near the surface of the earth, the resultant disturbance at a distant point is due not merely to the radiation traveling directly to the point but also to that which is first reflected from the earth and then reaches the receiving point. The interference effects here can lead to considerable variation in the received intensity, depending on the ratio of the distance between source and receiver to the wavelength. The analytical details of this problem for both air and water transmission are worked out in Secs. 3.6 and 10.5. In fact, all sound transmission in the atmosphere and the sea involves both diffraction and interference in a rather complicated way, and the same is true for bounded solids. It is fortunate that in many such cases ray analysis (Sec. 1.12) is adequate for the practical description.

It must be emphasized again that the treatment in this section is highly approximate and not at all rigorous. It is intended merely to provide a descriptive basis for the mathematical discussion in the next section.

2.4. Analytical Theory of Diffraction. Huygens' Principle

To discuss the diffraction of waves mathematically it is essential to put Huygens' principle on a more substantial foundation than is usual in elementary presentations. It will be recalled that the principle in its elementary formulation says that, if we know the wavefront of a traveling disturbance at a given instant and wish to find the corresponding wavefront at an infinitesimal time later, we treat each point on the original wavefront as the source of a hemispherical wavelet of radius equal to the phase velocity of the wave multiplied by the time interval in question. The new wavefront is then the mathematical envelope of all the wavelets so constructed. The elementary presentation contains no explanation of why hemispherical wavelets are chosen instead of spherical wavelets, except the fact that the latter would lead to backward, as well as forward, motion of the wavefront.

We revert to the general wave equation (1.12-1)

$$\nabla^2 f = \frac{\ddot{f}}{V^2} \tag{1}$$

and examine its solution for disturbances harmonic in time with angular frequency ω, that is, $f = F(x,y,z)e^{i\omega t}$. In this case (1) reduces to

$$\nabla^2 F + k^2 F = 0 \tag{2}$$

with $k = \omega/V$, as usual. We wish to find a solution of (1) in terms of the values of f and its space and time derivatives over any given closed surface. This will enable us, starting from a given wavefront, to construct a new wavefront and hence to follow the wave propagation.

Concentrating first on (2), we employ Green's theorem. If $\mathbf{Q}$ is an arbitrary vector function of position, that is,

$$\mathbf{Q} = \mathbf{i}Q_x + \mathbf{j}Q_y + \mathbf{k}Q_z \tag{3}$$

where Q_x, Q_y, Q_z are, respectively, the x, y, z components of $\mathbf{Q}$, the divergence theorem[1] says that

$$\int \mathbf{Q} \cdot d\mathbf{S} = \int \nabla \cdot \mathbf{Q} \, d\tau \tag{4}$$

where the left-hand side is the surface integral of the normal component of $\mathbf{Q}$ over a closed surface and the right-hand side is the volume integral of the *divergence* of $\mathbf{Q}$ over the volume enclosed by the surface (the element of volume is $d\tau$ and that of surface $d\mathbf{S}$). If we let

$$\mathbf{Q} = U\nabla U' \tag{5}$$

where U and U' are continuous and twice differentiable scalar functions of x, y, z, (4) becomes

$$\int \nabla U \cdot \nabla U' \, d\tau + \int U\nabla^2 U' \, d\tau = \int U \frac{\partial U'}{\partial n} \, dS \tag{6}$$

where $\partial U'/\partial n$ is the rate of change of U' along the outward normal to the surface, that is $(\partial U'/\partial n) \, dS = \nabla U' \cdot d\mathbf{S}$. Writing $\mathbf{Q} = U'\nabla U$, we get in place of (6)

$$\int \nabla U' \cdot \nabla U \, d\tau + \int U'\nabla^2 U \, d\tau = \int U' \frac{\partial U}{\partial n} \, dS \tag{7}$$

Subtraction of (7) from (6) gives

$$\int (U\nabla^2 U' - U'\nabla^2 U) \, d\tau = \int \left(U \frac{\partial U'}{\partial n} - U' \frac{\partial U}{\partial n} \right) dS \tag{8}$$

which, with the meaning already given to the functions U and U' and the

---

[1] R. B. Lindsay, "Concepts and Methods of Theoretical Physics," pp. 282ff., D. Van Nostrand Company, Inc., Princeton, N.J., 1951. For the mathematical conditions under which the divergence theorem holds, see Philip Franklin, "Treatise on Advanced Calculus," p. 378, John Wiley & Sons, Inc., New York, 1940. Note that though the theorem is most readily derivable for simply connected regions (i.e., those in which any simple closed polygon made up entirely of points of the region has all its interior points inside the region), it is also applicable, under conditions encountered in experience, in multiply connected regions—for example, a sphere with a hole in it, or a torus.

nature of the integrals, constitutes one form of Green's theorem and indeed the one we find useful in the solution of our problem.

Let us put

$$U = \frac{e^{-ikr}}{r} \tag{9}$$

where r is the distance from the chosen point P to the volume element $d\tau$, and let $U' = F$ in (2). The function U chosen here is known as a Green function.[1] Its key position in the solution by the method being outlined here will become clearer as we proceed.

We now suppose P is surrounded by the surface S_1 (Fig. 2.7) and further by the small sphere S_2. The volume over which the volume integration in (8) is to be conducted is that enclosed between S_1 and S_2, and the surface integral on the right of (8) is taken over the combination of S_1 and S_2.

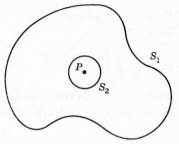

Fig. 2.7. Surfaces for illustration of Green's theorem.

From (9) it follows by direct inspection that

$$\nabla^2 U + k^2 U = 0 \tag{10}$$

The volume integral in (8) therefore becomes

$$\int U(\nabla^2 U' + k^2 U') \, d\tau$$

which vanishes because of (2). The surface integral must likewise equal zero. This is made up of two parts: one over S_1 and the other over S_2. Let us consider first the integral over S_2, which takes the form

$$\int \left[\frac{e^{-ika}}{a} \left(-\frac{\partial F}{\partial a} \right) + F \frac{\partial}{\partial a} \left(\frac{e^{-ika}}{a} \right) \right] dS_2 \tag{11}$$

where we have denoted the radius of the sphere S_2 by a. The expression $\partial F/\partial a$ is $\partial F/\partial n$ calculated for $r = a$. Recalling that $dS_2 = a^2 \, d\Omega$, where $d\Omega$ is the element of solid angle about P, and realizing that F and $\partial F/\partial a$ must stay finite as $a \to 0$, we see that the only nonvanishing part of the integral in (11) comes from the second term in the integral and yields

$$-4\pi F_P \tag{12}$$

---

[1] For a lengthy discussion of Green's functions and their role in the solution of partial differential equations subject to boundary conditions, see P. M. Morse and H. Feshbach, "Methods of Theoretical Physics," pp. 791ff., McGraw-Hill Book Company, Inc., New York, 1953.

where F_P is the value of F at the point P.   Hence

$$F_P = \frac{1}{4\pi} \int \left[\frac{e^{-ikr}}{r} \frac{\partial F}{\partial n} - F \frac{\partial}{\partial n} \left(\frac{e^{-ikr}}{r} \right) \right] dS_1$$

which can be expanded as

$$F_P = \frac{1}{4\pi} \int \left[\frac{e^{-ikr}}{r} \frac{\partial F}{\partial n} - Fe^{-ikr} \frac{\partial}{\partial n} \left(\frac{1}{r} \right) + ikF \frac{e^{-ikr}}{r} \frac{\partial r}{\partial n} \right] dS_1 \quad (13)$$

Hence, remembering that $k = \omega/V$ and the relation between F and f, we have

$$f_P = \frac{1}{4\pi} \int \left[\frac{e^{i\omega(t-r/V)}}{r} \frac{\partial F}{\partial n} - Fe^{i\omega(t-r/V)} \frac{\partial}{\partial n} \left(\frac{1}{r} \right) + ikF \frac{e^{i\omega(t-r/V)}}{r} \frac{\partial r}{\partial n} \right] dS_1 \quad (14)$$

Now $Fe^{i\omega(t-r/V)}$ is the same as f taken at time $t - r/V$ instead of at time t. We indicate this retarded character by writing

$$Fe^{i\omega(t-r/V)} = [f] \quad (15)$$

In this notation (14) has the form

$$f_p = \frac{1}{4\pi} \int \left\{ \frac{1}{r} \left[\frac{\partial f}{\partial n} \right] - \frac{\partial}{\partial n} \left(\frac{1}{r} \right) [f] + \frac{1}{rV} \frac{\partial r}{\partial n} \left[\frac{\partial f}{\partial t} \right] \right\} dS_1 \quad (16)$$

This equation emphasizes that the value of f at any point P is the sum of contributions from the various surface elements dS_1.   This is recognized as analogous to Huygens' principle in the elementary physics treatment of wave propagation.   It is indeed the generalized form of the principle. To get the value of the disturbance at time t at point P we must consider the corresponding values of f, $\partial f/\partial n$, and $\partial f/\partial t$ on the surface S_1 at time $t - r/V$, where r/V is the time necessary for the disturbance to travel the distance r from dS_1 to P.

The connection with the elementary form of Huygens' principle appears in clearer light if we apply (16) to a special problem.   In Fig. 2.8, let us

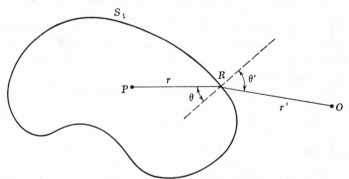

Fig. 2.8. Generalized Huygens' principle.

suppose that O is a point source of spherical harmonic waves. We wish to calculate the resultant disturbance at P in terms of the disturbance and its derivatives on the surface S_1 enclosing P. We draw the line OR from O to R, where the element dS_1 is located, and let $PR = r$ and $RO = r'$. The angles between the outward drawn normal at R and the lines PR and RO are θ and θ', respectively. The disturbance at R due to the point source at O is (to use the real part only)

$$f = \frac{A}{r'} \cos(\omega t - kr') \tag{17}$$

whence we find

$$\frac{\partial f}{\partial n} \doteq - \frac{Ak \cos \theta'}{r'} \sin(\omega t - kr') \tag{18}$$

to the approximation which assumes that the wavelength λ $(= 2\pi/k)$ is very small compared with r'. Recalling that

$$\frac{\partial(1/r)}{\partial n} = - \frac{\cos \theta}{r^2} \tag{19}$$

we finally get from (16) the result (paying due regard to the retarded character)

$$f_P = \frac{1}{4\pi} \int \left\{ - \frac{Ak \cos \theta'}{rr'} \sin[\omega t - k(r + r')] \right.$$
$$+ \frac{A \cos \theta}{r'r^2} \cos[\omega t - k(r + r')]$$
$$\left. - \frac{Ak \cos \theta}{r'r} \sin[\omega t - k(r + r')] \right\} dS_1 \tag{20}$$

But the approximation $\lambda \ll r'$ further reduces this to

$$f_P = - \frac{A}{2\lambda} \int \frac{1}{r'r} (\cos \theta + \cos \theta') \sin[\omega t - k(r + r')] \, dS_1 \tag{21}$$

This means that the resultant disturbance at P is obtained from the superposition of spherical wavelets from each element dS_1, each having the amplitude

$$\frac{A}{\lambda r' r} \frac{\cos \theta + \cos \theta'}{2}$$

and with a phase difference represented by the difference between $\sin[\omega t - k(r + r')]$ and $\cos(\omega t - kr')$.

The approximate expression (21) is commonly called the Fresnel-Kirchhoff diffraction formula.[1] The attenuation suffered by the various

[1] B. B. Baker and E. T. Copson, "The Mathematical Theory of Huygens' Principle," pp. 72ff., Clarendon Press, Oxford, 1939.

wavelets is exhibited by the product $r'r$ in the denominator. The actual evaluation of the integral is difficult except in special cases, and then only by approximation. However, it is possible to apply to it Kelvin's so-called "principle of stationary phase"[1] and conclude that for large k (small wavelength) the most significant contribution to the integral is made when the phase $k(r + r')$ is stationary. This means[2] that, if we draw the line OP from the source O to the point P at which the ultimate effect of the radiation is to be calculated, only those elements dS_1 of the surface S_1 which lie near this line will make a significant contribution to the integral and hence will be important in the computation of the resultant effect at P. In the evaluation of the integral, therefore, it is sufficient (for small wavelength) to consider $\cos \theta$ and $\cos \theta'$ close to unity, so that the term $(\cos \theta + \cos \theta')/2$ becomes practically unity itself. This mathematical formulation removes the difficulty inherent in the original presentation of Huygens' principle, as already mentioned at the beginning of the section, namely, the neglect of the contribution of the wavelets *back* of the original wavefront to the construction of the new wavefront. We see that in the backward direction from any surface element dS_1 (keeping in mind the stationary phase idea already emphasized) $\cos \theta \doteq - \cos \theta'$ and hence the contribution to the integral will become vanishingly small.

2.5. Polarization of Waves

In Sec. 1.5 we discussed the superposition of waves traveling in the same direction. There it was tacitly assumed that the two traveling disturbances were summable by direct addition—in other words, that, if motions, they were in the same direction. This is the case, for example, if the disturbances are displacements in the same direction as that of propagation, that is, if the waves are longitudinal. On the other hand, if the disturbance in each case is at right angles to the direction of propagation (transverse wave), the composition is more involved and leads to more interesting consequences.

To illustrate, let us imagine two harmonic waves of the same angular frequency ω progressing along the x axis with the same velocity V. In the first the disturbance is a displacement of the medium in the y direction, and in the second it is a displacement in the z direction (see Fig. 2.9). If we denote the first displacement as η and the second as ζ, we have

$$\begin{aligned} \eta &= A_1 \cos (\omega t - kx + \epsilon_1) \\ \zeta &= A_2 \cos (\omega t - kx + \epsilon_2) \end{aligned} \tag{1}$$

[1] J. J. Stoker, "Water Waves," pp. 163f., Interscience Publishers, Inc., New York, 1957.

[2] J. Larmor, *Proc. London Math. Soc.*, **19** (2), 174 (1919).

where we have assumed the waves to have the amplitudes A_1 and A_2, respectively, and likewise the different phases ϵ_1 and ϵ_2, respectively. The question is, What is the resultant disturbance corresponding to the superposition of η and ζ? The simplest way to handle this is to place

$$\omega t - kx + \epsilon_1 = \varphi \tag{2}$$

and
$$\omega t - kx + \epsilon_2 = \varphi + \epsilon_2 - \epsilon_1 = \varphi + \psi \tag{3}$$

Then if we eliminate φ between η and ζ, the result is

$$\frac{\eta^2}{A_1{}^2 \sin^2 \psi} - \frac{2\eta\zeta}{A_1 A_2 \sin \psi \tan \psi} + \frac{\zeta^2}{A_2{}^2 \sin^2 \psi} = 1 \tag{4}$$

which is the equation of a conic. Application of the usual test indicates that the conic is an ellipse. This means that the particles of the medium whose disturbance from equilibrium is propagated as a harmonic wave

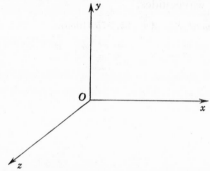

Fig. 2.9. Rectangular coordinates to illustrate polarization of waves.

move in such a way that the projection of their motion on any plane perpendicular to the direction of propagation is an ellipse with semiaxes $A_1 \sin \psi$ and $A_2 \sin \psi$, respectively. The result is termed an *elliptically* polarized harmonic wave. Since the disturbance in the first of the two harmonic waves is in the y direction and confined to the xy plane, we call it a *plane* polarized wave; the same is true for the wave whose disturbance is a displacement in the z direction. We have thus shown that the superposition of two plane polarized harmonic waves proceeding in a common direction with the same velocity but with different amplitudes and initial phases leads to an elliptically polarized wave.

Certain special cases are of interest. If the amplitudes A_1 and A_2 are equal and $\psi = \pi/2$, the ellipse reduces to a circle, and the resultant wave is termed *circularly* polarized. On the other hand, if $\psi = 0$, the resultant disturbance lies in the plane through the x axis given by the equation

$$\frac{\eta}{A_1} = \frac{\zeta}{A_2} \tag{5}$$

This disturbance is still a plane polarized wave, but the plane of polarization has been rotated through the angle arctan (A_2/A_1) from the y axis.

The standard illustrations of polarized waves are, of course, provided by light and electromagnetic radiation in general, with which we shall not have much to deal in this book (see, however, Sec. 6.7). In fact, it is the phenomenon of optical polarization which convinced early workers in optics that light waves must be transverse in character. We shall expect to find similar effects in transverse elastic waves (shear waves) in solids. This has historical interest in connection with the so-called "elastic solid theory of light," which has long since been replaced by the electromagnetic theory. For discussion of shear waves in solids, see Chaps. 6 and 7, as well as Sec. 10.6 on seismic waves. For longitudinal waves the polarization effects here being considered do not exist. However, interesting effects very similar to the polarization of transverse waves occur in so-called acoustical waveguides.[1]

[1] W. E. Kock, *J. Acoust. Soc. Am.*, **25**, 575 (1953).

CHAPTER 3

WAVES SUBJECT TO BOUNDARY CONDITIONS.
HARMONIC ANALYSIS

3.1. Boundary Conditions. Normal Modes. Fourier Analysis

We have already had occasion to note the effect of rigid boundaries, in a medium in which radiation exists, in setting up standing waves (Sec. 1.5) with certain characteristic, or normal-mode, frequencies. We now wish to carry the discussion further and, in particular, to find the precise expression for the wave disturbance in bounded media.

We revert to the simplest case of a finite one-dimensional medium in which a wave disturbance vanishes at all times at $x = 0$ and $x = l$. We showed in Sec. 1.5 that under these conditions the normal modes have frequencies of the form

$$\nu_n = \frac{nV}{2l} \tag{1}$$

where V is, as usual, the wave velocity and n any positive integer. The wave disturbance corresponding to frequency ν_n then becomes

$$f_n = (A_n \sin \omega_n t + B_n \cos \omega_n t) \sin \frac{n\pi x}{l} \tag{2}$$

where $\omega_n = 2\pi\nu_n =$ angular frequency of the nth normal mode, and A_n and B_n are arbitrary amplitude coefficients whose values obviously depend on the initial state of the disturbance. But the initial conditions may not relate to the nth harmonic; in general it is not to be expected that a particular harmonic will be excited when the medium is disturbed. Here we fall back on an assumption, the so-called "principle of superposition," first enunciated by Daniel Bernoulli in 1755. According to this, any possible wave disturbance in the bounded linear medium can be represented as the sum or superposition of expressions like (2) for all n. The complete disturbance then has the form

$$f = \sum_{n=1}^{\infty} (A_n \sin \omega_n t + B_n \cos \omega_n t) \sin \frac{n\pi x}{l} \tag{3}$$

It must be emphasized that this is a postulate whose value is to be judged by its success in predicting experience. From the mathematical standpoint it is true that, since the fundamental wave equation is linear, the sum of any finite number of individual solutions is also a solution (Sec. 1.7). However, this by no means guarantees the existence of a solution like (3) involving an *infinite* sum of terms. Much mathematics is involved in this problem.[1] It suffices for our purposes here to state that, if we fix x and consider f in (3) as a function of t alone and if the coefficients A_n and B_n are such that the series converges uniformly in the domain $0 \le t \le 2l/V$ [recall (1)], it will converge for all values of t and represent a periodic function of time with period equal to $2l/V$.

There are many ways in which the initial conditions can be expressed: we might, for example, specify the precise value of f for every value of x from 0 to l for two different instants of time. It is more conventional, however, to specify the values of f and $\dot{f}$ for all x in the interval at one instant of time, say, for convenience, $t = 0$. Calling these functions $f_0(x)$ and $\dot{f}_0(x)$, respectively, we have, from (3),

$$f_0(x) = \sum_{n=1}^{\infty} B_n \sin \frac{n\pi x}{l} \qquad (4)$$

$$\dot{f}_0(x) = \sum_{n=1}^{\infty} A_n \omega_n \sin \frac{n\pi x}{l} \qquad (5)$$

Each of these series is termed a Fourier series, specialized indeed since only sine and no cosine terms are present. The possibility of representing an arbitrary function like $f_0(x)$ in terms of such a series involves mathematical problems. It turns out to be sufficient for the representation that $f_0(x)$ and its first derivative with respect to x shall be piecewise continuous in the interval (that is, $0 \le x \le l$) in question. This means that they are continuous for all save a finite number of points in the interval. It may be shown that coefficients may be determined so that the series (4) converges to $f_0(x)$ at all points of continuity and to

$$\tfrac{1}{2}[f_0(x+) + f_0(x-)]$$

at points of discontinuity. Here $f_0(x+)$ means the value of the function at the discontinuity at x as the point is approached from the right, and $f_0(x-)$ means, correspondingly, the value when approached from the left.

Assuming the possibility of the expansion, we can calculate the coefficients A_n and B_n in the following way. Multiplying both sides of (4)

---

[1] Philip Franklin, "Methods of Advanced Calculus," pp. 401ff., McGraw-Hill Book Company, Inc., New York, 1944.

by $\sin (n'\pi x/l)$, where n' is any integer, we then integrate the result from 0 to l. Thus

$$\int_0^l f_0(x) \sin \frac{n'\pi x}{l} \, dx = \int_0^l B_n \sin \frac{n\pi x}{l} \sin \frac{n'\pi x}{l} \, dx$$

But since

$$\int_0^l \sin \frac{n\pi x}{l} \sin \frac{n'\pi x}{l} \, dx = 0 \qquad \text{for } n \neq n'$$

$$= \frac{l}{2} \qquad \text{for } n = n'$$

we obtain

$$B_n = \frac{2}{l} \int_0^l f_0(x) \sin \frac{n\pi x}{l} \, dx \tag{6}$$

Similarly,

$$A_n = \frac{2}{\pi n V} \int_0^l \dot{f}_0(x) \sin \frac{n\pi x}{l} \, dx \tag{7}$$

Resubstitution into (3) completes the solution of the problem. It is at once clear that, if the initial disturbance involves no initial velocity, all $A_n = 0$, whereas if the medium is initially in its undisturbed state, though subject to an initial velocity, all $B_n = 0$. This type of analysis is commonly applied to the transverse disturbances in a finite stretched string (see Chap. 4).

The same general method is available for bounded two- and three-dimensional media. In Sec. 1.8 we discussed the case of plane waves in a rectangular parallelepiped with sides a_1, a_2, a_3, respectively, and with rigid walls, on each one of which the disturbance vanishes identically for all t. The normal-mode frequencies are

$$\nu_n = \frac{V}{2} \sqrt{\frac{n_1^2}{a_1^2} + \frac{n_2^2}{a_2^2} + \frac{n_3^2}{a_3^2}} \tag{8}$$

where n_1, n_2, n_3 are any three integers. The corresponding solution for frequency ν_n, where the subscript n now stands for the triplet n_1, n_2, n_3, is then

$$f_n = (A_n \sin \omega_n t + B_n \cos \omega_n t) \sin \frac{n_1 \pi x}{a_1} \sin \frac{n_2 \pi y}{a_2} \sin \frac{n_3 \pi z}{a_3} \tag{9}$$

and we are led to seek the general solution as before in the form

$$f = \sum_{n=1}^{\infty} f_n \tag{10}$$

The coefficients a_n and b_n are evaluated by the same kind of technique used for the one-dimensional medium. Thus

$$f_0(x,y,z) = \sum B_n \sin \frac{n_1 \pi x}{a_1} \sin \frac{n_2 \pi y}{a_2} \sin \frac{n_3 \pi z}{a_3}$$

and therefore

$$B_n = \frac{8}{a_1 a_2 a_3} \int_0^{a_1} \int_0^{a_2} \int_0^{a_3} f_0(x,y,z) \sin \frac{n_1 \pi x}{a_1} \sin \frac{n_2 \pi y}{a_2} \sin \frac{n_3 \pi z}{a_3} \, dx \, dy \, dz \quad (11)$$

$$A_n = \frac{4}{\pi a_1 a_2 a_3 \nu_n} \int_0^{a_1} \int_0^{a_2} \int_0^{a_3} \dot{f}_0(x,y,z) \sin \frac{n_1 \pi x}{a_1} \sin \frac{n_2 \pi y}{a_2} \sin \frac{n_3 \pi z}{a_3} \, dx \, dy \, dz \tag{12}$$

More important are the nodes implied in the solution (9). We see that on the planes given by the equations

$$x = \frac{n_1'}{n_1} a_1 \qquad y = \frac{n_2'}{n_2} a_2 \qquad z = \frac{n_3'}{n_3} a_3 \tag{13}$$

where n_1', n_2', n_3' are integers less than or equal to n_1, n_2, n_3, respectively, the disturbance vanishes at all times. These are then nodal planes. The whole enclosure thus is filled with a rectangular pattern of nodes and loops. This is well illustrated by stationary sound waves in a closed rectangular room.

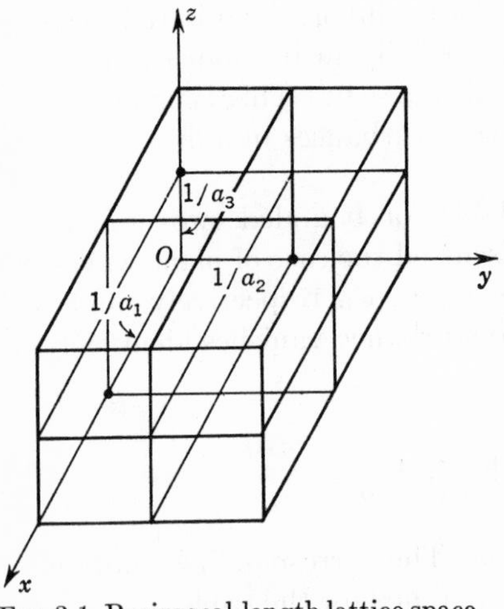

Often the distribution of the normal modes (8) is of importance. Thus one would like to know how many modes lie between any two given frequency values. Since n_1, n_2, n_3 are integers, this is strictly a problem in the theory of numbers, and a rather difficult one. However, we can simplify it somewhat by a geometrical treatment. We can construct in imagination a point lattice filling one octant of a rectangular space (see Fig. 3.1) in which the unit cell has dimensions $\frac{1}{a_1}, \frac{1}{a_2}, \frac{1}{a_3}$, respectively. This space may properly be called a reciprocal-length space; an ideal space, it is of course not the usual space of three dimensions. Any point in it has the coordinates $\frac{n_1}{a_1}, \frac{n_2}{a_2}, \frac{n_3}{a_3}$. The "distance" from the origin to such a point [Eq. (8)], when multiplied by $V/2$, then gives a possible normal-mode frequency. It is of interest to observe that, as the physical enclosure for

FIG. 3.1. Reciprocal-length lattice space.

the radiation becomes larger, the lattice points move closer together and the separation between normal-mode frequencies becomes less; thus what may be called the discrete spectrum of normal modes approaches more nearly a continuous spectrum. The converse accompanies a shrinkage in the size of the confining box.

The number of modes with frequencies lying in the interval ν, $\nu + d\nu$ is simply the number of lattice points lying between the octant of the sphere whose radius corresponds to ν and the octant of the sphere whose radius corresponds to $\nu + d\nu$. If the lattice points are sufficiently close together and we are dealing with a sufficiently large ν, the number of lattice points becomes approximately equivalent to the number of lattice cells in the region in question, since we can associate a point with each cell in the limit of a large number of cells. But the number of cells in a given region equals the volume in lattice space in this region divided by the volume of the unit cell. The latter is $1/\tau = 1/a_1 a_2 a_3$, where τ is the physical volume of the parallelepiped. If we denote the radius of the sphere corresponding to ν by r, then the modes between ν and $\nu + d\nu$ correspond to lattice points lying in the octant spherical shell having the volume

$$\frac{4\pi}{8} r^2 \, dr$$

with
$$r = \sqrt{\frac{n_1^2}{a_1^2} + \frac{n_2^2}{a_2^2} + \frac{n_3^2}{a_3^2}} = \frac{2\nu}{V} \tag{14}$$

Hence the number of normal modes in the interval in question is approximately

$$dN = \frac{\dfrac{4\pi}{8} \left(\dfrac{2\nu}{V}\right)^2 \dfrac{2}{V} \, d\nu}{1/a_1 a_2 a_3} = \frac{4\pi \nu^2 \tau \, d\nu}{V^3} \tag{15}$$

It should be emphasized that this result holds only for frequencies so large that $d\nu \ll \nu$. It therefore may possess little value in the study of acoustical modes in rooms. Here it is usually necessary to separate the various modes into groups, depending on whether two of the n values are zero (axial waves), one of the n values is zero (tangential waves), or none of the n values is zero (oblique waves). These are treated in greater detail[1] in Chap. 11.

It is worthwhile, however, to point out here that the frequency distribution law (15) is of considerable importance in the theory of thermal radiation. If it is assumed that such radiation is in a cavity whose walls radiate and absorb at equal rates at absolute temperature T, so that thermal equilibrium prevails, and if it is further assumed that to each normal

[1] P. M. Morse, "Vibration and Sound," 2d ed., pp. 391ff., McGraw-Hill Book Company, Inc., New York, 1948.

mode is assigned on the average the energy kT, where k is Boltzmann's gas constant per molecule (1.37×10^{-16} erg/°C), the energy dE contained in the frequency interval $d\nu$ in the neighborhood of frequency ν becomes

$$(dE)_\nu = \frac{4\pi\nu^2\tau kT\,d\nu}{c^3} \tag{16}$$

where c is the velocity of light.   Put in terms of wavelength, this takes the form

$$(dE)_\lambda = \frac{4\pi\tau kT\,d\lambda}{\lambda^4} \tag{17}$$

which, except for a factor of 2, is the famous Rayleigh-Jeans law for the distribution of energy in the spectrum of black body radiation at temperature T.   The factor of 2 is usually explained by the transverse character of the radiation.   The law holds only for the long-wavelength part of the electromagnetic spectrum and has, of course, been supplanted by the Planck radiation law over the spectrum as a whole.[1]

3.2. Wave Propagation across Boundaries

The preceding section deals with rigid boundaries at which radiation is completely reflected.   Such conditions do not in general exist in nature; all boundaries separate media in which wave propagation may be possible.   Hence we have to take into consideration the possibility of *transmission* across the boundary from the first medium to the second, as well as reflection.   We shall here put emphasis on energy, as distinct from the purely geometrical considerations in Sec. 2.1.

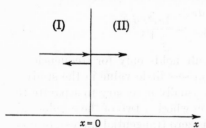

(I)   (II)

$x = 0$ x

FIG. 3.2. Wave transmission across a plane interface.

For simplicity we confine our discussion to a linear medium along the x axis.   Medium I (Fig. 3.2) will lie everywhere left of the origin and medium II everywhere right.   In medium I the velocity of the type of radiation under consideration is V_1, whereas in II it is V_2.   Let us imagine that a plane harmonic wave of angular frequency ω travels from left to right in medium I.   The incident disturbance is then

$$f_i = A_i e^{i(\omega t - k_1 x)} \tag{1}$$

with $k_1 = \omega/V_1$ and A_i the incident amplitude.   The reflected wave in I

[1] Max Born, "Atomic Physics," p. 190, G. E. Stechert & Company, New York, 1936.

will have the form

$$f_r = A_r e^{i(\omega t + k_1 x)} \tag{2}$$

Finally, the transmitted wave may be written

$$f_t = A_t e^{i(\omega t - k_2 x)} \tag{3}$$

with $k_2 = \omega/V_2$. Note that the incident, reflected, and transmitted waves are all assumed to have the same frequency. We make the fundamental hypothesis that a harmonic wave of given frequency will retain this frequency no matter through what medium it travels. This ignores such matters as the possible motion of the source or receiver of the radiation, to be considered in Sec. 10.3 under the Doppler effect.

The relations connecting f_i, f_r, and f_t clearly depend on the nature of the conditions which hold at the boundary, which we shall assume remains rigidly fixed. In order to obtain A_r and A_t in terms of A_i, we need two, and only two, such conditions. The two simplest mathematical ones we can think of would demand that both f and its gradient, or slope, $\partial f/\partial x$ shall be continuous at the boundary for all t. We must, however, be careful that these conditions make sense physically before we apply them blindly. It seems that the continuity of f itself meets the physical significance test all right, if f is an elastic displacement from equilibrium, for example. The continuity of $\partial f/\partial x$ is in a somewhat different category.

We recall, for example, from Sec. 1.10, that if f denotes an actual elastic displacement of a material medium from equilibrium, $\partial f/\partial x$ represents the elastic strain. There is no good reason for supposing that at the boundary of two different elastic media the strain should be continuous, though we might indeed experiment by trying this assumption and then comparing the result with what is actually observed. Disagreement would be found, and we should then be forced to examine the assumption more carefully. We should then probably conclude that it is physically more reasonable to suppose that it is the elastic *stress*, rather than the strain, which is continuous at the boundary. The stress [see (1.10-2)] is given by

$$X = Y \frac{\partial f}{\partial x} \tag{4}$$

where Y is an elastic constant which in general will differ for the two media in question. We can rationalize this alternative hypothesis by reflecting that, if the elastic stress were not the same in the two media at the boundary, there would necessarily be acceleration of mass there, so that the boundary could not remain fixed in position as we are assuming. Continuity of stress saves us from this uncomfortable contingency.

Let us apply the two boundary conditions. The continuity of f leads simply to

$$A_i + A_r = A_t \tag{5}$$

whereas the continuity of $Y(\partial f/\partial x)$ gives us

$$A_i - A_r = \frac{Y_2 k_2}{Y_1 k_1} A_t \tag{6}$$

Algebraic manipulation produces from these

$$A_r = \frac{Y_1 k_1 - Y_2 k_2}{Y_1 k_1 + Y_2 k_2} A_i \tag{7}$$

$$A_t = \frac{2 Y_1 k_1}{Y_1 k_1 + Y_2 k_2} A_i \tag{8}$$

In Sec. 1.7 we showed that, for a simple linear medium, $Y = \rho V^2$, where ρ is the mean density and V is the elastic wave velocity. We can therefore rewrite (7) and (8) in terms of density and velocity as follows

$$A_r = \frac{1 - \rho_2 V_2/\rho_1 V_1}{1 + \rho_2 V_2/\rho_1 V_1} A_i \tag{9}$$

$$A_t = \frac{2}{1 + \rho_2 V_2/\rho_1 V_1} A_i \tag{10}$$

For the limiting case in which $\rho_1 V_1 = \rho_2 V_2$, the above equations say that $A_r = 0$ and $A_t = A_i$. This agrees with the physical situation. If, on the other hand, $\rho_2 V_2 \gg \rho_1 V_1$, they yield

$$A_r \doteq - A_i \qquad A_t \doteq 0 \tag{11}$$

or the disturbance is almost entirely reflected, but with a change in phase of π, as implied in the minus sign. Curiously enough, the situation is not the same if $\rho_1 V_1 \gg \rho_2 V_2$, since then we have

$$A_r \doteq A_i \qquad A_t \doteq 2A_i \tag{12}$$

which seems to indicate that, though the reflected amplitude is still approximately equal to the incident, there is now a transmitted amplitude which is nearly twice the incident. This can be understood by introducing some energy considerations.

From Sec. 1.10 it will be recalled that for mechanical radiation in which f denotes an actual elastic displacement of the medium from equilibrium, the power per unit area conveyed by the radiation is proportional to the product of the partial time rate of change of f and the partial space rate of change of f. Thus to repeat (1.10-3), we have

$$P = Y \dot{f} \frac{\partial f}{\partial x} \tag{13}$$

This type of expression for power transmission per unit area is more general than might at first appear. For example, as we shall see later (Sec. 9.1), if we use the velocity potential φ as the wave function for elastic propagation in a fluid, the product of $\dot{\varphi}$ and $\partial\varphi/\partial x$ with the mean density of the fluid is also equal to P (for a plane wave in the x direction). Here, however, we shall stick to the meaning for f already established in this section.

The incident average power per unit area becomes [Eq. (1.10-9)]

$$\bar{P}_i = \tfrac{1}{2}\rho_1 V_1 \omega^2 A_i{}^2 \tag{14}$$

and the transmitted average power likewise

$$\bar{P}_t = \tfrac{1}{2}\rho_2 V_2 \omega^2 A_t{}^2 \tag{15}$$

Consequently, $$\bar{P}_t = \frac{4\rho_2 V_2/\rho_1 V_1}{(1 + \rho_2 V_2/\rho_1 V_1)^2}\, \bar{P}_i \tag{16}$$

where the fraction is usually called the transmission coefficient. It is at once clear that, if $\rho_1 V_1 \gg \rho_2 V_2$, $\bar{P}_t \ll \bar{P}_i$, and hence practically no energy is transmitted across the boundary, even if $A_t \doteq 2A_i$. This is confirmed by an examination of $\bar{P}_r$, for we have in general

$$\bar{P}_r = \left[\frac{1 - \rho_2 V_2/\rho_1 V_1}{1 + \rho_2 V_2/\rho_1 V_1}\right]^2 \bar{P}_i \tag{17}$$

where the coefficient of $\bar{P}_i$ is usually termed the reflection coefficient. Under the conditions just cited, $\bar{P}_r \doteq \bar{P}_i$, or practically all the energy is reflected. Of course the same result ensues if $\rho_2 V_2 \gg \rho_1 V_1$. We shall later see reason for giving the quantity ρV the special designation *specific acoustic resistance for a plane wave* (Sec. 9.3). It is clear that it controls the transmission of energy from the one medium to the other. If the media are well matched, the ρV values are close together, and considerable energy transmission takes place; if the media are badly matched, the ρV values differ greatly, with corresponding poor energy transmission.

The foregoing considerations have applied to two media, neither of which is dissipative. It is often important, however, to discuss the reflection of a plane wave at normal incidence from the interface of two absorbing media. Referring to Sec. 1.9 for the expression for a damped wave and assuming that the absorption coefficients in media I and II (Fig. 3.2) are α_1 and α_2, respectively, we now write in place of the f's in (1), (2), (3), respectively,

$$\begin{aligned}
f_i &= A_i e^{-\alpha_1 x} e^{i(\omega t - k_1 x)} \\
f_r &= A_r e^{-\alpha_1 x} e^{i(\omega t + k_1 x)} \\
f_t &= A_t e^{-\alpha_2 x} e^{i(\omega t - k_2 x)}
\end{aligned} \tag{18}$$

Similarly, the stress components are

$$\begin{aligned}
X_i &= -Y_1(\alpha_1 + ik_1)f_i \\
X_r &= -Y_1(\alpha_1 - ik_1)f_r \\
X_t &= -Y_2(\alpha_2 + ik_2)f_t
\end{aligned} \tag{19}$$

The continuity of f at the boundary $(x = 0)$ gives the relation

$$A_i + A_r = A_t \tag{20}$$

whereas the continuity of X gives

$$(\alpha_1 + ik_1)A_i + (\alpha_1 - ik_1)A_r = \frac{Y_2}{Y_1}(\alpha_2 + ik_2)A_t \tag{21}$$

Elimination of A_r gives

$$A_t = \frac{2ik_1 Y_1 A_i}{Y_2(\alpha_2 + ik_2) - Y_1(\alpha_1 - ik_1)} \tag{22}$$

and elimination of A_t gives

$$A_r = -\frac{Y_2(\alpha_2 + ik_2) - Y_1(\alpha_1 + ik_1)}{Y_2(\alpha_2 + ik_2) - Y_1(\alpha_1 - ik_1)} A_i \tag{23}$$

In calculating the power transmission across the boundary, we must now take account of the fact that the amplitude factors A_i, A_r, A_t are in general complex. It readily follows that (14) in this case becomes [for a detailed demonstration, see (3.3-8)]

$$\bar{P}_i = \tfrac{1}{2}\rho_1 V_1 \omega^2 |A_i|^2 \tag{24}$$

with a similar expression for $\bar{P}_t$. Hence we obtain

$$\frac{\bar{P}_t}{\bar{P}_i} = \frac{4r_{12}}{(1 + r_{12})^2 + \left(r_{12}\dfrac{V_2}{\omega}\alpha_2 - \dfrac{V_1}{\omega}\alpha_1\right)^2} \tag{25}$$

where $r_{12} = \rho_2 V_2/\rho_1 V_1$, the ratio of the specific acoustic plane wave resistances of the two media, respectively. If $\alpha_1 = \alpha_2 = 0$, this reduces to the transmission formula (16) for the nondissipative case. It is interesting to note that if

$$\frac{\alpha_2}{\alpha_1} = \frac{\rho_1 V_1^2}{\rho_2 V_2^2}$$

the power transmission ratio also reduces to that for nondissipative media.

3.3. Selective Wave Transmission

An important, though not unexpected, feature of the transmission of radiation across an interface separating two media, as illustrated in the previous section, is its independence of frequency. The question arises: Are there circumstances in which such transmission is selective with respect to frequency? We shall find that this is indeed the case when radiation from one medium passes through a *finite* layer of a second medium and emerges into a third medium which may be the same as the first. We illustrate with the simple case of linear nondissipative media. Figure 3.3 exhibits schematically the passage of plane radiation in the x direction from medium I through a thickness l of medium II and back into medium I, all at normal incidence. We again assume harmonic waves, as in Sec. 3.2, but alter the notation slightly by making A_t the

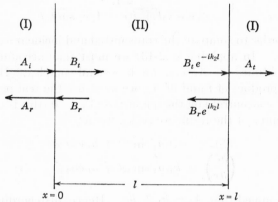

FIG. 3.3. Wave transmission through a finite layer.

amplitude of the transmitted wave into medium I after the passage through medium II. We denote amplitudes in medium II by B with subscripts, as shown in the figure. Note that in II it is now necessary to allow for radiation progressing in both positive and negative directions at both interfaces (which, incidentally, we take for convenience at $x = 0$ and $x = l$, respectively). If B_t represents the amplitude of the wave in II at $x = 0$ proceeding to the right, the corresponding wave at $x = l$ will have amplitude $B_t e^{-ik_2 l}$, since it will have changed in phase only by the multiplicative factor $e^{-ik_2 l}$. There is no change in magnitude since there is no dissipation. The wave parameters in media I and II are k_1 and k_2, respectively, as in Sec. 3.2.

The boundary conditions remain of the same kind as in Sec. 3.2, though there are now four (two for each interface). They take the form

$$A_i + A_r = B_t + B_r \tag{1}$$

$$\rho_1 V_1 (A_i - A_r) = \rho_2 V_2 (B_t - B_r) \tag{2}$$

$$B_t e^{-ik_2 l} + B_r e^{ik_2 l} = A_t \tag{3}$$

$$\rho_2 V_2 (B_t e^{-ik_2 l} - B_r e^{ik_2 l}) = \rho_1 V_1 A_t \tag{4}$$

where the first two hold at the left-hand interface and the second two at the right-hand interface. It might be thought that $A_t e^{-ik_1 l}$ should be used in place of A_t in (3) and (4), since we strictly should always measure x from the chosen origin. However, it will turn out that the transmission coefficient depends only on the absolute value of A_t, and hence any multiplicative phase factor of absolute value unity has no significance for the result we are seeking. The solution of (1), (2), (3), and (4) involves the elimination of A_r, B_r, and B_t and the expression of A_t in terms of A_i. To simplify matters, we write $\rho_i V_i = R_i$ and further $R_2/R_1 = r$. Algebra then produces

$$A_t = \frac{2A_i}{2\cos k_1 l + i(r + 1/r)\sin k_1 l} \tag{5}$$

It is now in order to compare the transmitted and incident average power per unit area. In applying (3.2-13) we must take account of the fact that the amplitudes A_i, A_t, etc., are in general complex. Hence, in calculating the product of $\dot{f}$ and $\partial f/\partial x$, we must use the real parts (see Sec. 1.10). If we concentrate on the quantities at $x = 0$ (this is no limitation on the generality of the result we seek), we get

$$(\dot{f}_i)_r = -\omega(a_1 \sin \omega t + b_1 \cos \omega t) \tag{6}$$

$$\left(\frac{\partial f_i}{\partial x}\right)_r = k_1(a_1 \sin \omega t + b_1 \cos \omega t) \tag{7}$$

where it is assumed that $A_i = a_1 + ib_1$. Hence, disregarding the minus sign [see (1.10-8) and the accompanying discussion],

$$\bar{P}_i = \omega^2 R_1(a_1{}^2 \overline{\sin^2 \omega t} + b_1{}^2 \overline{\cos^2 \omega t} + 2a_1 b_1 \overline{\cos \omega t \sin \omega t})$$

$$= \frac{\omega^2 R_1}{2}(a_1{}^2 + b_1{}^2) = \frac{\omega^2 R_1}{2}|A_i|^2 \tag{8}$$

This means that the average power per unit area is always proportional to the square of the absolute value of the elastic displacement from equilibrium. Though this has been shown for the incident radiation, it is true for any progressive plane wave. We can apply the result directly to (5) and get

$$\bar{P}_t = \frac{|A_t|^2}{|A_i|^2}\bar{P}_i = \frac{\bar{P}_i}{\cos^2 k_1 l + \dfrac{(r + 1/r)^2}{4}\sin^2 k_1 l} \tag{9}$$

The reciprocal of the denominator on the right is the transmission coefficient T. It may also be written more conveniently

$$T = \frac{1}{1 - \dfrac{(r^2 - 1)(1/r^2 - 1)}{4}\sin^2 k_1 l} \tag{10}$$

We see that T is a function not only of r and l but also of ω and the velocity of the radiation. In particular, for $\omega \doteq 0$, $T \doteq 1$. The transmission coefficient then goes through a succession of maxima and minima as the frequency is increased. The plot of T vs. ω has the form shown in Fig. 3.4. The maximum values of T are all equal to unity and occur for $\omega l/V_1 = n\pi$, where n is integral. The minimum values of T are all equal to $2/[1 + \frac{1}{2}(r^2 + 1/r^2)]$ and occur for $\omega l/V_1 = (2n + 1)\pi/2$. When $r = 1$, the transmission is unity for all frequencies, as is evident from the physical situation. This type of transmission is termed *selective*, since some frequency ranges are transmitted better than others. In fact it is about the simplest illustration of an important radiation device known as a *filter*, which passes radiation of certain frequencies and refuses passage to others. Of course the single layer here contemplated is not a complete filter, since for no frequency is the transmission reduced com-

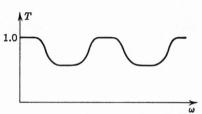

FIG. 3.4. Transmission coefficient as a function of frequency for a finite layer.

pletely to zero. However, it suggests that, if we were to provide an iterated series of alternating layers of two different media, we might expect this to manifest filter characteristics of the low-pass variety, that is, to pass low frequencies and then follow with a series of attenuation and passbands similar to the succession of minima and maxima in the T vs. ω plot for the single-layer example just discussed. This prognostication turns out to be correct.

3.4. Wave Propagation in Iterated Structures. Filtration

Let us imagine an iterated linear structure made up of alternate layers of two different media I and II with specific acoustic resistances R_1 and

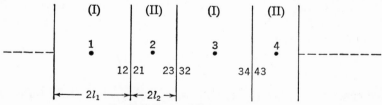

FIG. 3.5. Iterated linear structure.

R_2, respectively. The thicknesses of the layers are $2l_1$ and $2l_2$, respectively. The situation is shown diagrammatically in Fig. 3.5. For convenience, we attach the subscripts 1, 2, 3, 4, respectively, to quantities referring to behavior at the mid-points of the various layers. At the interfaces the corresponding quantities are characterized by two indices, such as 12, 21. For further simplicity it is assumed that the structure is infinite to both left and right. This idealization can be readily removed, and we can work with finite structures, but it is desirable at first to study the infinite variety.

Waves in general travel in both directions in the structure, which is assumed to lie along the x direction. Hence the elastic disturbance f takes the general form

$$f = F_1 e^{i(\omega t - kx)} + F_2 e^{i(\omega t + kx)} \tag{1}$$

with the k appropriate to the medium. The factor $e^{i\omega t}$ is unnecessary in the subsequent discussion and may therefore be omitted. Consequently we write for $\dot{f}$ and $\dfrac{\partial f}{\partial x}$

$$\dot{f} = i\omega(F_1 e^{-ikx} + F_2 e^{ikx}) \tag{2}$$

$$\frac{\partial f}{\partial x} = f' = -ik(F_1 e^{-ikx} - F_2 e^{ikx}) \tag{3}$$

Since the structure is symmetrical about the mid-point of any layer, the choice of origin is arbitrary. We shall take the mid-point of the layer marked 1 as corresponding to $x = 0$, and, in accordance with the convention already agreed upon, denote the values there as $\dot{f}_1$ and f'_1, respectively. We may therefore solve for F_1 and F_2 in terms of $\dot{f}_1$ and f'_1 as follows:

$$\begin{aligned} F_1 &= \frac{i}{2}\left(-\frac{\dot{f}_1}{\omega} + \frac{f'_1}{k_1}\right) \\ F_2 &= -\frac{i}{2}\left(\frac{\dot{f}_1}{\omega} + \frac{f'_1}{k_1}\right) \end{aligned} \tag{4}$$

If now we substitute these values back into (2) and (3), we can express $\dot{f}$ and f' anywhere in the first layer in terms of $\dot{f}_1$ and f'_1. The result is

$$\dot{f} = \dot{f}_1 \cos k_1 x + \frac{i\omega}{k_1} f_1 \sin k_1 x \tag{5}$$

$$f' = f'_1 \cos k_1 x + \frac{ik_1}{\omega} \dot{f}_1 \sin k_1 x \tag{6}$$

We can now employ (5) and (6) to express $\dot{f}_{12}$ and f'_{12} in terms of $\dot{f}_1$ and f'_1. Thus we have

$$\begin{aligned} \dot{f}_{12} &= \dot{f}_1 \cos k_1 l_1 + \frac{i\omega}{k_1} f'_1 \sin k_1 l_1 \\ f'_{12} &= f'_1 \cos k_1 l_1 + \frac{ik_1}{\omega} \dot{f}_1 \sin k_1 l_1 \end{aligned} \tag{7}$$

Since the choice of origin is arbitrary, we may equally well write in layer 2

$$\dot{f}_{23} = \dot{f}_{21} \cos 2k_2l_2 + \frac{i\omega}{k_2} f'_{21} \sin 2k_2l_2$$
$$f'_{23} = f'_{21} \cos 2k_2l_2 + \frac{ik_2}{\omega} f'_{21} \sin 2k_2l_2$$

(8)

and finally, in similar fashion,

$$\dot{f}_3 = \dot{f}_{32} \cos k_1l_1 + \frac{i\omega}{k_1} f'_{32} \sin k_1l_1$$
$$f'_3 = f'_{32} \cos k_1l_1 + \frac{ik_1}{\omega} \dot{f}_{32} \sin k_1l_1$$

(9)

Our problem is to express $\dot{f}_3$ and f'_3 in terms of $\dot{f}_1$ and f'_1 or, in general, $\dot{f}_{j+2}$ and f'_{j+2} in terms of $\dot{f}_j$ and f'_j, where j is any integer. From the symmetry of the structure it suffices to do this for $j = 1$. We need to set down the boundary conditions. From Secs. 3.2 and 3.3, with the choice again of $R_1 = \rho_1 V_1$ and $R_2 = \rho_2 V_2$, we obtain

$$\dot{f}_{12} = \dot{f}_{21} \qquad \dot{f}_{23} = \dot{f}_{32}$$
$$R_1 V_1 f'_{12} = R_2 V_2 f'_{21} \qquad R_2 V_2 f'_{23} = R_1 V_1 f'_{32}$$

(10)

If we introduce these into the preceding equations, we get the following equations expressing $\dot{f}_3$ and f'_3 in terms of $\dot{f}_1$ and f'_1, respectively:

$$f'_3 = Af'_1 + \frac{iB}{V_1} \dot{f}_1$$
$$\dot{f}_3 = A\dot{f}_1 + iCV_1 f'_1$$

(11)

where the parameters A, B, C have the form

$$A = \cos 2k_1l_1 \cos 2k_2l_2 - \frac{1}{2}\left(\frac{R_1}{R_2} + \frac{R_2}{R_1}\right) \sin 2k_1l_1 \sin 2k_2l_2$$

$$B = \cos 2k_2l_2 \sin 2k_1l_1 + \left(\frac{R_2}{R_1} \cos^2 k_1l_1 - \frac{R_1}{R_2} \sin^2 k_1l_1\right) \sin 2k_2l_2 \quad (12)$$

$$C = \cos 2k_2l_2 \sin 2k_1l_1 + \left(\frac{R_1}{R_2} \cos^2 k_1l_1 - \frac{R_2}{R_1} \sin^2 k_1l_1\right) \sin 2k_2l_2$$

Because of the symmetry we are entitled to write (11) in the more general form

$$f'_{j+2} = Af'_j + i \frac{B}{V_1} \dot{f}_j$$
$$\dot{f}_{j+2} = A\dot{f}_j + iCV_1 f'_j$$

(13)

assuming that j corresponds to medium I in each case. Examination discloses that A, B, C are connected by the relation

$$A^2 + BC = 1$$

(14)

which suggests that we introduce the angle W (which may be real or complex) such that

$$A = \cos W \qquad BC = \sin^2 W \qquad (15)$$

We can then rewrite (13) in the form

$$f'_{j+2} = f'_j \cos W + \frac{i \sqrt{B/C}}{V_1} \dot{f}_j \sin W$$

$$\dot{f}_{j+2} = \dot{f}_j \cos W + iV_1 \sqrt{\frac{C}{B}} f'_j \sin W \qquad (16)$$

It will now be assumed that

$$\frac{\rho_j V_j^2 f'_j}{\dot{f}_j} = -Z_0 \qquad (17)$$

where Z_0 is a constant independent of j, that is, is the same at the mid-point of every layer. [Note that, if j is even in (17), $\rho_j V_j^2$ becomes $\rho_2 V_2^2$, whereas if j is odd, it is $\rho_1 V_1^2$.] Physically this assumption expresses our confidence that, because of the symmetry and infinite character of the structure, Z_0, which is the ratio of the compressive stress (i.e., negative tensile stress) to the velocity of elastic disturbance, will be the same at the mid-point of every layer. Z_0 is termed the characteristic impedance of the structure, since from its form it is analogous to the ratio of electromotive force to current in electric transmission lines. (For more details about the impedance notation in wave propagation, see Sec. 9.3.) If we divide the first equation in (16) by the second, we readily show that

$$Z_0 = R_1 \sqrt{\frac{B}{C}} \qquad (18)$$

This in combination with (17) enables us to write (16) in the form

$$f'_{j+2} = f'_j e^{-iW}$$
$$\dot{f}_{j+2} = \dot{f}_j e^{-iW} \qquad (19)$$

which at once provides a clue to the transmission characteristics of the structure under study. For if W is a *real* angle

$$|\dot{f}_{j+2}| = |\dot{f}_j|$$
$$|f'_{j+2}| = |f'_j|$$

and the quantity at $j + 2$ differs from that at j in phase only. Under these conditions the structure transmits radiation without attenuation. On the other hand, if W is a complex angle

$$|\dot{f}_{j+2}| \neq |\dot{f}_j|$$

and the structure attenuates, each pair of layers reducing the amplitude of f' and $\dot{f}$ in the same proportion.   Now, W is real when $|\cos W| \leq 1$, whereas W is complex when $|\cos W| > 1$.   [It is to be noted, incidentally, that $\cos W$ in (12) is always real.]   Hence the transmission can be studied by plotting $\cos W$ as a function of frequency.   If this is done, the result in general looks like Fig. 3.6.   In particular, for $\nu = 0$, $\cos W = 1$.   As the frequency increases, $\cos W$ decreases, ultimately becomes negative, and finally becomes less than -1 at ν_1.   Thereafter it oscillates more or less as shown.   We may then divide the frequency scale into unshaded and shaded regions.   In the former, $|\cos W| \leq 1$, and the corresponding

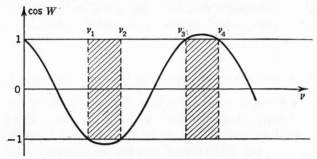

Fig. 3.6. Filtration characteristics of an iterated linear structure. Cos W versus frequency.

frequencies are transmitted.   In the latter $|\cos W| > 1$, and radiation of the corresponding frequency is attenuated.   From zero to ν_1 constitutes a transmission band or passband; from ν_1 to ν_2, an attenuation band, etc. The structure is really a bandpass filter, though since the first passband is of low frequency, it is usual to call it a low-pass filter.

The location and width of the bands are controlled by the relation between the k and l values, or, physically, the wavelength of the radiation and the thickness of the layers.   Inspection shows that the transmission- and attenuation-band boundaries occur for those frequencies which make $\sin k_1 l_1$ or $\sin k_2 l_2$ equal to unity or zero, respectively.   It is qualitatively clear that, if the thickness values are large compared with the mean wavelength range of the radiation, the attenuation and transmission bands will be narrow.   On the other hand, if the thickness values are of the order of magnitude of the mean wavelength, the bands will be broader.   Of course the term $\frac{1}{2}(R_1/R_2 + R_2/R_1)$ also enters into the picture.   It is possible to design a layered medium filter of the kind discussed here to meet a wide variety of practical conditions.[1]   Acoustic filters of this and similar types are discussed in Chap. 9.

[1] For more details on such filters, see R. B. Lindsay, *J. Appl. Phys.*, **9**, 612 (1938); and **10**, 680 (1939).   Also R. B. Lindsay, C. R. Lewis, and R. D. Albright, *J. Acoust. Soc. Am.*, **5**, 202 (1934); and W. P. Mason, "Electromechanical Transducers and Wave Filters," D. Van Nostrand Company, Inc., Princeton, N.J., 1942.

It is of interest to observe that the preceding analysis can be applied, with little change, to selective electromagnetic radiation. Light passing through a succession of layers of optically transparent media of alternating properties will be selectively transmitted. It is not difficult to show that the corresponding cos W function in this case is

$$\cos W = \cos 2k_1l_1 \cos 2k_2l_2 - \frac{1}{2}\left(\frac{n_1}{n_2} + \frac{n_2}{n_1}\right) \sin 2k_1l_1 \sin 2k_2l_2 \quad (20)$$

where n_1 and n_2 are the optical indices of refraction of the two alternating media, respectively. Since optical frequencies are so much higher than those usual in mechanical radiation, the pass- and attenuation bands will be very narrow indeed unless the l_1 and l_2 values are extremely small.[1]

3.5. Radiation from a Radially Vibrating Sphere.   Radiation Reaction

An important boundary problem in radiation is provided by radiation produced by a finite vibrator, where the conditions prevailing at the surface of the vibrator are obviously vital.   Since all actual sources of radiation are finite in size, this type of problem is of universal occurrence, though in practice we may find it possible to idealize by considering point sources, etc.   But it is obviously essential not to overlook the relation between the source of radiation and the resulting radiation field.

We shall choose a particularly simple case as a first illustration. Others will occur at various appropriate places farther on.   Here we concern ourselves with a spherical shell of equilibrium radius a vibrating radially with angular frequency ω in an elastic fluid medium.   This means that the velocity $\dot{f}_a$ of the spherical surface is the following function of the time:

$$\dot{f}_a = \dot{f}_0 e^{i\omega t} \quad (1)$$

In order to go forward with this problem it is necessary to ascertain the physical nature of the quantity which satisfies the general wave equation in an elastic fluid, that is, the quantity which we have denoted as f in the preceding sections.   In the case of plane waves in a one-dimensional medium we saw that it could be the actual displacement of the medium from equilibrium.   It does not follow that this will be true of spreading waves in a three-dimensional fluid medium.

We shall indulge here in a rather more general discussion than we gave in Sec. 1.7 in deriving the simple one-dimensional wave equation in a solid rod.   When we disturb a fluid, not only do we cause parts of it to

[1] C. H. Cartwright and A. F. Turner, *Phys. Rev.*, **55**, 595, 1128 (1939); and R. B. Lindsay, *Phys. Rev.*, **60**, 169 (1941).

move with respect to each other, but we alter the equilibrium pressure and density at the point of disturbance. In this process mass must be conserved; the expression for this conservation is the so-called "equation of continuity" in hydrodynamics. Physically, this says that in a continuous, indestructible fluid the excess of mass flow out of a small volume element over mass flow into the element is equal to the negative time rate of change of mass inside the element represented essentially by a change of the internal density. In formal fashion[1] the equation may be written

$$\nabla \cdot (\rho \mathbf{v}) = -\dot{\rho} \tag{2}$$

where ρ is the variable density and $\mathbf{v}$ is the fluid velocity. The divergence of $\rho \mathbf{v}$ is the excess mass flow per unit volume. If we write

$$\rho = \rho_0 + \rho_e \tag{3}$$

where ρ_0 is the mean equilibrium density (a constant in time) and ρ_e is the excess density due to the disturbance, it is clear that we may replace $\dot{\rho}$ in (2) by $\dot{\rho}_e$. Moreover, if $\rho_e \ll \rho_0$, as will happen in the small disturbances from equilibrium which we are considering here, we can safely replace ρ in $\nabla \cdot (\rho \mathbf{v})$ by ρ_0.

Now in any fluid there is a relation between the change in density and the associated change in pressure. This can be evaluated from the so-called equation of state of the fluid, that is, the relation connecting density, pressure, and temperature. If we ignore for the moment the precise form of the latter but merely make the simplest possible assumption that the excess pressure p_e (equal to the difference between the actual pressure p and the mean equilibrium pressure p_0) is directly proportional to ρ_e, we write

$$p_e = V^2 \rho_e \tag{4}$$

where V^2 here appears at first as a mere proportionality factor, though its further physical significance will shortly be evident. We may also interpret (4) as the equation reflecting the *elastic* behavior of the fluid when its equilibrium is disturbed (Hooke's law). The equation of continuity now assumes the form

$$\nabla \cdot (\rho_0 \mathbf{v}) = -\frac{\dot{p}_e}{V^2} \tag{5}$$

To solve the problem of the behavior of small disturbances from equilibrium we need another equation connecting $\mathbf{v}$ and p_e. This will obviously be the equation of motion of the fluid under the pressure change associated with the disturbance. From hydrodynamics[2] this has the

[1] Leigh Page, "Introduction to Theoretical Physics," 2d ed., pp. 25f., D. Van Nostrand Company, Inc., Princeton, N.J., 1935.
[2] *Ibid.*, p. 220.

general form

$$\dot{\mathbf{v}} + \mathbf{v} \cdot \nabla \mathbf{v} = -\frac{\nabla p}{\rho} \tag{6}$$

But if we again restrict attention to small flows, the term $\mathbf{v} \cdot \nabla \mathbf{v}$ can be neglected and ρ can be replaced by ρ_0, whereas ∇p becomes ∇p_e. Thus

$$\rho_0 \dot{\mathbf{v}} = -\nabla p_e \tag{7}$$

If we take the divergence of both sides of (7) and also differentiate both sides of (5) with respect to the time, the equations will have identical left-hand sides. Hence, putting the right-hand sides equal yields

$$\nabla^2 p_e = \frac{\ddot{p}_e}{V^2} \tag{8}$$

But this is the three-dimensional wave equation (see Sec. 1.7), which says, physically, that the excess pressure is the quantity propagated when an elastic fluid is subjected to a small disturbance from equilibrium.

In the radiation problem considered in this section, we are restricting our attention to spherical waves, since the radiator is a spherical shell. For this we need to express the Laplacian of p_e, namely, $\nabla^2 p_e$, in terms of spherical coordinates r, θ, φ. This is done in Appendix A with a mathematical reference, though we repeat the expression here for convenience. In spherical coordinates (8) becomes

$$\frac{1}{r^2} \frac{\partial}{\partial r} \left(r^2 \frac{\partial p_e}{\partial r} \right) + \frac{1}{r^2 \sin \theta} \frac{\partial}{\partial \theta} \left(\sin \theta \frac{\partial p_e}{\partial \theta} \right) + \frac{1}{r^2 \sin^2 \theta} \frac{\partial^2 p_e}{\partial \theta^2} = \frac{\ddot{p}_e}{V^2} \tag{9}$$

Symmetry indicates that in the present problem p_e does not depend on the latitude and longitude; that is, the terms in θ and φ go out, and the equation reduces to

$$\frac{1}{r^2} \frac{\partial}{\partial r} \left(r^2 \frac{\partial p_e}{\partial r} \right) = \frac{\ddot{p}_e}{V^2} \tag{10}$$

where r is the distance from the center of the shell (i.e., the effective point of origin of the spreading spherical wave). The vector equation of motion (7) reduces to

$$\rho_0 \ddot{f} = -\frac{\partial p_e}{\partial r} \tag{11}$$

where f is the particle displacement in the fluid, directed entirely along the radius vector and a function of r and t, as is p_e.

Note that (10) can be written, by direct expansion and rearrangement,

$$\frac{\partial^2}{\partial r^2} (r p_e) = \frac{r \ddot{p}_e}{V^2} \tag{12}$$

with the general solution

$$p_e = \frac{1}{r} g_1(r - Vt) + \frac{1}{r} g_2(r + Vt) \tag{13}$$

It is clear from the form of (11) and (12) that f will not satisfy the wave equation for spherical waves. On the other hand, from (4), rp_e will do so, if V is constant.

We now seek a harmonic solution p_e of (12) corresponding to an outgoing wave which will satisfy the boundary condition (1). This can be done by taking

$$p_e = \frac{A}{r} e^{i[\omega t - k(r-a)]} \tag{14}$$

where $k = \omega/V$, as usual. For now, by use of (11), we have

$$f = \frac{1}{\rho_0 \omega^2} \frac{\partial p_e}{\partial r} = -\frac{A}{\rho_0 r^2 \omega^2} (1 + ikr) e^{i[\omega t - k(r-a)]} \tag{15}$$

and

$$\dot{f}_a = -\frac{iA}{\rho_0 a^2 \omega} (1 + ika) e^{i\omega t} \tag{16}$$

Hence to satisfy the boundary condition we need

$$A = \frac{i \dot{f}_0 a^2 \omega \rho_0}{1 + ika} \tag{17}$$

The fluid flow velocity $\dot{f}_r$ at any point distant r from the center of the spherical shell greater than or equal to a is therefore

$$\dot{f}_r = \frac{\dot{f}_0 a^2}{r^2} \frac{1 + ikr}{1 + ika} e^{i[\omega t - k(r-a)]} \tag{18}$$

and the corresponding excess pressure p_e at the same place is given by (14) with A inserted from (17):

$$p_e = \frac{i \omega \dot{f}_0 a^2 \rho_0}{r(1 + ika)} e^{i[\omega t - k(r-a)]} \tag{19}$$

With this material in hand we can now solve a very interesting and fundamental problem in radiation, expressed physically as follows. In the act of radiating, the vibrating sphere must exert a force on the fluid medium in contact with its surface; it is, indeed, as a result of this force that the fluid is disturbed from equilibrium and the disturbance is propagated away from the sphere. At the same time, Newton's third law assures that the medium must react on the sphere with the same force with which it is itself acted on. Hence there must exist what may logically be called a *radiation reaction* on the sphere. We can compute it very simply by multiplying the value of p_e for $r = a$ by the area of the sphere.   The result may be written, by rationalizing the denominator in (19), as the sum of two terms, the first proportional to $\dot{f}_a$ and the second proportional to $\ddot{f}_a$.   Thus, if we denote the reaction force by F_a, we have

$$F_a = \frac{4\pi a^4 \omega \rho_0 k}{1 + k^2 a^2} \dot{f}_a + \frac{4\pi a^3 \rho_0}{1 + k^2 a^2} \ddot{f}_a \tag{20}$$

The part of the reaction force which is proportional to the velocity $\dot{f}_a$ of the surface of the sphere may be looked upon as a resisting force, whereas the part which is proportional to the acceleration $\ddot{f}_a$ may be considered an inertia force.

Now if the sphere were vibrating in a vacuum under the impressed harmonic force $F_0 e^{i\omega t}$, its equation of motion, with f_a as the radial displacement, would be

$$m\ddot{f}_a + R\dot{f}_a + f_a/C = F_0 e^{i\omega t} \tag{21}$$

where m is the effective mass, $1/C$ the effective stiffness (C is sometimes called the compliance), and R the effective mechanical damping coefficient of the vibrator.[1]   Because of the reaction of the radiation on the vibrator, as represented in (20), the resultant equation of motion takes the form

$$\left(m + \frac{4\pi a^3 \rho_0}{1 + k^2 a^2}\right)\ddot{f}_a + \left(R + \frac{4\pi a^4 \omega \rho_0 k}{1 + k^2 a^2}\right)\dot{f}_a + \frac{f_a}{C} = F_0 e^{i\omega t} \tag{22}$$

The term

$$\frac{4\pi a^3 \rho_0}{1 + k^2 a^2} = m_r \tag{23}$$

appears as a kind of radiation inertia or mass which increases the effective mass of the vibrator.   The term

$$\frac{4\pi a^4 \omega \rho_0 k}{1 + k^2 a^2} = R_r \tag{24}$$

appears as a kind of radiation damping coefficient which increases the effective damping of the vibrator.   It may be observed, of course, that since $\ddot{f}_a = -\omega^2 f_a$ we could quite legitimately treat $-m_r \omega^2$ as an effective *negative* addition to the mechanical stiffness of the sphere; this effect of the radiation may be interpreted as either an addition to the effective mass or a diminution in the effective stiffness.   The former point of view seems physically preferable.   The relative magnitudes of m_r and R_r depend on the frequency.   At very low frequencies for which $a \ll \lambda$, $ka \ll 1$, and m_r approaches the mass of a volume of the medium equal to three times the volume of the sphere, whereas R_r approaches the area of

[1] Leigh Page, "Introduction to Theoretical Physics," 2d ed., p. 77, D. Van Nostrand Company, Inc., Princeton, N.J., 1935.

the sphere multiplied by $\omega^2 \rho_0 / V$, which will be a relatively small quantity compared with R. We can therefore say that at low frequencies the principal reaction of the radiation on the source is to increase its effective mass. On the other hand, for sufficiently high frequencies, $ka \gg 1$, and m_r becomes very small, whereas $R_r \rightarrow 4\pi a^2 \rho_0 V$, which is just the area of the sphere multiplied by the specific acoustic resistance of a plane wave. In this case we can say that the principal effect of the radiation is to increase the rate of dissipation of energy (for given f_a) from the sphere, since this rate is simply $(R + R_r)\dot{f}_a{}^2$. We draw the conclusion that the sphere is a more efficient radiator into the medium at high frequencies than at low. The practical consequences of this will be discussed in the treatment of high-frequency sound radiation, or ultrasonics (Chap. 9).

The foregoing considerations are, of course, independent of the relation connecting m, R, C, and ω. It is well known[1] that if the driving force has the angular frequency

$$\omega = \sqrt{\frac{1}{Cm}} \tag{25}$$

the vibrator (*in vacuo*) will be in *resonance* and the average rate of energy inflow into the vibrator from the force will be a *maximum;* moreover, the average rate of dissipation $R\dot{f}_a{}^2$ will also be a maximum. It is clear that the radiation reaction alters both the resonance frequency and the average rate of energy dissipation. Thus the angular resonance frequency becomes

$$\omega_{\text{res}} = \sqrt{\frac{1/C}{m + 4\pi a^3 \rho_0 / (1 + k^2 a^2)}} \tag{26}$$

and the average rate of energy dissipation

$$\left(R + \frac{4\pi a^4 \omega \rho_0 k}{1 + k^2 a^2} \right) \overline{\dot{f}_a{}^2}$$

The significance of the dependence of this on ρ_0 (i.e., the density of the surrounding medium) should not be overlooked.

3.6. Scattering of a Scalar Wave by Obstacles

We have already considered (Secs. 2.1 and 3.2) the behavior of a progressive wave when it is incident on the boundary separating the original medium from another with different propagation properties. The phenomena of reflection and refraction then ensue. In treating these, we tacitly assumed that the boundary was infinite in extent, or at least

[1] R. B. Lindsay, "Physical Mechanics," 2d ed., p. 276, D. Van Nostrand Company, Inc., Princeton, N.J., 1950.

very large compared with the dimensions of the wavefront of the incident radiation.   We now wish to investigate the behavior of a radiation field in the presence of obstacles in the form of surfaces of discontinuity which are smaller than the wavefront area.   For example, a sound beam of large cross section in water may encounter a collection of air bubbles; a sound beam in the atmosphere, a grove of trees.   An elastic wave in a solid casting that meets a blowhole or other defect provides another illustration.   In all these cases the originally incident radiation is said to be scattered, in the sense that at any point the intensity of the radiation differs from what it would have been in the absence of the obstacles.

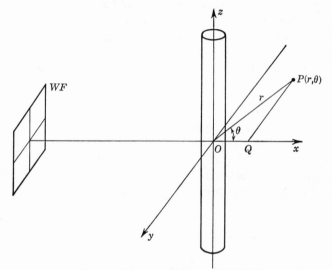

Fig. 3.7. Scattering of sound by a rigid cylinder.

The physical reasons for the scattering may be numerous: diffraction, reflection, refraction.   We have now to see how the scattered wave can be calculated in certain simple cases.   In this section we shall confine our attention to the scattering of an incident plane wave in a fluid by (1) a rigid solid right circular cylinder with its axis normal to the direction of propagation and (2) a rigid solid sphere.

We take up first the cylinder.   Figure 3.7 indicates the geometry of the situation.   Here WF represents a part of the incident plane wavefront advancing in the x direction.   The axis of the cylinder (radius a) is the z axis of a system of rectangular coordinates with origin O.   The length of the cylinder is not specified. P is any point in the xy plane and is fixed by the polar coordinates r and θ.   The solution of the scattering problem consists in finding the resultant excess pressure and intensity at the point P.

As in Sec. 3.5, we shall use the excess pressure p_e as the fundamental quantity which is propagated, but for the sake of convenience we shall leave off the subscript e. The incident wave will then be the harmonic plane wave advancing in the x direction

$$p_p = A_p e^{i(\omega t - kx)} \tag{1}$$

The incidence of this primary wave on the cylinder gives rise to a scattered wave for which the excess pressure will be denoted by p_s.

In view of the cylindrical symmetry imposed by the obstacle, it is desirable to express both primary and scattered waves as summations of cylindrical waves. This demands, first, that we express the wave equation (3.5-8) in terms of cylindrical coordinates r, θ, z. This is shown in standard mathematical texts (or see page 132) and yields

$$\frac{\partial^2 p}{\partial r^2} + \frac{1}{r}\frac{\partial p}{\partial r} + \frac{1}{r^2}\frac{\partial^2 p}{\partial \theta^2} + \frac{\partial^2 p}{\partial z^2} = \frac{\ddot{p}}{V^2} \tag{2}$$

where z lies along the axis of the cylinder. Since we shall be dealing entirely with waves harmonic in time, we shall set

$$\ddot{p} = -\omega^2 p \tag{3}$$

and rewrite the equation (with $k = \omega/V$)

$$\frac{\partial^2 p}{\partial r^2} + \frac{1}{r}\frac{\partial p}{\partial r} + \frac{1}{r^2}\frac{\partial^2 p}{\partial \theta^2} + \frac{\partial^2 p}{\partial z^2} + k^2 p = 0 \tag{4}$$

This may be handled by the method of separation of variables already mentioned in Sec. 1.8. Thus we get

$$p = F(r)G(\theta)Z(z) \tag{5}$$

By the usual manipulation this reduces to the three second-order ordinary differential equations

$$\frac{d^2 G}{d\theta^2} + m^2 G = 0$$

$$\frac{d^2 Z}{dz^2} + l^2 Z = 0 \tag{6}$$

$$\frac{d^2 F}{dr^2} + \frac{1}{r}\frac{dF}{dr} + \left(k^2 - l^2 - \frac{m^2}{r^2}\right)F = 0$$

In these equations m must be integral in order that G shall be a single-valued function of θ. For convenience we shall set $n^2 = k^2 - l^2$.

The first two equations in (6) need no comment.   The third is Bessel's equation[1] with the general solution

$$F = AJ_m(nr) + BN_m(nr) \tag{7}$$

Here $J_m(nr)$ is called the mth-order Bessel function of the first kind, whereas $N_m(nr)$ is the mth-order Bessel function of the second kind (sometimes called the Neumann function).   These may be written in the form of series as follows:

$$J_m(x) = \frac{m!}{\Gamma(m+1)} \sum_{j=0}^{\infty} \frac{(-1)^j x^{m+2j}}{2^{m+2j} \cdot j!(m+j)!} \tag{8}$$

where $\Gamma(m+1)$ denotes the gamma function

$$\Gamma(m+1) = \int_0^\infty x^m e^{-x}\, dx \tag{9}$$

In (8) m need not be integral, though in the present case it is, as we have observed.   For m integral

$$\Gamma(m+1) = m! \tag{10}$$

The Bessel function of the second kind is given in series form by

$$N_m(x) = J_m(x) \ln x - \frac{x^{-m}}{2^{1-m}} \sum_{j=0}^{\infty} \frac{(m-j-1)!\, x^{2j}}{2^{2j} \cdot j!}$$

$$- \frac{x^m}{2^{1+m}} \sum_{j=0}^{\infty} \frac{(-1)^j}{(m+j)!\, j!} \left[\Omega_j + \Omega_{j+m} \left(\frac{x}{2}\right)^{2j} \right] \tag{11}$$

where

$$\Omega_j = 1 + \frac{1}{2} + \frac{1}{3} + \cdots + \frac{1}{j} \tag{12}$$

$N_m(x)$ can be written more concisely in terms of $J_m(x)$ in the form

$$N_m(x) = J_m(x) \cot m\pi - J_{-m}(x) \csc m\pi \tag{13}$$

where

$$J_{-m}(x) = (-1)^m J_m(x) \tag{14}$$

It should be noted that $N_m(x)$ has an infinite discontinuity at $x = 0$, and

[1] H. Margenau and G. M. Murphy, "The Mathematics of Physics and Chemistry," p. 74, D. Van Nostrand Company, Inc., Princeton, N.J., 1943.   For useful formulas and tabulated values, see P. M. Morse, "Vibration and Sound," 2d ed., pp. 6, 188, 444, McGraw-Hill Book Company, Inc., New York, 1948.   For further tables and formulas, see H. B. Dwight, "Tables of Integrals and Other Mathematical Data," rev. ed., The Macmillan Company, New York, 1947; and E. Jahnke and F. Emde, "Tables of Functions with Formulae and Curves," Dover Publications, New York, 1945.

hence is not always useful for the expression of progressive cylindrical waves. For $x \gg 1$ the following asymptotic expressions are very useful:

$$J_m(x) \doteq \sqrt{\frac{2}{\pi x}} \cos \left[x - \frac{(2m + 1)\pi}{4} \right]$$

$$N_m(x) \doteq \sqrt{\frac{2}{\pi x}} \sin \left[x - \frac{(2m + 1)\pi}{4} \right] \tag{15}$$

This emphasizes that the Bessel functions for sufficiently large arguments are oscillatory functions modulated by an amplitude that decreases with distance x from the origin as $1/\sqrt{x}$. This gives a physical clue to their suitability for the representation of periodic waves.

Just as one can combine $\cos x$ and $\sin x$ to obtain an imaginary exponential, that is,

$$e^{ix} = \cos x + i \sin x$$

so one can develop new functions by the superposition of the Bessel functions of the first and second kind. Thus we write

$$H_m{}^{(1)}(x) = J_m(x) + iN_m(x)$$
$$H_m{}^{(2)}(x) = J_m(x) - iN_m(x) \tag{16}$$

The H functions are called Hankel functions, or Bessel functions of the third kind. For $x \gg 1$ they can be approximated by

$$H_m{}^{(1)}(x) \doteq \sqrt{\frac{2}{\pi x}} \exp \left\{ i \left[x - \frac{(2m + 1)\pi}{4} \right] \right\}$$

$$H_m{}^{(2)}(x) \doteq \sqrt{\frac{2}{\pi x}} \exp \left\{ -i \left[x - \frac{(2m + 1)\pi}{4} \right] \right\} \tag{17}$$

In view of the different characteristic behavior of $J_m(x)$ and $N_m(x)$, it is not usually feasible to use for F the combination in (7). Rather, one picks either the $J_m(x)$ or the $N_m(x)$ [or, in the second case, the $H_m(x)$], depending on the physical problem being studied. If a finite domain including the value $r = 0$ is in question, $J_m(x)$ is indicated. Hence we can get an appropriate solution to the wave equation in the form

$$p = A(n)J_m(nr)e^{im\theta}e^{i(\omega t - lz)} \tag{18}$$

with $A(n)$ as the amplitude factor and

$$n = \sqrt{k^2 - l^2} \qquad \omega = kV \tag{19}$$

To put (18) into a form suitable for the representation of a radially diverging cylindrical wave, we must of course take $l = 0$. The space variation in the wave is then contained in the term $J_m(nr)$, and n becomes k. By the superposition principle applying to linear equations, the general solution of the wave equation can be represented as a summation of individual solutions of the form (18) with all values of n.†

It will be recalled that the primary wave in the scattering problem being discussed in this section is assumed to be a harmonic wave progressing in the x direction [Eq. (1)]. In order to take advantage of the cylindrical symmetry exhibited by the obstacle, we shall expand $e^{-ikx} = e^{-ikr\cos\theta}$ (see Fig. 3.7) in terms of Bessel functions of the first kind. We first expand in a Fourier series. Thus

$$e^{-ikr\cos\theta} = \sum_{n=0}^{\infty} C_n(r)\cos n\theta \tag{20}$$

Assuming that the expansion is mathematically possible, we employ the usual rule [Eqs. (3.1-6, 7)] for the evaluation of the coefficients to obtain

$$C_n(r) = \frac{1}{\pi} \int_0^{2\pi} e^{-ikr\cos\theta} \cos n\theta \, d\theta \tag{21}$$

The integral representation of Bessel functions permits us to write[1]

$$C_n(r) = 2(-1)^n J_n(kr) \tag{22}$$

for $n \geq 1$ and

$$C_0(r) = J_0(kr) \tag{23}$$

The excess pressure in the primary plane wave then takes the form

$$p_p = A_p e^{i\omega t} \left[J_0(kr) + 2 \sum_{n=1}^{\infty} (-1)J_n(kr)\cos n\theta \right] \tag{24}$$

In order to satisfy the boundary conditions it is necessary to express the excess pressure in the scattered wave in terms of a similar expansion. We recall that at distances from the cylinder that are large compared with the wavelength the scattered wave must behave as an outgoing wave, that is, must depend on r through a term of the form e^{-ikr}. From (16) and (17) it is seen that for this purpose we must use the Hankel functions $H_n^{(2)}(kr)$ and hence write

$$p_s = e^{i\omega t} \sum_{n=0}^{\infty} B_n H_n^{(2)}(kr) \cos n\theta \tag{25}$$

The B_n coefficients are to be determined from the boundary condition

† For the Bessel function formulas given here, consult the references listed in the preceding footnote; see also B. O. Peirce, "A Short Table of Integrals," 4th ed., Ginn & Company, Boston, 1956.

[1] E. T. Whittaker and G. N. Watson, "A Course of Modern Analysis," 4th ed., p. 363, Cambridge University Press, London, 1940.

which demands that the resultant velocity normal to the surface of the cylinder shall vanish (it is assumed that the cylinder is rigid).

Now from (3.5-7) the velocity component normal to the cylinder is given (for harmonic waves such as we are dealing with here) by

$$v = \frac{i}{\omega \rho_0} \frac{\partial p}{\partial r} \tag{26}$$

Hence the boundary condition becomes

$$\left[\frac{\partial}{\partial r} (p_p + p_s) \right]_{r=a} = 0 \tag{27}$$

We employ the following formulas for the differentiation of Bessel functions:

$$\frac{dJ_0(kr)}{dr} = -kJ_1(kr) \qquad \frac{dJ_n(kr)}{dr} = \frac{k}{2} [J_{n-1}(kr) - J_{n+1}(kr)] \qquad n > 0$$

$$\frac{dN_0(kr)}{dr} = -kN_1(kr) \qquad \frac{dN_n(kr)}{dr} = \frac{k}{2} [N_{n-1}(kr) - N_{n+1}(kr)] \qquad n > 0$$

Carrying out the differentiation gives for (27) the equation

$$kA_p \left\{ -J_1(ka) + \sum_{n=1}^{\infty} (-i)^n [J_{n-1}(ka) - J_{n+1}(ka)] \cos n\theta \right\}$$

$$+ k \left\{ -B_0 H_1^{(2)}(ka) + \tfrac{1}{2} \sum_{n=1}^{\infty} B_n [H_{n-1}^{(2)}(ka) \right.$$

$$\left. - H_{n+1}^{(2)}(ka)] \cos n\theta \right\} = 0 \tag{28}$$

which must hold for all values of θ. This leads at once to

$$B_0 = -A_p \frac{J_1(ka)}{H_1^{(2)}(ka)}$$

$$B_n = (-2)(-1)^n A_p \frac{J_{n+1}(ka) - J_{n-1}(ka)}{H_{n+1}^{(2)}(ka) - H_{n-1}^{(2)}(ka)} \qquad n > 0 \tag{29}$$

Reverting to the J and N functions,

$$B_0 = A_p \frac{1}{1 - i[N_1(ka)/J_1(ka)]} \tag{30}$$

$$B_n = (-2)(-1)^n A_p \frac{1}{1 - i \cdot \dfrac{N_{n+1}(ka) - N_{n-1}(ka)}{J_{n+1}(ka) - J_{n-1}(ka)}} \tag{31}$$

These are both in the form

$$\frac{1}{1 - iq} = \frac{1}{1 + q^2} + \frac{iq}{1 + q^2}$$

and if we let $q = \cot \gamma$, we can write

$$B_0 = - A_p i \sin \gamma_0 e^{-i\gamma_0} \tag{32}$$

$$B_n = 2(-1)^{n+1} A_p \sin \gamma_n e^{-i\gamma_n} \tag{33}$$

with

$$\cot \gamma_0 = \frac{N_1(ka)}{J_1(ka)} \tag{34}$$

$$\cot \gamma_n = \frac{N_{n+1}(ka) - N_{n-1}(ka)}{J_{n+1}(ka) - J_{n-1}(ka)} \tag{35}$$

The pressure for the scattered wave then takes the form

$$p_s = A_p e^{i\omega t} \left[-i \sin \gamma_0 e^{-i\gamma_0} H_0^{(2)}(kr) \right.$$

$$\left. + 2 \sum_{n=1}^{\infty} (-i)^{n+1} \sin \gamma_n e^{-i\gamma_n} H_n^{(2)}(kr) \cos n\theta \right] \tag{36}$$

For values of r such that $kr \gg 1$, we can use the approximate formula (17) for $H_n^{(2)}(kr)$ and write

$$p_s = A_p \sqrt{\frac{2}{\pi kr}} e^{i(\omega t - kr)} \left\{ -i \sin \gamma_0 e^{-i(\gamma_0 - \pi/4)} \right.$$

$$\left. + 2 \sum_{n=1}^{\infty} (-i)^{n+1} \sin \gamma_n \exp\left[-i\left(\gamma_n - \frac{2n+1}{4}\pi \right) \right] \cos n\theta \right\} \tag{37}$$

Thus the scattered wave at relatively great distances from the source behaves like a cylindrical wave, but with an amplitude which is azimuth-modulated. For $kr \gg 1$, the intensity of the scattered wave is therefore given by (Sec. 1.10)

$$I = \overline{v_s p_s} = \frac{\overline{p_s^2}}{\rho_0 V} = \frac{A_p^2}{\pi r \rho_0 \omega} |\psi_s(\theta)|^2 \tag{38}$$

where $\psi_s(\theta)$ is the expression enclosed in braces in (37).

The total average rate at which energy is scattered by unit height of the cylinder or the total scattered power is P_s, where

$$P_s = \int_0^{2\pi} I r \, d\theta$$

$$= \frac{A_p^2}{\pi \omega \rho_0} \int_0^{2\pi} |\psi_s(\theta)|^2 \, d\theta$$

$$= \frac{2I_0}{\pi k} \int_0^{2\pi} |\psi_s(\theta)|^2 \, d\theta \tag{39}$$

where I_0 is the intensity of the primary wave. The integration can be carried out by the use of the well-known integral

$$\int_0^{2\pi} \cos n\theta \cos m\theta \, d\theta = 0 \qquad n \neq m$$
$$= \pi \qquad n = m$$

and leads ultimately to

$$P_s = \frac{4I_0}{k} \sum_{n=0}^{\infty} \epsilon_n \sin^2 \gamma_n \qquad (40)$$

where $\epsilon_0 = 1$, $\epsilon_n = 2$ $(n = 1, 2, \ldots)$. The evaluation of the sum in (40) depends on the value of $ka = 2\pi a/\lambda$. Use of (34) and (35) yields the following approximations for the extreme values of ka:

$$P_s \doteq \frac{6\pi^5 a^4}{\lambda^3} I_0 \qquad ka \ll 1 \qquad (41)$$

$$P_s \doteq 4aI_0 \qquad ka \gg 1 \qquad (42)$$

When $P_s/4aI_0$ is plotted as a function of ka, the curve is as indicated in Fig. 3.8.

For any given value of r the distribution of scattered intensity in angle is given by $|\psi_s(\theta)|^2$. This varies with the value of ka. Two sample polar diagrams are presented in Fig. 3.9.

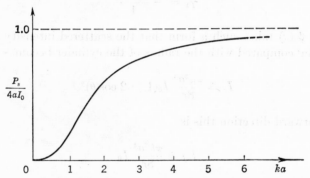

FIG. 3.8. Total scattered power (cylindrical scattering) as a function of ka.

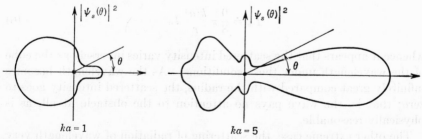

FIG. 3.9. Angular distribution in cylindrical scattering. (*Reprinted by permission from P. M. Morse, "Vibration and Sound," 2d ed., p. 349, McGraw-Hill Book Company, Inc., New York, 1948, with certain changes.*)

In each case the arrow indicates the direction of the primary radiation. When the wavelength is of the same order as the radius of the obstacle, the scattering is mainly in the backward direction and is rather uniformly distributed in angle.   There is little forward scattering.   As the wavelength is decreased (frequency increased), the forward scattering increases relatively to the backward scattering, and more peaks appear.

Indeed, as Fig. 3.9 suggests, increase in ka (corresponding for given a to a decrease in wavelength or increase in frequency) produces $|\psi_s(\theta)|^2$ patterns of increasing complexity with additional side lobes appearing along with the backward and forward peaks.   The forward peak (the shadow-forming wave) becomes sharp and high as ka increases, whereas the backward peak (the reflected wave) has the average shape of a cardioid.   This corresponds approximately to Fraunhofer diffraction in optics.

From the properties of Bessel functions it turns out that for $ka \ll 1$, the only γ's which are not negligible are γ_0 and γ_1 and indeed

$$\gamma_0 \doteq \frac{\pi k^2 a^2}{4}$$
$$\gamma_1 \doteq -\frac{\pi k^2 a^2}{4} \tag{43}$$

and hence $\psi_s(\theta)$ takes such a form that the scattered intensity at wavelengths long compared with the radius of the cylinder becomes

$$I_s \doteq \frac{\pi k^3 a^4}{8r} I_0 (1 - 2\cos\theta)^2 \tag{44}$$

For the forward direction this is

$$I_{sf} \doteq \frac{\pi k^3 a^4}{8r} I_0 \tag{45}$$

whereas for the backward direction

$$I_{sb} \doteq \frac{9}{8} \pi \frac{k^3 a^4}{r} I_0 \tag{46}$$

whence it appears that the scattered intensity varies inversely as the cube of the wavelength under these conditions.   As the wavelength becomes infinitely great compared with the radius, the scattered intensity goes to zero; that is, the wave pays no attention to the obstacle at all, as is physically reasonable.

The other extreme case, the scattering of radiation of wavelength very small compared with the radius of the cylinder, would appear to provide a good illustration of geometrical acoustics in which the wave propagation can be followed rather accurately by ray tracing (Sec. 1.12).   In this case we expect that a more or less sharp shadow zone will be formed on the forward side of the obstacle (see Fig. 3.10), whereas on the backward side reflection will take place more or less as in the corresponding optical case.   The mathematical details for this case are rather complicated[1] and will not be presented here.

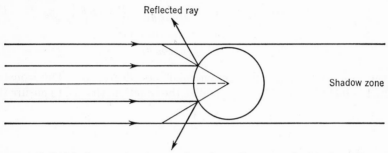

Reflected ray

Shadow zone

Fig. 3.10. Cylindrical scattering for wavelength small compared with the radius of the cylinder.   Shadow zone.

We now pass to the scattering of a plane wave by a rigid sphere, which for many purposes is more important than that by a cylinder.   The same general method will be followed; that is, we shall first expand the excess pressure for a plane harmonic progressive wave in terms of spherical coordinates r, θ, and ϕ.   The wave equation then becomes (see Appendix A)

$$\frac{1}{r^2}\frac{\partial}{\partial r}\left(r^2\frac{\partial p}{\partial r}\right) + \frac{1}{r^2\sin\theta}\frac{\partial}{\partial\theta}\left(\sin\theta\frac{\partial p}{\partial\theta}\right) + \frac{1}{r^2\sin^2\theta}\frac{\partial^2 p}{\partial\phi^2} = \frac{\ddot{p}}{V^2} \quad (47)$$

The usual scheme of separation of variables, that is, substituting

$$p = R(r)\Theta(\theta)\Phi(\phi)T(t) \quad (48)$$

leads to the following second-order ordinary differential equations:

$$\frac{d^2R}{dr^2} + \frac{2}{r}\frac{dR}{dr} + \left[k^2 - \frac{n(n+1)}{r^2}\right]R = 0 \quad (49)$$

$$\frac{1}{\sin\theta}\frac{d}{d\theta}\left(\sin\theta\frac{d\Theta}{d\theta}\right) + \left[n(n+1) - \frac{m^2}{\sin^2\theta}\right]\Theta = 0 \quad (50)$$

$$\frac{d^2\Phi}{d\phi^2} + m^2\Phi = 0 \quad (51)$$

$$\frac{d^2T}{dt^2} + V^2k^2T = 0 \quad (52)$$

where k, m, n are arbitrary constants.   If the solutions to (51) are to be single-valued, m must be an integer.   The solutions to (50) are the

[1] Morse, "Vibration and Sound," p. 350.

associated Legendre functions[1] usually expressed in the form

$$\Theta = P_n^{|m|}(\cos \theta) \tag{53}$$

with n having integral values to keep Θ finite over the whole permissible range in θ.   The mathematical treatment shows that we can write

$$P_n^{|m|}(\cos \theta) = \sin^{|m|} \theta \, \frac{d^{|m|}}{d(\cos \theta)^{|m|}} [P_n(\cos \theta)] \tag{54}$$

where $\qquad P_n(\cos \theta) = \dfrac{1}{2^n n!} \dfrac{d^n(\cos^2 \theta - 1)^n}{d(\cos \theta)^n} \tag{55}$

is the so-called "Legendre polynomial" of degree n.   The constant $1/2^n n!$ is included in (55) to normalize the function, that is, to ensure that

$$\int_{-1}^{+1} [P_n(\cos \theta)]^2 \, d(\cos \theta) = \frac{2}{2n + 1} \tag{56}$$

To handle (49), we place $R = Q/r$ and let $kr = z$.   These substitutions yield

$$\frac{d^2Q}{dz^2} + \left[1 - \frac{m(m + 1)}{z^2}\right] Q = 0 \tag{57}$$

Finally we set $Q = \sqrt{z}\, S$, whence (57) becomes

$$\frac{d^2S}{dz^2} + \frac{1}{z} \frac{dS}{dz} + \left[1 - \frac{(m + \frac{1}{2})^2}{z^2}\right] S = 0 \tag{58}$$

This again is Bessel's equation [see (6)], and the solution is

$$S = A J_{m+\frac{1}{2}}(z) + B N_{m+\frac{1}{2}}(z) \tag{59}$$

Hence $\qquad R = \dfrac{A'}{\sqrt{r}} J_{m+\frac{1}{2}}(kr) + \dfrac{B'}{\sqrt{r}} N_{m+\frac{1}{2}}(kr) \tag{60}$

The consideration of the problem of scattering by a sphere then proceeds similarly to that for a cylinder.   We must first expand the excess pressure in the primary plane wave in terms of the spherical wave functions (48), which in view of the symmetry of the situation reduce to Legendre polynomials.   Thus we write

$$e^{-ikr \cos \theta} = \sum_{n=0}^{\infty} A_n(r) P_n(\cos \theta) \tag{61}$$

To evaluate the coefficients $A_n(r)$ we employ the technique of multiplying through by $P_n(\cos \theta)$ and integrating with respect to $\cos \theta$ from -1 to

[1] Margenau and Murphy, "Mathematics of Physics and Chemistry," p. 68.

$+1$. Then

$$\int_{-1}^{+1} P_n(\cos \theta) e^{-ikr \cos \theta} \, d(\cos \theta) = A_n(r) \int_{-1}^{+1} [P_n(\cos \theta)]^2 \, d(\cos \theta)$$

whence, from (56),

$$A_n(r) = \frac{2n + 1}{2} \int_{-1}^{+1} P_n(\cos \theta) e^{-ikr \cos \theta} \, d(\cos \theta) \tag{62}$$

By carrying out the integration,[1] we finally arrive at

$$A_n(r) = \frac{2n + 1}{2} (-i)^n \sqrt{\frac{\pi}{2kr}} J_{n+\frac{1}{2}}(kr) \tag{63}$$

The excess pressure in the primary wave then has the form

$$p_p = A_p e^{i\omega t} \sum (2n + 1)(-i)^n \sqrt{\frac{\pi}{2kr}} J_{n+\frac{1}{2}}(kr) P_n(\cos \theta) \tag{64}$$

Now for values of r such that $kr \gg 1$, we have, from (15),

$$\sqrt{\frac{\pi}{2kr}} J_{n+\frac{1}{2}}(kr) \doteq \frac{1}{kr} \cos \left[kr - \left(\frac{n+1}{2} \right) \pi \right]$$

$$\sqrt{\frac{\pi}{2kr}} N_{n+\frac{1}{2}}(kr) \doteq \frac{1}{kr} \sin \left[kr - \left(\frac{n+1}{2} \right) \pi \right] \tag{65}$$

Hence, to assure that the scattered excess pressure at great distances from the sphere shall act as an outgoing spherical wave, we must expand in terms of

$$\sqrt{\frac{\pi}{2kr}} [J_{n+\frac{1}{2}}(kr) - i N_{n+\frac{1}{2}}(kr)] = \sqrt{\frac{\pi}{2kr}} H_{n+\frac{1}{2}}^{(2)}(kr) \tag{66}$$

The scattered excess pressure should therefore have the form

$$p_s = e^{i\omega t} \sqrt{\frac{\pi}{2kr}} \sum C_n H_{n+\frac{1}{2}}^{(2)}(kr) P_n(\cos \theta) \tag{67}$$

where once more the coefficients C_n are to be evaluated from the boundary condition at the surface of the sphere. This is of precisely the same form as (27). To employ it we find it convenient to introduce the notation

$$j_n(kr) = \sqrt{\frac{\pi}{2kr}} J_{n+\frac{1}{2}}(kr)$$

$$n_n(kr) = \sqrt{\frac{\pi}{2kr}} N_{n+\frac{1}{2}}(kr) \tag{68}$$

[1] Lord Rayleigh, "Theory of Sound," 2d ed., vol. 2, pp. 261f., Dover Publications, New York, 1945.

The properties of j_n and n_n are given by P. M. Morse.[1]   Then (67) and (64) become respectively

$$p_s = e^{i\omega t}\Sigma C_n[j_n(kr) - in_n(kr)]P_n(\cos \theta) \tag{69}$$

$$p_p = A_p e^{i\omega t}\Sigma(2n + 1)(-i)^n j_n(kr)P_n(\cos \theta) \tag{70}$$

Imposition of the boundary condition (27) yields

$$kA_p\{-j_1(ka) + \Sigma(-i)^n[nj_{n-1}(ka) - (n + 1)j_{n+1}(ka)]P_n(\cos \theta)\}$$
$$+ k(-C_0[j_1(ka) - in_1(ka)] + \Sigma C_n\{n[j_{n-1}(ka) - in_{n-1}(ka)] \cdot$$
$$- (n + 1)[j_{n+1}(ka) - in_{n+1}(ka)]\}P_n(\cos \theta)) = 0 \tag{71}$$

which must hold for all values of θ.   Hence

$$C_0 = \frac{A_p j_1(ka)}{j_1(ka) - in_1(ka)}$$

$$C_n = -(-i)^n A_p \frac{nj_{n-1}(ka) - (n + 1)j_{n+1}(ka)}{n[j_{n-1}(ka) - in_{n-1}(ka)] - (n + 1)[j_{n+1}(ka) - in_{n+1}(ka)]}$$
$$n \geq 1 \tag{72}$$

Following the analogy of the cylindrical case, we naturally set

$$(n + 1)j_{n+1}(ka) - nj_{n-1}(ka) = (2n + 1)D_n \sin \delta_n$$
$$nn_{n-1}(ka) - (n + 1)n_{n+1}(ka) = (2n + 1)D_n \cos \delta_n \tag{73}$$

where D_n and δ_n are amplitudes and phase factors, respectively.   In this notation the excess pressure in the scattered wave becomes

$$p_s = -A_p e^{i\omega t}\Sigma(2n + 1)(-i)^{n+1}e^{-i\delta_n}P_n(\cos \theta)[j_n(kr) - in_n(kr)] \tag{74}$$

The rest of the story follows the earlier treatment of the cylindrical case very closely.   We wind up with the following expression for the total scattered power:

$$P_s = \frac{4\pi I_0}{k^2} \sum (2n + 1) \sin^2 \delta_n \tag{75}$$

where I_0 is, as before, the intensity in the primary plane wave.   From the properties of the j_n and n_n functions it turns out that

$$P_s \doteq \frac{256\pi^5 a^6}{9\lambda^4} I_0 \qquad ka \ll 1 \tag{76}$$

$$P_s \doteq 2\pi a^2 I_0 \qquad ka \gg 1 \tag{77}$$

The dependence of P_s on the inverse fourth power of the wavelength for wavelengths long compared with the radius of the sphere is significant.

---

[1] "Vibration and Sound," p. 316.

This is known as Rayleigh scattering and occurs in a great variety of radiation problems, such as the scattering of light in the atmosphere and underwater sound scattering.

The plots of the scattered intensity as a function of angle are similar to those encountered in cylindrical scattering.[1]

3.7. Wave Pulses

The continuous progressive wave already discussed in considerable detail in the preceding sections is of course an idealization of the radiation encountered in practice.   No physically realizable progressive wave on the surface of the earth is infinite in either space or time.   All waves produced by sources on the earth are actually finite in spatial extent and temporal duration.   It is therefore necessary to examine to what extent a finite wave train, that is, a wave disturbance which at any instant in its propagation through a medium is different from zero over only a finite interval of space, can be represented in terms of progressive harmonic waves.   One example of such a wave, usually called a wave pulse, is the following:

$$f(x - Vt) = C = \text{nonvanishing constant} \qquad \text{for } |x - Vt| < \frac{L}{2}$$

$$f(x - Vt) = 0 \qquad \text{for } |x - Vt| > \frac{L}{2} \tag{1}$$

This is a square wave pulse moving in the x direction, which at any instant has the length L.   Another example is the sinusoidal pulse

$$f(x - Vt) = \cos k_0(x - Vt) \qquad \text{for } |x - Vt| < \frac{L}{2}$$

$$f(x - Vt) = 0 \qquad \text{for } |x - Vt| > \frac{L}{2} \tag{2}$$

where k_0 is the wave parameter (see Sec. 1.4).

Now the Fourier theorem already mentioned (Sec. 3.1) makes possible the analysis of an arbitrary function of a single variable (i.e., either space or time) in terms of a series of harmonic components in this variable, the representation being in general valid only for a finite interval of the variable.   Only periodic functions can be represented by Fourier series over an indefinitely large range of the variable.   To represent an arbitrary function like a finite wave train or pulse clearly demands another technique.   This is provided by the Fourier integral theorem, which states that a piecewise continuous function $f(x)$ (see Sec. 3.1) which also pos-

[1] *Ibid.*, p. 355.

sesses a piecewise continuous first derivative and is such that the integral

$$\int_{-\infty}^{+\infty} |f(x)|\, dx$$

exists can be expanded in a set of harmonic components with *continuously* varying frequencies and amplitudes depending on the frequencies.[1] Symbolically we may write

$$f(x) = \frac{1}{2\pi} \int_{-\infty}^{+\infty} e^{i\omega x}\, d\omega \int_{-\infty}^{+\infty} f(u)e^{-i\omega u}\, du \tag{3}$$

Here ω is the angular frequency of the component and its amplitude is

$$\frac{1}{2\pi} \int_{-\infty}^{+\infty} f(u)e^{-i\omega u}\, du \tag{4}$$

It is customary to call

$$\overline{f(\omega)} = \frac{1}{\sqrt{2\pi}} \int_{-\infty}^{+\infty} f(u)e^{-i\omega u}\, du \tag{5}$$

the *Fourier transform* of $f(u)$. It is then possible to express $f(x)$ in terms of its Fourier transform as follows

$$f(x) = \frac{1}{\sqrt{2\pi}} \int_{-\infty}^{+\infty} \overline{f(\omega)}e^{i\omega x}\, d\omega \tag{6}$$

If $f(x)$ is a real and even function, it turns out that we can write for its integral expansion

$$f(x) = \frac{1}{2\pi} \int_{-\infty}^{+\infty} \cos \omega x\, d\omega \int_{-\infty}^{+\infty} f(u) \cos \omega u\, du \tag{7}$$

We can extend this to a function of x and t in the form $x - Vt$ by writing

$$f(x - Vt) = \frac{1}{2\pi} \int_{-\infty}^{+\infty} \cos k(x - Vt)\, dk$$
$$\int_{-\infty}^{+\infty} f(u - V\tau) \cos k(u - V\tau)\, d(u - V\tau) \tag{8}$$

where we now need *two* dummy parameters u and τ in expressing the transform. Moreover, here we are employing the wave parameter k instead of the angular frequency ω to characterize the harmonic component waves.

[1] The mathematical literature on Fourier integrals is very extensive. See, for example, E. C. Titchmarsh, "Introduction to the Theory of Fourier Integrals," Oxford University Press, London, 1937. For a more modern approach, see M. J. Lighthill, "Introduction to Fourier Analysis and Generalized Functions," Cambridge University Press, London, 1958.

If we examine the case shown in (2), we have effectively for the Fourier transform (letting $u - V\tau = w$ for simplicity)

$$\overline{f(k)} = \frac{1}{\sqrt{2\pi}} \int_{-L/2}^{+L/2} \cos k_0 w \cos kw \, dw$$

$$= \frac{1}{\sqrt{2\pi}} \left[\frac{\sin (k_0 - k)L/2}{k_0 - k} + \frac{\sin (k_0 + k)L/2}{k_0 + k} \right] \qquad (9)$$

The first term in the brackets will predominate over the second for most of the range (i.e., everywhere except $k \doteq 0$), and we need consider it alone.   Hence the amplitude of the harmonic wave component of wave number k is very closely

$$\frac{1}{\pi} \frac{\sin (k_0 - k)L/2}{k_0 - k} \qquad (10)$$

which is plotted as a function of $k_0 - k$ in Fig. 3.11.   The amplitude attains an absolute maximum for $k = k_0$ (i.e., at A), and all subsequent

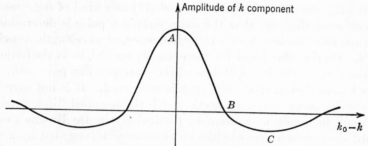

FIG. 3.11. Amplitude of the harmonic components in a wave pulse.

maxima and minima decline progressively in absolute value.   In particular, the absolute value of the amplitude at C is about one-fifth of that at A.   Moreover, the amplitude drops to zero for

$$(k_0 - k)L = \pm 2n\pi \qquad (11)$$

where n is any integer.   Most of the contribution to the harmonic analysis is confined to the range out to the first zero (that is, B) for which $n = 1$.   Accordingly, if we denote by Δk the range of $k_0 - k$ needed to represent the wave pulse satisfactorily as a superposition of harmonic continuous wave components holding for all x and t, we have approximately

$$\Delta k = \frac{2n\pi}{L} \qquad (12)$$

Now L is the length of the wave pulse.   If we denote this by Δx, (12) becomes

$$\Delta k \, \Delta x \geq 2\pi \qquad (13)$$

The physical meaning of this result is as follows. The shorter the wave pulse, the greater is the range of wave parameter necessary for its resolution into harmonic continuous waves, and vice versa. As the pulse is made longer, it approaches a continuous wave of practically single frequency (strictly, however, only if $\Delta x \to \infty$, of course). But a very short pulse requires a very large k spread. From the definition of k we see that this implies the same result for frequency. The corresponding relation in terms of wavelength takes the form

$$\Delta x \, \Delta \frac{1}{\lambda} \geq 1 \tag{14}$$

The practical consequence of this relation can be considerable. If, for example, it is desired to amplify the pulse by some device without altering its shape, it is necessary that the device shall have a frequency response sufficiently wide to take care of the whole frequency spread associated with the pulse length. Otherwise distortion will result.

It is suggestive to look upon (13) and (14) as a kind of *indeterminacy* relation, since they say that the more sharply a pulse is determined in space and time, the less definite is the frequency, or wavelength, associated with it. On the other hand, the more sharply we wish to fix the frequency of a given wave, the less well defined the corresponding pulse will be, so far as localization in space and time is concerned. It is not surprising that this has suggested a connection with the so-called "indeterminacy principle" in quantum mechanics, particularly in De Broglie's earlier picture of an atomic particle like an electron as represented by a wave pulse whose wavelength is connected with the momentum p of the particle by the celebrated relation

$$\lambda = \frac{h}{p} \tag{15}$$

where h is Planck's constant of action (6.55×10^{-27} erg-sec). If we suppose that the particle is somehow localized in the wave pulse, Δx in (14) will denote the indeterminacy in its position. Hence, substituting from (15) gives

$$\Delta x \, \Delta p \geq h \tag{16}$$

where Δp is a measure of the indeterminacy in the momentum of the particle. Thus, the more precisely the position of the particle is determined, the greater is the indefiniteness in the momentum p, the constant h providing a measure of the magnitude of the indeterminacy. Since De Broglie's elementary picture has been abandoned, this interpretation of the indeterminacy principle is now of historical interest only; the principle is a direct deduction from the formal hypotheses of quantum mechanics, which is a logical structure having no connection with any particular picture of atomic particles. Nevertheless the wave view is still helpful to many people.

3.8. Wave Pulses in Dispersive Media. Group Velocity

In the development of the previous section it was taken for granted that the wave velocity V is constant, that is, the same for all frequencies. As was pointed out in Sec. 1.10, however, this is by no means universally true. There are many media in which the velocity is a function of the frequency; these are *dispersive*. All material media are dispersive for electromagnetic waves of certain frequency. All material media are also dispersive for elastic radiation, though the effect is often very slight and difficult to detect save at very high frequencies; this is especially true for liquids (Sec. 12.2).

At any rate it is desirable to extend our discussion of wave pulses to dispersive media, in which $V = V(\omega)$, or, more conveniently expressed,

$$\omega = \omega(k) \tag{1}$$

that is, the angular frequency is a function of the wave parameter k, which we recall is equal to $2\pi/\lambda$ (see, for example, Sec. 1.4). The relation $\omega = 2\pi V/\lambda$ still holds universally. Hence $k = \omega/V(\omega)$, from which ω can be solved in terms of k. Let us now suppose that we are able to expand any arbitrary pulse $f(x,t)$ in terms of the harmonic components $\cos(kx - \omega t)$, where ω is subject to (1), thus:

$$f(x,t) = \int_{-\infty}^{+\infty} A(k) \cos(kx - \omega t)\, dk \tag{2}$$

where $A(k)$ is the amplitude associated with the wave parameter k. It must be emphasized that there is no immediate assurance that this expansion is justified from a mathematical point of view in this case;[1] we are merely going to investigate the consequences of the hypothesis. As a matter of fact, we shall further assume that a certain mean wave parameter k_0 and the corresponding angular frequency ω_0 are associated with the pulse and that in the representation (2) it is necessary to consider only a finite range of variation Δk on either side of k_0 in order to provide a satisfactory resolution. This means that we can substitute for the phase $kx - \omega t$ in (2) a Taylor expansion of the form

---

[1] A. Sommerfeld, "Mechanics of Deformable Bodies," pp. 189ff., Academic Press, Inc., New York, 1950; also J. A. Stratton, "Electromagnetic Theory," pp. 330ff., McGraw-Hill Book Company, Inc., New York, 1941.

$$kx - \omega t = k_0 x - \omega_0 t + \left(\frac{dk}{dk}\right)_0 (k - k_0)x - \left(\frac{d\omega}{dk}\right)_0 (k - k_0)t + \cdots$$

$$= k_0 x - \omega_0 t + (k - k_0)\left[x - \left(\frac{d\omega}{dk}\right)_0 t\right] + \cdots \tag{3}$$

in which $(d\omega/dk)_0$ means that the value of the derivative is calculated from (1) but evaluated at $k = k_0$ and $\omega = \omega_0$. Our assumption above justifies the limitation of the expansion to the first two terms. Substitution into (2) yields

$$f(x,t) = \cos(k_0 x - \omega_0 t) \int_{k_0 - \Delta k}^{k_0 + \Delta k} A(k) \cos(k - k_0)\left[x - \left(\frac{d\omega}{dk}\right)_0 t\right] dk$$

$$- \sin(k_0 x - \omega_0 t) \int_{k_0 - \Delta k}^{k_0 + \Delta k} A(k) \sin(k - k_0)\left[x - \left(\frac{d\omega}{dk}\right)_0 t\right] dk \tag{4}$$

It is here, of course, assumed that effectively

$$A(k) = 0 \qquad \text{for } |k| \geq k_0 + \Delta k \tag{5}$$

We can write (4) more compactly by calling the integral multiplying $\cos(k_0 x - \omega_0 t)$ the function $F(x,t)$ and that multiplying $\sin(k_0 x - \omega_0 t)$ the function $G(x,t)$. Then

$$f(x,t) = R(x,t) \cos[(k_0 x - \omega_0 t) + \alpha(x,t)] \tag{6}$$

with $\qquad\qquad R(x,t) = \sqrt{F^2 + G^2}$

and $\qquad\qquad \alpha(x,t) = \arctan \dfrac{G}{F}$ $\qquad\qquad\qquad\qquad$ (7)

This expresses the given wave pulse in terms of a single sinusoidal wave of angular frequency ω_0 but modulated with time- and space-dependent amplitude R and phase α, respectively. From an inspection of (4), it is clear that the time and space dependence is through the quantity $x - (d\omega/dk)_0 t$. If this quantity were to stay *constant* while x and t vary, we could clearly think of the pulse as represented by the single sinusoidal wave with fixed amplitude and phase. But the critical quantity in question will remain constant to one who moves along the x axis with the velocity

$$U = \left(\frac{d\omega}{dk}\right)_0 \tag{8}$$

Hence, to one who moves along the x axis with this velocity, the various component waves into which the pulse is resolved will appear to be superposed. There will certainly be a point at which the superposition results in maximum amplitude due to phase agreement. The velocity with which this point of maximum amplitude moves through the medium is designated by U and is called the *group velocity*. We say that the pulse has been analyzed into a group of waves.

There are several ways of expressing the group velocity to show how it differs from the wave velocity for the various components of the group. Thus we can write

$$\frac{1}{U} = \left[\frac{d(\omega/V)}{d\omega}\right]_0 = \frac{1}{V_0} - \frac{\omega_0}{V_0^2}\left(\frac{dV}{d\omega}\right)_0 \tag{9}$$

whence
$$U = \frac{V_0}{1 - (\omega_0/V_0)(dV/d\omega)_0} \tag{10}$$

This shows that, if $(dV/d\omega)_0 = 0$, that is, if there is no dependence of velocity on frequency, $U = V_0$, the mean phase velocity, which of course is then the velocity of all components; the group velocity is the same as the phase velocity. On the other hand, if $(dV/d\omega)_0 < 0$, $U < V_0$; and if $(dV/d\omega)_0 > 0$, $U > V_0$.

It is sometimes advantageous to express the group velocity in terms of the variation of phase velocity with wavelength. By the use of the fundamental relationship $\lambda = V/\nu$, we deduce from (10) that

$$U = V_0 - \lambda_0\left(\frac{dV}{d\lambda}\right)_0 \tag{11}$$

In the normal dispersion of visible light, $(dV/d\omega)_0 < 0$ (the velocity increases with the *wavelength*—recall the behavior of the index of refraction), and hence the group velocity should be less than the mean wave velocity in a pulse.

This is well illustrated in the experimental determination of the velocity of light in a dispersive medium, which in the region of normal dispersion in all cases yields a value less than that which would be predicted from the index of refraction. Thus Michelson, in the direct measurement of the velocity of light in CS_2 by his modification of the Foucault rotating-mirror arrangement, found a value 0.57 the velocity *in vacuo*, whereas the index of refraction would imply a value 0.61 for the same quantity. He naturally concluded that he had measured the group velocity in the dispersive medium, and indeed, if one uses the appropriate value of $(dV/d\omega)_0$ for this case in (10), the measured value is found. Evidently the phase velocity is the one involved in the geometrical bending of the wavefront in refraction, whereas the group velocity appears to be the rate of flow of energy in the beam. We should be cautious, however, in drawing this conclusion in general. For we must recall that in defining the group velocity at all it is necessary to assume that we can represent the wave pulse by a group of waves in which the variation of the wave parameter k is limited to a small interval Δk on either side of the mean parameter k_0 [see the analysis leading to (3)]. This is admissible if the pulse is not too short [see (3.7-13)].   However, for short pulses the range Δk may become too great to justify the expansion (3), so that the group velocity loses its meaning.   Another way of expressing this physically is to say that, if Δk is large, the wave pulse becomes deformed and diffuses as it moves through the medium.   It is only if the wave pulse retains its shape and dimensions as it moves that we can think of the energy of the pulse as more or less concentrated and moving through the medium with the group velocity.   This, then, will be the case if the dispersion is rather moderate, but not if the dispersion is large; in the latter case more terms must be taken to make the expansion (3) meaningful.   (For further discussion of the relation between group velocity and the rate of energy transfer in a dispersive medium, see Secs. 6.6 and 8.2.)

In the so-called "anomalous" dispersion of light, one passes through a region in which $(dV/d\omega)_0 > 0$, so that $U > V_0$.   This could lead to values of the group velocity greater than c, the velocity of light in free space, and the existence of such values contradicts the deduction from Einstein's theory of special relativity that no signal can ever be transmitted with a velocity greater than c.   It was believed at one time that this indicated the invalidity of the theory of relativity.   But this was based on the assumption that the group velocity is necessarily the same as the signal velocity, or the velocity of energy transfer in every medium in all circumstances.   As would perhaps be surmised from the previous paragraph, this is not the case.

CHAPTER 4

WAVES IN STRINGS

4.1. Wave Equation for a Uniform Flexible String

In the first three chapters we discussed some important general properties of waves. Though most of the illustrations related to mechanical waves in material media, the characteristics applied to waves of arbitrary nature. In the remainder of the book we shall be concerned more specifically with the various important varieties of mechanical radiation and their detailed description.

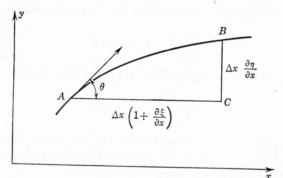

FIG. 4.1. Rectangular components of disturbed segment of uniform flexible string.

It is convenient to begin with what is perhaps the best illustration of mechanical wave propagation in a one-dimensional medium, namely, waves on a uniform flexible string. We imagine a perfectly flexible string of density ρ (mass per unit volume) lying along the x axis and, when in the equilibrium condition, stretched with tension T_0. The string is disturbed from equilibrium by being pulled aside in the xy plane. We denote the x and y components of the resultant displacement of the point on the string which originally was at $(x,0)$ by ξ and η, respectively. We then assume that the elementary segment of the string which was Δx before displacement becomes, as a result of the disturbance, the distorted and displaced segment AB whose x and y projections AC and BC (Fig. 4.1) are, respectively, $\Delta x(1 + \partial \xi/\partial x)$ and $(\partial \eta/\partial x) \Delta x$ to the approximation which retains only the term of the first degree in Δx and neglects higher powers. The tension in the disturbed configuration will be T and the angle which the tangent to AB at A makes with the x axis will be denoted by θ, whose sin is given by

$$\sin \theta = \frac{\partial \eta / \partial x}{\sqrt{(1 + \partial \xi / \partial x)^2 + (\partial \eta / \partial x)^2}} \tag{1}$$

The tension T is given by the assumed stress-strain relation for the string. Thus the excess tension per unit area should be equal to the product of an elastic constant (Young's modulus) and the strain (change in length per unit length). If S is the area of cross section of the string, we can write

$$T - T_0 = YS[\sqrt{(1 + \partial \xi / \partial x)^2 + (\partial \eta / \partial x)^2} - 1] \tag{2}$$

if Y is Young's modulus.

The component equations of motion of the string are now readily written. The vertical component of the tension on AB at A is $T \sin \theta$ and at B is $T \sin \theta + (\partial / \partial x)(T \sin \theta) \Delta x$, again retaining terms of the first degree in Δx. Hence the net vertical force is $(\partial / \partial x)(T \sin \theta) \Delta x$, and the corresponding equation of motion for the displacement becomes

$$\frac{\partial}{\partial x} (T \sin \theta) = \rho S \ddot{\eta} \tag{3}$$

The equation of motion for the displacement ξ is similarly

$$\frac{\partial}{\partial x} (T \cos \theta) = \rho S \ddot{\xi} \tag{4}$$

Note that the mass of the element AB is strictly $\rho S \Delta x$. As the original segment is altered, ρ and S also change, but the product $\rho S \Delta x$ must remain unaltered since mass must be conserved.

If we substitute from (1) and (2) into (3), the resulting equation of motion for η is

$$\rho S \ddot{\eta} = \frac{\partial^2 \eta}{\partial x^2} \left\{ \frac{T_0 + YS[\sqrt{(1 + \partial \xi / \partial x)^2 + (\partial \eta / \partial x)^2} - 1]}{\sqrt{(1 + \partial \xi / \partial x)^2 + (\partial \eta / \partial x)^2}} \right\}$$
$$- (T_0 - YS) \frac{\partial \eta}{\partial x} \left\{ \frac{\frac{\partial^2 \xi}{\partial x^2} \frac{\partial \eta}{\partial x} \left(1 + \frac{\partial \xi}{\partial x}\right) + \frac{\partial^2 \eta}{\partial x^2} \left(\frac{\partial \eta}{\partial x}\right)^2}{[(1 + \partial \xi / \partial x)^2 + (\partial \eta / \partial x)^2]^{\frac{3}{2}}} \right\} \tag{5}$$

There is a similar equation obtained from (4), which we shall not trouble to write. The important thing to note is that (5) is a rather complicated nonlinear equation, since it contains squares of derivatives of ξ and η. We have made no assumptions with regard to the magnitude of $\partial \xi / \partial x$ and $\partial \eta / \partial x$. However, let us for the sake of simplicity suppose that both these quantities are so small in magnitude that they can be neglected in comparison with unity. Equation (5) then reduces to the form

$$\rho S \ddot{\eta} = T_0 \frac{\partial^2 \eta}{\partial x^2} \tag{6}$$

or, if we revert to the line density ρ_l,

$$\ddot{\eta} = \frac{T_0}{\rho_l} \frac{\partial^2 \eta}{\partial x^2} \tag{7}$$

Under the same approximation, (4) takes the form

$$\ddot{\xi} = \frac{Y}{\rho} \frac{\partial^2 \xi}{\partial x^2} \tag{8}$$

These equations say that, when the disturbance in the string is sufficiently small so that the gradients of the x and y displacements with respect to x are small compared with unity, both displacements are propagated as waves along the x direction. It is of interest that their velocities are unequal in general. The velocity of the transverse component displacement is

$$V_T = \sqrt{\frac{T_0}{\rho_l}} \tag{9}$$

whereas that of the longitudinal component displacement is

$$V_L = \sqrt{\frac{Y}{\rho}} \tag{10}$$

We have already encountered the latter in Sec. 1.7. These are the velocities of waves of so-called "infinitesimal" amplitude in the stretched string.[1]

4.2. Energy Transport in a Vibrating String

Though the situation in Sec. 4.1 is idealized in the sense that the string is taken to be infinite in extent and yet stretched with nonvanishing tension, much valuable information can be obtained from it. The general solution of (4.1-7) is, of course,

$$\eta = f_1(x - V_T t) + f_2(x + V_T t) \tag{1}$$

All the considerations developed in Chap. 1 concerning waves in one-dimensional media apply here. In particular we can readily calculate the average rate of flow of energy involved in the wave transmission. As was pointed out in Sec. 1.10, there are two ways in which this can be

---

[1] For waves of large amplitude for which an equation of the form (5) applies, see G. F. Carrier, *Quart. Appl. Math.*, **3**, 157 (1945).

carried out. The first consists in forming the product of the resultant force producing the disturbance and the displacement velocity and then taking the time average of this product. This gives the average power transmission. The second proceeds by calculating the kinetic energy per unit length (a variant of the kinetic energy density discussed in Sec. 1.10) and the potential energy per unit length. The sum, when averaged over the time and multiplied by the velocity of propagation, yields the average power transmission.

We proceed to use the second method. The kinetic energy per unit length for the *transverse wave* is

$$W_{K,l} = \frac{\rho_l \dot{\eta}^2}{2} \tag{2}$$

The potential energy associated with the element dx is equal to the work done in stretching this element to the length $ds = \sqrt{1 + (\partial\eta/\partial x)^2}\, dx$. If we make the usual approximation that the tension remains fixed at T_0, the work in question is

$$W = T_0 \left[\sqrt{1 + \left(\frac{\partial\eta}{\partial x}\right)^2}\, dx - dx \right]$$

and hence the potential energy per unit length is, to the approximation already employed,

$$W_{P,l} = T_0 \frac{(\partial\eta/\partial x)^2}{2} \tag{3}$$

For a harmonic wave with displacement in the form

$$\eta = A \cos(\omega t - kx) \tag{4}$$

the average power transmission becomes

$$\bar{w} = \frac{\rho_l V_T \omega^2 A^2}{2} \tag{5}$$

This is precisely the result one gets by forming the average of

$$T_0 \frac{\partial\eta}{\partial x}\,\dot{\eta}$$

in accordance with the first method cited.

4.3. Stationary Waves in a Finite String.   Normal Modes

It is unnecessary to go through the details leading to the normal modes of the finite string, as they have been developed for the general linear medium in Secs. 1.5 and 3.1. We remind ourselves that the characteristic frequencies of a uniform, perfectly flexible string of length l, fastened rigidly at the two ends and stretched with tension T_0, are

$$\nu_n = \frac{nV}{2l} = \frac{n}{2l}\sqrt{\frac{T_0}{\rho_l}} \tag{1}$$

and the resultant transverse displacement η at any point x on the string at time t is given by f in (3.1-3), where the coefficients A_n and B_n are further given by (3.1-6) and (3.1-7).

The standard methods of exciting the finite stretched string are plucking, striking, and bowing. The analysis is simplest for the plucked string. Let us suppose that the string is pulled aside a distance h at its mid-point and let go. It is then clear that, since $\dot{f}_0(x)$ in (3.1-7) vanishes, all the A_n vanish identically. Since

$$
\begin{aligned}
f_0(x) &= \frac{2hx}{l} & 0 \leq x \leq \frac{l}{2} \\
f_0(x) &= \frac{2h}{l}(l-x) & \frac{l}{2} \leq x \leq l
\end{aligned} \tag{2}
$$

(3.1-6) yields

$$B_n = \frac{8h}{\pi^2 n^2}\sin\frac{n\pi}{2} \tag{3}$$

or
$$
\begin{aligned}
B_n &= 0 & \text{for } n \text{ even} \\
&= (-1)^{(n-1)/2}\frac{8h}{\pi^2 n^2} & \text{for } n \text{ odd}
\end{aligned} \tag{4}
$$

Consequently, the complete solution (using η in place of f) is

$$\eta = \frac{8h}{\pi^2}\sum_{n=0}^{\infty}\frac{1}{n^2}\sin\frac{n\pi}{2}\cdot\sin\frac{n\pi x}{l}\cos\frac{n\pi Vt}{l} \tag{5}$$

where, for convenience, we now use V in place of V_t. The absence of the even harmonics and the falling off of the higher odd harmonics in amplitude inversely as n^2 are the two most important physical facts inherent in (5). The latter suggests some attention to the energy represented in the various modes. The nth harmonic in the string fastened at the two ends has the general form

$$\eta = A\sin\frac{n\pi x}{l}\cos\frac{n\pi Vt}{l} \tag{6}$$

The time-average total energy in the string while it is vibrating in this mode is obtained by forming the total energy density $W_{K,l} + W_{P,l}$ from (4.2-2, 3), integrating over the length of the string from 0 to l, and forming the time average. The result is

$$\bar{E}_n = \frac{\pi^2 V^2 n^2 \rho_l A^2}{4l} \tag{7}$$

Actually it turns out that this is not only the time average of the total energy but the instantaneous energy as well. The kinetic and potential energies balance each other in such a way that the total energy remains constant in time. For the special case of the plucked string we have just seen that

$$A = \frac{8h}{\pi^2 n^2} \sin \frac{n\pi}{2}$$

and hence

$$\bar{E}_n = \frac{16h^2 V^2 \rho l}{\pi^2 n^2 l} \sin^2 \frac{n\pi}{2} \tag{8}$$

which, of course, vanishes for n even, and equals

$$\bar{E}_n = \frac{16h^2 V^2 \rho l}{\pi^2 n^2 l} \tag{9}$$

for n odd.

The above is for a single harmonic. How does it stand with the resultant displacement (5)? If we carry out the corresponding calculation in this case, we arrive at the interesting result that the total energy is simply the *sum* of the energies associated with the individual modes. This is by no means immediately evident, since the energy involves square terms, but the fact that it is true provides the justification for terming the individual harmonics *normal* modes.

The total energy associated with the actual motion of the string can be found by summing (9) over all the normal modes, that is, over all odd values of n. This is equivalent to

$$\bar{E}_{\text{tot}} = \frac{16h^2 V^2 \rho l}{\pi^2 l} \sum_{n=0}^{\infty} \left(\frac{1}{2n+1} \right)^2 \tag{10}$$

where n takes on all integral values. The value of the above sum turns out to be $\pi^2/8$, and hence

$$\bar{E}_{\text{tot}} = \frac{2h^2 V^2 \rho l}{l} \tag{11}$$

It is not difficult to verify that this is precisely equal to the original potential energy given to the string when it was plucked aside and just before it was let go. From the conservation of energy this result must, of course, follow.

4.4. Normal Coordinates for the Vibrating String.   External Driving Forces

We recall from Sec. 3.1 and the discussion of the previous section that the displacement η at any point on the finite vibrating string of length l

fastened rigidly at both ends can be written in the form

$$\eta = \sum_{n=1}^{\infty} \sin \frac{n\pi x}{l} (A_n \sin \omega_n t + B_n \cos \omega_n t) \tag{1}$$

where ω_n is the angular frequency of the nth mode and the coefficients A_n and B_n are given by (3.1-7) and (3.1-6), respectively. Now there is a certain advantage in considering the coefficient of $\sin (n\pi x/l)$ in the summation in (1) as a kind of coordinate of the motion, since it expresses the time dependence of the nth normal mode once the initial conditions have been established. We see its significance if we use (1) to evaluate the kinetic and potential energies of the string in terms of it.

We set, for convenience,

$$\varphi_n = A_n \sin \omega_n t + B_n \cos \omega_n t \tag{2}$$

Then
$$\dot{\eta} = \sum \dot{\varphi}_n \sin \frac{n\pi x}{l} \tag{3}$$

The total kinetic energy of the string is therefore

$$W_K = \frac{1}{2} \rho_l \int_0^l \left(\sum \dot{\varphi}_n{}^2 \sin^2 \frac{n\pi x}{l} + 2 \sum_{j \neq k} \dot{\varphi}_j \dot{\varphi}_k \sin \frac{j\pi x}{l} \sin \frac{k\pi x}{l} \right) dx \tag{4}$$

Now we have already seen in Sec. 3.1 that

$$\int_0^l \sin \frac{j\pi x}{l} \sin \frac{k\pi x}{l} dx = 0 \qquad \text{for } j \neq k$$

$$= \frac{l}{2} \qquad \text{for } j = k$$

Hence
$$W_K = \frac{l\rho_l}{4} \sum_{n=1}^{\infty} \dot{\varphi}_n{}^2 \tag{5}$$

It thus appears that the total kinetic energy of the string is a simple sum of squares of the $\dot{\varphi}_n$. Let us now form the total potential energy from (4.2-3). We have

$$W_P = \frac{T_0}{2} \int_0^l \left(\frac{\partial \eta}{\partial x} \right)^2 dx$$

$$= \frac{T_0}{2} \int_0^l \left(\sum_{n=1}^{\infty} \frac{n\pi}{l} \varphi_n \cos \frac{n\pi x}{l} \right)^2 dx \tag{6}$$

Carrying out the integration in the usual fashion yields

$$W_P = \frac{T_0 l}{4} \sum_{n=1}^{\infty} \frac{n^2 \pi^2}{l^2} \varphi_n{}^2 \tag{7}$$

or a simple quadratic function of the φ_n involving only square terms. Hence the total energy of the string as a function of time is

$$W = \frac{M}{4} \sum_{n=1}^{\infty} \left(\dot{\varphi}_n{}^2 + \frac{n^2\pi^2 V^2}{l^2} \varphi_n{}^2 \right) \tag{8}$$

where $V = \sqrt{T_0/\rho_l}$ is the velocity of transverse waves in the string and M is the total mass $= l\rho_l$. The interesting thing about this result is that the total energy is made up of a sum of terms, each of which relates to *one* mode only. It is for this reason that importance attaches to φ_n and it is referred to as a *normal coordinate*. We can now indeed treat the φ_n as generalized coordinates of a dynamical system and utilize the method of Lagrange to write the general equations of motion. Recalling that the Lagrangian function $L = W_K - W_P$, we have the Lagrangian equations of motion (see Sec. 1.11)

$$\frac{d}{dt}\left(\frac{\partial L}{\partial \dot{\varphi}_n}\right) - \frac{\partial L}{\partial \varphi_n} = \Phi_n \tag{9}$$

where Φ_n is the part of the generalized force not included in the elastic restoring force associated with the potential energy W_P. Equation (9) immediately becomes

$$\ddot{\varphi}_n + \frac{n^2\pi^2 V^2}{l^2} \varphi_n = \frac{2}{M} \Phi_n \tag{10}$$

If there are no external driving forces, $\Phi_n = 0$ for all n, and the solution of (10) becomes simply

$$\varphi_n = A_n \sin \omega_n t + B_n \cos \omega_n t \tag{11}$$

with

$$\omega_n = \frac{n\pi V}{l} \tag{12}$$

which is not surprising. The value of (10) to handle problems is more apparent in the case where applied driving forces exist. We recall from the Lagrangian theory[1] that the meaning of the generalized forces Φ_n is found in the fact that, if the normal or generalized coordinate φ_n undergoes a change $\delta\varphi_n$, the corresponding generalized force Φ_n does the *work*

$$\Phi_n \, \delta\varphi_n$$

Now, if we go back to (1), we see that the change $\delta\varphi_n$ corresponds to a change in the vertical displacement η of $\delta\eta$, where

$$\delta\eta = \sin \frac{n\pi x}{l} \delta\varphi_n \tag{13}$$

[1] R. B. Lindsay, "Concepts and Methods of Theoretical Physics," p. 141, D. Van Nostrand Company, Inc., Princeton, N.J., 1951.

If an actual force $F(x,t)$ per unit length acts in the vertical direction at time t on the element of mass $\rho_l\,dx$ of the string around the point x, the work associated with displacement $\delta\eta$ for the whole string becomes

$$\rho_l \int_0^l F(x,t)\,\delta\eta\,dx \;=\; \delta\varphi_n \int_0^l \rho_l F(x,t)\,\sin\frac{n\pi x}{l}\,dx \qquad (14)$$

Hence
$$\Phi_n \;=\; \int_0^l \rho_l F(x,t)\,\sin\frac{n\pi x}{l}\,dx \qquad (15)$$

is the generalized force associated with the nth normal coordinate. A rather common situation is that in which the force is concentrated in the vicinity of one point (e.g., a plucked string). We can then represent F by a so-called "delta function" (due to Dirac,[1] who has used it in quantum mechanics). Thus

$$F(x,t) \;=\; \delta(x - x_0)F(x_0,t) \qquad (16)$$

The function $\delta(x - x_0)$ is discontinuous and defined by

$$\int_0^\infty \delta(x - x_0)\,dx \;=\; 1 \qquad (17)$$

It vanishes everywhere save at $x = x_0$, where it is undefined (physically very large, however) but of such a nature that when it is integrated over the whole range of x the result is unity. The most important property of the delta function is that for any function $f(x)$

$$\int_0^\infty f(x)\delta(x - x_0)\,dx \;=\; f(x_0) \qquad (18)$$

In the case of the string in which $0 < x_0 < l$, we can equally well replace ∞ by l without disturbing the result.

We can now apply the delta-function technique to the determination of Φ_n for a driving force applied to a point x_0. With the choice of (16) for the applied force,

$$\Phi_n \;=\; \rho_l F(x_0,t)\,\sin\frac{n\pi x_0}{l} \qquad (19)$$

The nodal points are given by

$$x_0 \;=\; \frac{n'l}{n}$$

with $n' \le n$ (and both integral). For these, Φ_n vanishes, and the driving force has no effect on the string; one cannot excite a given mode by applying a force at a node of that mode.

Let us consider the general case of an arbitrary Φ_n. This involves the

---

[1] M. J. Lighthill, "Introduction to Fourier Analysis and Generalized Functions," pp. 16f., Cambridge University Press, London, 1958.

general solution of (10). Following the method suggested by Rayleigh,[1] we write the solution of

$$\ddot{\varphi}_n + p^2 \varphi_n = 0 \tag{20}$$

where $p = n\pi V/l$, in the form containing the initial value of φ_n, namely, φ_{n0}, and the initial value of the rate of change of φ_n, namely, $\dot{\varphi}_{n0}$. Thus

$$\varphi_n = \frac{\dot{\varphi}_{n0}}{p} \sin pt + \varphi_{n0} \cos pt \tag{21}$$

Now this says that the rate of change $\dot{\varphi}_{n0}$ at time $t = 0$ produces a φ_n at time t equal to

$$\frac{\dot{\varphi}_{n0}}{p} \sin pt$$

Hence a rate of change in φ_n of $\dot{\varphi}_{nt'}$ at $t = t'$ should produce a φ_n at time t equal to

$$\frac{\dot{\varphi}_{nt'}}{p} \sin p(t - t')$$

But from (10) we can see that the effect of $2\Phi_n/M$ is to produce in time dt' a rate of change in $d\varphi_n$ equal to

$$\frac{2\Phi_n}{M} dt'$$

Hence the $d\varphi_n$ produced at time t becomes

$$d\varphi_n = \frac{2}{M} \frac{\Phi_n}{p} \sin p(t - t') \, dt'$$

Since the generalized force operates from $t' = 0$ to $t' = t$, the *resultant* φ_n produced at time t will be

$$\varphi_n = \frac{2}{Mp} \int_0^t \Phi_n \sin p(t - t') \, dt' \tag{22}$$

which is the particular integral of (10) for arbitrary Φ_n. The complete solution of (10) becomes

$$\varphi_n = \frac{\dot{\varphi}_{n0}}{p} \sin pt + \varphi_{n0} \cos pt + \frac{2}{Mp} \int_0^t \Phi_n \sin p(t - t') \, dt' \tag{23}$$

Let us assume that the harmonic force

$$\rho_l F(x_0, t) = F_0 \cos \omega t \tag{24}$$

---

[1] "Theory of Sound," 2d ed., vol. 1, paragraph 66, Dover Publications, New York, 1945.

acts at the point x_0 on the string. Then, from (19),

$$\Phi_n = F_0 \cos \omega t' \sin \frac{n\pi x_0}{l} \tag{25}$$

and the integral in (23) becomes

$$\frac{2}{Mp} F_0 \sin \frac{n\pi x_0}{l} \int_0^t \cos \omega t' \sin p(t - t') \, dt'$$

which, on evaluation, yields

$$\varphi_n = \frac{\dot{\varphi}_{n0}}{p} \sin pt + \varphi_{n0} \cos pt + \frac{2F_0}{M} \sin \frac{n\pi x_0}{l} \frac{1}{p^2 - \omega^2} (\cos \omega t - \cos pt) \tag{26}$$

Though this is a precise solution satisfying the initial conditions, it is not, indeed, exactly in the form which the reader will recall is found for the forced oscillation of a linear oscillating system with the equation

$$m\ddot{x} + kx = F_0 \cos \omega t \tag{27}$$

This has the form, with $\sqrt{k/m} = p$,

$$x = A \cos pt + B \sin pt + \frac{F_0 \cos \omega t}{p^2 - \omega^2} \tag{28}$$

Here $F_0 \cos \omega t/(p^2 - \omega^2)$ is the so-called "forced" oscillation. By proper choice of $A = x_0 - F_0/(p^2 - \omega^2)$, we can put (28) in the form of (26) or, alternatively, can rewrite (26) as

$$\varphi_n = A \sin pt + B \cos pt + \frac{2F_0}{M} \sin \frac{n\pi x_0}{l} \frac{1}{p^2 - \omega^2} \cos \omega t \tag{29}$$

in the more usual fashion.

Of course the above is rather artificial, since we have omitted the effects of damping, which are always present and which bring out the effect of the resonance denominator $p^2 - \omega^2$ more explicitly. If we include dissipation and replace (10) by an equation of the form

$$\ddot{\varphi}_n + R\dot{\varphi}_n + p^2\varphi_n = \frac{2}{M} \Phi_n \tag{30}$$

we expect that the steady-state solution—as distinct from the transient, which dies out as $e^{-Rt/2}$—will have the form (for Φ_n harmonic in time)[1]

$$\varphi_n = \frac{2F_0}{M} \sin \frac{n\pi x_0}{l} \frac{\cos (\omega t - \alpha)}{\sqrt{\omega^2 R^2 + (p^2 - \omega^2)^2}} \tag{31}$$

[1] W. V. Houston, "Principles of Mathematical Physics," 2d ed., p. 73, McGraw-Hill Book Company, Inc., New York, 1948.

or $$\dot{\varphi}_n = \frac{2F_0}{M} \sin \frac{n\pi x_0}{l} \frac{\cos(\omega t - \beta)}{\sqrt{R^2 + [(p^2 - \omega^2)/\omega]^2}} \qquad (32)$$

Resonance occurs for $\omega = p$. The phase angles α and β differ by $\pi/2$. The important point is that, if the applied force has the same frequency as the natural frequency of the equivalent undamped system, namely, the frequency corresponding to the nth normal mode, the force will deliver energy to the string at a maximum rate, unless indeed the force is applied at a node of this mode, in which case no energy at all is (ideally) communicated. This significance of resonance is one that is worthy of emphasis in general.

4.5. Waves on a Loaded String. Selective Transmission and Filtration

Of considerable interest from the standpoint of wave propagation is the uniform flexible string loaded at intervals with mass particles. The simplest case considers an infinite string stretched with tension T_0 and with particles of mass m equally spaced at intervals $2l$ along the string (see Fig. 4.2). If the string were finite, we could attack the problem in

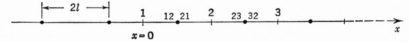

FIG. 4.2. Filtration of waves on a loaded string.

terms of the small oscillations from equilibrium of a system of a number of degrees of freedom equal to the number of the particles. However, we shall proceed otherwise and examine how the propagation of transverse elastic waves is affected by the presence of the particles. In the light of Sec. 3.4 we should expect that we might understand what goes on by treating the loaded string as an elastic medium with continuously iterated change of properties. It would then appear that the string should behave as an elastic wave filter. This turns out to be the case. In fact we can employ much of the analysis of Sec. 3.4 in our discussion.

The quantities most suited for the analytical treatment are, of course, the transverse displacement velocity $\dot{\eta}$ and the normal component of the tension, which will be here denoted by τ. Clearly

$$\tau = T_0 \frac{\partial \eta}{\partial x} \qquad (1)$$

where we are ignoring the change in actual tension during the motion (i.e., we assume small displacements). For the transverse displacement corresponding to harmonic waves traveling in both directions in the string, we first write (following the lead of Sec. 3.4)

$$\eta = \eta_0 e^{i(\omega t - kx)} + \eta_1 e^{i(\omega t + kx)} \tag{2}$$

Hence for $\dot{\eta}$ and τ we have (leaving off the $e^{i\omega t}$ factor)

$$\dot{\eta} = i\omega(\eta_0 e^{-ikx} + \eta_1 e^{ikx})$$
$$\tau = i\omega\rho_l V(-\eta_0 e^{-ikx} + \eta_1 e^{ikx}) \tag{3}$$

where ρ_l is the line density of the string and

$$V = \sqrt{\frac{T_0}{\rho_l}} \tag{4}$$

is the transverse wave velocity. Denoting $\dot{\eta}$ at $x = 0$ by $\dot{\eta}_1$ and τ at $x = 0$ by τ_1, we have [from (3)] for any value of x on the string

$$\dot{\eta} = \dot{\eta}_1 \cos kx + \frac{i\tau_1}{\rho_l V} \sin kx$$
$$\tau = \tau_1 \cos kx + i\rho_l V \dot{\eta}_1 \sin kx \tag{5}$$

It is now necessary to introduce the boundary conditions prevailing at the mass particles. We follow the convention indicated in Fig. 4.2, taking the origin on the x axis midway between two mass particles and using single subscripts to refer to quantities at the relevant mid-points. Double subscripts refer to quantities in the string *at* the particles. We then have the conditions

$$\dot{\eta}_{12} = \dot{\eta}_{21} = \dot{\eta}_L \tag{6}$$
$$\tau_{21} - \tau_{12} = m\ddot{\eta}_L \tag{7}$$

Equation (6) merely expresses the continuity of transverse displacement velocity at each particle, where η_L denotes the displacement of the particle itself. Equation (7) is the equation of vertical motion of the particle.

We now follow precisely the technique of Sec. 3.4 and find that for any two successive mid-points characterized by the subscripts n and $n + 1$, respectively,

$$\dot{\eta}_{n+1} = \dot{\eta}_n e^{-iW}$$
$$\tau_{n+1} = \tau_n e^{-iW} \tag{8}$$

where

$$\cos W = \cos 2kl - \frac{\omega m V}{2T_0} \sin 2kl \tag{9}$$

The infinite loaded string thus acts as a filter for transverse waves with passbands given by

$$|\cos W| \leq 1 \tag{10}$$

and attenuation bands by

$$|\cos W| > 1 \tag{11}$$

We readily see that the filter is low-pass and that the cutoff frequency for the first transmission band is given by

$$\omega = \frac{2T_0}{mV} \cot kl \tag{12}$$

If $kl \ll 1$, that is, if the masses are very close together, we have $\cot kl \doteq kl$ and get for the cutoff frequency

$$\nu = \frac{1}{2\pi} \sqrt{\frac{2T_0}{ml}} \tag{13}$$

The average line density of the loaded string is $nm/(2n - 2)l$ for n masses and thus approaches $m/2l$ as n increases indefinitely. If we call this ρ_l, we can write (13) as

$$\nu = \frac{1}{2\pi l} \sqrt{\frac{T_0}{\rho_l}} \tag{14}$$

The relation between this result and the fundamental mode of the finite vibrating string fastened at the two ends [Eq. (4.3-1)] should be examined and the difference noted. Our treatment is idealized. However, the study of the *finite* filter can be carried through on somewhat similar lines, and it will be of value to examine the finite loaded string in this way.

We shall suppose, to consult Fig. 4.2 again, that the horizontal string is fastened rigidly at $x = 0$ (denoted by the subscript 1) and is also fastened at $x = 2nl$, where n is the number of mass particles. This means that it is fastened at a distance l from the nth particle. The distance between successive particles still remains $2l$. If we follow the method of Sec. 3.4, we arrive at

$$\begin{aligned}
\tau_{j+1} &= \tau_j \cos W + iZ\dot{\eta}_j \sqrt{\frac{B}{C}} \sin W \\
\dot{\eta}_{j+1} &= \dot{\eta}_j \cos W + \frac{i}{Z}\tau_j \sqrt{\frac{C}{B}} \sin W
\end{aligned} \tag{15}$$

for the quantities at any mid-point $j + 1$ in terms of the corresponding quantities at the immediately preceding mid-point j. Here $Z = \rho_l V$, and

$$A = \cos W = \cos 2kl - \frac{\omega m}{2Z} \sin 2kl \tag{16}$$

$$B = \sin 2kl + \frac{\omega m}{Z} \cos^2 kl \tag{17}$$

$$C = \sin 2kl - \frac{\omega m}{Z} \sin^2 kl \tag{18}$$

Clearly
$$A^2 + BC = 1 \tag{19}$$

and it is from the foregoing that we were able to write (8). But now we wish to observe that by mathematical induction one can establish from

(15) that

$$\tau_{j+1} = \tau_1 \cos jW + iZ\dot{\eta}_1 \sqrt{\frac{B}{C}} \sin jW \tag{20}$$

$$\dot{\eta}_{j+1} = \dot{\eta}_1 \cos jW + \frac{i}{Z}\tau_1 \sqrt{\frac{C}{B}} \sin jW \tag{21}$$

which holds for $j = 1, 2, 3, \ldots, n$. Since the string is fastened at the two ends, we have

$$\dot{\eta}_1 = \dot{\eta}_{n+1} = 0 \tag{22}$$

Hence $$\sin nW = 0 \tag{23}$$

since neither τ_1 nor $\sqrt{C/B}$ can be identically equal to zero.   From this it follows that

$$W = \frac{j\pi}{n} \tag{24}$$

where j is any integer.   These values of W then give the characteristic frequencies, or normal modes, of the structure through the solution of the transcendental equation

$$\cos 2kl - \frac{\omega m}{2Z} \sin 2kl = \cos \frac{j\pi}{n} \tag{25}$$

It is instructive to consider the approximation

$$kl \ll 1 \tag{26}$$

implying that the distance between successive particles is very small compared with the shortest wavelength allowed.   Equation (25) then takes the form

$$\frac{\omega mkl}{Z} = 1 - \cos \frac{j\pi}{n} \tag{27}$$

which in turn leads to the set of frequencies

$$\nu_j = \frac{1}{2\pi} \sqrt{\frac{2T_0}{ml}} \sin \frac{j\pi}{2n} \tag{28}$$

There are n different frequencies in this set, as j takes on the values $1, 2, \ldots, n$.   These are valid, of course, only if

$$\nu_{\max} \ll \frac{V}{2\pi l} \tag{29}$$

or if $$m \gg 2\rho_l l \tag{30}$$

In words, the approximation implies that the mass of each particle is large compared with the mass of the section of string between successive particles.   Another way to look at it is to note that, if (26) is satisfied, the phase change in the wave along the string from one particle to the next is a small fraction of 2π; that is, each section of string essentially vibrates as a whole. This is indeed the physical basis of the common method of treating the loaded string problem as a set of coupled oscillators.[1]

Actually the standard treatment does not give quite the frequencies stated in (28), since the conditions are slightly different. Thus in the usual problem the first and last masses are distant $2l$, respectively, from the beginning and end of the string, whereas in the wave treatment just given, the corresponding distance is l. We can easily adjust the method of this section to the standard scheme, however. Let us suppose that the string is now fastened at the distance $2l$ from the first mass and denote quantities there by the subscript zero. Likewise, we assume that the other end is fastened at distance $2l$ from the nth particle and denote quantities there by the subscript f. We then have, in line with (5),

$$\dot{\eta}_1 = \dot{\eta}_0 \cos kl + \frac{i\tau_0}{Z} \sin kl \tag{31}$$

$$\tau_1 = \tau_0 \cos kl + iZ\dot{\eta}_0 \sin kl$$

$$\dot{\eta}_f = \dot{\eta}_{n+1} \cos kl + i\frac{\tau_{n+1}}{Z} \sin kl \tag{32}$$

$$\tau_f = \tau_{n+1} \cos kl + iZ\dot{\eta}_{n+1} \sin kl$$

We solve for $\dot{\eta}_0$, τ_0, $\dot{\eta}_{n+1}$, and τ_{n+1} in terms of $\dot{\eta}_1$, τ_1, $\dot{\eta}_f$, and τ_f, respectively, and introduce the conditions $\dot{\eta}_0 = \dot{\eta}_f = 0$. This leads to

$$\dot{\eta}_1 = \frac{i\tau_0}{Z} \sin kl$$

$$\tau_1 = \tau_0 \cos kl$$

$$\dot{\eta}_{n+1} = \frac{-i\tau_f}{Z} \sin kl$$

$$\tau_{n+1} = \tau_f \cos kl$$

These equations, coupled with (20) and (21), yield two equivalent values of the ratio τ_f/τ_0 which, when equated, give

$$\sin (n + 1)W = 0 \tag{33}$$

in place of (23). The corresponding characteristic frequencies then become (using the approximation $kl \ll 1$ as before)

$$\nu_j = \frac{1}{2\pi} \sqrt{\frac{2T_0}{ml}} \sin \frac{j\pi}{2(n + 1)} \tag{34}$$

in place of (28). The frequencies (34) are precisely those given where the loaded string is treated in conventional fashion.

[1] Houston, op. cit., pp. 121ff.

Some other special limiting cases are not without interest as providing checks on the preceding analysis and a further connection with the case of the continuous string. Thus let us suppose that $m = 0$. Then in (9)

$$\cos W = \cos 2kl$$

and transmission takes place for all frequencies, as is certainly the case for the infinite continuous string. On the other hand, for the finite string, if $m = 0$ in (25),

$$2kl = \frac{j\pi}{n}$$

and since $2nl$ is the length L of the string,

$$kL = j\pi \tag{35}$$

or precisely the condition for the harmonics of the finite stretched string.

On the other hand, if we suppose that n increases without limit but that m goes to zero in such a way that $mn = M =$ mass of the string (supposed now to be made up of an infinite number of infinitesimally small material particles), we see that in (28)

$$\nu_j \rightarrow \frac{j}{2L} \sqrt{\frac{T_0}{\rho_l}} \tag{36}$$

where now $\rho_l = M/L$. This is precisely the expression for the normal modes of the finite uniform stretched string. The more general character of the radiation treatment of the problem is evident in the fundamental transcendental equation (25) for the normal modes, independent of the approximation (30).

It is also instructive to look at the problem from the standpoint of the transmission of energy through the finite loaded string. We visualize a wave in a continuous string to the left of the collection of mass particles; it enters the finite filter and then emerges at the other end. The rate of energy flow into the filter at the origin (taken now to be at a distance l to the left of the first mass particle) may be written as

$$\tfrac{1}{2}Z_i|\tau_i|^2 \tag{37}$$

where τ_i is the vertical component of the tension in the incident wave at the origin, and $Z_i = \rho_i V_i$, where ρ_i is the line density of the continuous string to the left and V_i the transverse wave velocity in this part. Similarly, the rate of energy flow out of the filter at the point a distance l from the last mass particle will have the form

$$\tfrac{1}{2}Z_t|\tau_{n+1}|^2 \tag{38}$$

with $Z_t = \rho_t V_t$, etc. We shall call

$$P_r = \frac{Z_t |\tau_{n+1}|^2}{Z_i |\tau_i|^2} \tag{39}$$

the *power transmission ratio* of the finite loaded string filter.

If we denote the vertical component of tension in the wave *reflected* from the origin back into the string to the left by τ_i', we have the boundary conditions at the origin

$$\tau_1 = \tau_i + \tau_i'$$
$$\dot{\eta}_1 = -\frac{1}{\rho_i V_i}(\tau_i - \tau_i') \tag{40}$$

Utilizing these equations together with (20) and (21) enables us to eliminate τ_i' and finally to obtain for the required power transmission ratio

$$P_r = \frac{Z_i}{Z_t} \frac{4}{(1 + Z_i/Z_t)^2 \cos^2 nW + [(Z_i/Z)\sqrt{C/B} + (Z/Z_t)\sqrt{B/C}]\sin^2 nW} \tag{41}$$

We may profitably examine the simple case in which $Z_i = Z_t = Z$ (i.e., the same string throughout). Then (41) reduces to

$$P_r = \frac{1}{1 + (\omega^2 m^2/Z^2)(\sin^2 nW)/(4\sin^2 W)} \tag{42}$$

If $|\cos W| \leq 1$, which is the criterion for a passband of the equivalent infinitely long loaded string filter, W is a real angle, and both $\sin nW$ and $\sin W$ are in absolute value less than or equal to unity. In particular, $\sin nW = 0$ for $W = j\pi/n$, where j is any integer. Hence for the values of W for which $j = 1, 2, \ldots, n-1$, $P_r = 1$, corresponding to complete transmission through the finite structure. On the other hand, if $|\cos W| > 1$, which is the criterion for an attenuation band of the equivalent infinite filter, W is the complex angle

$$W = W_r + iW_i \tag{43}$$

with real part W_r and imaginary part W_i. Since $\cos W$ is real, $W_r = j\pi$, where j is integral. Then

$$\begin{aligned} \cos nW &= \pm \cosh nW_i \\ \sin nW &= \pm i \sinh nW_i \\ \sin W &= \pm i \sinh W_i \end{aligned} \tag{44}$$

As n increases, the term $(\sin^2 nW)/(\sin^2 W)$ in (42) increases and P_r approaches zero. This provides the connection between the theory of the finite loaded string and the equivalent infinite filter. As a matter of fact, we see that the condition (24) for the normal modes of the finite loaded string is precisely the condition for $P_r = 1$ for the finite filter.

CHAPTER 5

WAVES IN MEMBRANES

5.1. Wave Equation for a Membrane

Next in order of complexity to the vibrating string is the membrane, here treated as an ideal two-dimensional, perfectly flexible continuum possessing a uniform surface density, or mass per unit area, σ and stretched with a uniform surface tension T, or the force per unit length with which the part of the membrane on one side of any line drawn in the membrane pulls on the part on the other side. It is assumed that the equilibrium position of the membrane is a plane, treated for convenience as the xy plane in rectangular coordinates, and that the disturbance contemplated is a displacement at any point (x,y) by an amount ξ in the z direction. As in the case of the string, the displacement is considered everywhere small compared with the dimensions of the membrane and is assumed insufficient to produce a noticeable change in the surface tension T and surface density σ.

In Fig. 5.1 dS represents an element of the membrane and ds an element in the boundary (treated as a scalar). The unit vector in the plane of the membrane normal to the boundary at ds is denoted by $\mathbf{n}$. The equation of motion of the membrane is found by equating the upward component of the force due to the surface tension over the whole

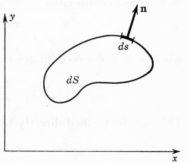

Fig. 5.1. Surface element of a vibrating membrane.

membrane to the integrated mass times acceleration associated with the vertical motion. The upward component of the force at any point is given by

$$T \frac{d\xi}{dn} ds$$

since $d\xi/dn$ is the cosine of the angle between the vertical and the direction of the normal. Hence the total upward force is

$$T \int \nabla \xi \cdot \mathbf{n} \, ds \tag{1}$$

131

since $\nabla \xi \cdot \mathbf{n} = \nabla \xi \cdot d\mathbf{n}/dn = d\xi/dn$, where here $\nabla \xi = \mathbf{i}\, \partial \xi/\partial x + \mathbf{j}\, \partial \xi/\partial y$. The kinetic reaction on the element is

$$\sigma \ddot{\xi}\, dS$$

and hence the equation of motion for the membrane as a whole is

$$\int\!\!\int \sigma \ddot{\xi}\, dS = T\!\int \nabla \xi \cdot \mathbf{n}\, ds \tag{2}$$

We can now apply the divergence theorem for the two-dimensional case and write for the right-hand side

$$T\!\int \nabla \xi \cdot \mathbf{n}\, ds = T\!\int \nabla^2 \xi\, dS \tag{3}$$

This leads to the equation of motion in the form

$$\ddot{\xi} = \frac{T}{\sigma}\, \nabla^2 \xi \tag{4}$$

which is the wave equation for transverse waves in the membrane with velocity

$$V = \sqrt{\frac{T}{\sigma}} \tag{5}$$

In this equation, of course, $\nabla^2 \xi$ is the two-dimensional Laplacian. In rectangular coordinates

$$\nabla^2 \xi = \frac{\partial^2 \xi}{\partial x^2} + \frac{\partial^2 \xi}{\partial y^2} \tag{6}$$

whereas in polar coordinates r and θ, we have

$$\nabla^2 \xi = \frac{1}{r}\frac{\partial}{\partial r}\left(r\frac{\partial \xi}{\partial r}\right) + \frac{1}{r^2}\frac{\partial^2 \xi}{\partial \theta^2} \tag{7}$$

This can be verified directly by the use of the transformation equations

$$x = r \cos \theta \qquad y = r \sin \theta$$

or perhaps more effectively as the two-dimensional case of the general expression for the operator ∇^2 in orthogonal curvilinear coordinates[1] q_1, q_2, q_3; that is,

$$\nabla^2 \xi = \frac{1}{h_1 h_2 h_3}\left[\frac{\partial}{\partial q_1}\left(\frac{h_2 h_3}{h_1}\frac{\partial \xi}{\partial q_1}\right) + \frac{\partial}{\partial q_2}\left(\frac{h_1 h_3}{h_2}\frac{\partial \xi}{\partial q_2}\right) + \frac{\partial}{\partial q_3}\left(\frac{h_1 h_2}{h_3}\frac{\partial \xi}{\partial q_3}\right)\right]$$

where for cylindrical coordinates $h_1 = h_3 = 1$ and $h_2 = r$ ($q_1 = r$, $q_2 = \theta$, $q_3 = z$). If ξ is independent of z, we get the two-dimensional case, and (7) results.

[1] W. V. Houston, "Principles of Mathematical Physics," 2d ed., p. 242, McGraw-Hill Book Company, Inc., New York, 1948.

The wave equation (4) for a membrane can also be derived by the variational method set forth in Sec. 1.11. The reader may show that for the membrane the variational integral is

$$\int_{t_0}^{t_1}\int_0^{a_1}\int_0^{a_2}\left\{\frac{1}{2}\sigma\dot{\xi}^2 - \frac{1}{2}T\left[\left(\frac{\partial\xi}{\partial x}\right)^2 + \left(\frac{\partial\xi}{\partial y}\right)^2\right]\right\}dx\,dy\,dt \tag{8}$$

where the membrane in equilibrium is treated as a rectangle with sides a_1 and a_2.

5.2. Waves in a Rectangular Membrane

The choice of coordinates for the expression of the wave equation for a membrane is clearly dictated by its shape, since every actual membrane is finite in size and the wave propagation in it is therefore materially controlled by the boundary conditions. We shall first direct attention to a rectangular membrane and therefore use the wave equation in the form

$$\ddot{\xi} = V^2\left(\frac{\partial^2\xi}{\partial x^2} + \frac{\partial^2\xi}{\partial y^2}\right) \tag{1}$$

The considerations of Sec. 1.3 suggest that a possible general solution of this equation is

$$\xi = f(\alpha x + \beta y - Vt) \tag{2}$$

if

$$\alpha^2 + \beta^2 = 1 \tag{3}$$

This corresponds to a plane wave progressing in the direction having direction cosines α and β with respect to the x and y axes, respectively. Direct substitution verifies this solution.

More interest inheres in harmonic waves subject to boundary conditions, and this suggests the use of the method of separation of variables already developed in general fashion in Sec. 1.8. The reduction from three to two dimensions involves no difficulty. Thus, if we express the solution of (1) in the form

$$\xi = X(x)Y(y)(Ae^{i\omega t} + Be^{-i\omega t}) \tag{4}$$

the result is

$$\begin{aligned} X &= A_1e^{ik_1x} + B_1e^{-ik_1x}\\ Y &= A_2e^{ik_2x} + B_2e^{-ik_2x} \end{aligned} \tag{5}$$

with

$$k_1^2 + k_2^2 = k^2 = \frac{\omega^2}{V^2} \tag{6}$$

A, B, A_1, B_1, A_2, B_2 are arbitrary constants.

Let us suppose now that the rectangular membrane has side a_1 along the x axis and side a_2 along the y axis, as in Fig. 5.2, and further that it is fastened firmly along its whole periphery, so that $\xi = 0$ at all times there. Application of this boundary condition to the above solution shows that ω can take on only the discrete set of values given by the equation [see (1.8-15)]

$$\omega^2 = \pi^2 V^2 \left(\frac{n_1{}^2}{a_1{}^2} + \frac{n_2{}^2}{a_2{}^2} \right) \tag{7}$$

where n_1 and n_2 are any integers (excluding zero, which gives rise to identically vanishing ξ). Corresponding to each choice of n_1 and n_2, the solution for the displacement ξ is

$$\xi_{n_1 n_2} = \sin \frac{n_1 \pi x}{a_1} \sin \frac{n_2 \pi y}{a_2} \left(A_{n_1 n_2} \cos \omega t + B_{n_1 n_2} \sin \omega t \right) \tag{8}$$

A general solution will clearly be the sum of $\xi_{n_1 n_2}$ for all possible n_1 and n_2. Each $\xi_{n_1 n_2}$ denotes a so-called "normal-mode solution" for the rectangular membrane.[1] The fundamental mode corresponds to the smallest, or fundamental, angular frequency

$$\omega_{11} = \pi V \sqrt{\frac{1}{a_1{}^2} + \frac{1}{a_2{}^2}} \tag{9}$$

It is interesting to observe that, though the list of allowed or characteristic frequencies includes the harmonics $\omega_{22} = 2\omega_{11}$, $\omega_{33} = 3\omega_{11}$, etc., there are many other frequencies which are not harmonic, such as ω_{12}, ω_{21}, ω_{23}, etc.

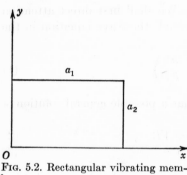

FIG. 5.2. Rectangular vibrating membrane.

Just as a vibrating string fastened at both ends exhibits nodal points associated with the various normal modes, so the vibrating membrane exhibits nodal lines, which, from (8), are seen to be straight lines parallel to the x and y axes, respectively, and having equations

$$\begin{aligned} x &= \frac{a_1}{n_1}, \frac{2a_1}{n_1}, \ldots, \frac{(n_1 - 1)a_1}{n_1} \\ y &= \frac{a_2}{n_2}, \frac{2a_2}{n_2}, \ldots, \frac{(n_2 - 1)a_2}{n_2} \end{aligned} \tag{10}$$

5.3. The Circular Membrane

From the standpoint of practical applications, the circular membrane is somewhat more important than the rectangular membrane. It can be

---

[1] Instructive diagrams illustrating some of the simpler normal modes of a rectangular membrane are found in P. M. Morse, "Vibration and Sound," 2d ed., pp. 180f., McGraw-Hill Book Company, Inc., New York, 1948.

readily handled by writing the wave equation (5.1-4) in terms of polar coordinates [see (5.1-7)]. If we assume disturbances harmonic in time with angular frequency ω, this equation becomes (with $k = \omega/V$)

$$\frac{\partial^2 \xi}{\partial r^2} + \frac{1}{r}\frac{\partial \xi}{\partial r} + \frac{1}{r^2}\frac{\partial^2 \xi}{\partial \theta^2} + k^2 \xi = 0 \tag{1}$$

The natural attack is by separation of variables:

$$\xi = R(r)\Theta(\theta) \tag{2}$$

whence (1) gives rise to the two equations

$$\frac{d^2 \Theta}{d\theta^2} + n^2 \Theta = 0 \tag{3}$$

$$\frac{d^2 R}{dr^2} + \frac{1}{r}\frac{dR}{dr} + \left(k^2 - \frac{n^2}{r^2}\right) R = 0 \tag{4}$$

In (3) n must be a real number and, indeed, an integer in order to satisfy the condition that ξ shall be a single-valued function of θ; that is,

$$\xi(\theta + 2\pi) = \xi(\theta)$$

The solution of (3) is

$$\Theta = A \sin (n\theta + \alpha) \tag{5}$$

where α and A are arbitrary constants. Equation (4) can be rewritten in the form

$$\frac{d^2 R}{dr'^2} + \frac{1}{r'}\frac{dR}{dr'} + \left(1 - \frac{n^2}{r'^2}\right) R = 0 \tag{6}$$

where $r' = kr$. Equation (6) is Bessel's equation [see (3.6-6)] with the general solution (for n integral)

$$R = CJ_n(kr) + DN_n(kr) \tag{7}$$

where we have already introduced the J and N functions in Sec. 3.6 [Eqs. (3.6-8, 11)]. We recall that $N_n(kr)$ has an infinite discontinuity at $r = 0$ and hence can be of no value for a continuous membrane, though it clearly must be used in discussing waves in a membrane with a circular hole at its center (see Sec. 7.3). We therefore choose $D = 0$ in (7) and write the complete solution in the form

$$\xi = CJ_n(kr) \cos (n\theta + \alpha)e^{i\omega t} \tag{8}$$

The fact that $J_n(kr)$ for given n and k oscillates with increasing r with steadily decreasing amplitude suggests, from the physical point of view, that attenuated radial waves are moving outward from the center of the membrane.[1] But the amplitude also depends on the angular orientation. Consequently the waves are of rather complicated pattern. When membranes are used as sources of compressional radiation in a surrounding medium, they are usually clamped at the periphery, leading to the production of stationary waves. The characteristic frequencies, or normal modes, for given n are given by the condition

$$J_n(ka) = 0 \tag{9}$$

if a is the radius of the membrane. Various sets of modes are provided by solving (9) with $n = 0, 1, 2, \ldots$, in turn. Thus the first three roots of $J_0(ka) = 0$ are, in increasing order of magnitude,

$$ka = 0.7655\pi,\ 1.7571\pi,\ 2.7546\pi \tag{10}$$

The corresponding roots of $J_1(ka) = 0$ are

$$ka = 1.2197\pi,\ 2.2330\pi,\ 3.2383\pi \tag{11}$$

and the corresponding roots of $J_2(ka) = 0$ are

$$ka = 1.6347\pi,\ 2.6793\pi,\ 3.6987\pi \tag{12}$$

The three lowest frequencies of the clamped membrane are then

$$\nu = 0.7655\,\frac{V}{2a},\ 1.2197\,\frac{V}{2a},\ 1.6347\,\frac{V}{2a} \tag{13}$$

where V is the velocity (5.1-5). The first of these is the fundamental frequency. The frequencies in (13) do not form a harmonic sequence. However, examination discloses[2] that the following approximate formula holds for large n:

$$\nu_{jn} \doteq \left(n + \frac{j}{2} - \frac{1}{4}\right)\frac{V}{2a} \tag{14}$$

Just as nodal points are associated with a stationary wave in a string, so there are nodal lines in the vibration of a membrane clamped at the periphery. There are concentric nodal circles, along which the displacement vanishes, whose radii are given by the equation

$$J_n(kr) = 0 \tag{15}$$

[1] We are here confining attention to the case of waves harmonic in time, and in practice these are the most important type. It is worthwhile to point out here, however, that if one tries to establish a general solution of the form (1.3-4) for radially diverging waves in a membrane, it proves to be impossible. It is not possible for a circular wave disturbance to spread out from a point source and leave no effect behind it, as we have seen that it is possible for plane and spherical waves to do. A circular wave leaves a wake between the head of the disturbance and the source. The same is true of a cylindrical wave in three dimensions (see *ibid.*, pp. 184f.).

[2] *Ibid.*, p. 189.

and nodal diameters making angles θ with a given reference diameter having the values

$$\theta = \frac{(2j + 1)\pi}{2n} - \frac{\alpha}{n} \tag{16}$$

where j is integral. For given n there are n diameters ranged uniformly about the center. If the first s roots of (15), arranged in order of increasing magnitude, are (letting $z = kr$) $z_{n1}, \ldots, z_{ns}$, the radii of the corresponding nodal circles are

$$a, \frac{z_{n1}}{z_{ns}} a, \frac{z_{n2}}{z_{ns}} a, \ldots, \frac{z_{n,s-1}}{z_{ns}} a \tag{17}$$

For small values of n the differences between the radii of successive nodal circles are approximately constant and equal to a half wavelength of the corresponding radial standing wave. For given n the approximation improves with increasing s. On the other hand, though the existence of nodal diameters might seem to correspond to circumferential waves, we can no longer associate in any simple way a wavelength with the nodal separation. Strictly speaking, the attempt to identify radial and circumferential waves in a membrane is artificial.

Since there are 44 characteristic frequencies in the first three octaves above the fundamental for a circular membrane, the membrane exhibits marked resonance activity over a wide range. The only way to avoid this is to excite the membrane well below its fundamental frequency. In this case it is often convenient to treat the membrane as effectively a vibrating system with one degree of freedom, that is, in a certain sense as a piston. We can find the effective mass of the vibrator by assuming that, below its fundamental, the shape of the membrane is paraboloidal. This is indeed what the first approximation to $J_0(kr)$ amounts to for $kr \ll 1$; that is [from (3.6-8)],

$$J_0(kr) = 1 - \frac{k^2 r^2}{4} \tag{18}$$

The maximum kinetic energy of the membrane in this circumstance is [see (8)]

$$W_{K,\max} = \frac{C^2 \omega^2}{2} \sigma \int_0^a \left(1 - \frac{k^2 r^2}{4}\right)^2 2\pi r \, dr \tag{19}$$

Evaluation of the integral leads to

$$W_{K,\max} = \frac{1}{2} \left(\frac{\pi a^2 \sigma}{3}\right) \dot{\xi}_0{}^2 \tag{20}$$

where $\dot{\xi}_0$ is the velocity amplitude at the center of the membrane. This means, however, that when we consider the membrane as an equivalent piston its effective mass is equal to one-third the actual mass.

In similar fashion we can find the effective stiffness. By a simple generalization of the result for a vibrating string (see Sec. 4.2) we can write for the maximum potential energy of the membrane

$$W_{P,\max} = \frac{1}{2} \int_0^a \left(\frac{\partial \xi}{\partial r}\right)^2 2\pi r T \, dr \tag{21}$$

Again using (18) with (8), we arrive at

$$W_{P,\max} = \tfrac{1}{2}(2\pi T)\xi_0{}^2 \tag{22}$$

The effective stiffness becomes $2\pi T$. From Sec. 4.4 (see also Sec. 3.6), the resonance frequency of a vibrating system of mass m and stiffness f is

$$\nu = \frac{1}{2\pi} \sqrt{\frac{f}{m}} \tag{23}$$

For the piston equivalent to the membrane this becomes

$$\nu = \frac{1.22}{\pi a} \sqrt{\frac{T}{\sigma}} = \frac{0.78V}{2a} \tag{24}$$

It is interesting to observe that this frequency differs from the actual fundamental frequency of the membrane as given in (13) by only a little over 1 per cent. This means, physically, that the substitution of the equivalent piston for the actual membrane is justified for frequencies below the fundamental. This is often of practical utility.

The above considerations have another valuable consequence, since they suggest a method of evaluating the normal modes approximately even when the solution of the wave equation for the membrane is not precisely known. This might be the case, for example, in a membrane with a variable surface density. We shall illustrate for the standard membrane, treated as a vibrating system with one degree of freedom. Let us assume the displacement harmonic in time with angular frequency ω and write the dependence on r as $\xi(r)$. The maximum kinetic energy then is [see (19)]

$$W_{K,\max} = \frac{\sigma \omega^2}{2} \int_0^a 2\pi r[\xi(r)]^2 \, dr \tag{25}$$

and the maximum potential energy is

$$W_{P,\max} = \frac{T}{2} \int_0^a \left[\frac{d\xi(r)}{dr}\right]^2 2\pi r \, dr \tag{26}$$

Now in any vibrating system with one degree of freedom, when the kinetic energy is a maximum, the potential energy is zero. Hence conservation of energy dictates

$$W_{K,\max} = W_{P,\max} \tag{27}$$

leading to

$$\omega^2 = \frac{T}{\sigma} \frac{\int_0^a \left(\frac{d\xi}{dr}\right)^2 2\pi r \, dr}{\int_0^a \xi^2 \, 2\pi r \, dr} \tag{28}$$

If we knew ξ as a function of r for each mode, we could of course evaluate the integrals and hence calculate ω for each mode. This is essentially what we did for the fundamental above by assuming that ξ is parabolic in r to a first approximation. Even if we do not know ξ precisely as a function of r, can we still use (28)? The answer is yes, for we know that the choice of ξ as a function of r which makes ω^2 smaller than for any other ξ will be the most nearly correct ξ for the fundamental mode, since ω is a minimum for this mode. Hence, if by some guesswork we hit upon a ξ which, when substituted into (28), yields a value of ω smaller than that corresponding to ν in (24), we shall know that it is more nearly right. We have plausible reason to suppose, for example, that

$$\xi = c_1 \cos \frac{\pi r}{2a} \tag{29}$$

should be a better approximation than the parabolic form (18). Note that this solution satisfies the boundary condition $\xi = 0$ for $r = a$. The analytical details, involving rather simple integrals, are left for the reader to work out. The result of calculating (28) with the use of (29) is

$$\omega^2 = \frac{T}{\sigma a^2} \frac{\pi^2}{4} \left(\frac{\pi/2 + 2/\pi}{\pi/2 - 2/\pi}\right)$$

or

$$\omega = \frac{2.41}{a} \sqrt{\frac{T}{\sigma}} \tag{30}$$

from which

$$\nu = \frac{1.205}{\pi a} \sqrt{\frac{T}{\sigma}} \tag{31}$$

which is indeed smaller than ν in (24) and indeed almost indistinguishable from the rigorous solution (13).

We might expect to do even better by adding another circular function term to (29), writing

$$\xi = \cos \frac{\pi r}{2a} + c \cos \frac{3\pi r}{2a} \tag{32}$$

which again satisfies the boundary condition at $r = a$ independently of the arbitrary constant c. [Note that there is no point in introducing an arbitrary constant before $\cos (\pi r/2a)$ since it is only the ratio of the coefficients of the second and first terms which counts.] We now substitute (32) into (28) and eventually get for ω^2 the following function of c:

$$\omega^2 = \frac{T}{\sigma a^2} \frac{\dfrac{\pi^2}{4}\left(\dfrac{\pi}{2} + \dfrac{2}{\pi}\right) - 3\pi c + \dfrac{9\pi^2}{4}\left(\dfrac{\pi}{2} + \dfrac{2}{9\pi}\right)c^2}{(\pi/2 - 2/\pi) - (4/\pi)c + (\pi/2 - 2/9\pi)c^2} \tag{33}$$

But we must choose c so that ω^2 is a minimum. Hence we introduce the condition

$$\frac{d(\omega^2)}{dc} = 0 \tag{34}$$

This leads to a quadratic equation in c of which the appropriate root, when substituted back into (28), yields

$$\omega = \frac{2.406}{a}\sqrt{\frac{T}{\sigma}} \tag{35}$$

somewhat smaller than ω in (30) and in still better agreement with the actual fundamental frequency. It yields indeed $0.7659V/2a$ for ν in comparison with the exact value $0.7655V/2a$ in (13).

The scheme we have been illustrating is known as the Rayleigh-Ritz method[1] and is a very useful one for the approximate evaluation of the fundamental frequency in a complicated vibrating system in which the exact displacement cannot readily be determined. As a matter of fact, it is possible to extend the method to the evaluation of the higher-mode frequencies.

[1] C. H. Page, "Physical Mathematics," pp. 65ff., D. Van Nostrand Company, Inc., Princeton, N.J., 1955.

CHAPTER 6

PROPAGATION OF DEFORMATION DISTURBANCES THROUGH ELASTIC MEDIA

6.1. Strain and Stress in a Deformable Medium

From the physical standpoint the key problem in mechanical radiation is the study of the propagation of deformations in an elastic deformable medium. A deformable medium is one in which it is possible to change the separation between any two identifiable points by the application of appropriate forces. If the medium is elastic, the removal of the forces results in the ultimate restoration of the original separation. In the meantime the continuity of the elastic medium assures that a deformation will not remain localized but will move through the medium. This indeed proves to be a result of the analysis based on the equation of motion of the medium.

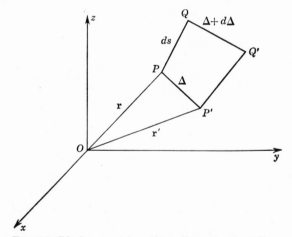

FIG. 6.1. Displacement in a three-dimensional medium.

The deformation of a medium is commonly studied in terms of the concepts of *strain* and *stress*. We shall set up a rectangular frame of reference (Fig. 6.1) in the medium we are discussing and shall consider any point P with position vector $\mathbf{r}$, having the rectangular components x, y, z; that is,

$$\mathbf{r} = \mathbf{i}x + \mathbf{j}y + \mathbf{k}z \tag{1}$$

Let us assume that after deformation the part of the medium which was originally at P has moved to P', with position vector $\mathbf{r}'$, where $\mathbf{r}' - \mathbf{r} = \mathbf{\Delta}$, which will be called the *displacement vector*. Now of course a point P can move to P' without having the medium actually deformed; a simple translation or rotation of the whole medium might readily carry P to P'. To study deformation we have to ask ourselves what happens to another nearby point Q. Let us suppose that when P moves to P', Q moves to Q', suffering a displacement which we shall call $\mathbf{\Delta} + d\mathbf{\Delta}$. Then $d\mathbf{\Delta}$ can serve as a representation of the deformation of the medium. Strictly, Q may have any original separation from P. But if we are to build differential equations to describe the deformation, it is essential to treat Q as very close to P. Then the representation of the deformation in the *neighborhood* of P becomes

$$d\mathbf{\Delta} = d(d\mathbf{r}) \tag{2}$$

We shall let $\mathbf{\Delta}$ have the rectangular components ξ, η, ζ; that is,

$$\mathbf{\Delta} = \mathbf{i}\xi + \mathbf{j}\eta + \mathbf{k}\zeta \tag{3}$$

in the usual vector notation. Then

$$\begin{aligned}
d\mathbf{\Delta} = \ &\mathbf{i}(\xi_x\,dx + \xi_y\,dy + \xi_z\,dz) \\
+ \ &\mathbf{j}(\eta_x\,dx + \eta_y\,dy + \eta_z\,dz) \\
+ \ &\mathbf{k}(\zeta_x\,dx + \zeta_y\,dy + \zeta_z\,dz)
\end{aligned} \tag{4}$$

where we are using the partial derivative notation $\xi_x = \partial\xi/\partial x$, etc. This can be rewritten in the form

$$\begin{aligned}
d\mathbf{\Delta} = \ &\mathbf{i}[\xi_x\,dx + \tfrac{1}{2}(\eta_x + \xi_y)\,dy + \tfrac{1}{2}(\zeta_x + \xi_z)\,dz] \\
+ \ &\mathbf{j}[\tfrac{1}{2}(\xi_y + \eta_x)\,dx + \eta_y\,dy + \tfrac{1}{2}(\zeta_y + \eta_z)\,dz] \\
+ \ &\mathbf{k}[\tfrac{1}{2}(\xi_z + \zeta_x)\,dx + \tfrac{1}{2}(\eta_z + \zeta_y)\,dy + \zeta_z\,dz] \\
+ \ &\mathbf{i}[\tfrac{1}{2}(\xi_y - \eta_x)\,dy + \tfrac{1}{2}(\xi_z - \zeta_x)\,dz] \\
+ \ &\mathbf{j}[\tfrac{1}{2}(\eta_x - \xi_y)\,dx + \tfrac{1}{2}(\eta_z - \zeta_y)\,dz] \\
+ \ &\mathbf{k}[\tfrac{1}{2}(\zeta_x - \xi_z)\,dx + \tfrac{1}{2}(\zeta_y - \eta_z)\,dy]
\end{aligned} \tag{5}$$

The purpose of this decomposition becomes clearer when we examine the nature of the second vector containing the differences of the partial derivatives as components. If we form the curl of the vector $\mathbf{\Delta}$, we obtain[1]

$$\nabla \times \mathbf{\Delta} = \begin{vmatrix} \mathbf{i} & \mathbf{j} & \mathbf{k} \\ \dfrac{\partial}{\partial x} & \dfrac{\partial}{\partial y} & \dfrac{\partial}{\partial z} \\ \xi & \eta & \zeta \end{vmatrix}$$

$$= \mathbf{i}(\zeta_y - \eta_z) + \mathbf{j}(\xi_z - \zeta_x) + \mathbf{k}(\eta_x - \xi_y) \tag{6}$$

[1] For a good brief treatment of vector analysis including the vector operators, consult Philip Franklin, "Methods of Advanced Calculus," pp. 303ff., McGraw-Hill Book Company, Inc., New York, 1944.

Further, let us form the cross product of $\frac{1}{2}\nabla \times \Delta$ with the differential of $\mathbf{r}$ as given in (1), namely,

$$d\mathbf{r} = \mathbf{i}\,dx + \mathbf{j}\,dy + \mathbf{k}\,dz \tag{7}$$

and get

$$\frac{1}{2}(\nabla \times \Delta) \times d\mathbf{r} = \frac{1}{2}\begin{vmatrix} \mathbf{i} & \mathbf{j} & \mathbf{k} \\ \zeta_y - \eta_z & \xi_z - \zeta_x & \eta_x - \xi_y \\ dx & dy & dz \end{vmatrix} \tag{8}$$

This is precisely equal to the second vector appearing in (5). It remains to ascertain its physical significance. By virtue of the nature of the cross product, this vector, which has, of course, the dimensions of displacement, must be perpendicular to both $\nabla \times \Delta$ and $d\mathbf{r}$. Hence it cannot correspond to any change in $d\mathbf{r}$ (the vector separation of two nearby points of the medium) which involves a change in the length of $d\mathbf{r}$. It must therefore be a displacement corresponding to a *rotation* of the point Q about the point P.

This result may be confirmed by noting that, if Δ is a small displacement of a rigid body due to rotation alone about some fixed point, $\nabla \times \Delta$ turns out to be twice the actual small angle of rotation.[1] Hence $\frac{1}{2}(\nabla \times \Delta) \times d\mathbf{r}$ must be a displacement due to rotation only. The second part of the deformation vector (5) therefore corresponds to a rotation which does not involve genuine deformation, that is, change of mutual distances of particles. Hence the true deformation must be found in the first vector in $d\Delta$, which we may denote by $(d\Delta)_1$.

The coefficients ξ_x, $\frac{1}{2}(\eta_x + \xi_y)$, etc., can be most simply written in the form of the symmetric square-array matrix or

$$\left\| \begin{array}{ccc} \xi_x & \frac{1}{2}(\eta_x + \xi_y) & \frac{1}{2}(\zeta_x + \xi_z) \\ \frac{1}{2}(\xi_y + \eta_x) & \eta_y & \frac{1}{2}(\zeta_y + \eta_z) \\ \frac{1}{2}(\xi_y + \zeta_x) & \frac{1}{2}(\eta_z + \zeta_y) & \zeta_z \end{array} \right\| \tag{9}$$

Examination shows that ξ_x means the increase in length per unit length in the x direction. It is called a linear or dilatational strain component. Similarly, η_y and ζ_z are the linear strain components in the y and z direction, respectively (see Secs. 1.7 and 1.10).

Inspection further discloses that $(\xi_z + \zeta_x)$ is the sum of the two shearing angles associated with a shearing of the medium about the y axis. We see this by looking at Fig. 6.2, which represents by the rectangle $OABC$ one side of an elementary parallelepiped in the deformable medium with OC along the z axis and OA along the x axis. If the deformation is such that CB slides along itself to $C'B'$, whereas OA remains fixed, the original rectangle becomes the parallelogram $OAB'C''$, and we say that the

[1] R. B. Lindsay, "Concepts and Methods of Theoretical Physics," p. 305, D. Van Nostrand Company, Inc., Princeton, N.J., 1951.

result is a *shear* (or shearing strain). The measure of the shear is arbitrarily taken to be $\dfrac{CC'}{OC}$, which is equal to $\dfrac{\partial \xi}{\partial z}\dfrac{dz}{dz}$, or simply $\dfrac{\partial \xi}{\partial z}$. For this shear there is no displacement along the y axis. The only other shear for which this is true is that which takes A into A' in the z direction and B into B''. The representation of this shear is $\partial \zeta / \partial x$. The total shear about the y axis is then defined to be $(\partial \xi / \partial z + \partial \zeta / \partial x)$. Similarly,

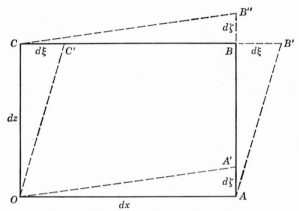

FIG. 6.2. Shear strain in an elastic medium.

$(\zeta_x + \xi_z)$ and $(\zeta_y + \eta_z)$ are measures of the shears about the y and x axes, respectively. Since the choice of numerical measure is to a certain extent arbitrary, the use of the factor $\frac{1}{2}$ in the array (9) should cause no concern. We shall retain it because of the gain in symmetry. The matrix, or array, (9) will be called the *strain matrix* and written

$$D = \left\| \begin{array}{ccc} \delta_{xx} & \delta_{xy} & \delta_{xz} \\ \delta_{yx} & \delta_{yy} & \delta_{yz} \\ \delta_{zx} & \delta_{zy} & \delta_{zz} \end{array} \right\| \tag{10}$$

with the δ's replacing the partial derivatives. The symmetrical character of the matrix demands that $\delta_{xy} = \delta_{yx}$, etc.

The strain matrix has the character of a covariant tensor of the second order. What this means is seen most readily by replacing x, y, z by x_1, x_2, x_3, respectively, and noting that the quadratic form

$$\Sigma \delta_{x_j x_k} \, dx_j \; dx_k \tag{11}$$

is equal to the scalar product

$$(d\mathbf{\Delta})_1 \cdot d\mathbf{r} \tag{12}$$

This in turn may be shown to be equal to one-half the change in ds^2 (or the square of the distance between the two nearby points P and Q) due to the deformation $(d\mathbf{\Delta})_1$. The quadratic form (11) must preserve its form independent of the coordinate system used (as long as it is orthogonal). This means[1] that if we transform to new coordinates x_1', x_2', x_3' the new $\delta_{x_j x_k}'$ which satisfy the requirement will have to be given in terms of the old by the relation

$$\delta_{x_j x_k}' = \sum_{i,l=1}^{3} \delta_{x_i x_l} \frac{\partial x_i}{\partial x_j'} \frac{\partial x_l}{\partial x_k'} \tag{13}$$

Any aggregate with this transformation property is said to be a *covariant tensor of the second order*.

Associated with the deformation of the medium are forces usually represented in terms of *stresses*, or forces per unit area. In Fig. 6.3 we

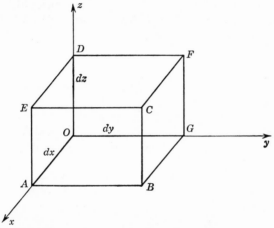

Fig. 6.3. Elementary parallelepiped for elastic stresses.

refer the stresses to the infinitesimal parallelepiped $dx\,dy\,dz$. Thus on the face $OGFD$, which is perpendicular to the x axis, the stress acting along the x axis is denoted by X_{xx}. The shearing stresses on this same face in the y and z directions are written as X_{xy} and X_{xz}, respectively. With similar notation for the faces perpendicular to the y and z axes, respectively, we can set up the following array of nine quantities as representative of the stress on the element:

$$S = \begin{Vmatrix} X_{xx} & X_{xy} & X_{xz} \\ X_{yx} & X_{yy} & X_{yz} \\ X_{zx} & X_{zy} & X_{zz} \end{Vmatrix} \tag{14}$$

It can be shown that this is also a covariant tensor of the second order. It is also a symmetric tensor; that is, $X_{xy} = X_{yx}$, etc., as can be shown by invoking the condition of rotational equilibrium under the action of the torques due to the stresses.

[1] *Ibid.*, pp. 306ff.

6.2. Relation between Strain and Stress in Elastic Media. Hooke's Law

For small strains in homogeneous, isotropic media each stress is directly proportional to the corresponding strain, a relation known as Hooke's law. This in fact can be generalized to apply to anisotropic media, like crystals, but at the moment we shall confine our attention to isotropic bodies. The definitions of the three fundamental moduli of elasticity for such bodies, namely, Young's modulus Y, the bulk modulus B, and the shear modulus μ, depend on Hooke's law for their meaning and are well known from elementary physics. We also have to recall Poisson's ratio σ, which is the ratio of the lateral strain to the associated linear strain in any given direction. The following relations connecting these quantities are commonly derived in physics texts:[1]

$$Y = 3B(1 - 2\sigma) \tag{1}$$

$$Y = 2\mu(1 + \sigma) \tag{2}$$

$$Y = \frac{9B\mu}{\mu + 3B} \tag{3}$$

If in Fig. 6.3 we suppose that the stresses X_{xx}, X_{yy}, and X_{zz} act along their respective axes, Hooke's law yields for the resultant associated linear strains

$$
\begin{aligned}
\delta_{xx} &= \frac{X_{xx} - \sigma(X_{yy} + X_{zz})}{Y} \\
\delta_{yy} &= \frac{X_{yy} - \sigma(X_{zz} + X_{xx})}{Y} \\
\delta_{zz} &= \frac{X_{zz} - \sigma(X_{xx} + X_{yy})}{Y}
\end{aligned}
\tag{4}
$$

where, for example, $\sigma X_{yy}/Y$ denotes the negative strain along the x axis due to the tensile stress along the y axis by virtue of the lateral contraction. If we add these equations and utilize (1) and (2), we can express the stresses in terms of the strains thus:

$$
\begin{aligned}
X_{xx} &= \left(B - \frac{2\mu}{3}\right)\Theta + 2\mu\delta_{xx} \\
X_{yy} &= \left(B - \frac{2\mu}{3}\right)\Theta + 2\mu\delta_{yy} \\
X_{zz} &= \left(B - \frac{2\mu}{3}\right)\Theta + 2\mu\delta_{zz}
\end{aligned}
\tag{5}
$$

where
$$\Theta = \delta_{xx} + \delta_{yy} + \delta_{zz} = \nabla \cdot \mathbf{\Delta} \tag{6}$$

[1] See, for instance, Edwin Edser, "General Physics for Students," p. 231, Macmillan & Co., Ltd., London, 1913.

is called the total dilatational strain. We can add to (5) Hooke's law for the shearing stresses and strains in the form (see Sec. 6.1)

$$X_{xy} = 2\mu\delta_{xy} \qquad X_{yz} = 2\mu\delta_{yz} \qquad X_{zx} = 2\mu\delta_{zx} \tag{7}$$

It is customary to write $B - 2\mu/3 = \Lambda$ (the so-called Lamé coefficient) and to replace (5) and (7) by the single matrix relation

$$S = \left\|\begin{matrix} \Lambda\Theta + 2\mu\delta_{xx} & 2\mu\delta_{xy} & 2\mu\delta_{xz} \\ 2\mu\delta_{yx} & \Lambda\Theta + 2\mu\delta_{yy} & 2\mu\delta_{yz} \\ 2\mu\delta_{zx} & 2\mu\delta_{zy} & \Lambda\Theta + 2\mu\delta_{zz} \end{matrix}\right\| \tag{8}$$

which may be further expressed in the form

$$S = 2\mu D + \Lambda D' \tag{9}$$

in which D' is the diagonal matrix

$$D' = \left\|\begin{matrix} \Theta & 0 & 0 \\ 0 & \Theta & 0 \\ 0 & 0 & \Theta \end{matrix}\right\| \tag{10}$$

The matrix equation (9) is the generalized form of Hooke's law for a homogeneous, isotropic elastic medium.

6.3. Motion of a Homogeneous, Isotropic Elastic Medium. Elastic Waves

If an elastic medium is disturbed from its equilibrium position and then let go, its motion will be due to the excess stresses set up by the disturbances. The components of the resultant force acting on the element $dx\,dy\,dz$ in Fig. 6.3 can be written as follows:

$$\left(\frac{\partial X_{xx}}{\partial x} + \frac{\partial X_{yx}}{\partial y} + \frac{\partial X_{zx}}{\partial z}\right) dx\,dy\,dz$$

$$\left(\frac{\partial X_{xy}}{\partial x} + \frac{\partial X_{yy}}{\partial y} + \frac{\partial X_{zy}}{\partial z}\right) dx\,dy\,dz \tag{1}$$

$$\left(\frac{\partial X_{xz}}{\partial x} + \frac{\partial X_{yz}}{\partial y} + \frac{\partial X_{zz}}{\partial z}\right) dx\,dy\,dz$$

By the use of the tensor relation (6.2-9) the parentheses become, respectively,

$$\left(B + \frac{\mu}{3}\right)\frac{\partial\Theta}{\partial x} + \mu\nabla^2\xi$$

$$\left(B + \frac{\mu}{3}\right)\frac{\partial\Theta}{\partial y} + \mu\nabla^2\eta \tag{2}$$

$$\left(B + \frac{\mu}{3}\right)\frac{\partial\Theta}{\partial z} + \mu\nabla^2\zeta$$

so that the resultant force vector per unit volume is

$$\left(B + \frac{\mu}{3}\right)\nabla\Theta + \mu\nabla\cdot\nabla\mathbf{\Delta} \tag{3}$$

The vector equation of motion results from placing the above expression equal to the product of the density and the resultant acceleration. In this connection we must remember that the acceleration of a particle in a continuous medium involves not merely the time rate of change of velocity *at* a point of the medium but also the time rate of change due to the displacement of the particle in the medium. This statement is fairly obvious for a fluid which is a continuous medium possessing the possibility of flow, but it also applies to any deformable continuous medium.

If we denote the particle displacement velocity by $\mathbf{v}$, that is,

$$\mathbf{v} = \dot{\mathbf{\Delta}}$$

it is shown in texts on hydrodynamics[1] that the actual particle acceleration $\mathbf{a}$ is

$$\mathbf{a} = \dot{\mathbf{v}} + \mathbf{v}\cdot\nabla\mathbf{v} \tag{4}$$

where $\dot{\mathbf{v}} = \partial\mathbf{v}/\partial t$. If the deformation velocity and its gradient are small, the term $\mathbf{v}\cdot\nabla\mathbf{v}$ will be of second order compared with $\dot{\mathbf{v}}$, and to a first approximation we can say $\mathbf{a} = \dot{\mathbf{v}}$. This permits us to write the vector equation of motion of the deformable medium under stress forces alone and for small deformations from equilibrium in the form

$$\rho\ddot{\mathbf{\Delta}} = \left(B + \frac{\mu}{3}\right)\nabla\Theta + \mu\nabla\cdot\nabla\mathbf{\Delta} \tag{5}$$

It is desirable to write this in another form by using the vector identity

$$\nabla\times\nabla\times\mathbf{\Delta} = \nabla\nabla\cdot\mathbf{\Delta} - \nabla\cdot\nabla\mathbf{\Delta} \tag{6}$$

where
$$\nabla\cdot\nabla\mathbf{\Delta} = \mathbf{i}\nabla^2\xi + \mathbf{j}\nabla^2\eta + \mathbf{k}\nabla^2\zeta \tag{7}$$

Then (5) becomes

$$\rho\ddot{\mathbf{\Delta}} = \left(B + \frac{4\mu}{3}\right)\nabla\nabla\cdot\mathbf{\Delta} - \mu\nabla\times\nabla\times\mathbf{\Delta} \tag{8}$$

This is in a favorable form for the examination of two special cases: (1) $\mathbf{\Delta}$ is an *irrotational* vector for which $\nabla\times\mathbf{\Delta} = 0$, and (2) $\mathbf{\Delta}$ is a *solenoidal* vector for which $\nabla\cdot\mathbf{\Delta} = 0$. We consider these in turn.

If $\nabla\times\mathbf{\Delta} = 0$, (8) becomes

$$\rho\ddot{\mathbf{\Delta}} = \left(B + \frac{4\mu}{3}\right)\nabla^2\mathbf{\Delta} \tag{9}$$

---

[1] Or see, for example, Leigh Page, "Introduction to Theoretical Physics," 2d ed., p. 213, D. Van Nostrand Company, Inc., Princeton, N.J., 1935.

This says that Δ is propagated as a wave with velocity

$$V = \sqrt{\frac{B + 4\mu/3}{\rho}} \tag{10}$$

which means that each component of Δ, that is, ξ, η, ζ, is propagated with the same velocity. The corresponding wave is termed an irrotational wave. Let us concentrate attention on a plane wave of this type by assuming that ξ, η, ζ are functions of x and t only and do not depend on y and z. Equation (9) then reduces to the three equations

$$\ddot{\xi} = V^2 \frac{\partial^2 \xi}{\partial x^2} \qquad \ddot{\eta} = V^2 \frac{\partial^2 \eta}{\partial x^2} \qquad \ddot{\zeta} = V^2 \frac{\partial^2 \zeta}{\partial x^2} \tag{11}$$

with general solution (see Sec. 1.7) for each component of Δ in the form

$$\xi = \xi_1(x - Vt) + \xi_2(x + Vt) \tag{12}$$

Now, since $\nabla \times \Delta = 0$, it follows that

$$\frac{\partial \zeta}{\partial y} = \frac{\partial \eta}{\partial z} \qquad \frac{\partial \xi}{\partial z} = \frac{\partial \zeta}{\partial x} \qquad \frac{\partial \eta}{\partial x} = \frac{\partial \xi}{\partial y} \tag{13}$$

But since the three components are functions of x and t only, this leads to $\partial \eta/\partial x = \partial \zeta/\partial x = 0$, and hence η and ζ are constants in space and are not propagated as waves. The only propagated displacement is ξ, which is directed along the direction of propagation. The wave is thus termed *longitudinal*. A plane irrotational wave is then a longitudinal wave. No shears are involved in this type of wave, which is purely dilatational, though it is interesting to note that the shear modulus still enters into the wave velocity.

There is another important way of looking at an irrotational wave. Since $\nabla \times \Delta = 0$, it also follows that $\nabla \times \mathbf{v} = 0$. It is clear that this will be satisfied identically if

$$\mathbf{v} = \nabla\varphi \tag{14}$$

where φ is a scalar function of space and time. It is customary to call φ a *velocity potential*. The existence of such a function is not merely a sufficient condition for the irrotational character of $\mathbf{v}$; it can be shown by Stokes' theorem to be a necessary condition. Thus, since this theorem says[1]

$$\int_{\text{surf}} (\nabla \times \mathbf{v}) \cdot \mathbf{n} \, dS = \int_{\text{cont}} \mathbf{v} \cdot d\mathbf{s} \tag{15}$$

where the surface integral on the left is taken over any surface cap on the closed contour over which the line or contour integral on the right is taken, dS is the element of area with $\mathbf{n}$ the unit normal, and $d\mathbf{s}$ is the

[1] *Ibid.*, p. 36.

arc element of the contour. If $\nabla \times \mathbf{v}$ vanishes identically, it follows that around any closed contour in the region the contour integral of $\mathbf{v}$ must vanish. But this means that the value of the contour integral between *any* two points in the medium is independent of the path, so that $\mathbf{v} \cdot d\mathbf{s}$ must be equal to a perfect differential, which we may call $d\varphi$. This guarantees that $\mathbf{v} = \nabla\varphi$.

If we now differentiate (9) with respect to time, we have

$$\ddot{\mathbf{v}} = V^2\nabla^2\mathbf{v} \tag{16}$$

which becomes, with $\mathbf{v} = \nabla\varphi$,

$$\nabla\ddot{\varphi} = V^2\nabla^2(\nabla\varphi) \tag{17}$$

If φ is a well-behaved mathematical function,[1] we can now set

$$\nabla^2(\nabla\varphi) = \nabla(\nabla^2\varphi)$$

whence if V is constant we can say that $\ddot{\varphi}$ and $V^2\nabla^2\varphi$ differ by only a quantity constant in space. If we are interested only in quantities that vary in both space and time (i.e., quantities that can be propagated), (17) takes the form

$$\ddot{\varphi} = V^2\nabla^2\varphi \tag{18}$$

which indicates that φ, if it is propagated at all, is also propagated as a wave with velocity V.

It is of interest to specialize the above results to a medium without shear elasticity, that is, an ideal fluid in which $\mu = 0$. For this the velocity V becomes

$$V = \sqrt{\frac{B}{\rho}} \tag{19}$$

There are also some other significant relations. Hooke's law (6.2-9) now reduces to the form

$$S = \Lambda D' \tag{20}$$

In an ideal fluid there are no shearing stresses; the stress is indeed wholly compressive, commonly known simply as excess pressure p_e (see Secs. 3.5 and 3.6). The total dilatation Θ now becomes simply δ_v, or the change in volume per unit volume, whereas S is the diagonal pressure matrix, all nonvanishing components of which are equal, there being complete symmetry with respect to compressive stress in a fluid at any point. (This is strictly an assumption for fluids subject to unbalanced deforming stresses, but one which is well borne out by experience.)

---

[1] For the conditions under which the order of partial differentiation of a function of several variables is immaterial, see R. S. Burington and C. C. Torrance, "Higher Mathematics with Applications to Science and Engineering," p. 97, McGraw-Hill Book Company, Inc., New York, 1939.

Hence (20) becomes

$$p_e = -B\delta_v \tag{21}$$

It is customary to introduce in place of δ_v the so-called *condensation s*, which is defined as the fractional change in density associated with the volume strain. We then have $\delta_v = -s$ and can write (21) in the form

$$p_e = Bs \tag{22}$$

Since the dilatation Θ is $\nabla \cdot \mathbf{\Delta}$, we also have

$$s = -\nabla \cdot \mathbf{\Delta} \tag{23}$$

With the use of these relations it follows that both s and p_e satisfy the wave equation (18) and are propagated with the velocity V.

The physical significance of differentiating (23) with respect to the time should not be overlooked. We get

$$\dot{s} + \nabla \cdot \mathbf{v} = 0 \tag{24}$$

which, if we multiply through by ρ_0 (here treated as a *constant mean* density in space, though variable in time), becomes

$$\dot{\rho} + \nabla \cdot (\rho_0 \mathbf{v}) = 0 \tag{25}$$

This is a *special* case of the *equation of continuity* of flow in hydrodynamics, which expresses the conservation of mass in the flow of the deformable medium [see (3.5-2)]. The more general equation of continuity, in which ρ is variable in space as well as in time, is treated in Chap. 9 [see also (8.1-1)].

We now wish to examine the form assumed by the general equation of motion (8) of a deformable medium subject to stresses alone, when the displacement vector $\mathbf{\Delta}$ is solenoidal. Then $\nabla \cdot \mathbf{\Delta} = 0$, and the equation becomes

$$\rho\ddot{\mathbf{\Delta}} = \mu\nabla^2\mathbf{\Delta} \tag{26}$$

which says that a solenoidal displacement is propagated as a wave with velocity

$$V = \sqrt{\frac{\mu}{\rho}} \tag{27}$$

clearly less than the velocity of an irrotational wave. If we examine particularly a plane wave in which $\mathbf{\Delta}$ depends on x and t alone, we readily see that in this case $\partial\xi/\partial x = 0$ and hence ξ is not propagated as a wave. This means that the propagated displacement is at right angles to the direction of propagation and hence that a plane solenoidal elastic wave is transverse. It is, of course, a pure shear wave, which could not exist in an ideal fluid.

It is of some interest to examine the case of a spherical elastic wave. We first take an irrotational wave. The components of $\nabla \times \boldsymbol{\Delta}$ expressed in spherical coordinates r, θ, ϕ are[1]

$$(\nabla \times \boldsymbol{\Delta})_r = \frac{1}{r^2 \sin \theta} \left[\frac{\partial}{\partial \theta} (r \sin \theta \, \Delta_\phi) - \frac{\partial}{\partial \phi} (r \Delta_\theta) \right]$$

$$(\nabla \times \boldsymbol{\Delta})_\theta = \frac{1}{r \sin \theta} \left[\frac{\partial \Delta_\theta}{\partial \phi} - \frac{\partial}{\partial r} (r \sin \theta \, \Delta_\phi) \right] \tag{28}$$

$$(\nabla \times \boldsymbol{\Delta})_\phi = \frac{1}{r} \left[\frac{\partial}{\partial r} (r \Delta_\theta) - \frac{\partial \Delta_r}{\partial \theta} \right]$$

where $$\boldsymbol{\Delta} = \mathbf{r}_1 \Delta_r + \boldsymbol{\theta}_1 \Delta_\theta + \boldsymbol{\phi}_1 \Delta_\phi \tag{29}$$

in spherical coordinates.   If the wave is irrotational, each component of $\nabla \times \boldsymbol{\Delta}$ is equal to zero.   If we further assume that Δ_r, Δ_θ, and Δ_ϕ depend on r and t only, the equation of motion (9) becomes the three equations

$$\ddot{\Delta}_r = \frac{(B + 4\mu/3)}{r} \frac{\partial^2}{\partial r^2} (r \Delta_r)$$

$$\ddot{\Delta}_\theta = \frac{(B + 4\mu/3)}{r} \frac{\partial^2}{\partial r^2} (r \Delta_\theta) \tag{30}$$

$$\ddot{\Delta}_\phi = \frac{(B + 4\mu/3)}{r} \frac{\partial^2}{\partial r^2} (r \Delta_\phi)$$

where, moreover, the irrotationality condition from (28) leads at once to

$$\Delta_\phi = 0$$

and $$\frac{\partial}{\partial r} (r \Delta_\theta) = 0 \tag{31}$$

so that $r \Delta_\theta$ is independent of r and depends on t alone. Hence Δ_ϕ and $r \Delta_\theta$ are not propagated as waves, whereas $r \Delta_r$ is. It follows that the spherical irrotational wave is longitudinal in the sense that at any place the direction of the wave propagation is equivalent to the direction of the displacement in the medium.

We now consider the solenoidal spherical wave.   In spherical coordinates[2]

$$\nabla \cdot \boldsymbol{\Delta} = \frac{1}{r^2} \frac{\partial}{\partial r} (r^2 \Delta_r) + \frac{1}{r \sin \theta} \frac{\partial}{\partial \theta} (\Delta_\theta \sin \theta) + \frac{1}{r \sin \theta} \frac{\partial \Delta_\phi}{\partial \varphi} \tag{32}$$

If again we assume that $\boldsymbol{\Delta}$ is a function of r and t only, $\partial \Delta_\phi / \partial \phi = 0$ and $(\partial / \partial \theta)(\Delta_\theta \sin \theta) = (\cos \theta) \Delta_\theta$.   Hence,   from   the   solenoidal   condition

---

[1] For a discussion of the components of the curl of a vector in curvilinear orthogonal coordinates, see Franklin, "Methods of Advanced Calculus," p. 318.

[2] See *ibid.*

$\nabla \cdot \mathbf{\Delta} = 0$, we cannot conclude that $r\Delta_r$ is independent of r, since

$$\frac{\partial}{\partial r} (r^2 \Delta_r) = -(\cot \theta) r \Delta_\theta$$

and hence the wave is not necessarily transverse, as is a plane solenoidal wave. We must therefore be careful not to assume that a solenoidal wave is always transverse.

6.4. Energy in an Elastic Radiation Field

Let us now introduce some general considerations of energy into the radiation of elastic waves. We revert to the fundamental equation of motion (6.3-5)

$$\rho \ddot{\mathbf{\Delta}} = \left(B + \frac{\mu}{3} \right) \nabla \nabla \cdot \mathbf{\Delta} + \mu \nabla \cdot \nabla \mathbf{\Delta} \tag{1}$$

To get an energy equation out of this, the obvious course is to form the scalar product of each side with $\dot{\mathbf{\Delta}}$, that is,

$$\rho \dot{\mathbf{\Delta}} \cdot \ddot{\mathbf{\Delta}} = C \dot{\mathbf{\Delta}} \cdot (\nabla \nabla \cdot \mathbf{\Delta}) + \mu \dot{\mathbf{\Delta}} \cdot (\nabla \cdot \nabla \mathbf{\Delta}) \tag{2}$$

where $C = B + \mu/3$ for convenience. Now, from (6.3-23), $\nabla \cdot \mathbf{\Delta} = -s$; hence the first term on the right becomes $-C \dot{\mathbf{\Delta}} \cdot \nabla s$. We can use a vector identity for this and write

$$\nabla \cdot (s \dot{\mathbf{\Delta}}) = s \nabla \cdot \dot{\mathbf{\Delta}} + \dot{\mathbf{\Delta}} \cdot \nabla s \tag{3}$$

Moreover, there is another identity[1] of the form

$$\nabla \cdot (\dot{\mathbf{\Delta}} \cdot \nabla \mathbf{\Delta}) = \dot{\mathbf{\Delta}} \cdot (\nabla \cdot \nabla \mathbf{\Delta}) + \nabla \dot{\mathbf{\Delta}} : \nabla \mathbf{\Delta} \tag{4}$$

where
$$\nabla \dot{\mathbf{\Delta}} : \nabla \mathbf{\Delta} = \sum_{j,k} \frac{\partial \dot{\Delta}_j}{\partial x_k} \frac{\partial \Delta_k}{\partial x_j} \tag{5}$$

in which for simplicity we denote x, y, z, by x_1, y_2, z_3, respectively, and $\dot{\Delta}_j$ means the jth component of $\dot{\mathbf{\Delta}}$, etc.

We can therefore rewrite (2) in the form

$$\rho \dot{\mathbf{\Delta}} \cdot \ddot{\mathbf{\Delta}} = -C[\nabla \cdot (s \dot{\mathbf{\Delta}}) - s \nabla \cdot \dot{\mathbf{\Delta}}] + \mu[\nabla \cdot (\dot{\mathbf{\Delta}} \cdot \nabla \mathbf{\Delta}) - \nabla \dot{\mathbf{\Delta}} : \nabla \mathbf{\Delta}] \tag{6}$$

The next step is to integrate both sides over a finite volume of the elastic medium. Thus we get

$$\int \left[\frac{\rho}{2} \frac{\partial}{\partial t} (\dot{\mathbf{\Delta}} \cdot \dot{\mathbf{\Delta}}) + \frac{C}{2} \frac{\partial}{\partial t} s^2 + \frac{\mu}{2} \frac{\partial}{\partial t} (\nabla \mathbf{\Delta} : \nabla \mathbf{\Delta}) \right] d\tau$$

$$= -\int C \nabla \cdot (s \dot{\mathbf{\Delta}}) \, d\tau + \int \mu \nabla \cdot (\dot{\mathbf{\Delta}} \cdot \nabla \mathbf{\Delta}) \, d\tau \tag{7}$$

---

[1] P. M. Morse and H. Feshbach, "Methods of Theoretical Physics," p. 150, McGraw-Hill Book Company, Inc., New York, 1953.

By combination of terms and the use of the divergence theorem this may be rewritten as

$$\frac{\partial}{\partial t} \int \left[\frac{\rho}{2} \dot{\Delta}^2 + \frac{C}{2} s^2 + \frac{\mu}{2} (\nabla \Delta : \nabla \Delta) \right] d\tau = \int (-Cs\dot{\Delta} + \mu \dot{\Delta} \cdot \nabla \Delta) \cdot \mathbf{n} \, d\sigma \quad (8)$$

in which $d\tau$ represents the element of volume and $d\sigma$ the corresponding element in the surface surrounding the volume. The normal to the surface element is $\mathbf{n}$.

To interpret this result physically, it will be simplest to take first the case in which the medium is an ideal fluid with $\mu = 0$. Then (8) reduces to

$$\frac{\partial}{\partial t} \int \left(\frac{\rho \dot{\Delta}^2}{2} + \frac{Bs^2}{2} \right) d\tau = - \int (Bs\dot{\Delta}) \cdot \mathbf{n} \, d\sigma \quad (9)$$

The term $\rho \dot{\Delta}^2/2$ clearly is the kinetic energy per unit volume of the fluid. Similarly $Bs^2/2$ is the potential energy per unit volume [see (1.10-32)]. The integral on the left is therefore the total energy in the volume in question at a given instant, and the whole left-hand side is the instantaneous time rate of change of this. In the surface integral on the right

$$Bs\dot{\Delta} = p_e \dot{\Delta} \quad (10)$$

since the excess pressure $p_e = \rho_0 V^2 s$ [Eq. (6.3-22)] and $B = \rho_0 V^2$. Hence the surface integral represents the rate at which work is done by the fluid medium inside the volume surrounded by the surface on the medium outside; in other words, it is the rate at which energy is instantaneously leaving the volume through the surface. The result we have demonstrated therefore constitutes a kind of energy-conservation theorem for the case of disturbances in an elastic fluid. It is indeed precisely analogous to the Poynting theorem in electromagnetic radiation (see Sec. 6.7).

We have now to look at the more general case of an arbitrary elastic medium which can support shears ($\mu \neq 0$). We expect that the term $(\mu/2)(\nabla \Delta : \nabla \Delta)$ is a contribution to the elastic strain potential energy involving the shear strains. Closer examination[1] shows that this is indeed the case. The term $\int \mu (\dot{\Delta} \cdot \nabla \Delta) \cdot \mathbf{n} \, d\sigma$ is likewise a contribution to the rate of flow of elastic energy across the boundary of a medium which is shearable as well as compressible. The term

$$(-Cs\dot{\Delta} + \mu \dot{\Delta} \cdot \nabla \Delta) \cdot \mathbf{n}$$

represents the total instantaneous ratio of flow of energy per unit area in the elastic radiation field. When averaged over the time, it becomes the intensity of the radiation.

[1] *Ibid.*, p. 150.

6.5. Elastic Waves in Anisotropic Media

The equations of motion of a deformable elastic medium disturbed from equilibrium and let go under the action of its own internal stresses have been set up and discussed in Sec. 6.3 for the special case of isotropic media. We now wish to generalize them to anisotropic media. The main difference we shall encounter is due to the more elaborate character of Hooke's law for such media. If we look back to (6.3-1), we see that the component equations of motion for small deformations are, in perfectly general form,

$$
\rho\ddot{\xi} = \frac{\partial X_{xx}}{\partial x} + \frac{\partial X_{yx}}{\partial y} + \frac{\partial X_{zx}}{\partial z}
$$
$$
\rho\ddot{\eta} = \frac{\partial X_{xy}}{\partial x} + \frac{\partial X_{yy}}{\partial y} + \frac{\partial X_{zy}}{\partial z} \tag{1}
$$
$$
\rho\ddot{\zeta} = \frac{\partial X_{xz}}{\partial x} + \frac{\partial X_{yz}}{\partial y} + \frac{\partial X_{zz}}{\partial z}
$$

For anisotropic media Hooke's law no longer has the simple form (6.2-9). Rather, each stress component is a linear function of all the strain components. To write the relationship, it is simpler to adopt another notation and set

$$
\begin{array}{lll}
X_{xx} = X_1 & X_{yy} = X_2 & X_{zz} = X_3 \\
X_{yz} = X_{zy} = X_4 & X_{xz} = X_{zx} = X_5 & X_{xy} = X_{yx} = X_6
\end{array} \tag{2}
$$

Similarly, we write the strain components in the form

$$
\begin{array}{lll}
\delta_{xx} = \delta_1 & \delta_{yy} = \delta_2 & \delta_{zz} = \delta_3 \\
\delta_{yz} = \delta_{zy} = \dfrac{\delta_4}{2} & \delta_{xz} = \delta_{zx} = \dfrac{\delta_5}{2} & \delta_{xy} = \delta_{yx} = \dfrac{\delta_6}{2}
\end{array} \tag{3}
$$

The generalized Hooke's law may then be written as the six equations

$$
X_k = \sum_{j=1}^{6} c_{kj}\delta_j \qquad k = 1, \ldots, 6 \tag{4}
$$

where the 36 quantities c_{kj} are known as the *elastic coefficients* of the anisotropic medium. We can equally well solve for the δ_j in terms of the X_k and get

$$
\delta_j = \sum_{k=1}^{6} s_{jk}X_k \qquad j = 1, \ldots, 6 \tag{5}
$$

The 36 quantities s_{jk} are termed the *elastic constants*. By direct substitution of δ_j from (5) into (4) it develops that

$$\sum_{j=1}^{6} c_{kj}s_{jk'} = 1 \qquad \text{for } k = k'$$
$$= 0 \qquad \text{for } k \neq k' \tag{6}$$

If we think of the quantities c_{kj} as forming the matrix $\|c\|$ and the quantities s_{jk} the matrix $\|s\|$, the relations (6) are equivalent to the matrix relation

$$\|c\| \cdot \|s\| = \|1\| \tag{7}$$

where $\|1\|$ is the unit matrix, that is,

$$\|1\| = \begin{Vmatrix} 1 & 0 & 0 & 0 & 0 & 0 \\ 0 & 1 & 0 & 0 & 0 & 0 \\ 0 & 0 & 1 & 0 & 0 & 0 \\ 0 & 0 & 0 & 1 & 0 & 0 \\ 0 & 0 & 0 & 0 & 1 & 0 \\ 0 & 0 & 0 & 0 & 0 & 1 \end{Vmatrix} \tag{8}$$

It will be recalled that matrix multiplication is defined in such a way that if $\|p\|$ is the product $\|c\| \cdot \|s\|$ we have

$$p_{lm} = \sum_{j=1}^{6} c_{lj}s_{jm} \tag{9}$$

Thus the matrix $\|c\|$ is the *reciprocal* of the matrix $\|s\|$. The components of the $\|c\|$ matrix are not all different. In fact we can prove that it is a symmetric matrix, that is,

$$c_{kj} = c_{jk} \tag{10}$$

Moreover,
$$s_{kj} = s_{jk} \tag{11}$$

Hence the number of independent elastic coefficients is 21 instead of 36. We can prove this by examining the internal potential energy associated with the strain. For a change in volume strain $d\delta_1$ associated with the tensile stress X_1, the change in internal energy of the elementary parallelepiped $dx\, dy\, dz$ is

$$X_1\, d\delta_1\, dx\, dy\, dz \tag{12}$$

By applying the same reasoning to the shearing deformations, we finally find the change in total internal energy U per unit volume due to all possible deformations to be

$$dU = \Sigma X_k\, d\delta_k \tag{13}$$

Hence
$$\frac{\partial U}{\partial \delta_k} = X_k$$

and, from (4),

$$c_{kj} = \frac{\partial X_k}{\partial \delta_j} = \frac{\partial^2 U}{\partial \delta_k \, \partial \delta_j} \tag{14}$$

Also

$$c_{jk} = \frac{\partial X_j}{\partial \delta_k} = \frac{\partial^2 U}{\partial \delta_j \, \partial \delta_k} \tag{15}$$

Since the order of differentiation is here immaterial, the conclusion (10) follows. Similarly, $s_{kj} = s_{jk}$.

The number of independent elastic constants is, of course, reduced from 21 to 2 for a homogeneous, isotropic medium. This may be thought of as due to the symmetry connected with the invariance of Hooke's law under an arbitrary rotation of axes.[1]

We may now rewrite (1) in vector form by employing the notation introduced in (2) and the following equations, coupled with the choice of $x = x_1$, $y = x_2$, $z = x_3$. The result is

$$\rho \ddot{\Delta}_j = \sum_{k=1}^{3} \frac{\partial X_{kj}}{\partial x_k} \tag{16}$$

if we choose $\Delta_1 = \xi$, $\Delta_2 = \eta$, $\Delta_3 = \zeta$ and, shifting notation again for convenience, set $X_{xx} = X_{11}$, $X_{xy} = X_{12}$, etc. The summation sign may be omitted in (16) by the employment of the summation convention in tensor analysis, whereby an expression is summed over any repeated index (in the above case, k).

Let us now investigate the propagation of a plane harmonic wave through the medium. For this

$$\Delta_j = \Delta_{j0} \exp \left[i(\omega t - k \Sigma l_i x_i) \right] \tag{17}$$

where the l_i are the direction cosines of the normal to the wavefront, that is,

$$\sum_{i=1}^{3} l_i^2 = 1$$

Recalling the relations between the components of Δ and the strains δ_j set forth in Sec. 6.1 and employing (17) in combination with (4), we get

$$X_{11} = X_{xx} = -ik[c_{11}l_1\Delta_1 + c_{12}l_2\Delta_2 + c_{13}l_3\Delta_3 + c_{14}(l_2\Delta_3 + l_3\Delta_2) + c_{15}(l_1\Delta_3 + l_3\Delta_1) + c_{16}(l_1\Delta_2 + l_2\Delta_1)]$$

or, collecting terms,

$$X_{11} = -ik[\Delta_1(c_{11}l_1 + c_{15}l_3 + c_{16}l_2) + \Delta_2(c_{12}l_2 + c_{14}l_3 + c_{16}l_1) + \Delta_3(c_{13}l_3 + c_{14}l_2 + c_{15}l_3)] \tag{18}$$

[1] A. Sommerfeld, "Mechanics of Deformable Bodies," pp. 62ff., Academic Press, Inc., New York, 1950.

whence, by differentiating with respect to x_1 and again using (17),

$$\frac{\partial X_{11}}{\partial x_1} = -ikl_1X_{11} \tag{19}$$

Similarly,

$$\begin{aligned}
X_{yx} = X_{12} = -ik[&\Delta_1(c_{61}l_1 + c_{66}l_2 + c_{65}l_3) \\
&+ \Delta_2(c_{66}l_1 + c_{62}l_2 + c_{64}l_3) \\
&+ \Delta_3(c_{65}l_1 + c_{64}l_2 + c_{63}l_3)]
\end{aligned} \tag{20}$$

and

$$\frac{\partial X_{12}}{\partial x_2} = -ikl_2X_{12} \tag{21}$$

Finally,

$$\begin{aligned}
X_{zx} = X_{13} = -ik[&\Delta_1(c_{51}l_1 + c_{56}l_2 + c_{55}l_3) \\
&+ \Delta_2(c_{56}l_1 + c_{52}l_2 + c_{54}l_3) \\
&+ \Delta_3(c_{55}l_1 + c_{54}l_2 + c_{53}l_3)]
\end{aligned} \tag{22}$$

and

$$\frac{\partial X_{13}}{\partial x_3} = -ikl_3X_{13} \tag{23}$$

The first of (1) now takes the form

$$\begin{aligned}
\rho\ddot{\Delta}_1 = -ik[&l_1X_{11} + l_2X_{12} + l_3X_{13}] \\
= -k^2\{&\Delta_1[c_{11}l_1{}^2 + c_{66}l_2{}^2 + c_{55}l_3{}^2 + 2\overset{*}{c}_{16}l_1l_2 + 2c_{56}l_2l_3 + 2c_{15}l_1l_2] \\
&+ \Delta_2[c_{16}l_1{}^2 + c_{26}l_2{}^2 + c_{45}l_3{}^2 + (c_{12} + c_{66})l_1l_2 + (c_{25} + c_{46})l_2l_3 \\
&\qquad\qquad\qquad\qquad\qquad\qquad\qquad\qquad\qquad + (c_{14} + c_{56})l_1l_3] \\
&+ \Delta_3[c_{15}l_1{}^2 + c_{46}l_2{}^2 + c_{35}l_3{}^2 + (c_{14} + c_{56})l_1l_2 + (c_{36} + c_{45})l_2l_3 \\
&\qquad\qquad\qquad\qquad\qquad\qquad\qquad\qquad\qquad + (c_{13} + c_{55})l_1l_3]\}
\end{aligned} \tag{24}$$

where we have utilized the relations (10) to simplify the expression somewhat. Since $k^2 = \omega^2/V^2$, where V is the wave velocity, and $\ddot{\Delta}_1 = -\omega^2\Delta_1$, we can rewrite the above in the form

$$\rho V^2\Delta_1 = A_{11}\Delta_1 + A_{12}\Delta_2 + A_{13}\Delta_3 \tag{25}$$

where the A_{11}, etc., are the bracket terms in (24). Precisely similar analysis yields

$$\rho V^2\Delta_2 = A_{12}\Delta_1 + A_{22}\Delta_2 + A_{23}\Delta_3 \tag{26}$$

$$\rho V^2\Delta_3 = A_{13}\Delta_1 + A_{23}\Delta_2 + A_{33}\Delta_3 \tag{27}$$

where

$$\begin{aligned}
A_{22} &= c_{66}l_1{}^2 + c_{22}l_2{}^2 + c_{44}l_3{}^2 + 2c_{26}l_1l_2 + 2c_{24}l_2l_3 + 2c_{46}l_1l_3 \\
A_{33} &= c_{55}l_1{}^2 + c_{44}l_2{}^2 + c_{33}l_3{}^2 + 2c_{45}l_1l_2 + 2c_{34}l_2l_3 + 2c_{35}l_1l_3 \\
A_{23} &= c_{56}l_1{}^2 + c_{24}l_2{}^2 + c_{34}l_3{}^2 + (c_{25} + c_{46})l_1l_2 + (c_{23} + c_{44})l_2l_3 \\
&\qquad\qquad\qquad\qquad\qquad\qquad\qquad\qquad\qquad + (c_{36} + c_{45})l_1l_3
\end{aligned} \tag{28}$$

The condition that the three homogeneous equations (25), (26), (27) have a nonvanishing solution is that

$$\begin{vmatrix} A_{11} - \rho V^2 & A_{12} & A_{13} \\ A_{12} & A_{22} - \rho V^2 & A_{23} \\ A_{13} & A_{23} & A_{33} - \rho V^2 \end{vmatrix} = 0 \tag{29}$$

This equation is a cubic in V^2, leading in general to three different velocities of elastic radiation in the anisotropic medium. Each velocity depends on the values of the 21 independent elastic coefficients as well as the direction cosines l_1, l_2, l_3.

It will pay to illustrate the above with a couple of examples. Let us take first the so-called cubic crystal (of which gold and copper are good examples).[1] Here the 21 coefficients c_{ij} reduce to 3 nonvanishing ones, namely, c_{11}, c_{12}, and c_{44}. All the rest are zero. Then the A_{ij} coefficients become

$$A_{11} = c_{11}l_1{}^2 \qquad A_{12} = c_{12}l_1l_2 \qquad A_{13} = 0$$
$$A_{22} = c_{44}l_3{}^2 \qquad A_{23} = c_{44}l_2l_3 \qquad A_{33} = c_{44}l_2{}^2 \qquad (30)$$

For a wave propagated along the x axis we have $l_1 = 1$, $l_2 = l_3 = 0$, and the above simplify to

$$A_{11} = c_{11}$$

corresponding to velocity

$$V_d = \sqrt{\frac{c_{11}}{\rho}} \qquad (31)$$

On the other hand, for a wave along the y axis, $l_2 = 1$ and the other l's are zero, so that we get the velocity

$$V_s = \sqrt{\frac{c_{44}}{\rho}} \qquad (32)$$

A wave along the z axis yields the same velocity. From the physical significance of the c coefficients it follows that V_d is the velocity of a dilatational wave, whereas V_s corresponds to a shear wave.

Another common crystallographic form is the hexagonal, characteristic of normal ice crystals, for example, near 0°C and 1 atm pressure. Here the nonvanishing c_{ij} are as follows:[2]

$$c_{11} = c_{22} \qquad c_{13} = c_{23} \qquad c_{44} = c_{55}$$
$$c_{12} \qquad\qquad c_{13} \qquad\qquad c_{66} = \frac{c_{11} - c_{12}}{2} \qquad (33)$$

The A_{ij} then take the form

$$A_{11} = c_{11}l_1{}^2 + \frac{c_{11} - c_{12}}{2} l_2{}^2 + c_{44}l_3{}^2 \qquad A_{12} = \frac{c_{11} + c_{12}}{2} l_1l_2$$
$$A_{13} = (c_{13} + c_{44})l_1l_3 \qquad\qquad A_{23} = (c_{13} + c_{44})l_2l_3$$
$$A_{22} = \frac{c_{11} - c_{12}}{2} l_1{}^2 + c_{11}l_2{}^2 + c_{44}l_3{}^2 \qquad A_{33} = c_{44}l_1{}^2 + c_{44}l_2{}^2 + c_{33}l_3{}^2 \qquad (34)$$

---

[1] C. Zener, "Elasticity and Anelasticity of Metals," chaps. 1, 2, University of Chicago Press, Chicago, 1948.

[2] A. H. A. Penny, *Proc. Cambridge Phil. Soc.*, **44**, 423 (1948).

The so-called optic axis of the hexagonal crystal corresponds to

$$l_1 = l_2 = 0$$

$l_3 = 1$. Hence the determinantal equation (29) becomes

$$\begin{vmatrix} c_{44} - \rho V^2 & 0 & 0 \\ 0 & c_{44} - \rho V^2 & 0 \\ 0 & 0 & c_{33} - \rho V^2 \end{vmatrix} = 0 \tag{35}$$

with roots

$$V_d = \sqrt{\frac{c_{33}}{\rho}} \tag{36}$$

$$V_s = \sqrt{\frac{c_{44}}{\rho}} \tag{37}$$

respectively. Again V_d is a dilatational wave velocity, whereas V_s corresponds to a shear.

For $l_1 = l_3 = 0$, $l_2 = 1$, one gets another shear wave velocity

$$V_s = \sqrt{\frac{c_{11} - c_{12}}{2\rho}} \tag{38}$$

6.6. Wave Propagation in Crystal Lattices

The continuous elastic medium is an ideal construct. Actually, according to the atomic theory, all material media are composed of atoms; material properties depend on the mutual arrangement and interaction of the constituent atoms and ultimately on the atomic structure. If we deal with relatively large disturbances, that is, those in which relatively large aggregates of atoms act as a whole, the continuum theory may be expected to provide a satisfactory approximation. This should be true for elastic wave propagation for wavelengths which are large compared with the average interatomic distance. However, as the wavelength decreases, we naturally expect to encounter effects due to the atomic particles individually. It is true that in the case of solids the frequency at which this would occur is higher than can be produced by macroscopic elastic disturbances of the conventional sort. In gases at very low pressure, however, the situation is different (see Sec. 12.2).

It therefore seems desirable to examine the propagation of a wave through a collection of discrete particles which act on each other with definite assigned forces. By a mechanical wave in such an aggregate we mean the following. Whenever any one particle is disturbed from its equilibrium position, the disturbance is communicated somehow to neighboring particles, which also move from their equilibrium positions, and so on through the collection. The simplest type of aggregate we can deal with is, of course, a crystal lattice, that is, a collection of particles whose equilibrium positions form an orderly periodic spatial pattern. The easiest example of this to begin with is a linear aggregate of equally spaced particles all of the same mass, which is considered to be disturbed by displacement either in the direction of the length or perpendicular thereto.

It will be recalled that we encountered a similar situation in the loaded string in Sec. 4.5. There, it is true, the material particles were thought of as influencing the propagation along the continuous string so as to produce selective transmission with respect to frequency. Nevertheless, we can extract some useful information from this problem concerning the wave propagation along an equally spaced set of equal particles acting only on their nearest neighbors with a harmonic restoring force. We observed the filtration properties of such a structure and calculated the power transmission as a function of frequency. We might also have noted that the structure acts effectively as a dispersive medium; that is, the effective phase velocity is a function of wavelength, or frequency. We can see this readily from (4.5-21), which gives the displacement velocity $\dot{\eta}_{j+1}$ at the mid-point between the jth and the $(j + 1)$st particles in terms of $\dot{\eta}_1$, the displacement at the mid-point between the first and second particles. To repeat,

$$\dot{\eta}_{j+1} = \dot{\eta}_1 \cos jW + \frac{i}{Z} \tau_1 \sqrt{\frac{C}{B}} \sin jW \tag{1}$$

where
$$\cos W = \cos 2kl - \frac{\omega m}{2Z} \sin 2kl$$

$$B = \sin 2kl + \frac{\omega m}{Z} \cos^2 kl \tag{2}$$

$$C = \sin 2kl - \frac{\omega m}{Z} \sin^2 kl$$

and τ_1 is the normal component of the tension. The equilibrium separation of adjacent particles (each of mass m) is $2l$. $Z = \rho_l V$, where ρ_l is the mass per unit length of the connecting string and V = velocity of the transverse wave in the string ($= \sqrt{T_0/\rho_l}$, where T_0 is the mean tension). We recall that the wave parameter $k = \omega/V$.

The above result is based on the assumption that harmonic waves of angular frequency ω move in both directions along the loaded string. The vanishing of $\dot{\eta}_{j+1}$ means that the corresponding point is a node, and if both $\dot{\eta}_{j+1}$ and $\dot{\eta}_1$ vanish identically with no other $\dot{\eta}$'s vanishing in between it means that the distance $2jl$ is a half wavelength of the effective transverse radiation in the loaded string. But from (1) the condition that $\dot{\eta}_{j+1}$ and $\dot{\eta}_1$ shall vanish simultaneously is

$$\sin jW = 0 \tag{3}$$

or
$$W = \frac{\pi}{j} \tag{4}$$

taking the lowest root.   Hence the relation between wavelength and frequency is

$$\cos 2kl - \frac{\omega m}{2Z} \sin 2kl = \cos \frac{\pi}{j} = \cos \frac{4\pi l}{\lambda} \tag{5}$$

where λ is the effective wavelength.   If we assume, as we did in Sec. 4.5, that

$$kl \ll 1$$

the above can be approximated by

$$\omega = \sqrt{\frac{2T_0}{ml}} \sin \frac{2\pi l}{\lambda} \tag{6}$$

corresponding to effective velocity $V_l = \nu\lambda$, where

$$V_l = l \sqrt{\frac{2T_0}{ml}} \frac{\sin (2\pi l/\lambda)}{2\pi l/\lambda} \tag{7}$$

We must be careful here to avoid confusion between this velocity and the velocity V with which waves travel in the continuous string of mean line density ρ_l when stretched with tension T_0.   Actually, only as $l/\lambda \to 0$ or the wavelength λ becomes very great does

$$V_l \to \sqrt{\frac{2lT_0}{m}} \tag{8}$$

or precisely V, since $m/2l = \rho_l$ if the number of particles is very great. In terms of frequency the dispersion law takes the form

$$V_l = \frac{\omega l}{\arcsin (\omega l/V)} \tag{9}$$

The above results can of course be deduced by a direct dynamical analysis of the lattice.   We present in Fig. 6.4 a schematic diagram show-

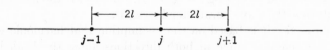

Fig. 6.4. Linear lattice.

ing the equilibrium positions of any three particles of the lattice (each of mass m) numbered as $j - 1, j$, and $j + 1$, respectively, the equilibrium spacing between successive particles being $2l$.   Let us suppose that, when any particle is displaced, there is a restoring force proportional to the change in its distances from the two neighboring particles *only*.   If we denote the equivalent stiffness by f and continue to denote the displacements from equilibrium by η, the equation of motion of the jth particle becomes

$$m\ddot{\eta}_j + f(2\eta_j - \eta_{j-1} - \eta_{j+1}) = 0 \tag{10}$$

We now ask the condition that this be satisfied by a plane wave of the form

$$\eta_j = A e^{i(\omega t - kx_j)} \tag{11}$$

where x_j is the distance of the jth particle from some chosen origin $(x_j = 2jl)$. Substitution reveals that (11) can satisfy the equation of motion if

$$\omega^2 = \frac{2f}{m}(1 - \cos 2kl) = \frac{4f}{m}\sin^2 kl \tag{12}$$

The velocity of the wave is

$$V_l = \frac{\omega}{k} = 2l\sqrt{\frac{f}{m}}\frac{\sin kl}{kl} \tag{13}$$

which is reminiscent of (7). Here $k = 2\pi/\lambda$, as usual. For very long waves $kl \to 0$ and

$$V_l = V_\infty \doteq 2l\sqrt{\frac{f}{m}} \tag{14}$$

independent of the wavelength. As the wavelength decreases, V_l decreases. For $\lambda/2 = 2l$, or the separation between the particles equal to a half wavelength, $V_l = 2V_\infty/\pi$. When $\lambda = 2l$, $V_l = 0$. As λ increases, V_l oscillates as shown in Fig. 6.5. The filtering characteristic

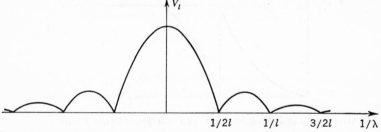

FIG. 6.5. Dependence of propagation velocity on wavelength in a linear lattice.

of the lattice is clear from (12), since the angular frequency ω has the maximum value

$$\omega_m = 2\sqrt{\frac{f}{m}} \tag{15}$$

This then constitutes a cutoff frequency above which there is no attenuation-free transmission. We can indeed satisfy the equation of motion by (11) for higher frequencies, but only for *complex* k. This corresponds to attenuation (see Sec. 1.9). Thus if we let

$$k = k_r + i k_i \tag{16}$$

(12) becomes

$$\omega^2 = \frac{4f}{m} (\sin^2 k_r l \cosh^2 k_i l - \cos^2 k_r l \sinh^2 k_i l$$

$$+ 2i \sin k_r l \cos k_r l \sinh k_i l \cosh k_i l) \tag{17}$$

but since ω^2 must be real and positive, the coefficient of i on the right-hand side of (17) must vanish. In view of the nature of the real part, this means that $\cos k_r l = 0$ or $\sinh k_i l = 0$. But since the latter would involve $k_i = 0$, we must choose the former and write

$$\omega = 2 \sqrt{\frac{f}{m}} \cosh k_i l \tag{18}$$

Frequencies with these values are attenuated with the attenuation coefficient k_i; that is, the displacement η_j becomes

$$\eta_j = A e^{-k_i x_i} e^{i(\omega t - k_r x_i)} \tag{19}$$

From (18) it is clear that the attenuation coefficient k_i increases as ω increases from ω_m, so that the higher frequencies are more strongly attenuated. The situation is depicted graphically in Fig. 6.6, which plots k_r (full curve) and k_i (broken curve) as functions of ω.

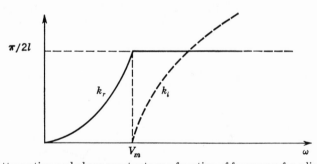

FIG. 6.6. Attenuation and phase constants as a function of frequency for a linear lattice.

From (7) or the equivalent (13) we can calculate the group velocity, using the analysis of Sec. 3.8. Thus

$$U = V_0 - \lambda_0 \left(\frac{dV}{d\lambda} \right)_0 = 2l \sqrt{\frac{f}{m}} \cos \frac{2\pi l}{\lambda_0} \tag{20}$$

where λ_0 is the mean wavelength of the group. The connection between this and the flow of energy along the lattice will now be examined. The average kinetic energy density is

$$\bar{w}_K = \frac{1}{2l} \frac{m}{2} \overline{\dot{\eta}_{jr}^2} \tag{21}$$

where to calculate $\dot{\eta}_j$ we use (11). We must take the real part. Hence we get at once

$$\bar{w}_K = \frac{m}{8l} \omega^2 A^2 \tag{22}$$

The average potential energy density is [from the equation of motion (10)]

$$\bar{w}_P = \frac{1}{2l} \frac{f}{2} \overline{(\eta_j - \eta_j - 1)_r^2} \tag{23}$$

Now $\quad (\eta_j - \eta_{j-1})_r = A[\cos (\omega t - kx_j) - \cos (\omega t - kx_{j-1})]$
$$= -2A \sin \tfrac{1}{2}[2\omega t - 2kl(2j - 1)] \sin kl$$

Therefore $\qquad\qquad \bar{w}_P = \dfrac{fA^2}{2l} \sin^2 kl \tag{24}$

If we substitute ω^2 from (12) into the expression for the kinetic energy density, it is at once clear that

$$\bar{w}_K = \bar{w}_P = \frac{fA^2}{2l} \sin^2 kl \tag{25}$$

Hence the total average energy density is

$$\bar{w} = \frac{fA^2}{l} \sin^2 kl \tag{26}$$

Next let us calculate the average rate of energy flow along the lattice. In accordance with our general discussion of energy propagation in waves in Sec. 1.10, we find the above quantity by averaging the product of $\dot{\eta}_j$ and the reaction force on the jth particle due to the $(j + 1)$st particle. This is the average power, denoted by $\bar{P}$. Thus

$$\bar{P} = \overline{f\dot{\eta}_j(\eta_j - \eta_{j+1})} \tag{27}$$

in which, of course, real parts of all quantities are understood. Substitution gives

$$\bar{P} = 2f\omega A^2 \overline{\sin (\omega t - kx_j) \sin (\omega t - kx_j + kl) \sin kl}$$
$$= 2A^2 \sqrt{\frac{f}{m}} \sin^2 kl \cos kl \tag{28}$$

The ratio of $\bar{P}$ to $\bar{w}$ has the dimensions of velocity and may be taken to represent physically the average velocity with which energy flows along the lattice due to the wave propagation. Thus

$$\frac{\bar{P}}{\bar{w}} = 2l \sqrt{\frac{f}{m}} \cos kl \tag{29}$$

Comparison with (20) shows that, if we take $k = 2\pi/\lambda_0$, this is precisely the group velocity U associated with the lattice behaving as a dispersive medium. This is physically a rather satisfying result. In Sec. 3.8 we learned that the group velocity in general is the velocity with which the superposition of a whole aggregate of wave trains of different frequencies, each proceeding with the phase velocity associated with its particular frequency, will travel through the dispersive medium. Any arbitrary disturbance in such a medium will be subject to a Fourier decomposition and hence may be expected to move with the group velocity and to carry the corresponding energy with it. One word of caution is necessary, however. From the definition of group velocity it is clear that it has a meaning only when k is real. When absorption is present and k is complex [Eq. (16)], the definition of U breaks down. Even in this case, however, the energy velocity still has a meaning and definite value.[1] It is significant that absorption is always associated with anomalous dispersion, that is, an "apparent" group velocity greater than the mean phase velocity.

6.7. Elastic and Electromagnetic Radiation

In this section we shall briefly compare elastic radiation of the kind with which we are mainly concerned in this book and electromagnetic wave propagation.

Elastic radiation occurs when a deformation is produced at some point in an elastic medium. Similarly, electromagnetic radiation is produced whenever there is a change in the electric and magnetic field intensities prevailing at any point in space. Thus an electric charge in accelerated motion will produce such field changes and lead to electromagnetic radiation, as, for example, from a radio antenna. The electric and magnetic field intensities $\mathbf{E}$ and $\mathbf{H}$, respectively, in space free of electric charges and currents satisfy the well-known field equations[2]

$$\nabla \cdot \kappa \mathbf{E} = 0 \qquad \nabla \cdot \mu \mathbf{H} = 0$$

$$\nabla \times \mathbf{H} = \frac{\kappa}{c} \dot{\mathbf{E}} \qquad \nabla \times \mathbf{E} = -\frac{\mu}{c} \dot{\mathbf{H}} \tag{1}$$

where κ is the dielectric constant of the medium and μ its permeability.[3] The quantity c is here at first merely the ratio of the size of the electromagnetic unit of electric charge to that of the electrostatic unit. The

---

[1] L. Brillouin, *Congr. intern. elec. Paris*, **2**, 739 (1932).

[2] W. V. Houston, "Principles of Mathematical Physics," 2d ed., p. 324, McGraw-Hill Book Company, Inc., New York, 1948.

[3] This will be distinguished without difficulty from the shear modulus μ introduced in Sec. 6.2.

reader who is familiar with electromagnetism will recall that the two upper equations are the consequence of Coulomb's law of inverse squares for the force interaction of electric charges and magnetic poles, respectively. The equation at the lower left comes from Ampère's law for the magnetic field associated with an electric current (in this case the displacement current of Maxwell, proportional to $\dot{\mathbf{E}}$, the only kind of electric current one can have in matter devoid of actual moving charges). The equation at the lower right is the differential form of Faraday's law of electromagnetic induction, that is, the production of electromotive force by a changing magnetic field.

If we assume that κ and μ are constant in the region considered and operate on $\nabla \times \mathbf{H}$ with the $\nabla \times$ operation, we have

$$\nabla \times \nabla \times \mathbf{H} = \frac{\kappa}{c} \nabla \times \dot{\mathbf{E}} = \frac{-\kappa\mu}{c^2} \ddot{\mathbf{H}} \tag{2}$$

Now from the vector identity for $\nabla \times \nabla \times$ we ultimately get from (2)

$$\nabla^2 \mathbf{H} = \frac{\kappa\mu}{c^2} \ddot{\mathbf{H}} \tag{3}$$

which implies that the vector $\mathbf{H}$ (i.e., each component of it) is propagated through the medium as a wave with the velocity

$$V = \frac{c}{\sqrt{\kappa\mu}} \tag{4}$$

Examination of the lower right-hand equation in (1) discloses that $\mathbf{E}$ is also propagated with this velocity. These are electromagnetic waves. Since $\mathbf{E}$ and $\mathbf{H}$ have zero divergence, the waves are solenoidal (see Sec. 6.3), in distinction to elastic waves, which appear in both irrotational and solenoidal forms. They travel without dissipation and with no dependence of velocity on frequency. Actual waves, like light and radio, give evidence of both attenuation and dispersion. Hence the simple theory reviewed here is inadequate, just as the simple theory of elastic radiation presented in the first part of this chapter also fails to meet the corresponding experimental requirements.

It turns out that, when the equations (1) are rewritten in a form appropriate to a *conducting* medium in which actual electric currents can flow, the corresponding harmonic electromagnetic waves are attenuated exponentially with an absorption coefficient proportional to the square root of the frequency as well as the square root of the electrical conductivity. This is reminiscent of the effect of viscosity and heat conduction on the transmission of elastic waves in fluids, though the mechanisms involved are of course different. The electromagnetic wave attenuation produced by the conductivity of the medium is also accompanied by dispersion (as in the elastic case), and the predicted values are experimentally verified for very long wavelengths or low frequencies. However, the agreement breaks down completely for high frequencies. Under these conditions it is impossible to account for the observed behavior of electromagnetic radiation by treating the medium as continuous; one must introduce the discrete nature of the medium as made up of atoms and free electrons which can scatter the radiation by absorbing energy from it and then reradiating it in all directions. The problem then becomes one in the quantum mechanics of the interaction of radiation and the constituent particles of matter. In particular, when the frequency of the radiation is equal to one of the resonance frequencies of an atom, absorption and dispersion become very pronounced.[1] We shall see in Sec. 12.1 that a rather similar situation prevails in elastic radiation in fluids. The transport properties of viscosity and heat conduction are, of course, due to the relative motion of the molecules on the kinetic theory, and thus the absorption of compressional elastic waves is a molecular phenomenon. It turns out, indeed, that in most fluids viscous and thermal-conduction absorption is not adequate to account for the observed attenuation. To handle this difficulty, recourse is had to the transfer of the translational kinetic energy of the molecules, as increased by the elastic wave, into internal states of rotation and vibration of the constituent molecules. The energy is ultimately fed back into the translational form, but only with a time lag which leads to some of it going into the purely random form we recognize as heat and therefore being lost to the wave. The situation is reminiscent of that in the electromagnetic case, though here it is not *resonance* which is involved, since the frequencies of the elastic waves are by no means high enough to correspond to the resonance frequencies of atoms and molecules. Rather, the phenomenon is one of so-called "relaxation," involving the average time taken by a molecule, after having absorbed some energy, to reemit it. Relatively large absorption takes place when this time (the *relaxation time*) is of the order of the period of the harmonic wave. The details of this process are presented in Sec. 12.1.

Another important analogy between electromagnetic and elastic radiation emerges as soon as we examine analytically the propagation of energy. Reverting to the field equations (1), we can write at once by scalar multiplication

$$\mathbf{H} \cdot (\nabla \times \mathbf{E}) = -\frac{\mu}{c} \mathbf{H} \cdot \dot{\mathbf{H}}$$

$$\mathbf{E} \cdot (\nabla \times \mathbf{H}) = \frac{\kappa}{c} \mathbf{E} \cdot \dot{\mathbf{E}}$$

(5)

[1] J. A. Stratton, "Electromagnetic Theory," pp. 321ff., McGraw-Hill Book Company, Inc., New York, 1941.

If we subtract the second of these equations from the first and employ a standard vector identity, the result is

$$\nabla \cdot (\mathbf{E} \times \mathbf{H}) = -\frac{1}{c} (\mu \mathbf{H} \cdot \dot{\mathbf{H}} + \kappa \mathbf{E} \cdot \dot{\mathbf{E}})$$

or
$$c\nabla \cdot (\mathbf{E} \times \mathbf{H}) = -\frac{\partial}{\partial t} \left[\frac{1}{2} (\mu H^2 + \kappa E^2) \right] \tag{6}$$

Integrating over a finite volume of space and employing the divergence theorem yields

$$c \int (\mathbf{E} \times \mathbf{H}) \cdot \mathbf{n} \, dS + \frac{\partial}{\partial t} \int \left[\frac{1}{2} (\mu H^2 + \kappa E^2) \right] d\tau = 0 \tag{7}$$

where the surface integral is taken over the surface bounding the given volume (dS is the surface element and $d\tau$ the volume element). It can be shown[1] that

$$\int \frac{1}{8\pi} (\mu H^2 + \kappa E^2) \, d\tau$$

is the total energy in the electromagnetic field. Equation (7) then can be interpreted as expressing the conservation of energy in the field. The time rate of change of the total energy in the field is equal to the negative of the expression

$$\frac{c}{4\pi} \int (\mathbf{E} \times \mathbf{H}) \cdot \mathbf{n} \, dS \tag{8}$$

which then must mean physically the rate at which energy flows across the boundary of the volume in question. This is the content of what is usually referred to as Poynting's theorem, and (8) is called the Poynting flux.

We note the analogy between the Poynting theorem and the equation for elastic radiation (6.4-9). The fact that electromagnetic waves are vector waves, whereas elastic radiation is scalar, does not destroy the essential physical significance of this analogy.

In view of the similarities between elastic and electromagnetic radiation just mentioned, it is not surprising that attempts have been made to view electromagnetic waves as having their origin in stresses and strains in some peculiar elastic medium. Maxwell succeeded in developing such a point of view[2] as part of a program for providing electromagnetism with a mechanical basis. Although such viewpoints are now considered out of date and of dubious practical worth, they are nevertheless important from the standpoint of the methodology of physics. As an illustration,

---

[1] Houston, "Principles of Mathematical Physics," pp. 278ff., 328ff.

[2] J. C. Maxwell, "Treatise on Electricity and Magnetism," 3d ed., vol. 2, Oxford University Press, London, 1904.

we shall consider the analogy between the velocity potential of a fluid as a propagated quantity, when its value at any point in the fluid is disturbed, and a certain electromagnetic quantity. We have already commented on the velocity potential φ in Sec. 6.3 as the quantity such that $\nabla\varphi$ equals the particle velocity in the fluid. There we found that in an ideal fluid the velocity potential φ is propagated as a wave in accordance with the wave equation

$$\nabla^2\varphi = \frac{\ddot{\varphi}}{V^2} \qquad (9)$$

It is of interest to note that the derivation of this equation can be looked at from a somewhat different formal point of view than that adopted in Sec. 6.3. The equation of motion of the fluid (shear modulus $\mu = 0$), from (6.3-8), becomes

$$\rho\ddot{\mathbf{\Delta}} = B\nabla\nabla \cdot \mathbf{\Delta} \qquad (10)$$

If we employ (6.3-23) and recall that $\ddot{\mathbf{\Delta}} = -\nabla\dot{\varphi}$, we can rewrite this as (with $B = \rho V^2$)

$$\nabla\dot{\varphi} = -V^2\nabla s \qquad (11)$$

or, integrating both sides by the method discussed in Sec. 6.3,

$$\dot{\varphi} = -V^2 s \qquad (12)$$

At the same time the equation of continuity (6.3-24) becomes

$$\dot{s} = -\nabla^2\varphi \qquad (13)$$

The elimination of s between (12) and (13) yields the wave equation (9) at once. The combination of the equation of motion for small disturbances from equilibrium with the equation of continuity to produce the wave equation is characteristic for elastic media. It is interesting to observe that we can put the deduction of the electromagnetic wave equation into this same form.

We first introduce the vector potential $\mathbf{A}$ defined so that

$$\mu\mathbf{H} = \nabla \times \mathbf{A} \qquad (14)$$

where μ is here once more the magnetic permeability. We also introduce the scalar potential ψ defined so that

$$-\nabla\psi = \mathbf{E} + \frac{\dot{\mathbf{A}}}{c} \qquad (15)$$

The existence of ψ is guaranteed by the fact that $\mathbf{E} + \dot{\mathbf{A}}/c$ is an irrotational vector [from the lower right-hand equation in (1)]. Since ψ and $\mathbf{A}$ are not uniquely defined by (14) and (15), H. A. Lorentz, for purposes of simplicity, fixed them further by the arbitrary assumption

$$\nabla \cdot \mathbf{A} + \frac{\mu \kappa \dot{\psi}}{c} = 0 \tag{16}$$

Now, from the lower left-hand equation in (1)

$$\nabla \times \nabla \times \mathbf{A} = -\nabla^2 \mathbf{A} + \nabla(\nabla \cdot \mathbf{A}) = \frac{\mu \kappa \dot{\mathbf{E}}}{c} \tag{17}$$

and by the use of (16) this yields

$$\nabla^2 \mathbf{A} = -\frac{\partial}{\partial t} \frac{\mu \kappa}{c} (\mathbf{E} + \nabla \psi) \tag{18}$$

and (15) becomes

$$\dot{\mathbf{A}} = -\frac{c^2}{\mu \kappa} \frac{\mu \kappa}{c} (\mathbf{E} + \nabla \psi) \tag{19}$$

Elimination of the quantity $(\mu\kappa/c)(\mathbf{E} + \nabla\psi)$ between (18) and (19) leads at once to the wave equation for $\mathbf{A}$:

$$\nabla^2 \mathbf{A} = \frac{\mu \kappa}{c^2} \ddot{\mathbf{A}} \tag{20}$$

The mathematical analogy between (13) and (18) on the one hand and between (12) and (19) on the other is striking. It suggests that we might consider the quantity $(\mu\kappa/c)(\mathbf{E} + \nabla\psi)$ as a kind of condensation in the electromagnetic field, whereas $\mathbf{A}$ appears as the analogue of the velocity potential in fluid flow.

Rather more interesting physically are cases in which elastic radiation and an electromagnetic field are present in the same medium. Effects of this kind are discussed in Chaps. 8 and 12.

CHAPTER 7

WAVES IN RODS AND PLATES

7.1. Longitudinal Waves in a Solid Rod.   Configurational Dispersion

For the purposes of the following discussion a rod will be assumed to be a rectangular parallelepiped or right cylinder whose length is much greater than any transverse dimension.   Any small elastic strain in the length direction whose magnitude and phase are uniform over the cross section will be propagated as a longitudinal elastic wave along the rod. We have already worked out the simple theory in Sec. 1.7 and found that the longitudinal wave velocity is

$$V_l = \sqrt{\frac{Y}{\rho}} \tag{1}$$

where Y is Young's modulus and ρ the density of the solid.

The idealized theory leading to the above result neglects entirely the lateral strain associated with the longitudinal strain.   For harmonic waves of low frequency this neglect is justified, but when the frequency increases to a value such that the corresponding wavelength is of the order of magnitude of the lateral dimensions, we may expect the lateral effects to play an increasingly great role in the longitudinal velocity.   In fact this has been experimentally shown: as the frequency increases, the longitudinal velocity has been found to decrease steadily from the value (1) and ultimately to approach a value close to the shear wave velocity [see (6.3-27)].   This type of dispersion has been called *configurational*, to distinguish it from the dispersion associated with the internal structure of the solid.   It is, of course, the kind of dispersion observed in the transmission of electromagnetic waves through waveguides as well as in the propagation of water waves in channels (Sec. 8.2).   The importance of configurational dispersion in rods is obvious when one considers that measurement of elastic wave velocity is often used as a basis for the calculation of elastic constants.

The study of elastic waves in a solid rod is a special case of wave propagation in a homogeneous, isotropic elastic medium.   The fundamental equation for this is (6.3-5), and we repeat it here for convenience:

$$\rho\ddot{\mathbf{\Delta}} = \left(B + \frac{\mu}{3} \right) \nabla\Theta + \mu\nabla \cdot \nabla\mathbf{\Delta} \tag{2}$$

where $\mathbf{\Delta}$ is the displacement vector, and the other quantities are precisely as in Sec. 6.3. There we showed that there are two principal types of waves which can satisfy (2), namely, the irrotational variety for which $\nabla \times \mathbf{\Delta} = 0$ and which are propagated with the velocity

$$V_i = \sqrt{\frac{B + 4\mu/3}{\rho}} \tag{3}$$

and the solenoidal type for which $\nabla \cdot \mathbf{\Delta} = 0$ with propagation velocity

$$V_s = \sqrt{\frac{\mu}{\rho}} \tag{4}$$

It is interesting to observe that if we introduce a displacement potential φ, the vector displacement

$$\mathbf{\Delta} = \nabla\varphi + \mathbf{\Delta}' \tag{5}$$

satisfies Eq. (2), provided that φ and $\mathbf{\Delta}'$ satisfy the equations

$$\begin{aligned} \ddot{\varphi} &= V_i^2 \nabla^2 \varphi \\ \ddot{\mathbf{\Delta}}' &= V_s^2 \nabla^2 \mathbf{\Delta}' \end{aligned} \tag{6}$$

and if, in addition, $\mathbf{\Delta}'$ is solenoidal. In other words both irrotational and solenoidal types of waves are involved in the general solution (5).

Following R. W. Morse,[1] we apply (5) and (6) to the case of a long, thin rod of rectangular cross section oriented along the z axis of a system of rectangular coordinates. The boundaries of the cross section are $x = \pm a$, $y = \pm b$. It is assumed that φ and the components of $\mathbf{\Delta}'$ are propagated in the z direction as harmonic waves with phase dependence of the form

$$e^{i(\omega t - kz)}$$

and with coefficients depending only on x and y. Then

$$\nabla^2 \varphi = \frac{\partial^2 \varphi}{\partial x^2} + \frac{\partial^2 \varphi}{\partial y^2} - k^2 \varphi$$

$$\ddot{\varphi} = -\omega^2 \varphi$$

Hence the first equation in (6) becomes

$$\left(\frac{\partial^2}{\partial x^2} + \frac{\partial^2}{\partial y^2} + \gamma_1^2 \right) \varphi = 0 \tag{7}$$

and the second

$$\left(\frac{\partial^2}{\partial x^2} + \frac{\partial^2}{\partial y^2} + \gamma_2^2 \right) \mathbf{\Delta}' = 0 \tag{8}$$

[1] R. W. Morse, *J. Acoust. Soc. Am.*, **22**, 219 (1950).

where
$$\gamma_1{}^2 = k^2 \left[\left(\frac{V}{V_i} \right)^2 - 1 \right] \tag{9}$$

$$\gamma_2{}^2 = k^2 \left[\left(\frac{V}{V_s} \right)^2 - 1 \right] \tag{10}$$

Here, of course, V = the actual phase velocity = ω/k.

By separation of variables we see that the solutions of (7) correspond to linear combinations of products of the form $\sin \alpha_1 x \sin \beta_1 y$, $\sin \alpha_1 x \cos \beta_1 y$, etc., where

$$\alpha_1{}^2 + \beta_1{}^2 = \gamma_1{}^2 \tag{11}$$

Similarly, Δ_x', Δ_y', Δ_z' (or ξ', η', ζ' in the notation of Sec. 6.1) can likewise satisfy (8) if they are each made up of linear combinations of the form $\sin \alpha_2 x \sin \beta_2 y$, $\sin \alpha_2 x \cos \beta_2 y$, etc., where

$$\alpha_2{}^2 + \beta_2{}^2 = \gamma_2{}^2 \tag{12}$$

We then get the solutions for Δ by using (5). But these must satisfy certain boundary conditions, which really contain the crux of the problem. If we assume that the rod may move freely everywhere (i.e., is not clamped anywhere), the normal components of stress over all the bounding surfaces must vanish at all times. Since there are three stress conditions for each pair of lateral surfaces, six simultaneous equations are involved. We may abbreviate these in terms of the stress components as

$$\left.\begin{matrix} X_{xx} \\ X_{yx} \\ X_{zx} \end{matrix}\right\} = 0 \text{ for } x = \pm a \qquad \left.\begin{matrix} X_{xy} \\ X_{yy} \\ X_{zy} \end{matrix}\right\} = 0 \text{ for } y = \pm b \tag{13}$$

To write these conditions we need to use (6.2-5, 7), expressing the stress components in terms of the strains, which, of course, involve derivatives of the displacement components with respect to x, y, z. To satisfy the conditions in simplest fashion, it is necessary to have the stress components factor into products of functions of x and y separately. We can do this by choosing either $\alpha_1 = \alpha_2$ or $\beta_1 = \beta_2$, but we shall proceed by keeping α_1 and α_2 independent and making $\beta_1 = \beta_2 = \beta$. This means that we shall concentrate attention only on the conditions at $x = \pm a$ and leave the other conditions out of consideration at the moment. This leads to displacement components of the form

$$\xi = (A \sin \alpha_1 x + B \sin \alpha_2 x) \cos \beta y$$
$$\eta = \left(\frac{\beta}{\alpha_1} A \cos \alpha_1 x + C \cos \alpha_2 x \right) \sin \beta y \tag{14}$$
$$\zeta = i \left[-\frac{k}{\alpha_1} A \cos \alpha_1 x + \frac{1}{k} (\alpha_2 B + \beta C) \cos \alpha_2 x \right] \cos \beta y$$

where the amplitude factors A, B, C are at first arbitrary. Use of (6.2-5, 7) for $x = \pm a$ leads to a set of homogeneous, simultaneous equations in A, B, C. The condition that these possess a nontrivial solution is the vanishing of the secular determinant, that is,

$$\begin{vmatrix} 2\beta \sin \alpha_1 a & \beta \sin \alpha_2 a & \alpha_2 \sin \alpha_2 a \\ -(k^2 + \beta^2 - \alpha_2^2) \cos \alpha_1 a & 2\alpha_1\alpha_2 \cos \alpha_2 a & 0 \\ 2(k^2 + \beta^2) \sin \alpha_1 a & (k^2 + \beta^2 - \alpha_2^2) \sin \alpha_2 a & 0 \end{vmatrix} = 0$$

(15)

For $\alpha_2 \neq 0$, this reduces to

$$\frac{\tan \alpha_2 a}{\tan \alpha_1 a} = -\frac{4\alpha_1\alpha_2(k^2 + \beta^2)}{(k^2 + \beta^2 - \alpha_2^2)^2}$$

(16)

For given β, this equation yields a relation between frequency and phase velocity; it is therefore a dispersion equation.

Continuing to follow Morse, we let $s = 2a/\lambda$ in order to emphasize the importance of the relation between the wavelength λ and the transverse dimensions of the rod. We further introduce the quantities P and Q, where

$$P = \frac{sV}{V_s}$$

$$Q = \sqrt{s^2 + \frac{a^2\beta^2}{\pi^2}}$$

(17)

Equation (16) then takes the form

$$\frac{\tan \pi \sqrt{P^2 - Q^2}}{\tan \pi \sqrt{\epsilon P^2 - Q^2}} = -\frac{4P^2 \sqrt{(P^2 - Q^2)(\epsilon P^2 - Q^2)}}{(2P^2 - Q^2)^2}$$

(18)

where $\epsilon = (V_s/V_i)^2 = (1 - 2\sigma)/2(1 - \sigma)$, σ being Poisson's ratio (see Sec. 6.2). Equation (18) can be solved as a transcendental equation for P/Q as a function of ϵ or σ. It is simplest to confine attention to principal-value solutions corresponding to the lowest mode. The general character of the solution is best seen by examining the special cases where, on the one hand, P and Q are very small and, on the other hand, P and Q are very large. It turns out that in both cases Q is a linear function of P for given σ. An actual solution of (18) for $\sigma = 0.3$ is given in Fig. 7.1.

All this is for given β, which can be determined only from the boundary conditions at $y = \pm b$. It is obviously impossible to satisfy the three stress conditions there by the adjustment of a single constant, but it is found that the two shear stresses X_{xy} and X_{zy} become negligibly small if the rod is sufficiently wide. We therefore feel safe in choosing β so that the dilatational stress X_{yy} vanishes for $y = \pm b$ as long as b is large enough (still small, of course, relative to the length of the rod). This

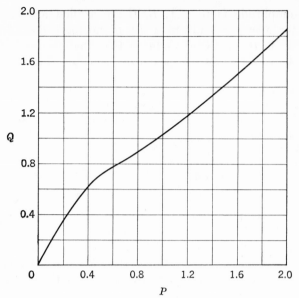

FIG. 7.1. Q as a function of P for a solid rod with Poisson's ratio 0.3.   [*Reprinted with permission from R. W. Morse, J. Acoust. Soc. Am.*, **22**, 219 (1950), *with certain changes.*]

condition on X_{yy} will be met [see the η expression in (14)] by

$$\beta b = (n + \tfrac{1}{2})\pi \qquad n = 0, 1, 2, 3, \ldots \qquad (19)$$

The fundamental corresponds to $n = 0$ with no nodal surfaces parallel to the length of the rod.   Our attention in this discussion is confined to this case.

The physical quantity of greatest interest is V/V_s, and we can readily express this in terms of s by means of (17), in which Q now becomes, from (19),

$$Q = \sqrt{\left(\frac{2a}{\lambda}\right)^2 + \left(\frac{a}{2b}\right)^2} \qquad (20)$$

The frequency is

$$\nu = \frac{V_s}{2a} P \qquad (21)$$

and

$$\frac{2a}{\lambda} = \sqrt{Q^2 - \left(\frac{a}{2b}\right)^2} \qquad (22)$$

Now, when $Q = a/2b$, λ becomes infinite, and hence the phase velocity becomes infinite for the frequency given [in (21)] by the value of P which corresponds to this value of Q.   This is the "cutoff" frequency, and no propagation takes place for lower frequencies, since for them λ

in (22) becomes imaginary.[1] The waveguide analogy is evident. Moreover, the significance of the lateral resonance for the configurational dispersion, already pointed out at the beginning of this section, now becomes clear. If, for example, we let $b \gg a$, $2a/\lambda \doteq Q = a/2b$, and the cutoff wavelength is $\lambda = 4b$, or the half wavelength equals the width of the rod. The calculated cutoff and those measured experimentally in special cases are in good agreement.[2]

Figure 7.2 is a plot of V/V_s as a function of $2a/\lambda$ as computed from the theory presented above for a rod in which $a/b = 0.5$, $\sigma = 0.30$, and $V_s = 2,160$ m/sec. The circles are experimental points. The agreement is rather good at the shorter wavelengths. The approach to a cutoff frequency is also well shown, and the approach of V to V_s is indicated.

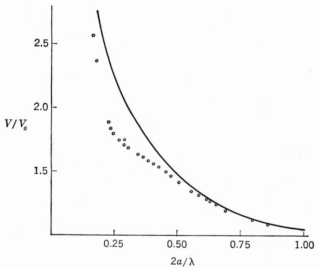

FIG. 7.2. Comparison of theoretical and experimental dependence of V/V_s on $2a/\lambda$ for a solid rod, with $a/b = 0.5$, $\sigma = 0.30$, and $V_s = 2,160$ m/sec. [*Reprinted with permission from R. W. Morse, J. Acoust. Soc. Am.*, **22**, 219 (1950), *with certain changes.*]

In addition to the "thickness" mode discussed above, we expect the appearance of another mode associated with the width dimension. The analysis for this follows similar lines, but we choose $\alpha_1 = \alpha_2 = \alpha$ and allow the β's to be independent of each other. The roles of x and y are now interchanged in the displacement functions, which are similar to those in (14) except that the x dependence is hyperbolic, that is, of form $\sinh \alpha x$, etc. It is readily verified that a solution of this form is

---

[1] It should be noted that if dissipative attenuation were included in this treatment, damped propagation would be possible below the cutoff frequency.

[2] R. W. Morse, *J. Acoust. Soc. Am.*, **22**, 219 (1950).

possible. We can of course write sinh αx in the form of a sine if α is pure imaginary. We now satisfy the boundary conditions (13) at $y = \pm b$ and obtain a dispersion equation identical in form with (18). If we denote quantities associated with this mode with primes, we have

$$\frac{V'}{V_s} = \frac{P'}{s'}$$

$$s' = \sqrt{Q'^2 - \left(\frac{\alpha b}{\pi}\right)^2}$$

(23)

α is to be determined by the conditions at $x = \pm a$. Since α has been assumed to be pure imaginary, there is no cutoff for this mode. No choice of α can satisfy all the stress conditions completely, but $\alpha = 0$ seems to be plausible for $b \gg a$. Figure 7.3 is a plot of V/V_s as a function of $2b/\lambda$ for this mode where $\sigma = 0.3$ and $V_s = 2,160$ m/sec. The circles correspond to measured values for an appropriate specimen.

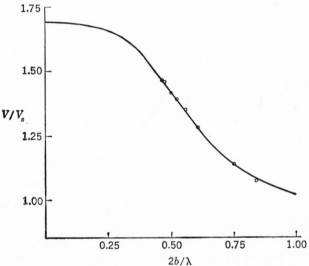

FIG. 7.3. Comparison of theoretical and experimental dependence of V/V_s on $2b/\lambda$ for a solid rod, with $\sigma = 0.30$ and $V_s = 2,160$ m/sec. [Reprinted with permission from R. W. Morse, J. Acoust. Soc. Am., **22**, 219 (1950), with certain changes.]

In general, the experimental study of configurational dispersion is carried out by exciting the rod with a vibrating quartz crystal coupled to it by a liquid medium. Lycopodium powder sprinkled on the vibrating rod tends to gather at the nodes of the longitudinal standing waves and hence provides a wavelength determination. This, together with the known frequency of excitation, makes possible the evaluation[1] of V.

[1] For another plan see A. E. Bakanowski and R. B. Lindsay, J. Acoust. Soc. Am., **22**, 14 (1950).

As might be expected, configurational dispersion of longitudinal waves has been observed in *cylindrical* rods of *circular* cross section, and the theory follows the same lines as for the case already described. Much study has been devoted to circular rods.[1]

We recall from Sec. 3.8 that, whenever dispersion exists, a wave pulse travels with the so-called group velocity

$$U = V_0 - \lambda \left(\frac{dV}{d\lambda}\right)_0 \tag{24}$$

where V_0 is the phase velocity for the mean wavelength of the pulse. Since V for a rectangular rod is expressed in terms of λ through the transcendental equation (18), it is impracticable to express U in this problem by an explicit formula. However, it can be computed in any particular case by differentiation of the curves in Figs. 7.2 and 7.3. From Fig. 7.3 we can readily see, for example, that for long wavelengths (that is, $2b/\lambda \ll 1$), since the change of V/V_s with $1/\lambda$ is small, U is nearly equal to V. As V/V_s decreases with $1/\lambda$, so does U, which, in fact, reaches a minimum when the slope of the V/V_s curve reaches a maximum. When V/V_s levels off again, U again approaches V. Curves giving U as a function of λ are shown in Kolsky's book, cited above. These considerations are important in pulse transmission along rods, since if the sound velocity is measured by direct counting of pulses and distance traveled, it is the group velocity which results, unless the wavefront of the pulse is very narrow compared with the lateral dimensions of the rod. The considerations of this section imply, of course, that the sound wavefront extends over the whole cross section of the rod.

7.2. Flexural Waves in a Rod

If a symmetrical solid rod originally in equilibrium in the horizontal direction is deformed so that any part of its axis of symmetry ceases to be horizontal, it is said to have suffered flexure. Our problem in this section is to see how such flexural disturbances are propagated along the rod. Figure 7.4 shows an element of the rod of length dx. Its area

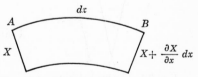

FIG. 7.4. Element of a solid rod in flexure.

of cross section is taken to be S. When deformed by flexure, the shearing stress at A is X, whereas at $B(x + dx)$ it is $X + (\partial X/\partial x)\, dx$. Associ-

[1] D. Bancroft, *Phys. Rev.*, **59**, 588 (1941); and G. E. Hudson, *Phys. Rev.*, **63**, 96 (1943). A good survey of the whole field is found in H. Kolsky, "Stress Waves in Solids," Oxford University Press, London, 1953.

ated with the shearing stress is the bending moment, or torque, L at A and $L + (\partial L/\partial x)\, dx$ at B. The mass of the element is $\rho S\, dx$, and its vertical acceleration (the only one it is assumed to have in flexure) is $\ddot{\eta}$ if η is the displacement normal to the x axis. Since the area of cross section is supposed to remain constant during flexure, the equation of motion of the element is

$$\rho\ddot{\eta} = \frac{\partial X}{\partial x} \tag{1}$$

To work with this equation we must express X in terms of the bending moment, which, in turn, must be expressed in terms of the change in η. If we were to neglect the rotation of the element during the bending, we should have, simply by taking static moments about the z axis (assumed to pass through the center of the element),

$$SX = -\frac{\partial L}{\partial x} \tag{2}$$

However, $(SX + \partial L/\partial x)\, dx$ is really the total unbalanced torque tending to produce rotation of the element about the z axis. Hence it must equal the moment of inertia I about this axis multiplied by the angular acceleration $\ddot{\theta}$. Thus

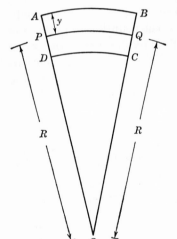

$$I\ddot{\theta} = \left(SX + \frac{\partial L}{\partial x}\right) dx \tag{3}$$

But $$\theta = \frac{\partial \eta}{\partial x} \tag{4}$$

and $$I = \rho S\, dx\, K^2 \tag{5}$$

where K is the radius of gyration about the z axis. Then we can rewrite (3) as

$$\rho K^2 \frac{\partial \ddot{\eta}}{\partial x} = X + \frac{1}{S}\frac{\partial L}{\partial x} \tag{6}$$

Using (1) with this gives

$$\ddot{\eta} - K^2 \frac{\partial^2 \ddot{\eta}}{\partial x^2} + \frac{1}{\rho S}\frac{\partial^2 L}{\partial x^2} = 0 \tag{7}$$

Fig. 7.5. Flexural strain.

To use this equation it is necessary to express L in terms of the dependence of η on x. In Fig. 7.5 let $ABCD$ represent an element of the rod in the plane of flexure and let PQ be the central axis with $R = OP = OQ$ the radius of the circle into which we may assume the central axis to be bent as a first approximation. The linear strain in the top layer of the rod is then y/R, if y is the distance PA. The corresponding tensile stress is (if Y is Young's modulus)

$$\frac{Yy}{R}$$

and the total force moment about the z axis, which is normal to the plane of flexure (i.e., the plane of the figure), becomes

$$L = \int \frac{Yy^2 \, dy \, dz}{R} = \frac{YSK^2}{R}$$

The curvature of the distorted central axis is

$$C = \frac{\partial^2\eta/\partial x^2}{[1 + (\partial\eta/\partial x)^2]^{\frac{3}{2}}}$$

and if $|\partial\eta/\partial x| \ll 1$, the radius of curvature becomes approximately

$$R = 1 \bigg/ \frac{\partial^2\eta}{\partial x^2}$$

Hence, to a good approximation we may write

$$L = YSK^2 \frac{\partial^2\eta}{\partial x^2} \tag{8}$$

The final equation for η as a function of x and t becomes

$$\ddot{\eta} - K^2 \frac{\partial^2\ddot{\eta}}{\partial x^2} + V_l^2 K^2 \frac{\partial^4\eta}{\partial x^4} = 0 \tag{9}$$

where V_l is the longitudinal wave velocity in a long rod [or for frequencies at which the wavelength is much longer than the lateral dimensions (see Sec. 7.1)]. For a rod of circular cross section, $K^2 = a^2/4$, where a is the radius, whereas for a rectangular rod, $K^2 = h^2/12$, if h is the thickness in the plane of vibration. We see that, if the curvature is very small, the middle term in (9) originating from the rotational inertia can be neglected and the approximate equation for flexural elastic disturbances is

$$\ddot{\eta} + V_l^2 K^2 \frac{\partial^4\eta}{\partial x^4} = 0 \tag{10}$$

This is not in the form of the ideal wave equation for waves in the x direction [Eq. (1.7-7)]. It does not have the general solution $\eta = f(x - ct)$. Hence an arbitrary flexural disturbance in the rod will not be transmitted without change in shape. Nevertheless we know from experience that something is transmitted. We therefore look for the condition under which a harmonic wave can satisfy (10). Substituting $\eta = \eta_0 e^{i(\omega t - kx)}$ into (10) indicates that this indeed is a solution, provided that the phase velocity V (which is ω/k) has the value

$$V = \sqrt{V_l K \omega} \tag{11}$$

or, in terms of the wavelength $\lambda = 2\pi/k$,

$$V = \frac{2\pi K V_l}{\lambda} \tag{12}$$

The dependence of phase velocity on the frequency indicates dispersion. The group velocity U then differs from the phase velocity, and, indeed, application of (3.8-11) shows at once that

$$U = 2V_0 \tag{13}$$

where as usual V_0 is the phase velocity for the mean frequency in the group. The inverse dependence of phase velocity on the wavelength is not physically reasonable, since it makes the velocity go to infinity as the wavelength goes to zero (or the frequency goes to infinity). This serves to emphasize the approximate character of (10). It not only neglects the rotational inertia implied in the term $K^2(\partial^2 \ddot{\eta}/\partial x^2)$ but, more importantly, says nothing about what happens when the wavelength becomes of the same order of magnitude as the lateral dimensions of the rod. As in the case of compressional waves discussed in Sec. 7.1, we expect that flexural waves in a rod will exhibit configurational dispersion. Hence it is reasonable to suppose that (12) applies only for wavelengths long compared with the lateral dimensions.

Actually it is possible to satisfy (9) with a harmonic wave of the form $\eta_0 e^{i(\omega t - kx)}$. This works if

$$V = \frac{V_l}{\sqrt{1 + \lambda^2/4\pi^2 K^2}} \tag{14}$$

which, for $\lambda \gg 2\pi K$, reduces to (12). On the other hand, for $\lambda \to 0$, $V \to V_l$. This gets around the infinity difficulty to which (12) is subject but, of course, takes no account of configurational dispersion.

The harmonic solution we have just considered is a special one, and to consider the behavior of a finite rod in which standing waves are to be expected, we naturally need the general one. If we still impose the condition of harmonicity in time with angular frequency ω, the dependence of η and x follows the fourth-order ordinary differential equation (including the rotational-inertia term)

$$\frac{d^4\eta}{dx^4} + \frac{\omega^2}{V_l^2}\frac{d^2\eta}{dx^2} - \frac{\omega^2\eta^2}{V_l^2 K^2} = 0 \tag{15}$$

The general solution thus demands four arbitrary constants and clearly can be written in the form

$$\eta = Ae^{-ikx} + Be^{ikx} + Ce^{-\alpha x} + De^{\alpha x} \tag{16}$$

where k and α are real. Substituting into (15) yields

$$k = \left(\sqrt{\frac{\omega^4}{4V_l^4} + \frac{\omega^2}{V_l^2 K^2}} + \frac{\omega^2}{2V_l^2}\right)^{\frac{1}{2}}$$
$$\alpha = \left(\sqrt{\frac{\omega^4}{4V_l^4} + \frac{\omega^2}{V_l^2 K^2}} - \frac{\omega^2}{2V_l^2}\right)^{\frac{1}{2}} \tag{17}$$

For very small K, $k \doteq \alpha$, and rotational inertia may be neglected.

We can now examine the behavior of the rod when subject to given boundary conditions. This enables the arbitrary constants in (16) to be evaluated. Let us take for example a rod of length l clamped at one end ($x = 0$) and free to vibrate in flexure at the other. This is the case of a vibrating reed. The conditions are

$$\eta = \frac{\partial \eta}{\partial x} = 0 \qquad \text{at } x = 0$$
$$L = YSK^2 \frac{\partial^2 \eta}{\partial x^2} = 0 \qquad \text{at } x = l \tag{18}$$

The first condition says that the rod has no motion at the end $x = 0$ and that its slope is also zero there. The condition at $x = l$ says that there is no torque there. These lead to three equations sufficient to evaluate three of the constants in (16). Thus we get for C and D in terms of A and B

$$C = -\frac{A}{2}\left(\frac{ik}{\alpha} + 1\right) + \frac{B}{2}\left(\frac{ik}{\alpha} - 1\right)$$
$$D = \frac{A}{2}\left(\frac{ik}{\alpha} - 1\right) - \frac{B}{2}\left(\frac{ik}{\alpha} + 1\right) \tag{19}$$

Now, differentiating (16) twice yields

$$\frac{\partial^2 \eta}{\partial x^2} = -k^2(Ae^{-ikx} + Be^{ikx}) + \alpha^2(Ce^{-\alpha x} + De^{\alpha x})$$

Putting this equal to zero, for $x = l$,

$$Ce^{-\alpha l} + De^{\alpha l} = \frac{k^2}{\alpha^2}(Ae^{-ikl} + Be^{ikl})$$

and introducing C and D from (19), we finally eliminate them and get

$$B = A\frac{(ik/\alpha - 1)e^{\alpha l} - (ik/\alpha + 1)e^{-\alpha l} - (2k^2/\alpha^2)e^{-ikl}}{(ik/\alpha + 1)e^{\alpha l} - (ik/\alpha - 1)e^{-\alpha l} + (2k^2/\alpha^2)e^{ikl}} \tag{20}$$

There is one more condition, namely, the vanishing of the shearing force

SX at $x = l$. This means [from (6)]

$$\rho \frac{\partial \ddot{\eta}}{\partial x} - Y \frac{\partial^3 \eta}{\partial x^3} = 0 \tag{21}$$

at $x = l$. Since

$$\rho \frac{\partial \ddot{\eta}}{\partial x} = -\omega^2 \rho \frac{\partial \eta}{\partial x} = ik\omega^2 \rho A e^{-ikx} - ik\omega^2 \rho B e^{ikx} + \omega^2 \rho \alpha C e^{-\alpha x} - \omega^2 \rho \alpha D e^{\alpha x}$$

and $\qquad \frac{\partial^3 \eta}{\partial x^3} = ik^3 (A e^{-ikx} - B e^{ikx}) - \alpha^3 (C e^{-\alpha x} - D e^{\alpha x})$

this condition becomes

$$ik(\omega^2 \rho - k^2 Y)(A e^{-ikl} - B e^{ikl}) + \alpha(\omega^2 \rho + \alpha^2 Y)(C e^{-\alpha l} - D e^{\alpha l}) = 0 \tag{22}$$

Using (19) and (20) to eliminate B, C, and D, we finally have, after some manipulation,

$$\frac{k^4 + \alpha^4}{2k^2 \alpha^2} \cos kl \cosh \alpha l + \frac{\alpha^2 - k^2}{2\alpha k} \sin kl \sinh \alpha l = -1 \tag{23}$$

In the limiting case for which $\alpha \doteq k$ (i.e., neglect of rotational inertia), the above equation reduces to

$$\cos kl \cosh kl = -1 \tag{24}$$

from which the characteristic frequencies, or normal modes, can be computed. The smallest value of kl which satisfies this equation is

$$kl = 1.875 \tag{25}$$

and this therefore gives the fundamental frequency, which is

$$\omega = \frac{(1.875)^2 V_l K}{l^2} \tag{26}$$

The higher modes were computed by Rayleigh.[1] The modes do not form a harmonic sequence. Incidentally, it can be shown that the normal-mode condition for a rod free at both ends or clamped at both ends is the same and is given by

$$\cos kl \cosh kl = 1 \tag{27}$$

to the approximation that neglects rotational inertia. The fundamental frequency for both these cases is the same and is given by (26) with 4.730 in place of 1.875.

The other limiting case for which (23) reduces to a simple form results when K is so large that $\alpha \to 0$. If we multiply (23) by α^2, it follows that

[1] Lord Rayleigh, "Theory of Sound," 2d ed., vol. 1, paragraph 174, Dover Publications, New York, 1945.

the condition for the equation to hold for small α is

$$\cos kl = 0$$

or

$$\omega = \frac{\pi V}{2l} = \frac{\pi V_l}{2l} \tag{28}$$

since $V = V_l$ in this limit [Eq. (14)]. Of course this again neglects configurational dispersion.

7.3. Torsional Waves in a Solid Rod

When a solid circular cylinder is twisted by the application of a shearing stress X applied at its periphery, the resultant shear is measured directly by the angle of twist θ, which in turn, by Hooke's law, is

$$\theta = \frac{X}{\mu} \tag{1}$$

where μ is the shear modulus. But from the definition of a shear

$$\theta = \frac{\partial D}{\partial x} \tag{2}$$

where D is the tangential displacement of any point on the periphery. If now we consider an element of rod of length dx (taking the axis of the rod along the x axis of a coordinate system), the difference between the shearing stresses at the two ends is

$$\mu \frac{\partial^2 D}{\partial x^2} \, dx \tag{3}$$

and hence the equation of tangential motion for the element is

$$\rho \ddot{D} = \mu \frac{\partial^2 D}{\partial x^2} \tag{4}$$

which is therefore the equation for a torsional wave and indicates that the velocity of such a wave along the rod is

$$V = \sqrt{\frac{\mu}{\rho}} \tag{5}$$

where ρ is the density. This is, of course, the velocity of shear waves in the bulk material of which the rod is made.

An interesting application of the above analysis is the filtration of torsional waves. Figure 7.6 represents schematically a solid circular cylinder RR supported by flexible membranes M at equal intervals $2l$ along its length. The membranes are rigidly attached both to the rod at its periphery and to the inner surface of the hollow circular cylinder C of inner radius h.

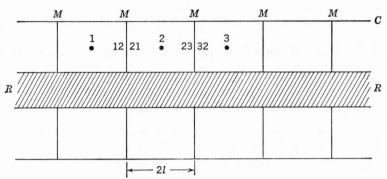

FIG. 7.6. Filtration of torsional waves in a membrane-supported rod in a hollow tube

This is an example of an iterated structure such as we have already discussed in Sec. 3.4, and we may expect it to exhibit filtration of torsional waves transmitted along the cylindrical rod due to the interaction with the branch membranes. We shall not present the analysis here[1] but merely point out that the structure is found to behave as a bandpass filter with the low frequencies attenuated; effectively, it is a high-pass filter. Radial torsional waves are set up in the membranes involving both the J and N Bessel functions introduced in Sec. 3.6.

7.4. Flexural Waves in a Flat Plate

The solid plate differs from a membrane (Sec. 5.1) in that it possesses stiffness associated with the elastic constants of the material of which it is composed. Probably the simplest way of deriving the equation of motion of such a plate is the variational, or Lagrangian, method. This has been described in Sec. 1.11, and it is clear from (1.11-6) that all we need to do in order to apply it to the present problem is to find an expression for the potential energy of the deformed plate. We go back to (6.2-4) for the dilatational strains in a solid elastic medium in terms of the corresponding stresses. We shall assume that the plate has its faces parallel to the xy plane and that the dilatational stress along the z axis vanishes, that is, $X_{zz} = 0$. If then we solve (6.2-4) for X_{xx} and X_{yy}, the result is

$$X_{xx} = \frac{Y}{1 - \sigma^2} (\delta_{xx} + \sigma\delta_{yy})$$

$$X_{yy} = \frac{Y}{1 - \sigma^2} (\delta_{yy} + \sigma\delta_{xx})$$

(1)

[1] R. B. Lindsay and T. G. Barnes, *J. Acoust. Soc. Am.*, **8**, 42 (1936).

If we assume that in the plate flexure (as somewhat similarly for the bent rod) the medial plane of the plate remains unextended, the dilatation of a point at height z above this plane is given by

$$\frac{(R + z)\theta - R\theta}{R\theta} = \frac{z}{R} \tag{2}$$

where R is the appropriate radius of curvature for the direction of dilatation and θ is the angle at the center of curvature. Hence, if we orient the x and y axes along the principal planes of bending, we have

$$\delta_{xx} = \frac{z}{R_1} \qquad \delta_{yy} = \frac{z}{R_2} \tag{3}$$

where R_1 and R_2 are the principal radii of curvature.[1]

The potential energy per unit volume of the deformed elastic medium is the work done on a unit volume by the stresses in producing the final strains. Since by Hooke's law the stress is directly proportional to the strain, this work for dilatational stresses is

$$\tfrac{1}{2}(X_{xx}\delta_{xx} + X_{yy}\delta_{yy} + X_{zz}\delta_{zz}) \tag{4}$$

which for a flat plate reduces to

$$\frac{1}{2}(X_{xx}\delta_{xx} + X_{yy}\delta_{yy}) = \frac{Y}{2(1 - \sigma^2)}(\delta_{xx}^2 + 2\sigma\delta_{xx}\delta_{yy} + \delta_{yy}^2) \tag{5}$$

We must now substitute for δ_{xx} and δ_{yy} from (3), whence the **potential** energy per unit area becomes

$$\frac{Y}{2(1 - \sigma^2)}\int_{-h/2}^{+h/2}\left(\frac{1}{R_1^2} + \frac{1}{R_2^2} + \frac{2\sigma}{R_1 R_2}\right)z^2\,dz$$

$$= \frac{Yh^3}{24(1 - \sigma^2)}\left(\frac{1}{R_1^2} + \frac{1}{R_2^2} + \frac{2\sigma}{R_1 R_2}\right) \tag{6}$$

where h is the thickness of the plate.

Now from differential geometry[2] we have

$$\frac{1}{R_1} + \frac{1}{R_2} = \text{mean curvature}$$

$$= \frac{\partial^2 \zeta}{\partial x^2} + \frac{\partial^2 \zeta}{\partial y^2} \tag{7}$$

whereas

$$\frac{1}{R_1 R_2} = \text{total curvature}$$

$$= \frac{\partial^2 \zeta}{\partial x^2}\frac{\partial^2 \zeta}{\partial y^2} - \left(\frac{\partial^2 \zeta}{\partial x\,\partial y}\right)^2 \tag{8}$$

where ζ is the displacement normal to the xy plane.

[1] E. B. Wilson, "Advanced Calculus," p. 148, Ginn & Company, Boston, 1912.
[2] *Ibid.*

The Lagrangian density (see Sec. 1-11) for the present problem then is

$$L = \frac{1}{2}\rho h \dot{\zeta}^2 - \frac{K}{2}\left\{(\nabla^2\zeta)^2 - 2(1-\sigma)\left[\frac{\partial^2\zeta}{\partial x^2}\frac{\partial^2\zeta}{\partial y^2} - \left(\frac{\partial^2\zeta}{\partial x\,\partial y}\right)^2\right]\right\} \qquad (9)$$

where ρ, as usual, is the volume density of the plate material and

$$\nabla^2\zeta = \frac{\partial^2\zeta}{\partial x^2} + \frac{\partial^2\zeta}{\partial y^2}$$

Moreover,
$$K = \frac{Yh^3}{12(1-\sigma^2)}$$

The condition that

$$\int L\,dt \qquad (10)$$

shall have a stationary value in the usual calculus of variations sense is the Eulerian (or generalized Lagrangian) equation (see Sec. 1.11)

$$\frac{\partial}{\partial t}\left(\frac{\partial L}{\partial \dot{\zeta}}\right) + \frac{\partial}{\partial x}\left[\frac{\partial L}{\partial(\partial\zeta/\partial x)}\right] + \frac{\partial}{\partial y}\left[\frac{\partial L}{\partial(\partial\zeta/\partial y)}\right] - \frac{\partial^2}{\partial x^2}\left[\frac{\partial L}{\partial(\partial^2\zeta/\partial x^2)}\right]$$
$$- \frac{\partial^2}{\partial y^2}\left[\frac{\partial L}{\partial(\partial^2\zeta/\partial y^2)}\right] - \frac{\partial^2}{\partial x\,\partial y}\left[\frac{\partial L}{\partial(\partial^2\zeta/\partial x\,\partial y)}\right] - \frac{\partial L}{\partial\zeta} = 0 \qquad (11)$$

If we carry out the indicated differentiations on L as given by (9), the result is the equation

$$\rho\ddot{\zeta} = -\frac{K}{h}\left\{\frac{\partial^2}{\partial x^2}\left[\nabla^2\zeta - (1-\sigma)\frac{\partial^2\zeta}{\partial y^2}\right] + \frac{\partial^2}{\partial y^2}\left[\nabla^2\zeta - (1-\sigma)\frac{\partial^2\zeta}{\partial x^2}\right]\right.$$
$$\left. + 2(1-\sigma)\frac{\partial}{\partial x\,\partial y}\left(\frac{\partial^2\zeta}{\partial x\,\partial y}\right)\right\} \qquad (12)$$

This can be reduced to

$$\ddot{\zeta} = -\frac{K}{\rho h}\nabla^4\zeta \qquad (13)$$

where
$$\nabla^4\zeta = \nabla^2(\nabla^2\zeta) = \frac{\partial^4\zeta}{\partial x^4} + \frac{\partial^4\zeta}{\partial y^4} + 2\frac{\partial^4\zeta}{\partial x^2\,\partial y^2} \qquad (14)$$

Since we are mainly interested in motions which are harmonic in time with angular frequency ω, (13) becomes

$$\nabla^4\zeta = \frac{\omega^2\zeta}{c'^4} \qquad (15)$$

where
$$c'^4 = \frac{Yh^2}{12\rho(1-\sigma^2)} \qquad (16)$$

Note that c' has the dimensions of $cm/\sqrt{sec}$ and is therefore not a velocity. However, it is convenient to write ω^2/c'^4 as k'^4 and have

$$\nabla^4\zeta = k'^4\zeta \qquad (17)$$

This equation can be factored as follows

$$(\nabla^2 + k'^2)(\nabla^2 - k'^2)\zeta = 0 \tag{18}$$

The complete integral of this for a circular plate has the form (omitting the time-dependent term)

$$\zeta = A[J_n(k'r) + qJ_n(ik'r)] \cos (n\theta + \alpha) \tag{19}$$

where q is an arbitrary constant. The equivalent wave velocity V is given by

$$V^2 = \frac{\omega^2}{k'^2} = c'^2\omega$$

$$= \omega \sqrt{\frac{Yh^2}{12\rho(1 - \sigma^2)}} \tag{20}$$

Here again, as in flexural waves in rods, we note the presence of dispersion. The group velocity, from (3.8-10), becomes

$$U = 2V_0 \tag{21}$$

if V_0 is the mean phase velocity of the waves in the group. The relation between this and the group velocity of flexural waves in a rod (7.2-13) is striking, though not unexpected.

The motion of a finite plate of course depends on the boundary conditions. For a circular plate of radius a, clamped around the periphery, the conditions are that ζ vanish at all points of the edge and that the slope of the profile of the plate also vanish there. This means that $d\zeta/dr$ vanishes at all points of the edge. We therefore have, from (19),

$$J_n(k'a) + qJ_n(ik'a) = 0$$
$$\left\{\frac{d}{dr}[J_n(k'r) + qJ_n(ik'r)]\right\}_{r=a} = 0 \tag{22}$$

The first condition enables q to be evaluated as

$$q = -\frac{J_n(k'a)}{J_n(ik'a)} \tag{23}$$

and the second condition fixes k' from

$$J_n(ik'a)\left[\frac{d}{dr}J_n(k'r)\right]_{r=a} = J_n(k'a)\left[\frac{d}{dr}J_n(ik'r)\right]_{r=a} \tag{24}$$

Rayleigh[1] found the first two roots of (24) as

$$k'a = 3.20, 6.30$$

[1] "Theory of Sound," vol. 1, p. 367.

The fundamental frequency therefore is

$$\nu = \frac{(3.2)^2}{4\pi a^2} \sqrt{\frac{Yh^2}{3\rho(1 - \sigma^2)}} \tag{25}$$

Again we note that the normal frequencies do not form a harmonic series. As in the case of the vibrating membrane, when a diaphragm is used as a source of sound, it is customary to work below the resonance frequency and treat the plate as an equivalent piston.

7.5. Surface Waves in Solids

In Sec. 6.3 we developed the general theory of elastic wave transmission in a homogeneous, isotropic medium and found that, if the medium is unbounded, both dilatational (irrotational) and shear (solenoidal) waves are in general propagated. This will always be true of a solid medium, though for an ideal fluid only dilatational waves are involved. We have seen in the present chapter how the radiation is affected by the presence of boundaries, as in rods and plates. In the next chapter we shall investigate waves propagated along the surface of an incompressible fluid, such as water. These are very commonly observed phenomena. It is of interest, however, that surface waves also exist in a solid having a bounding surface, as might indeed be expected. These surface waves, first investigated by Rayleigh[1] and usually known by his name, are similar to the well-known skin effect for electromagnetic waves in electrically conducting media in that they are more or less rapidly damped in amplitude as the distance from the surface increases. Moreover, the velocity is less than that in the unbounded medium.

We repeat for convenience the general equation (6.3-8) for an elastic medium:

$$\rho\ddot{\Delta} = \left(B + \frac{4\mu}{3}\right)\nabla\nabla \cdot \Delta - \mu\nabla \times \nabla \times \Delta \tag{1}$$

and apply this to a flat boundary surface of a solid taken to be the xy plane, confining our attention to waves propagated in the x direction. The z axis is directed from the surface to the interior of the solid. Since both types of waves are contemplated, we write for the displacement vector Δ

$$\Delta = \Delta_d + \Delta_s \tag{2}$$

where Δ_d is the part of the displacement corresponding to dilatation and

[1] Cf. Lord Rayleigh, *Proc. London Math. Soc.*, **17**, 4 (1885). Also consult Kolsky, "Stress Waves in Solids," pp. 16ff.

Δ_s that associated with shear. Thus, since Δ_d is irrotational and Δ_s is solenoidal, we can write

$$\Delta_d = \nabla\varphi \tag{3}$$

and

$$\Delta_s = \nabla \times \mathbf{S} \tag{4}$$

where φ is a scalar function and $\mathbf{S}$ a vector function of space and time. Hence

$$\nabla \cdot \Delta = \nabla \cdot \Delta_d = \nabla^2\varphi$$

and

$$\nabla \times \nabla \times \Delta = \nabla \times \nabla \times \Delta_s = -\nabla^2\Delta_s = -\nabla^2(\nabla \times \mathbf{S}) \tag{5}$$

In view of the assumption with regard to propagation, all these quantities are independent of y. For the sake of convenience, and with no real loss in generality, we take $\eta = 0$. Hence $\nabla \times \mathbf{S}$ reduces to

$$-\mathbf{i}\,\frac{\partial S_y}{\partial z} + \mathbf{k}\,\frac{\partial S_y}{\partial x} \tag{6}$$

and $\nabla^2(\nabla \times \mathbf{S})$ becomes

$$-\mathbf{i}\,\frac{\partial}{\partial z}\,\nabla^2 S_y + \mathbf{k}\,\frac{\partial}{\partial x}\,\nabla^2 S_y$$

The vector displacement Δ reduces to

$$\Delta = \mathbf{i}\left(\frac{\partial\varphi}{\partial x} - \frac{\partial S_y}{\partial z}\right) + \mathbf{k}\left(\frac{\partial\varphi}{\partial z} + \frac{\partial S_y}{\partial x}\right) \tag{7}$$

Hence the vector equation (1) reduces to the two component equations (calling $S_y = \varphi$ for convenience)

$$\rho\left(\frac{\partial\ddot{\varphi}}{\partial x} + \frac{\partial\ddot{\psi}}{\partial z}\right) = \left(B + \frac{4\mu}{3}\right)\frac{\partial}{\partial x}\,(\nabla^2\varphi) + \mu\frac{\partial}{\partial z}\,(\nabla^2\psi)$$

$$\rho\left(\frac{\partial\ddot{\varphi}}{\partial z} - \frac{\partial\ddot{\psi}}{\partial x}\right) = \left(B + \frac{4\mu}{3}\right)\frac{\partial}{\partial z}\,(\nabla^2\varphi) - \mu\frac{\partial}{\partial x}\,(\nabla^2\psi)$$

$$\tag{8}$$

It is clear that we can satisfy these equations if φ and ψ are solutions of the equations

$$\rho\ddot{\varphi} = \left(B + \frac{4\mu}{3}\right)\nabla^2\varphi \tag{9}$$

$$\rho\ddot{\psi} = \mu\nabla^2\psi \tag{10}$$

where, we recall, φ and ψ are functions of x, z, and t. We look for solutions of (9) and (10) in the form

$$\varphi = A(z)e^{i(\omega t - kx)}$$

$$\psi = C(z)e^{i(\omega t - kx)} \tag{11}$$

Since

$$\nabla^2\varphi = \frac{d^2A}{dz^2}\,e^{i(\omega t - kx)} - k^2 A e^{i(\omega t - kx)} \tag{12}$$

etc., the equations for A and C become

$$\frac{d^2A}{dz^2} = \left(k^2 - \frac{\omega^2}{V_i^2}\right) A \tag{13}$$

$$\frac{d^2C}{dz^2} = \left(k^2 - \frac{\omega^2}{V_s^2}\right) B \tag{14}$$

where
$$V_i = \sqrt{\frac{B + 4\mu/3}{\rho}}$$
$$\tag{15}$$
$$V_s = \sqrt{\frac{\mu}{\rho}}$$

The general solution of both (13) and (14) is in the form

$$A = \beta_1 e^{-\alpha z} + \beta_2 e^{\alpha z}$$
$$C = \beta_1' e^{-\alpha' z} + \beta_2' e^{\alpha' z} \tag{16}$$

where
$$\alpha = \sqrt{k^2 - \frac{\omega^2}{V_i^2}} \qquad \alpha' = \sqrt{k^2 - \frac{\omega^2}{V_s^2}} \tag{17}$$

and β_1 and β_2 are arbitrary. If $k > \omega/V$, so that α is real, φ and ψ are propagated as waves with amplitudes decaying exponentially with z, provided that $\beta_2 = 0$.

The boundary conditions are that the stress components X_{zz}, X_{zy}, and X_{zx} vanish at the surface, where $z = 0$. From (6.2-5) we recall that

$$X_{zz} = \left(B - \frac{2\mu}{3}\right) \nabla \cdot \mathbf{\Delta} + 2\mu \frac{\partial}{\partial z}\left(\frac{\partial \varphi}{\partial z} - \frac{\partial \psi}{\partial x}\right)$$
$$= \left(B - \frac{2\mu}{3}\right) \nabla^2 \varphi + 2\mu\left(\frac{\partial^2 \varphi}{\partial z^2} - \frac{\partial^2 \psi}{\partial z \, \partial x}\right) \tag{18}$$

Substituting from (11) and using (16) with $\beta_2 = 0$ gives

$$X_{zz} = \left(B - \frac{2\mu}{3}\right)\beta_1(\alpha^2 - k^2)e^{-\alpha z}e^{i(\omega t - kx)}$$
$$+ 2\mu\beta_1\alpha^2 e^{i(\omega t - kx)}e^{-\alpha z} - 2i\mu\alpha'\beta_1' k e^{-\alpha' z}e^{i(\omega t - kx)} \tag{19}$$

The condition that this vanish for $z = 0$ is

$$\beta_1\left[B(\alpha^2 - k^2) + \frac{2\mu}{3}(\alpha^2 + k^2)\right] - 2i\mu\alpha'\beta_1' k = 0 \tag{20}$$

Next, from (6.2-7), we have

$$X_{zx} = \mu\left(\frac{\partial \xi}{\partial z} + \frac{\partial \zeta}{\partial x}\right) = \mu\left(2\frac{\partial^2 \varphi}{\partial x \, \partial z} - \frac{\partial^2 \psi}{\partial x^2} + \frac{\partial^2 \psi}{\partial z^2}\right) \tag{21}$$

which, on substitution and putting $z = 0$, gives

$$2ik\alpha\beta_1 + (k^2 + \alpha'^2)\beta_1' = 0 \tag{22}$$

Elimination of β_1 and β_1' from (20) and (22) results in the following equation connecting α, α', and k:

$$4\mu\alpha'\alpha k^2 = \left[B(\alpha^2 - k^2) + \frac{2\mu}{3}(\alpha^2 + k^2) \right](k^2 + \alpha'^2) \qquad (23)$$

With the use of (17), this gives

$$4\mu\sqrt{\left(1 - \frac{V_R{}^2}{V_i{}^2}\right)\left(1 - \frac{V_R{}^2}{V_s{}^2}\right)} = \left[\frac{4\mu}{3} - \left(B + \frac{2\mu}{3}\right)\frac{V_R{}^2}{V_i{}^2} \right]\left[2 - \frac{V_R{}^2}{V_s{}^2} \right] \qquad (24)$$

where $V_R = \omega/k$ = phase velocity of the Rayleigh waves. From this equation V_R can, in principle, be solved in terms of the elastic constants and density. Since the frequency has disappeared there is *no* dispersion of Rayleigh waves.

The actual displacement components ξ and ζ are given by [see (2), (3), and (4)]

$$\begin{aligned}
\xi &= \frac{\partial\varphi}{\partial x} + \frac{\partial\psi}{\partial z} = -(ik\beta_1 e^{-\alpha z} + \beta_1'\alpha' e^{-\alpha' z})e^{i(\omega t - kx)} \\
\zeta &= \frac{\partial\varphi}{\partial z} - \frac{\partial\psi}{\partial x} = -(\beta_1\alpha e^{-\alpha z} - \beta_1' ik e^{-\alpha' z})e^{i(\omega t - kx)}
\end{aligned} \qquad (25)$$

Use of the relation connecting β_1 and β_1' leads to the real forms

$$\begin{aligned}
\xi_r &= \beta_1 k \left(e^{-\alpha z} - \frac{2\alpha\alpha'}{\alpha'^2 + k^2} e^{-\alpha' z} \right) \sin(\omega t - kx) \\
\zeta_r &= \beta_1\alpha \left(e^{-\alpha z} - \frac{2k^2}{\alpha'^2 + k^2} e^{-\alpha' z} \right) \cos(\omega t - kx)
\end{aligned} \qquad (26)$$

Examination discloses that the dissipation factor in parentheses in the expression for ξ_r decreases with increasing values of kz [note that, from (17), $\alpha/k = \sqrt{1 - V_R{}^2/V_i{}^2}$, $\alpha'/k = \sqrt{1 - V_R{}^2/V_s{}^2}$] and, indeed, becomes zero for a certain value; that is, there is not simply exponential decay of ξ with depth. This decay depends on frequency, since k is proportional to ω. Hence, the higher the frequency, the smaller the value of z for which ξ vanishes; the behavior is in this respect analogous to that of the skin effect in high-frequency electric currents in conductors. The situation with respect to ζ is not quite the same since the factor in parentheses does not change sign with increasing z. For Poisson's ratio in the neighborhood of 0.25, the velocity of the Rayleigh waves comes out to be approximately 0.9 of the velocity of shear waves.

If α and α' are pure imaginary (that is, $k < \omega/V$), φ and ψ are propagated as harmonic waves into the bulk of the solid, the direction cosines of the wave normal depending on ω/V_i and ω/V_s [see Eq. (11)]. In this case we do not get Rayleigh waves.   The details are left for the reader to work out.

7.6. Dissipation of Elastic Waves in Solids

Thus far in the discussion of the transmission of elastic waves in solid rods and plates it has been assumed that the intensity of the wave remains constant.   In Sec. 7.5 we did encounter a kind of damping effect in propagation along a surface, but this is associated with the amplitude of the disturbance as a function of distance from the surface and has nothing to do with dissipation in the direction of propagation.   Yet simple observation indicates the presence of such dissipation in rods and plates. It should be noted that this is quite different from the selective transmission and filtration phenomena associated with stratified media, loaded strings, or other nonhomogeneous media; it is an irreversible attenuation in which the wave energy ultimately is transformed into heat, that is, random energy of the constituent atoms and molecules of the solid.

We can immediately apply the reasoning of Sec. 1.10 and obtain the spatial intensity attenuation coefficient 2α in terms of the rate of change of the mean energy density $\bar{w}$ with distance in the direction of propagation.   Thus [see (1.10-23)]

$$2\alpha = -\frac{1}{\bar{w}} \frac{d\bar{w}}{dx} \tag{1}$$

If $\Delta\bar{w} = -(d\bar{w}/dx)\lambda$, where λ is the wavelength, the above becomes, for a harmonic wave,

$$2\alpha = \frac{1}{\lambda} \frac{\Delta\bar{w}}{\bar{w}} \tag{2}$$

where $\Delta\bar{w}/\bar{w}$ is the fractional loss in average energy density per wavelength (treated as a positive quantity).   In Sec. 1.10 we saw that

$$\frac{\Delta\bar{w}}{\bar{w}} = 2\alpha\lambda = 2\omega_i T \tag{3}$$

where T is the period of the wave and $2\omega_i$ is the *temporal* intensity attenuation coefficient.

This discussion is indeed limited to the case in which the attenuation is exponential.   Strictly speaking, we should verify this by setting up a theory for propagation through a medium in which the dissipation is due to an assumed mechanism and showing that the integration of the resulting propagation equations leads to exponential damping.   As a matter of fact, we shall do precisely this for fluid media in Chap. 9.   However, the situation for solids turns out to be much more difficult than for fluids, and for the moment we rest content with the assurance that actual experimental studies of propagation in solids to good approximation agree with the hypothesis of exponential dissipation (see Sec. 12.8 for further details).

The reference to the temporal attenuation suggests at once a standard way of representing wave dissipation in solid rods. When a suitably mounted rod of finite length is excited in one of its normal modes and the exciting force is cut off, the amplitude of the vibration decays at every point. In analogy with the behavior of a damped oscillator with one degree of freedom (e.g., an oscillating mass suspended from the end of a spring and immersed in a viscous liquid, or a simple a-c circuit with resistance, inductance, and capacitance in series), we can define the logarithmic decrement as the natural logarithm of the ratio between successive vibration maxima. Since the energy density for elastic disturbances is proportional to the square of the disturbance amplitude (see Sec. 1.10), if A_1 and A_2 are successive maxima, we have

$$\frac{\Delta \bar{w}}{\bar{w}} = \frac{A_1{}^2 - A_2{}^2}{A_1{}^2} \tag{4}$$

and if the damping is small

$$\frac{A_1{}^2 - A_2{}^2}{A_1{}^2} \doteq \frac{2(A_1 - A_2)}{A_1} \doteq 2 \ln \frac{A_1}{A_2}$$

so that

$$\frac{\Delta \bar{w}}{\bar{w}} \doteq 2\delta \tag{5}$$

where δ is the logarithmic decrement. Hence, from (3), we have

$$\omega_i = \frac{\delta}{T} \tag{6}$$

as the relation between the temporal attenuation coefficient and the decrement. The decrement can then be looked upon as a measure of what is commonly referred to as the internal friction or viscosity of the solid. It is found that the decrement tends, in general, to be higher for dielectric solids than for metals. Thus for steel it is 0.6×10^{-3} whereas for polystyrene it is 48×10^{-3}. In general, materials with large elastic constants have lower decrements. In fact the product of decrement and elastic constant is of the same order of magnitude for many materials.

CHAPTER 8

WAVES IN INCOMPRESSIBLE FLUIDS

8.1. Hydrodynamical Equations for an Incompressible Fluid

One of the most interesting and picturesque examples of wave propagation is provided by the waves on the surface of a liquid like water. Indeed these are commonly employed to illustrate the properties of waves in general, as in the use of a ripple tank with optical projection. To understand this type of wave motion, it is necessary to review the equations for the mechanical behavior of an incompressible fluid.

These equations include the condition that there be conservation of mass and momentum. The first is the so-called "equation of continuity," which takes the form [see (3.5-2)]

$$\nabla \cdot (\rho \mathbf{v}) + \dot{\rho} = 0 \tag{1}$$

if ρ is the density of the fluid and $\mathbf{v}$ is the flow velocity at any point. If the divergence term is expanded, we get

$$\rho \nabla \cdot \mathbf{v} + \mathbf{v} \cdot \nabla \rho + \dot{\rho} = 0 \tag{2}$$

The term $\dot{\rho}$ denotes the time rate of change of density at a specific point, irrespective of what particle of fluid occupies it. The total change in density as one follows a particular particle of fluid in its motion is[1]

$$\frac{d\rho}{dt} = \dot{\rho} + \mathbf{v} \cdot \nabla \rho \tag{3}$$

Hence, if the fluid is incompressible and there can be no changes in density as the particle moves from place to place, the equation of continuity becomes

$$\nabla \cdot \mathbf{v} = 0 \tag{4}$$

Moreover, as we have noted in Sec. 6.3, if the flow is irrotational, there exists a velocity potential function $\varphi(x,y,z)$ such that

$$\mathbf{v} = \nabla \varphi \tag{5}$$

[1] R. B. Lindsay, "Concepts and Methods of Theoretical Physics," p. 349, D. Van Nostrand Company, Inc., Princeton, N.J., 1951.

and in this case the equation of continuity reduces to Laplace's equation for φ, that is,

$$\nabla^2\varphi = 0 \tag{6}$$

The equation of motion expresses essentially the conservation of momentum and, for unit volume of fluid [Eq. (3.5-6)], may be put in the form

$$\frac{d\mathbf{v}}{dt} = -\frac{\nabla p}{\rho} + \mathbf{F} \tag{7}$$

where p is the pressure in the fluid as a function of space and time and $\mathbf{F}$ is the external force per unit mass, and where, in analogy with (3),

$$\frac{d\mathbf{v}}{dt} = \dot{\mathbf{v}} + \mathbf{v} \cdot \nabla\mathbf{v} \tag{8}$$

Another form of the equation of motion is readily available by the use of the vector identity for $\nabla(\mathbf{a} \cdot \mathbf{b})$. Thus we can write

$$\dot{\mathbf{v}} - \mathbf{v} \times (\nabla \times \mathbf{v}) = \mathbf{F} - \frac{\nabla p}{\rho} - \frac{1}{2}\nabla v^2 \tag{9}$$

For irrotational motion $\nabla \times \mathbf{v} = 0$ and $\dot{\mathbf{v}} = \nabla\dot{\varphi}$. We shall assume, moreover, that the external force $\mathbf{F}$ is conservative, so that $\mathbf{F} = -\nabla\Omega$, where Ω is the corresponding external potential function. Finally, we note from the definition of the ∇ operator that

$$\frac{\nabla p}{\rho} = \nabla \int \frac{dp}{\rho} \tag{10}$$

if p is a function of ρ, so that the integral exists. Under these conditions, (9) takes the form

$$\dot{\varphi} + \Omega + \int \frac{dp}{\rho} + \frac{v^2}{2} = C(t) \tag{11}$$

where $C(t)$ is a function of time alone. For steady flow in which $\dot{\varphi} = 0$, this is Bernoulli's equation, which here holds at all points of the fluid. Of course, even in nonirrotational steady flow it holds along *any* streamline, with the constant varying from streamline to streamline.[1]

For an incompressible fluid such as we shall consider in our surface wave study, $\int \frac{dp}{\rho}$ becomes $\frac{p}{\rho}$, and (11) takes the even simpler form

$$\frac{p}{\rho} + \Omega + \frac{v^2}{2} + \dot{\varphi} = C(t) \tag{12}$$

---

[1] L. M. Milne-Thomson, "Theoretical Hydrodynamics," 3d ed., p. 10, Macmillan & Co., Ltd., London, 1955.

8.2. Surface Waves in Liquids

We now apply the analysis set forth in the preceding section to the special case of gravity waves in a liquid in an infinitely long narrow tank of depth h.   By a gravity wave we shall mean the propagation of a surface deformation confined to the xy plane (the tank runs along the x axis, so that the undisturbed surface is parallel to this axis), with gravity as the only force tending to restore the surface to its equilibrium position. For the moment we neglect the effect of surface tension.

In Fig. 8.1 the y coordinate of any point on the liquid surface is denoted by $\eta + h$; that is, η is the displacement of the surface in the y direction from its equilibrium position for which $y = h$.   The propagation of the

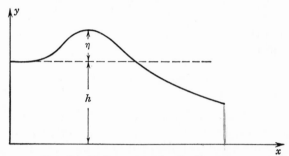

FIG. 8.1. Deformation of a liquid surface.

disturbance in the x direction will be studied by means of the solution of Laplace's equation (8.1-6) subject to the appropriate boundary conditions.   At the interface between the liquid and the rigid walls of the tank the condition is clearly that there shall be no motion normal to the wall. This means $\partial \varphi / \partial n = 0$, where n denotes the normal.   At the free surface the situation is different.   We can apply (8.1-12) with p/ρ set equal to a constant, namely, the steady pressure in the gaseous medium above the free surface of the liquid (e.g., the atmospheric pressure in a typical case) divided by the constant density of the liquid.   It will be assumed that the disturbance is sufficiently small so that the term $v^2/2$ can be neglected.   The potential Ω is the gravitational potential, that is,

$$\Omega = g\eta \tag{1}$$

where g is the acceleration of gravity.

We can consider $C(t)$ as absorbed in the $\dot\varphi$, adjust for the constancy of p/ρ, and finally write as a surface condition

$$\dot\varphi_{\text{surf}} = -g\eta \tag{2}$$

There is, however, a second condition.   Since a particle once on the surface must always remain there (the fluid being incompressible), it follows that

$$y - \eta(x,z,t) - h = 0 \tag{3}$$

for a particle on the surface. Hence the total time rate of change of the function $y - \eta - h$ must vanish identically. This means, from (8.1-3),

$$\frac{\partial(y - \eta)}{\partial t} + v_x \frac{\partial(y - \eta)}{\partial x} + v_y \frac{\partial(y - \eta)}{\partial y} + v_z \frac{\partial(y - \eta)}{\partial z} = 0$$

From this we conclude (neglecting second-order terms)

$$\frac{\partial \eta}{\partial t} = v_y = \frac{\partial \varphi}{\partial y} \tag{4}$$

If we combine this with (2), the result is

$$\ddot{\varphi} = -g \frac{\partial \varphi}{\partial y} \tag{5}$$

which is the second surface condition. We are now ready to get a solution for Laplace's equation subject to the boundary conditions cited, noting of course that φ in this case is a function of x, y, and t. We wish our solution to represent a harmonic wave progressing in the x direction and expect an amplitude depending on y. In view of the well-known fact that solutions of Laplace's equation are possible by separation of variables (see Secs. 1.8 and 3.6), it is plausible to assume a solution of the form

$$\varphi = (Ae^{ky} + Be^{-ky}) \cos k(x - Vt) \tag{6}$$

where the wave velocity V and the amplitude coefficients A and B are to be determined by the boundary conditions. If we impose the boundary condition $\partial \varphi / \partial y = 0$ at the bottom of the tank, where $y = 0$, we get $A = B$; and if, further, we apply (5) at the surface where $y = h$, the ultimate result is

$$V^2 = \frac{g}{k} \tanh kh \tag{7}$$

But $k = 2\pi/\lambda$, and hence the velocity in terms of the wavelength becomes

$$V^2 = \frac{g\lambda}{2\pi} \tanh \frac{2\pi h}{\lambda} \tag{8}$$

The actual displacement of any point of the surface is obtained from (2), which gives

$$\eta = \frac{kVA'}{g} \cosh kh \sin k(x - ct) \tag{9}$$

where A' is now the arbitrary amplitude constant. Note that we could equally well use sinh kh in (9) in place of cosh kh by appropriate change in the constant A'.   Indeed this form would result directly from the use of (4).   Particular interest attaches to the expression for the velocity. We see that, if the tank is very shallow and the wavelength is long, so that

$$\frac{h}{\lambda} \ll 1$$

$$\tanh \frac{2\pi h}{\lambda} \doteq \frac{2\pi h}{\lambda}$$

and $$V^2 \doteq gh \tag{10}$$

or a velocity dependent on gravity and the depth alone.   As a matter of fact, the velocity $\sqrt{gh}$ is the maximum velocity a surface gravity wave can have.   At the other extreme, that is, water depth very great compared with λ, $\tan(2\pi h/\lambda) \doteq 1$ and

$$V^2 \doteq \frac{g\lambda}{2\pi} \tag{11}$$

indicating that there is dispersion in the propagation.   The group velocity corresponding to this dispersion law is (see Sec. 3.8)

$$U = V_0 - \lambda_0 \left(\frac{dV}{d\lambda}\right)_0 = \frac{V_0}{2} \tag{12}$$

where $$V_0 = \sqrt{\frac{g\lambda_0}{2\pi}}$$

We now wish to include the effect of surface tension.   In Sec. 5.1 it was shown that, when a perfectly flexible membrane is disturbed from its equilibrium position by a vertical displacement η, there is a restoring force per unit area equal to

$$T\left(\frac{\partial^2\eta}{\partial x^2} + \frac{\partial^2\eta}{\partial z^2}\right) \tag{13}$$

if T is the tension in the membrane, and the equilibrium position is the xz plane [Eq. (5.1-4), with appropriate change in notation].   Now we can consider the surface of the liquid as effectively like a membrane under surface tension.   If we do this, we must modify (8.1-12) by including the term $-\dfrac{T}{\rho}\left(\dfrac{\partial^2\eta}{\partial x^2} + \dfrac{\partial^2\eta}{\partial z^2}\right)$ along with $\dfrac{p}{\rho}$ in Bernoulli's equation.   Hence the surface condition (2) must now take the form

$$\dot{\varphi}_{\text{surf}} = -g\eta + \frac{T}{\rho}\left(\frac{\partial^2\eta}{\partial x^2} + \frac{\partial^2\eta}{\partial z^2}\right) \tag{14}$$

Similarly, (5) must be modified to

$$\ddot{\varphi} = -g\frac{\partial\varphi}{\partial y} + \frac{T}{\rho}\left(\frac{\partial^2}{\partial x^2} + \frac{\partial^2}{\partial z^2}\right)\frac{\partial\varphi}{\partial y} \tag{15}$$

The other boundary conditions remain unaltered. It seems plausible to use for the solution of this more general equation an expression of the same form as (6), namely,

$$\varphi = A \cosh ky \cos k(x - Vt) \tag{16}$$

If we apply condition (15), the result is to replace (7) by

$$V^2 = \left(\frac{g}{k} + \frac{Tk}{\rho}\right) \tanh kh \tag{17}$$

If the surface tension T is small or, in particular, if

$$T \ll \frac{\rho g \lambda^2}{4\pi^2}$$

the expression for the wave velocity reduces to (8). This will certainly be the case for long waves in a liquid like water—for example, waves for which the wavelength is of the order of a meter, since the surface tension of water at room temperature is about 75 dynes/cm. However, the surface tension begins to play an important and ultimately predominant role for short wavelengths of the order of 1 cm or less. Thus for ripples on the surface of water (where h is so large that $\tanh kh \doteq 1$)

$$V = \sqrt{\frac{2\pi T}{\rho \lambda}} \tag{18}$$

whence the group velocity in this case turns out to be

$$U = \frac{3V_0}{2} \tag{19}$$

a rather striking result which has been experimentally verified in deep ripple tanks.

The displacement η at the surface has the same form in the general case of capillary plus gravity waves as for gravity waves alone; that is, (9) still holds.

It is of interest to determine the actual path of a particle of liquid with mean position (x,y) when such a wave as we have been discussing moves along the surface. Using (16), we see that the component velocities of a particle in the x and y directions, respectively, are

$$\dot{\xi} = \frac{\partial \varphi}{\partial x} = -Ak \cosh ky \sin k(x - Vt)$$

$$\dot{\eta} = \frac{\partial \varphi}{\partial y} = Ak \sinh ky \cos k(x - Vt) \tag{20}$$

These equations in turn yield

$$\xi = -\frac{A}{V} \cosh ky \cos k(x - Vt)$$

$$\eta = \frac{A}{V} \sinh ky \sin k(x - Vt)$$

(21)

The elimination of the time between these two gives the equation of the path

$$\frac{\xi^2}{(A^2 \cosh^2 ky)/V^2} + \frac{\eta^2}{(A^2 \sinh^2 ky)/V^2} = 1 \qquad (22)$$

This is the equation of an ellipse with semimajor and semiminor axes equal, respectively, to

$$\frac{A}{V} \cosh ky \qquad \frac{A}{V} \sinh ky \qquad (23)$$

For $ky \gg 1$, that is, short wavelength and deep water, the path approximates a circle.

Study of the propagation of energy in a surface wave permits the establishment of an interesting connection with the group velocity. We first obtain the kinetic and potential energy densities in the wave, restricting ourselves to gravity waves only. The kinetic energy of the liquid element with volume $d\tau$ is

$$\tfrac{1}{2}\rho(\dot{\xi}^2 + \dot{\eta}^2)\, d\tau$$

and the total kinetic energy of the whole liquid is

$$W_K = \frac{\rho}{2} \int (\dot{\xi}^2 + \dot{\eta}^2)\, d\tau \qquad (24)$$

Similarly, the potential energy of the mass of liquid standing on the element of area dS of the undisturbed surface is

$$\tfrac{1}{2}g\rho\eta^2\, dS \qquad (25)$$

since the mass of this liquid is $\rho g\eta\, dS$ and the height of its center of mass above the free surface is $\eta/2$. Hence the total potential energy of the liquid due to the wave disturbance is

$$W_P = \frac{g\rho}{2} \int \eta^2\, dS \qquad (26)$$

where the integral is taken over the whole surface of the liquid. Now we can write (24) in the form

$$W_K = \frac{\rho}{2} \int \left[\left(\frac{\partial\varphi}{\partial x}\right)^2 + \left(\frac{\partial\varphi}{\partial y}\right)^2 \right] d\tau \qquad (27)$$

which gives us a chance to apply Green's theorem. We recall that the technique is much like that employed in Sec. 2.4. We apply the divergence theorem to the function

$$\mathbf{Q} = \varphi \nabla \varphi \tag{28}$$

and get [see (2.4-6) and remember that φ satisfies Laplace's equation]

$$\int \nabla \varphi \cdot \nabla \varphi \, d\tau = \int \varphi \frac{\partial \varphi}{\partial n} \, dS \tag{29}$$

The volume integral is thus replaceable by a surface integral, which in the case of the wave motion here described reduces to an integral over the free surface, since the boundary condition $\frac{\partial \varphi}{\partial n} = 0$ prevails over all the rigid surfaces. Moreover, on the free surface, $\frac{\partial \varphi}{\partial n} \doteq \frac{\partial \varphi}{\partial y}$. So we have

$$W_K = \frac{\rho}{2} \int \varphi \frac{\partial \varphi}{\partial y} \, dS \tag{30}$$

From (16) and (20) the above integral now becomes (remembering that we are calculating quantities at the surface)

$$W_K = \frac{\rho A^2 k}{2} \sinh kh \cosh kh \int \cos^2 k(x - Vt) \, dS \tag{31}$$

whereas, from (21), the potential energy is

$$W_P = \frac{g\rho A^2}{2V^2} \sinh^2 kh \int \sin^2 k(x - Vt) \, dS \tag{32}$$

If we now use the expression for V^2 given in (7), we see that the quantities outside the integrals in (31) and (32) are precisely the same. If we carry out the integrations over a surface strip of unit width and length equal to one wavelength λ, both integrals are numerically equal to $\lambda/2$. Hence the kinetic and potential energies in one wavelength of the gravity surface wave are equal, and the total energy for one wavelength is

$$W = \pi \rho A^2 \sinh kh \cosh kh \tag{33}$$

We next calculate the power transmission in the wave, or the average rate at which work is done per unit width per unit time. In accordance with Sec. 1.10 this is simply the average of the product of the pressure in the liquid and the velocity $\dot{\xi}$ in the direction of propagation. But we must here integrate this product over y as y goes from zero to h, in order to include the whole of the liquid which is being disturbed. Thus, if we denote the instantaneous power transmission by P,

$$P = \int_0^h p\dot{\xi} \, dy \tag{34}$$

If we substitute p from Bernoulli's equation (8.1-12) and use $\dot{\xi} = \partial\varphi/\partial x$, P becomes (neglecting $v^2/2$, as usual)

$$P = -Ak \int_0^h (p_0 - \rho\dot{\varphi} - \rho g y) \cosh ky \sin k(x - Vt)\, dy \qquad (35)$$

where p_0 is the pressure in the gas above the liquid surface. From the dependence of φ on x, y, t [see (16)] it is seen that P is made up of the sum of two terms, as far as time is concerned, namely, an integral multiplied by $\sin k(x - Vt)$ and another integral multiplied by $\sin^2 k(x - Vt)$. When we perform a time average, the first vanishes and the second gives $\frac{1}{2}$. Hence,

$$\bar{P} = \frac{A^2 k^2 \rho V}{2} \int_0^h \cosh^2 ky\, dy \qquad (36)$$

Carrying out the integration gives

$$\bar{P} = \frac{A^2 k \rho V}{4} \sinh kh \cosh kh(1 + 2kh \operatorname{csch} 2kh) \qquad (37)$$

Now, from (33), the average energy per unit length (or energy density in this case) is

$$\bar{W} = \frac{k\rho A^2}{2} \sinh kh \cosh kh \qquad (38)$$

The average power transmission should be precisely this multiplied by the velocity with which the energy is transmitted by the wave. Hence the latter velocity is

$$U = \frac{V}{2} \left(1 + \frac{4\pi h}{\lambda} \operatorname{csch} \frac{4\pi h}{\lambda}\right) \qquad (39)$$

If we go back to the expression for the phase velocity V in (8) and evaluate from the expression

$$U = V_0 - \lambda_0 \left(\frac{dV}{d\lambda}\right)_0 \qquad (40)$$

the group velocity corresponding to the dependence of this phase velocity on the wavelength, we find that U in (39) is indeed the group velocity (40). In other words, the energy transfer in the surface wave takes place on the average with the group velocity. In Sec. 6.6 we discussed the same problem for transmission through a linear lattice and noted the limitations of the treatment.

8.3. Tidal Waves

It is customary to treat harmonic liquid surface waves in which the wavelength is very much longer than the depth as a special class and call them *tidal* waves, since the wave associated with the rise and fall of the tide is the principal illustration on the surface of the sea. Actually we have already treated this in Sec. 8.2 as a special case of surface waves in general, and we found that the velocity is independent of the wavelength and equal to $\sqrt{gh}$, where h is the depth. It will therefore not be necessary to provide a separate derivation.[1]

We content ourselves with pointing out an interesting consequence of tidal waves in a canal if no restriction is placed on the amplitude of the wave. For this purpose it is useful to employ a device known as "reduction to a steady wave." Consider a wave profile moving with velocity V with respect to an otherwise stationary liquid (i.e., at rest as far as motion in the direction of wave propagation is concerned). Imagine that the liquid as a whole is given a motion with speed V in the *opposite* direction to that of propagation. The wave profile then comes to rest with respect to the primary inertial system, and the liquid, so to speak, moves under it with average velocity $-V$. We "stop" the wave so that we can examine it. Now the actual velocity will not stay constant at V, since the cross-sectional area of the liquid varies with the height η of the profile above the equilibrium surface. Let us suppose that the resultant velocity is $V + V'$ when the amplitude of the wave is η (assuming that V here is the *average* velocity of the wave). The equation of continuity then demands that the total volume of liquid passing any plane perpendicular to the direction of propagation be constant. If we think of the width of the tidal canal as unity and if its depth is h, as usual, this constant must be hV. Hence we have

$$(h + \eta)(V + V') = hV \tag{1}$$

We must now revert to Bernoulli's equation (8.1-12) and reflect that, since the motion has been made steady by the reduction device, $\dot{\varphi}$ is zero. Moreover, p/ρ is still constant. We may now no longer neglect $v^2/2$ as we did in Sec. 8.2, since v here includes V. Thus the equation becomes

$$\frac{1}{2}(V + V')^2 + g\eta = \frac{V^2}{2} = \text{const} \tag{2}$$

We now eliminate V' between (1) and (2). The result is

$$V^2 = \frac{gh(1 + \eta/h)^2}{1 + \eta/2h} \tag{3}$$

If $\eta \ll h$, this yields $V \doteq \sqrt{gh}$, or the standard velocity for long-wave propagation of small-amplitude surface motion. However, our equation is no longer restricted to this approximation. In fact, we see that if $\eta > 0$, $V > \sqrt{gh}$, whereas if $\eta < 0$, $V < \sqrt{gh}$. But this means that

[1] C. A. Coulson, "Waves," p. 63, Interscience Publishers, Inc., New York, 1943.

all parts of the wave profile do not travel with the same velocity; the elevated parts (the crests, for which $\eta > 0$) move at somewhat greater velocity than the depressed parts (the troughs, for which $\eta < 0$).   Hence the wave profile cannot maintain its shape during the propagation; the crests tend to overtake the troughs, and this leads to a steepening of the forward part of the profile.   A wave of this sort must ultimately break, unless this is prevented through the action of viscous or other resisting forces not included in the discussion here.[1]   We shall have occasion to return to this behavior in considering finite-amplitude sound waves in Chap. 9.

We have said little about what produces the waves we observe on open water on the earth's surface, though we have mentioned the tides as one source.   Another is the wind, which clearly can raise waves of great amplitude.   Unfortunately, little is known of specific character about wind-generated waves, though various theories have been proposed.[2]

8.4. Magnetohydrodynamic Waves

We have already called attention in Sec. 6.7 to some analogies between electromagnetic radiation and elastic waves.   The special case of an incompressible fluid suggests examination of the influence of a magnetic field.   This can lead to the existence of a so-called *magnetohydrodynamic* wave.   Let us take, for example, an infinitely extended homogeneous, incompressible, conducting fluid of density ρ subjected to a uniform magnetic field of intensity $\mathbf{H}_0$.   Now let us suppose that the liquid is given a velocity $\mathbf{v}$ at some specified point.   What will happen?   Since the fluid is a conductor and it moves with respect to a magnetic field, there is a resultant electric field of intensity

$$\mathbf{E} = \frac{\mathbf{j}}{\sigma} - \frac{\mu}{c} \mathbf{v} \times (\mathbf{H}_0 + \mathbf{H}) \tag{1}$$

where μ is the permeability of the liquid, and we now have to write for the magnetic field $\mathbf{H}_0 + \mathbf{H}$, since the electric current induced will modify the original field slightly.   The quantity $\mathbf{j}$ is the current density, and σ is the electrical conductivity of the medium.   Equation (1) is essentially Ohm's law, giving the current density in terms of the resultant electric field intensity, that is, the $\mathbf{E}$ which goes into the field equation corresponding to Faraday's law plus the extra field due to the motional electro-

---

[1] For an excellent treatment of breaking water waves consult J. J. Stoker, "Water Waves," pp. 357ff., Interscience Publishers, Inc., New York, 1957.

[2] For a recent review, see F. Ursell, Wave Generation by Wind, in G. K. Batchelor and R. M. Davies (eds.), "Surveys of Mechanics," pp. 216ff., Cambridge University Press, London, 1956.

motive force. In the present case we shall assume that the conductivity of the medium is so great as to be effectively infinite. From the lower right-hand field equation (6.7-1) we therefore write

$$\nabla \times [\mathbf{v} \times (\mathbf{H}_0 + \mathbf{H})] = \dot{\mathbf{H}} \tag{2}$$

But now the liquid is exposed, not only to the normal pressure gradient and gravity, but to the new body force per unit volume equal to[1]

$$\frac{\mu}{c} \mathbf{j} \times (\mathbf{H}_0 + \mathbf{H})$$

where $\mathbf{j}$ is the resultant current density. From Ampère's law for conductors[2]

$$\mathbf{j} = \frac{c}{4\pi} \nabla \times (\mathbf{H}_0 + \mathbf{H}) \tag{3}$$

which replaces the lower left-hand field equation in (6.7-1) in the case of conductors. Hence the hydrodynamic equation of motion (8.1-7, 8) becomes

$$\rho[\dot{\mathbf{v}} + \mathbf{v} \cdot \nabla \mathbf{v}] = -\nabla p - \rho \nabla \Omega + \frac{\mu}{c} \mathbf{j} \times (\mathbf{H}_0 + \mathbf{H})$$

$$= -\nabla(p + \rho\Omega) + \frac{\mu}{4\pi} [\nabla \times (\mathbf{H}_0 + \mathbf{H})] \times (\mathbf{H}_0 + \mathbf{H}) \tag{4}$$

where Ω is the gravitational potential. We must now combine (2) and (4) to see how $\mathbf{v}$ and $\mathbf{H}$ vary with space and time. In carrying out this process we shall simplify by making the assumption that $\mathbf{v}$ is small enough so that $(\mathbf{v} \cdot \nabla \mathbf{v})$ may be neglected compared with $\dot{\mathbf{v}}$ and that products of $\mathbf{v}$ and $\mathbf{H}$ and squares of either quantity may likewise be neglected. This means that in $\nabla \times [\mathbf{v} \times (\mathbf{H}_0 + \mathbf{H})]$ we neglect $\nabla \times (\mathbf{v} \times \mathbf{H})$ compared with $\nabla \times (\mathbf{v} \times \mathbf{H}_0)$. The latter quantity, by the usual vector identity, becomes

$$\nabla \times (\mathbf{v} \times \mathbf{H}_0) = \mathbf{v}\nabla \cdot \mathbf{H}_0 - \mathbf{H}_0\nabla \cdot \mathbf{v} + (\mathbf{H}_0 \cdot \nabla)\mathbf{v} - (\mathbf{v} \cdot \nabla)\mathbf{H}_0$$

Since $\mathbf{H}_0$ is constant and the fluid is incompressible, the first, second, and fourth terms on the right vanish, and we are left with $(\mathbf{H}_0 \cdot \nabla)\mathbf{v}$ only. Hence (2) reduces to

$$\dot{\mathbf{H}} = (\mathbf{H}_0 \cdot \nabla)\mathbf{v} \tag{5}$$

Using the identity

$$\nabla(\mathbf{H}_0 \cdot \mathbf{H}) = (\mathbf{H}_0 \cdot \nabla)\mathbf{H} + (\mathbf{H} \cdot \nabla)\mathbf{H}_0 + \mathbf{H}_0 \times (\nabla \times \mathbf{H}) + \mathbf{H} \times (\nabla \times \mathbf{H}_0)$$

[1] J. A. Stratton, "Electromagnetic Theory," p. 96, McGraw-Hill Book Company, Inc., New York, 1941.

[2] Lindsay, "Concepts and Methods of Theoretical Physics," p. 393.

in which the second and fourth terms on the right vanish, and employing the approximations already mentioned, we can express (4) in the form

$$\rho \dot{\mathbf{v}} = -\nabla \left(p + \rho \Omega + \frac{\mu}{4\pi} \mathbf{H}_0 \cdot \mathbf{H} \right) + \frac{\mu}{4\pi} (\mathbf{H}_0 \cdot \nabla)\mathbf{H} \tag{6}$$

If we take the divergence of this equation, we find that

$$\nabla^2 \left(p + \rho \Omega + \frac{\mu}{4\pi} \mathbf{H}_0 \cdot \mathbf{H} \right) = 0 \tag{7}$$

Outside the region of the disturbance, $\mathbf{H} = 0$, and p and $\rho \Omega$ are constant. Hence, since $p + \rho \Omega + (\mu/4\pi)\mathbf{H}_0 \cdot \mathbf{H}$ is a solution of Laplace's equation which is constant outside a given region, it must be constant everywhere. Equation (6) therefore reduces to

$$\rho \dot{\mathbf{v}} = \frac{\mu}{4\pi} (\mathbf{H}_0 \cdot \nabla)\mathbf{H} \tag{8}$$

There is no loss in generality in taking $\mathbf{H}_0$ along the x axis, so that (5) becomes

$$\dot{\mathbf{H}} = H_0 \frac{\partial \mathbf{v}}{\partial x} \tag{9}$$

and (8) takes the form

$$\rho \dot{\mathbf{v}} = \frac{\mu}{4\pi} H_0 \frac{\partial \mathbf{H}}{\partial x} \tag{10}$$

If we eliminate $\mathbf{v}$, we get for $\mathbf{H}$ the equation

$$\frac{\partial^2 \mathbf{H}}{\partial x^2} = \frac{4\pi\rho}{\mu H_0^2} \ddot{\mathbf{H}} \tag{11}$$

Elimination of $\mathbf{H}$ likewise gives

$$\frac{\partial^2 \mathbf{v}}{\partial x^2} = \frac{4\pi\rho}{\mu H_0^2} \ddot{\mathbf{v}} \tag{12}$$

Hence both $\mathbf{v}$ and $\mathbf{H}$ are propagated as waves with velocity

$$V = H_0 \sqrt{\frac{\mu}{4\pi\rho}} \tag{13}$$

These are known as magnetohydrodynamic waves. They travel with the velocity given in (13) along the direction of $\mathbf{H}_0$. For mercury, in which such waves have been detected, the velocity for $H_0 = 10^3$ oersteds is about 75 cm/sec.

The above discussion has been confined to an incompressible fluid. However, it is not difficult to show that such waves can be propagated in a compressible fluid, provided that the velocity V is small compared with the velocity of sound in the same medium. This makes it possible to apply the theory of magnetohydrodynamic waves to the gas in the surface of the sun. H. Alfvén has used it to explain the observed behavior of sun spots.[1]

[1] T. G. Cowling, "Magnetohydrodynamics," pp. 34ff., Interscience Publishers, Inc., New York, 1957. Other cosmical applications of the waves in question are also discussed in this text.

CHAPTER 9

SOUND WAVES IN FLUIDS

9.1. Review of Basic Equations for Compressional Waves in Fluids

Sound propagation in a fluid is a very important illustration of compressional wave motion in a material medium. In the earlier chapters of this book (see, in particular, Chaps. 3 and 4) we touched on certain aspects of this type of mechanical radiation, but we now wish to explore it more thoroughly. For this purpose we review here the fundamental equations. In Sec. 3.5 we showed that the excess pressure p_e resulting from a small compressional disturbance in an ideal fluid is propagated in accordance with (3.5-8):

$$\nabla^2 p_e = \frac{\ddot{p}_e}{V^2} \tag{1}$$

where the wave velocity V is given by

$$V = \sqrt{\frac{p_e}{\rho_e}} \tag{2}$$

and the excess density associated with the excess pressure p_e is denoted by ρ_e. If we take the curl of both sides of the hydrodynamic equation of motion (3.5-7), the result is that

$$\rho_0 \frac{\partial}{\partial t} (\nabla \times \mathbf{v}) = 0 \tag{3}$$

since $\nabla \times \nabla p_e = 0$ identically. This means that $\nabla \times \mathbf{v}$ is independent of time; if it is zero at one instant, it must vanish for all time. Since in wave propagation we are interested only in quantities which vary in both space and time, the simplest assumption to make about $\nabla \times \mathbf{v}$ is to set it equal to zero. This leads to the existence of the velocity potential φ, that is,

$$\mathbf{v} = \nabla \varphi \tag{4}$$

There is thus plausibility in the assumption that small compressional disturbances in an ideal fluid are propagated irrotationally and that for sound waves in such a medium a velocity potential always exists. At any rate, such an assumption leads (as we shall see) to consequences which have been amply verified experimentally. We shall make the assumption and shall indeed find it convenient to use the velocity potential φ as a basic quantity in the treatment of many of the acoustical problems which follow. We have indeed already shown in Sec. 6.3 that an irrotational disturbance in a fluid medium is propagated in accordance with the equation

$$\ddot{\varphi} = V^2 \nabla^2 \varphi \tag{5}$$

which we shall therefore take as fundamental for the following discussion. It is desirable to express the other important quantities—excess pressure, excess density, and condensation—in terms of φ.

From (6.7-12) we have for the condensation

$$s = -\frac{\dot{\varphi}}{V^2} \tag{6}$$

and since by definition (Sec. 6.3)

$$s = \frac{\delta\rho}{\rho} = \frac{\rho_e}{\rho_0} \tag{7}$$

we obtain

$$\rho_e = -\frac{\rho_0 \dot{\varphi}}{V^2} \tag{8}$$

Finally, from the Hooke's-law relation [Eq. (3.5-4)]

$$p_e = V^2 \rho_e \tag{9}$$

the expression for the excess pressure becomes

$$p_e = -\rho_0 \dot{\varphi} \tag{10}$$

It is important for future considerations to note that the relation (9) is closely connected with the equation of state of the fluid. It is, in fact, immediately derivable from it.

9.2. Velocity of Sound Waves in Fluids

It is now in order to examine the nature of the velocity of compressional waves in a fluid as given by (9.1-2). Since the disturbances are assumed to be very small, we can safely replace p_e/ρ_e by $dp/d\rho$ and write for the velocity

$$V = \sqrt{\frac{dp}{d\rho}} \tag{1}$$

If the fluid is an ideal gas for which the equation of state is

$$p = R_m \rho T \tag{2}$$

where R_m is the gas constant per unit mass, we have

$$V = \sqrt{R_m T} = \sqrt{\frac{p}{\rho}} \tag{3}$$

if we assume that the temperature remains constant during the compression. This formula was first obtained by Newton.[1] It gives a value for the velocity of sound in air which falls short of that experimentally observed by about 20 per cent. Laplace[2] in 1816 suggested that the Newtonian formula (3) implies that the compressions and expansions in a sound wave are isothermal and that this is probably not the case. If, rather, one assumes that the disturbances are adiabatic and combines the adiabatic relation

$$\frac{p}{\rho^\gamma} = \text{const} \tag{4}$$

with the equation of state (2), one obtains in place of (3)

$$V = \sqrt{\frac{\gamma p}{\rho}} \tag{5}$$

in which $\gamma = c_p/c_v$, or the ratio of the specific heat at constant pressure to that at constant volume. This value agrees with experiment for low frequencies, and Laplace's explanation is now accepted to such an extent that (5) is used as the basis of a method for the precise determination of γ.

According to (5), the velocity of sound in an ideal gas does not depend on the pressure or density. It does depend on the temperature; in fact, from (2) we have

$$V = \sqrt{\gamma R_m T} \tag{6}$$

which also suggests that an instrument for the measurement of the velocity of sound could serve as a thermometer.

For fluids in general we may write (1) in the form

$$V = \sqrt{\frac{B_{ad}}{\rho}} \tag{7}$$

where B_{ad} is the adiabatic bulk modulus. Thus

$$B_{ad} = \rho \left(\frac{dp}{d\rho}\right)_{ad} = \gamma \rho \left(\frac{dp}{d\rho}\right)_{iso} \tag{8}$$

This enables us in principle to calculate the velocity of elastic waves in liquids, though it must be confessed that the equation of state of liquids

[1] Isaac Newton, "Principia Mathematica," trans. by Motte and rev. by Florian Cajori, p. 378, University of California Press, Berkeley, Calif., 1946.

[2] P. S. Laplace, *Ann. phys. chim.*, **3**, 288 (1816).

is not known with sufficient precision to make the theoretical calculation practical.

For a real gas whose equation of state is known, we can evaluate V from (7) and (8). A useful form of the equation of state is

$$p = \rho R_m T \left(1 + \frac{B\rho}{M} + \frac{C\rho^2}{M^2} + \cdots \right) \qquad (9)$$

in which M is the mass of the gas and the quantities B and C are called, respectively, the second and third virial coefficients.[1] Then (7) yields

$$V = \sqrt{\gamma R_m T \left(1 + \frac{2B\rho}{M} + \frac{3C\rho^2}{M^2} + \cdots \right)} \qquad (10)$$

which reduces to (6) for an ideal gas in which $B = C = 0$. It often happens that the use of the second virial coefficient alone is a sufficiently accurate representation in (9). We can rewrite (10) to this approximation as

$$V = \sqrt{\gamma(R_m T + 2Bp/M)} \qquad (11)$$

For a real gas, then, the velocity depends on the pressure independently of the temperature. It must be kept in mind in the use of (10) and (11) that γ is also a function of temperature and pressure and, for real gases at high temperature and pressure, can have quite different values from those for an ideal gas. It is therefore convenient to rewrite (10) and (11) in terms of γ_0, the value for the ideal gas. This demands the expression for the general specific-heat capacities at constant pressure and constant volume in terms of their values for the special case of an ideal gas. We shall not go through this thermodynamic reasoning here but shall merely quote the result, and indeed only for the case in which the second virial coefficient B alone is retained. Equation (11) then becomes[2]

$$V = \sqrt{\frac{\gamma_0 R T}{M} \left\{ 1 + \frac{\rho}{M} \left[2B + 2(\gamma_0 - 1)T \frac{dB}{dT} \right.\right.}$$
$$\left.\left. + \frac{(\gamma_0 - 1)^2}{\gamma_0} T^2 \frac{d^2B}{dT^2} \right] + \cdots \right\}} \qquad (12)$$

This formula will be of particular importance in the case of vapors whose equation of state below the critical point departs markedly from that of an ideal gas. For a gas like air, (11) is sufficiently accurate under not too extreme conditions with $\gamma \doteq \gamma_0$. Thus for air at 90°K the value of V at a pressure of 1 atm is about 188 m/sec, whereas at 0.2 atm it is

---

[1] J. O. Hirschfelder, C. F. Curtiss, and R. B. Bird, "Molecular Theory of Gases and Liquids," pp. 131ff., John Wiley & Sons, Inc., New York, 1954.

[2] *Ibid.*, p. 232.

191 m/sec. At very high pressures and at high frequency the effect is much more marked, and the velocity at given temperature increases with pressure.[1]

When the fluid is a liquid, the equation of state is more difficult to set up. However, we can readily establish a connection between V in (1) and the elastic properties of the liquid. For we know that, if the liquid has compressional elasticity only, its compressibility β is given by

$$\frac{1}{\beta} = -\frac{\Delta p}{\Delta v/v} = \rho \frac{\Delta p}{\Delta \rho} \tag{13}$$

where ρ may be taken with sufficient accuracy to be the mean density. Hence, if β is the adiabatic compressibility β_{ad}, we have

$$V = \sqrt{\frac{1}{\rho \beta_{ad}}} = \sqrt{\frac{\gamma}{\rho \beta_{iso}}} \tag{14}$$

where γ is the ratio of the specific heats for the liquid. The relation (14) is well substantiated experimentally.

A more detailed study of the velocity of sound in liquids demands attention to the equation of state. One can learn something here by assuming that the latter has the form of van der Waals' equation for a real gas. Actually one could use the general expansion of the equation of state in terms of the virial coefficients (9), remembering that the coefficients B and C are functions of temperature and density. For many purposes it is simpler to write van der Waals' equation directly as

$$p = \frac{RT}{M/\rho - b} - \frac{a\rho^2}{M^2} \tag{15}$$

where M is the molar mass, R is the equivalent molar gas constant, and a and b are the liquid van der Waals constants, here functions of temperature and density. Application of (1) leads to the velocity of sound V, where

$$V^2 = \frac{\gamma RT}{(M/\rho - b)^2}\left[\frac{M}{\rho^2} + \left(\frac{db}{d\rho}\right)_T\right] - \frac{\gamma \rho^2}{M^2}\left(\frac{da}{d\rho}\right)_T - \frac{2\gamma}{\rho}\left(\frac{RT}{M/\rho - b} - p\right) \tag{16}$$

Now at atmospheric pressure $2\gamma p/\rho$ for a liquid is of much smaller order of magnitude than the terms in the bracket, say of order 10^6, whereas the other terms[2] are approximately of order 10^{10}. Hence $2\gamma p/\rho$ may be

---

[1] The dependence in question is complicated by the further dependence of velocity on frequency, especially at high frequencies (see Chap. 12). Also consult L. Bergmann, "Der Ultraschall," 6th ed., pp. 501ff., S. Hirzel Verlag, Leipzig, 1954.

[2] Of course, for a gas, p will just balance $RT/(M/\rho - b)$, where b vanishes.

safely neglected. Moreover, for most liquids the term in $da/d\rho$ is too small to be retained. This leaves the approximate expression

$$V^2 = \frac{\gamma RT}{(M/\rho - b)^2}\left[\frac{M}{\rho^2} + \left(\frac{db}{d\rho}\right)_T\right] - \frac{2\gamma RT}{\rho(M/\rho - b)} \qquad (17)$$

We cannot, of course, expect this to reduce to the ideal gas value for V^2 when $b \to 0$, since we have discarded $\gamma p/\rho$ for the liquid case in our derivation.

Further progress depends on the choice of b as a function of ρ. It will be recalled that in the van der Waals theory for gases b represents four times the total volume of the molecules themselves considered as hard spheres of radius r; that is, for one mole

$$b = \frac{16\pi}{3} N r^3 \qquad (18)$$

where N = number of molecules per mole. It has been assumed by W. Schaaffs[1] that

$$b = \frac{b_g M/\rho}{M/\rho + b_g - b_0} \qquad (19)$$

where b_g is the value of b in the van der Waals equation for effectively infinite volume, whereas b_0 is the corresponding value for $T = 0$ and $p = 0$. These values can be obtained from critical data. From these, Schaaffs obtains semiempirically the result

$$\left(\frac{db}{d\rho}\right)_T \doteq -\frac{2}{3}\frac{M}{\rho^2} \qquad (20)$$

With this choice, (17) takes the form

$$V^2 = \frac{\gamma RT}{M - b}\left(\frac{M/3}{M - b\rho} - 2\right) \qquad (21)$$

Since b contains the radius r of the molecule, the most interesting use this can be put to physically is the evaluation of r in terms of the velocity of sound in the liquid. This can then be compared with the corresponding value calculated from critical data. Table 9–1 shows the extent of the agreement for certain organic liquids. The results are interesting from the standpoint of the order-of-magnitude agreement as well as the consistency in the progression in values. Unfortunately, the use of more elaborate equations of state in calculating V does not seem to improve the agreement markedly. (For further discussion of the relation between sound transmission and the structure of fluid media, see Chap. 12.)

[1] Z. Physik, **115**, 69 (1940). See also Ergeb. exakt. Naturw., **25**, 109 (1951).

TABLE 9-1. MOLECULAR RADII CALCULATED FROM SOUND VELOCITY IN LIQUIDS
(After Schaaffs)*

Liquid	V at 20°C, m/sec	$r \times 10^8$ cm (from V)	$r \times 10^8$ cm (from critical data)
Methyl alcohol	1,125	1.47	1.87
Carbon disulfide	1,158	1.73	1.97
Benzene	1,331	1.99	2.29
Carbon tetrachloride	943	2.03	2.33
Heptane	1,154	2.33	2.48

* L. Bergmann, "Der Ultraschall," 6th ed., S. Hirzel Verlag, Leipzig, 1954.

9.3. Intensity and Impedance of Compressional Waves in Fluids

Following the lead of Secs. 1.3 and 1.7 we can write a plane wave solution of the wave equation (9.1-5) in the form

$$\varphi = f(\alpha x + \beta y + \gamma z - Vt) \tag{1}$$

where α, β, γ are here the direction cosines of the normal to the wavefront, that is, $\alpha^2 + \beta^2 + \gamma^2 = 1$. Similarly, a spherical wave solution is in the form

$$\varphi = \frac{1}{r} f(r - Vt) \tag{2}$$

We now wish to extend the considerations of Sec. 1.10 to the determination of the intensity of a compressional wave in a fluid. This, as usual, is defined to be the average rate of flow of energy per unit area of wavefront in the direction normal to the wavefront. Let us find this first for a plane wave, which, without loss of generality, we may assume travels in the x direction, so that

$$\varphi = f(x - Vt) \tag{3}$$

Since the wave is dilatational, the disturbance is also directed wholly in the x direction, whence $\nabla \varphi$ reduces to $\mathbf{i} \, \partial \varphi / \partial x$ and the flow velocity has the magnitude

$$v = \dot{\xi} = \frac{\partial \varphi}{\partial x} = f'(x - Vt) \tag{4}$$

where f' is the derivative of f with respect to the whole argument $x - Vt$. The excess pressure is, from (9.1-10),

$$p_e = -\rho_0 \dot{\varphi} = \rho_0 V f'(x - Vt) \tag{5}$$

Now the instantaneous rate of energy flow per unit area is the instantaneous rate at which work is done per unit area by the passage of the disturbance, that is, the power per unit area. This is

$$p_e\dot{\xi} = \rho_0 V[f'(x - Vt)]^2 = \frac{p_e{}^2}{\rho_0 V} \tag{6}$$

The time average of this quantity is by definition the intensity I (Sec. 1.10) or

$$I = \frac{\overline{p_e{}^2}}{\rho_0 V} \tag{7}$$

If the plane wave is a harmonic one with angular frequency, so that

$$p_e = p_0 e^{i(\omega t - kx)} \tag{8}$$

we readily see that

$$I = \frac{p_0{}^2}{2\rho_0 V} \tag{9}$$

Next let us investigate the intensity of a spherical wave. The flow velocity now is in magnitude

$$v = |\nabla\varphi| = \frac{\partial\varphi}{\partial r} = -\frac{f}{r^2} + \frac{f'}{r} \tag{10}$$

(where, for simplicity, the argument of f is left out). Moreover,

$$p_e = \frac{\rho_0 V}{r} f' \tag{11}$$

so that

$$p_e v = -\frac{\rho_0 V f f'}{r^3} + \frac{\rho_0 V f'^2}{r^2} \tag{12}$$

The expression for the intensity of a spherical wave is thus rather more complicated than that for a plane wave. However, if the spherical wave is harmonic with angular frequency ω, the time average of ff' vanishes, and we still have the form (7) for I. The fall-off in intensity inversely with the square of r has already been commented on in Chap. 1.

The decibel notation is immediately applicable, as in Sec. 1.10. Thus, for a plane progressive harmonic wave with maximum excess pressure p_0, we have for the intensity in decibels (db) relative to a standard excess pressure p_s in the same medium

$$\delta = 20 \log_{10} \frac{p_0}{p_s} \tag{13}$$

The use of electrical analogies, particularly for sound sources, suggests the introduction of the *impedance* notation, which is often useful in sound-radiation problems. In the so-called "direct" analogy, the excess pressure in a sound wave is taken to correspond with the electromotive force, and the volume current (the product of the particle velocity $\dot{\xi}$ and the area of the wavefront S) is assumed to be analogous to the electric current.   Hence it is natural to define the acoustic impedance of a wave as

$$Z = \frac{p_e}{\dot{X}}$$ (14)

where $\dot{X}$ = volume current = $S\dot{\xi}$.   With the use of the complex notation for wave quantities the impedance will usually be complex.[1]

We first examine (14) for the case of a plane harmonic wave of angular frequency ω in which the velocity potential φ is

$$\varphi = \varphi_0 e^{i(\omega t - kx)}$$ (15)

leading to

$$\dot{\xi} = -ik\varphi_0 e^{i(\omega t - kx)}$$ (16)

and

$$p_e = -i\omega\rho_0\varphi_0 e^{i(\omega t - kx)}$$ (17)

The impedance of such a wave is then

$$Z = \frac{\rho_0 V}{S}$$ (18)

a real quantity.   The numerator is called the specific acoustic impedance of a plane wave and denoted by Z_s.   It is the impedance for a unit area of wavefront.   Because it is real, it is usually referred to as the specific acoustic resistance.   Its presence in the expression for the intensity [Eq. (9)] is significant.   We may write the latter

$$I = \frac{p_0^2}{Z_s}$$ (19)

The specific acoustic resistance then controls the magnitude of the intensity of a plane wave for a given maximum excess pressure.[2]

Let us now proceed to a spherical harmonic wave diverging from the origin in which the velocity potential has the form

$$\varphi = \frac{\varphi_0 e^{i(\omega t - kr)}}{r}$$ (20)

The excess pressure has the form

$$p_e = -\frac{i\omega\varphi_0\rho_0 e^{i(\omega t - kr)}}{r}$$ (21)

and the flow velocity

$$\dot{\xi} = -\frac{\varphi_0}{r^2}(1 + ikr)e^{i(\omega t - kr)}$$ (22)

---

[1] The use of $\dot{X}$ for volume current is now standard in acoustics and acoustical engineering.   The student is cautioned not to confuse it with the use of X for stress in earlier chapters.

[2] It will be recalled that in Sec. 3.2 we observed the important role which the specific acoustic resistance plays in the transmission of plane radiation across the interface of two different media.

Hence the acoustic impedance is now

$$Z = \frac{i\omega\rho_0(1 - ikr)}{4\pi r(1 + k^2r^2)} \tag{23}$$

since the area of the spherical wavefront at distance r from the origin is $4\pi r^2$. This is a complex impedance with real and imaginary parts respectively given by

$$Z_r = \frac{\rho_0\omega k}{4\pi(1 + k^2r^2)} \tag{24}$$

$$Z_i = \frac{\rho_0\omega}{4\pi r(1 + k^2r^2)} \tag{25}$$

More important is the specific acoustic impedance obtained by multiplying through by the area of the wavefront. Thus

$$Z_s = \frac{i\omega\rho_0 r(1 - ikr)}{1 + k^2r^2} \tag{26}$$

with the real and imaginary parts

$$Z_{sr} = \frac{\rho_0\omega k r^2}{1 + k^2r^2}$$
$$Z_{si} = \frac{\rho_0\omega r}{1 + k^2r^2} \tag{27}$$

For a spherical wave *converging* on the origin similar analysis yields the same value for Z_{sr} and a value of Z_{si} which is equal in magnitude but opposite in sign to that in (27). It is customary to call the real part the specific acoustic *resistance* and the imaginary part the specific acoustic *reactance*. The latter is a specific inertance for a diverging wave (corresponding to an inductance in the electrical analogy) and the negative of a specific compliance for a converging wave (corresponding to the reciprocal of a capacitance in the electrical analogy).

It is instructive to examine the forms assumed by (27) for the extreme cases of waves of very high and very low frequencies, respectively. The former case will correspond to a wavelength λ very small compared with r, so that $kr \gg 1$. Then

$$Z_{sr} \to \rho_0 V$$
$$Z_{si} \to \frac{\rho_0 V}{kr} \ll \rho_0 V \tag{28}$$

Under these conditions, then, the specific acoustic resistance of a spherical wave approaches that of a plane wave, whereas the specific acoustic reactance becomes vanishingly small compared with it.

On the other hand, for $kr \ll 1$, corresponding to very low frequency, or very long wavelength compared with r, we have

$$Z_{sr} \rightarrow \rho_0 V k^2 r^2$$
$$Z_{si} \rightarrow \rho_0 V k r \tag{29}$$

In this extreme case the specific acoustic reactance is much larger than the specific acoustic resistance, and both are small compared with $\rho_0 V$.

These considerations remind us of the discussion of radiation reaction on a vibrating source in Sec. 3.5, where the use of the impedance notation would have been useful. We introduced specific acoustic resistance as an appropriate terminology in Sec. 3.2.

As in the electrical analogy, we may define the resultant specific impedance as the absolute value

$$Z_s = \sqrt{Z_{sr}^2 + Z_{si}^2}$$
$$= \frac{\rho_0 \omega r}{\sqrt{1 + k^2 r^2}} \tag{30}$$

which again approaches $\rho_0 V$ for $kr \gg 1$ and $\rho_0 V k r$ for $kr \ll 1$.

Can we express the intensity of a spherical harmonic wave in terms of the impedance? If we return to (21) and (22), the maximum values of the real part of the excess pressure and the particle velocity become, respectively,

$$p_{e,\max} = \frac{\omega \varphi_0 \rho_0}{r} \tag{31}$$

and

$$\dot{\xi}_{\max} = \frac{\varphi_0 \sqrt{1 + k^2 r^2}}{r^2} \tag{32}$$

so that the intensity can be written

$$I = \frac{p_{e,\max}^2}{2\rho_0 V} = \frac{1}{2} p_{e,\max} \dot{\xi}_{\max} \frac{Z_s}{\rho_0 V} \tag{33}$$

This reminds us of the expression for the power developed by an alternating electric current in which $Z_s/\rho_0 V$ appears as the power factor, or the cosine of the phase angle between the current and electromotive force. In the case of acoustical transmission it is the cosine of the angle between the excess pressure and the particle velocity. The important result is that the power factor here is the absolute value of the specific impedance divided by the specific impedance of a plane wave. Another way of looking at this conclusion is often of importance. If we note that

$$\frac{p_{e,\max}}{\dot{\xi}_{\max}} = Z_s \tag{34}$$

we can write

$$I = \frac{1}{2} \dot{\xi}_{\max}^2 \frac{Z_s^2}{\rho_0 V} = \frac{1}{2} \dot{\xi}_{\max}^2 Z_{sr} \tag{35}$$

In other words, if the intensity is expressed in terms of the square of the particle velocity, the coefficient is half the *real* component of the specific acoustic impedance. For a spherical acoustic source with fixed particle velocity at a specified distance from the source, the output is proportional to the real part of the specific impedance at that place. This has a useful application to acoustic transducers (sources and receivers) generally.

The concept of impedance forms a useful mathematical link in the analogies connecting electrical, mechanical, and acoustical systems. For example, for a vibrating system of one degree of freedom with mass m, compliance C, and dissipation coefficient R, the equation of motion subject to a harmonic driving force $F = F_0 e^{i\omega t}$ is (Sec. 3.5)

$$m\ddot{f} + R\dot{f} + \frac{f}{C} = F_0 e^{i\omega t} \tag{36}$$

where f is the displacement from equilibrium. It is often convenient to write the expression for the complex velocity in the steady-state solution in the form

$$\dot{f} = \frac{F}{R + i(m\omega - 1/\omega C)} \tag{37}$$

where

$$R + i\left(m\omega - \frac{1}{\omega C}\right) = Z_m \tag{38}$$

is termed the complex mechanical impedance; it is the ratio of the driving force to the displacement velocity. The real part of the mechanical impedance is R, the mechanical resistance; the imaginary part is $m\omega - 1/\omega C$, or the mechanical reactance. The concept of specific impedance has, of course, no application to this situation. (For further discussion of mechanical impedance and analogies generally, see Sec. 9.8.)

9.4. Reflection and Refraction of Sound Waves

In Sec. 2.1 we developed the geometrical aspects of the reflection and refraction of waves at a plane boundary. In Sec. 3.2 we worked out the power transmission of harmonic waves across a boundary on which they are incident normally. It is now in order to generalize the discussion by considering the reflection and refraction of *oblique* compressional harmonic waves at a boundary and to include the transmission of energy as well. This problem was presumably first worked out by George Green in 1838.[1] It is related, of course, to the problem of the oblique reflection and refrac-

---

[1] George Green, *Trans. Cambridge Phil. Soc.*, **6**, 403 (1838). See also N. M. Ferrers, (ed.), "The Mathematical Papers of the Late George Green," Macmillan & Co., Ltd., London, 1871.

tion of light as treated from the standpoint of an elastic solid by Fresnel.[1] We are here concerned solely with a compressible ideal fluid.

In view of the results of Sec. 2.1, we shall simplify the discussion by assuming that the incident wavefront is parallel to the x axis. Its trace on the yz plane is AB (Fig. 9.1), which makes the angle θ_i with the y axis.

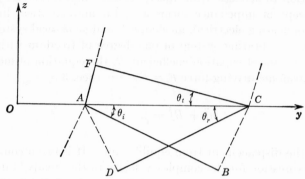

FIG. 9.1. Refraction of a plane sound wave at a plane interface.

The boundary surface at which the reflection and refraction are assumed to take place is the xy plane. The trace of the reflected wavefront on the yz plane is CD, where the angle ACD is $\theta_r = \theta_i$. Similarly, the trace of the refracted wavefront is FC and the angle of refraction or transmission is θ_t.

The velocity potential of the incident harmonic wave then is

$$\varphi_i = A_i e^{i[\omega t - k_1(\beta_i y + \gamma_i z)]} \tag{1}$$

where $k_1 = \omega/V_1$ (V_1 being the velocity in the incident medium, *below* the xy plane) and β_i and γ_i are the direction cosines of the incident ray or normal to the incident wavefront. (Note that α_i in this case is zero.) We therefore have

$$\beta_i = \sin \theta_i \qquad \gamma_i = \cos \theta_i \tag{2}$$

Similarly, the reflected velocity potential is

$$\varphi_r = A_r e^{i[\omega t - k_1(\beta_i y - \gamma_i z)]} \tag{3}$$

and the transmitted

$$\varphi_t = A_t e^{i[\omega t - k_2(\beta_t y + \gamma_t z)]} \tag{4}$$

where $k_2 = \omega/V_2$ (V_2 being the velocity in the second medium) and

$$\beta_t = \sin \theta_t \qquad \gamma_t = \cos \theta_t \tag{5}$$

[1] A. Fresnel, "Oeuvres," vol. 1, p. 767, Imprimerie Imperiale, Paris, 1866. See also the interesting discussion in E. T. Whittaker, "History of the Theories of Aether and Electricity," vol. 1, pp. 123f., Thomas Nelson and Sons, London, 1951.

We have already derived the law of refraction in the form

$$\frac{\sin \theta_i}{\sin \theta_t} = \frac{V_1}{V_2} = \frac{k_2}{k_1}$$

so that
$$k_2\beta_t = k_1\beta_i \tag{6}$$

The boundary conditions are (1) continuity of pressure and (2) continuity of flow velocity normal to the boundary surface. From $p_e = -\rho_0\dot{\varphi}$, the first condition yields, for $z = 0$,

$$\rho_1(\dot{\varphi}_i + \dot{\varphi}_r) = \rho_2\dot{\varphi}_t \tag{7}$$

where ρ_1 and ρ_2 are the mean densities in the two media, respectively. From $v_n = \partial\varphi/\partial z$ the second condition yields, at $z = 0$,

$$\frac{\partial\varphi_i}{\partial z} + \frac{\partial\varphi_r}{\partial z} = \frac{\partial\varphi_t}{\partial z} \tag{8}$$

Substitution from (1), (3), and (4) produces the two equations

$$\begin{aligned} \rho_1(A_i + A_r) &= \rho_2 A_t \\ k_1\gamma_i(A_i - A_r) &= k_2\gamma_t A_t \end{aligned} \tag{9}$$

If we are interested in reflection, we eliminate A_t and obtain

$$\frac{A_r}{A_i} = \frac{\rho_2 k_1\gamma_i - \rho_1 k_2\gamma_t}{\rho_2 k_1\gamma_i + \rho_1 k_2\gamma_t} \tag{10}$$

Use of the values of the γ's in terms of the angles, coupled with the law of refraction, transforms this equation into

$$\frac{A_r}{A_i} = \frac{\rho_2/\rho_1 - \cot \theta_t/\cot \theta_i}{\rho_2/\rho_1 + \cot \theta_t/\cot \theta_i} \tag{11}$$

Since, as usual, we may express the incident intensity as the mean-square excess pressure divided by the specific acoustic impedance, it follows that the ratio of the reflected to the incident intensity is

$$\left(\frac{A_r}{A_i}\right)^2 = \frac{(\rho_2/\rho_1 - \cot \theta_t/\cot \theta_i)^2}{(\rho_2/\rho_1 + \cot \theta_t/\cot \theta_i)^2} \tag{12}$$

For normal incidence $\cos \theta_i = \cos \theta_t = 1$, and the above reduces to the simpler form already obtained in Sec. 3.2. Examination of (11) shows that, in addition to the simple case in which the second medium has the same specific acoustic impedance as the first ($\rho_2 V_2 = \rho_1 V_1$), we also get *no* reflection at the boundary between two media of different specific acoustic impedance for the angle of incidence such that

$$\rho_2 \cot \theta_i = \rho_1 \cot \theta_t$$

This leads to

$$\cot \theta_i = \sqrt{\frac{V_1^2/V_2^2 - 1}{\rho_2^2/\rho_1^2 - V_1^2/V_2^2}} \tag{13}$$

If V_1/V_2 lies between unity and ρ_2/ρ_1, this angle is real, and for it the wave is wholly transmitted. It is, however, not easy to satisfy this condition with usually available materials.

For some purposes the transmission coefficient is more important than that for reflection. We can readily arrive at this from energy-conservation considerations. The average rate of flow of energy across the incident wavefront is equal to the sum of the corresponding quantities for the reflected and transmitted wavefronts, respectively. Hence, if we denote the incident wavefront area by S_i (equal of course to the reflected wavefront area) and the transmitted area by S_t, with the use of I_i, I_r, I_t to denote the incident, reflected, and transmitted intensities, respectively, conservation demands that

$$I_i S_i = I_r S_i + I_t S_t$$

or

$$\frac{I_t}{I_i} = \frac{S_i}{S_t}\left(1 - \frac{I_r}{I_i}\right) \tag{14}$$

Since $S_i/S_t = \cos \theta_i/\cos \theta_t$ (see Fig. 9.1), the above yields, with the use of (12),

$$\frac{I_t}{I_i} = \frac{4\rho_2 V_1/\rho_1 V_2}{(\rho_2/\rho_1 + \cot \theta_t/\cot \theta_i)^2} \tag{15}$$

It is readily verified that this also follows directly from

$$I_t = \frac{\omega^2 \rho_2 A_t^2}{2V_2}$$

and

$$I_i = \frac{\omega^2 \rho_1}{2V_1} A_i^2$$

In the analysis leading to (12) we tacitly assumed either that $V_1 > V_2$, so that there is a *real* angle θ_t for every angle of incidence θ_i, or, if $V_1 < V_2$, that $\theta_i < \arcsin (V_1/V_2)$. If these conditions are not satisfied, total reflection ensues, as is clear from the following considerations. Since in this case $\sin \theta_t > 1$, it follows from (5) that γ_t, which is $\cos \theta_t$, is pure imaginary. Hence we write it

$$\gamma_t = -i\gamma_t'$$

where γ_t' is real, and have in place of (4)

$$\varphi_t = A_t e^{-k_2 \gamma_t' z} e^{i(\omega t - k_2 \beta_t y)} \tag{16}$$

The application of the boundary conditions proceeds as before, only now (10) becomes

$$\frac{A_r}{A_i} = \frac{\rho_2 k_1 \gamma_i + i\rho_1 k_2 \gamma_t'}{\rho_2 k_1 \gamma_1 - i\rho_1 k_2 \gamma_t'} \tag{17}$$

Hence A_r and A_i are now complex quantities, equal in magnitude though different in phase. In fact,

$$\frac{|A_r|^2}{|A_i|^2} = 1 \tag{18}$$

and

$$A_r = A_i e^{-i\delta} \tag{19}$$

where

$$\delta = \arctan\left(-\frac{2ab}{a^2 - b^2}\right) \tag{20}$$

if $a = \rho_2 k_1 \gamma_i$ and $b = \rho_1 k_2 \gamma_t'$. The result is total reflection with a change in phase given by (20). This then always takes place when $V_1 < V_2$ and the angle of incidence is greater than the critical angle arcsin (V_1/V_2). The form of the transmitted velocity potential φ_t given by (16) is interesting, since it corresponds to a damped wave in the y direction, that is, along the boundary surface, with a dissipation coefficient equal to $\omega\gamma_t'/V_2 = (\omega/V_1)\sqrt{\sin^2\theta_i - V_1^2/V_2^2}$. In general it penetrates only a little distance across the boundary and can be shown to convey, on the average, no sound energy from the first to the second medium.[1]

The analogy with light and electromagnetic waves in general is instructive. We can pursue this a bit further if we go back to (11) and, confining our attention to *gases*, write

$$V_1 = \sqrt{\frac{\gamma p}{\rho_1}} \qquad V_2 = \sqrt{\frac{\gamma p}{\rho_2}} \tag{21}$$

where we assume that the gas on both sides is at the same pressure and has the same ratio of specific heats γ (do not confuse this γ with the direction cosines γ_i and γ_t). Hence in this case

$$\frac{\rho_2}{\rho_1} = \frac{V_1^2}{V_2^2}$$

Therefore (11) becomes

$$\begin{aligned}
\frac{A_r}{A_i} &= \frac{\dfrac{V_1^2}{V_2^2} - \dfrac{\cos\theta_t}{\sin\theta_t}\dfrac{\sin\theta_i}{\cos\theta_i}}{\dfrac{V_1^2}{V_2^2} + \dfrac{\cos\theta_t}{\sin\theta_t}\dfrac{\sin\theta_i}{\cos\theta_i}} \\
&= \frac{\sin 2\theta_i - \sin 2\theta_t}{\sin 2\theta_i + \sin 2\theta_t} \\
&= \frac{\tan(\theta_i - \theta_t)}{\tan(\theta_i + \theta_t)}
\end{aligned} \tag{22}$$

This is one of the well-known Fresnel formulas in the oblique reflection of light from a plane surface. It corresponds indeed to light polarized

[1] The analysis is similar to that for the corresponding electromagnetic case. Consult J. A. Stratton, "Electromagnetic Theory," pp. 497ff., McGraw-Hill Book Company, Inc., New York, 1941.

perpendicularly to the plane of incidence. Immediately, we deduce that, if $\theta_i + \theta_t = \pi/2$, $A_r/A_i = 0$, or there is no reflected amplitude. This condition on the angles is equivalent to

$$\tan \theta_i = \frac{V_1}{V_2} \tag{23}$$

which is Brewster's law in optics. We must note, of course, that, since there is no possibility of polarization in the optical sense for acoustic waves in extended media, the analogy is not complete (but see the reference in Sec. 2.5 to the special properties of acoustic waves in tubes).

Another illustration is provided by the case of two liquids with the same densities, $\rho_1 = \rho_2$, but with different bulk moduli, so that $V_1 \neq V_2$. Then (11) becomes

$$\frac{A_r}{A_i} = \frac{\sin \theta_t \cos \theta_i - \cos \theta_t \sin \theta_i}{\sin \theta_t \cos \theta_i + \cos \theta_t \sin \theta_i} = \frac{\sin (\theta_t - \theta_i)}{\sin (\theta_t + \theta_i)} \tag{24}$$

This corresponds to the Fresnel equation for light polarized in the plane of incidence.[1]

9.5. Diffraction and Scattering of Sound by Fluid Obstacles and Bubbles

In Sec. 3.6 we discussed the scattering of a compressional wave in a fluid medium by a rigid obstacle, treating specifically the cases of the cylinder and the sphere. There is considerable interest in scattering by objects which are not rigid, such as bubbles in water. The analysis in such a case proceeds similarly to that of Sec. 3.6, save that one must now consider the scattered wave inside the obstacle. Typical of this method are some calculations by S. J. Bezuszka[2] on the scattering of sound in one fluid (e.g., water) by thin-walled plastic cylinders containing liquids having different acoustical properties from the surrounding fluid. Experimental work along this line has also been carried out by P. Tamarkin.[3] The following development leans heavily on their results.

First it is worthwhile to make a few general observations. We expect that the nature of the scattering will depend on the ratio of the radius of the cylinder to the wavelength of the sound. If this ratio is much greater than unity, the simple diffraction considerations of Chap. 2 suggest that the obstacle will cast an acoustic shadow; in others words, ray

---

[1] Fresnel, "Oeuvres," vol. 1, p. 767; also F. A. Jenkins and H. E. White, "Fundamentals of Optics," 2d ed., pp. 560ff., McGraw-Hill Book Company, Inc., New York, 1950.

[2] *J. Acoust. Soc. Am.*, **25**, 1090 (1953).

[3] *J. Acoust. Soc. Am.*, **21**, 612 (1949).

acoustics will be adequate to describe the phenomenon. On the other hand, if the ratio is much smaller than unity, Rayleigh scattering will result, as would be expected from the discussion at the end of Sec. 3.6, since here the fact that the obstacle is not rigid will make little difference. The interesting case is that in which the radius of the cylinder is of the same order as the wavelength.

The geometry of the situation is shown in Fig. 9.2. The cylinder is placed with its axis along the x axis of a system of rectangular coordi-

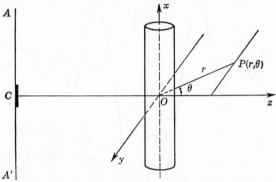

FIG. 9.2. Scattering of a plane sound wave by a fluid cylinder with axis parallel to the wavefront. [*Reprinted with permission from S. J. Bezuszka, J. Acoust. Soc. Am.*, **25**, 1090 (1953), *with certain changes.*]

nates. ACA' represents a plane wavefront parallel to the xy plane approaching the cylinder along the z axis. The fluid inside the cylinder is characterized by density ρ_i and elastic wave velocity V_i. The scattering is expressed by the calculated values of the root-mean-square excess pressure at any point P with polar coordinates r and θ with respect to the origin O. Actually it turns out to be simpler to plot the pressure against the lateral distance of P from the z axis, since this permits simpler comparison with experimental results.

No analytical details are presented here. A typical plot taken from Bezuszka's paper will indicate the nature of the theoretical results (Fig. 9.3). The quantity plotted is proportional to the total rms excess pressure (where total means the resultant of the incident and scattered radiation), the factor K being $\omega\rho_0/\sqrt{2}$, where ρ_0 is the density of the fluid surrounding the cylinder and ω is the angular frequency of the incident sound. V_i is the velocity of sound in the fluid in the cylinder, and $\rho_i V_i$ is the specific acoustic resistance (plane wave) for the cylinder fluid. The quantity $k_i a = 2\pi a/\lambda_i$, where λ_i is the wavelength in the cylinder fluid. For the value given in the figure, the radius is about four times the wavelength. This was chosen for the purpose of comparison with the experimental results of Tamarkin. The curve has the typical form of a

Fraunhofer diffraction pattern in optics, as indeed one would expect from the general setup.

The experimental curves of Tamarkin have indeed the same general form as those theoretically predicted, though the relative heights of the peaks do not agree. The principal reason for the discrepancy is probably to be found in the fact that it was impossible in the experimental study to secure incident plane waves; in any feasible tank one has to

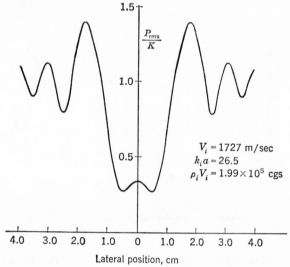

FIG. 9.3. Pressure distribution in a plane wave scattered by a 4.0 N NaCl-H$_2$O obstacle (24.5 cm from obstacle). [*Reprinted with permission from S. J. Bezuszka, J. Acoust. Soc. Am.*, **25**, 1090 (1953), *with certain changes.*]

settle for a sound beam which will not have a precisely plane wavefront over the surface of an obstacle of the size contemplated. Of course, in the experimental arrangement it is also necessary to enclose the cylindrical fluid in a container, and this might be expected to scatter by itself. Actually, with the thin-walled plastic cylinders employed, this scattering turns out to be negligible.

Another significant way of interpreting the theoretical scattering results is to plot as a function of $k_i a$ the ratio p/p_0, where p is the excess pressure at some suitably chosen point on the z axis (e.g., at the center of the diffracted wave) and p_0 is the value the pressure would have at this point if the obstacle were not there. This can be done if the calculations have been carried out for a sufficiently wide range of scattering liquids (as was the case with Bezuszka's work). Figure 9.4 shows the result, which may be interpreted as a kind of resonance curve. Thus, as a result of the diffraction, for certain values of $k_i a$, or the ratio of radius to wavelength, the total relative response (incident plus scattered) at a point in the center of the beam has maximum value, indicating a cooperation of the scattered with the incident radiation.   In terms of the obstacle this presumably means that the forced modes of radial oscillation in the cylinder are coinciding, or at any rate coming close to some of the natural modes. The theoretical resonance curve agrees rather well with the experimental one obtained by Tamarkin, though the latter is more severely limited in $k_i a$ range.

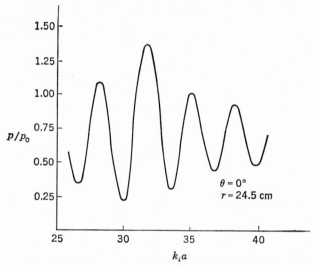

FIG. 9.4. Plot of the ratio of scattered and incident pressures vs. values of $k_i a$ for the various obstacles, at a point 24.5 cm directly ahead of them. [*Reprinted with permission from S. J. Bezuszka, J. Acoust. Soc. Am.*, **25**, 1090 (1953), *with certain changes.*]

   The mention of resonance in connection with sound scattering by liquid-filled cylinders suggests that this may be even more important with air bubbles in water.   We therefore pay some attention to scattering by a single bubble.   Here the phenomenon of resonance can be made to appear more explicitly in the analysis.   As in the case of the cylinder, the scattering by a spherical bubble will involve the production of stationary waves in the air or other gas inside the bubble.   These are of course very complicated, as is indicated by the somewhat simpler case of a circular membrane in Sec. 5.3.   The normal modes of a rectangular chamber, which are of importance in room acoustics, are relatively simpler (see Secs. 3.1 and 11.2).   Those for a sphere can be found in Rayleigh.[1]   We shall simplify the present discussion by assuming that only the spherically symmetrical modes are effective; in practice these are the most easily excited.

---

[1] Lord Rayleigh, "Theory of Sound," 2d ed., vol. 2, pp. 241ff., Dover Publications, New York, 1945.

If we were to follow the general outline of the analysis in Sec. 3.6, we should have to express the plane wave incident on the bubble as a summation of spherical waves, since from the above assumption the waves excited in the bubble will be spherical in character. We shall further simplify, however, by assuming that the bubble radius a is small compared with the wavelength of the incident sound. Then any change in phase of the incident disturbance over the space occupied by the bubble will be negligible, and we may safely take the disturbance as harmonically varying with time alone at the vicinity of the bubble. The velocity potential of the incident wave will therefore be taken as

$$\varphi_i = A e^{i\omega t} \tag{1}$$

and that for the scattered wave from the bubble will be

$$\varphi_s = \frac{B}{r} e^{i(\omega t - kr)} \tag{2}$$

where r is measured from the center of the bubble. The corresponding excess pressures are

$$p_i = -\rho_0 \dot{\varphi}_i = -i\omega\rho_0 A e^{i\omega t}$$
$$p_s = -\rho_0 \dot{\varphi}_s = \frac{-i\omega\rho_0 B}{r} e^{i(\omega t - kr)} \qquad r > a \tag{3}$$

For the excess pressure inside the bubble it will be sufficient (because of the small value of a compared with the wavelength) to set

$$p_b = C e^{i\omega t} \tag{4}$$

Since the excess pressure change inside the bubble is adiabatic in view of the rapid change due to the sound wave, we have, from the adiabatic gas relation,

$$\dot{p}_b = \frac{-3\gamma p_0 \dot{a}}{a} \tag{5}$$

where γ is the usual specific-heat ratio and p_0 is the average static pressure inside and outside the bubble when it is undisturbed by the sound wave. Combining (5) with (4), we obtain for the radial velocity of the bubble

$$\dot{a} = \frac{-i\omega a C e^{i\omega t}}{3\gamma p_0} \tag{6}$$

We must now employ the boundary conditions that at the surface of the bubble the excess pressure and radial velocity shall be continuous. The first gives

$$-i\omega\rho_0 A - \frac{i\omega\rho_0 B}{a} e^{-ika} = C \tag{7}$$

Since $ka \ll 1$, because of the assumed small size of the bubbles, we set $e^{-ika} = 1 - ika$ approximately and rewrite (7) as

$$A + \frac{B}{a}(1 - ika) = -\frac{C}{i\omega\rho_0} \tag{8}$$

To set up the radial velocity condition we need, in addition to $\dot{a}$, the radial flow velocity v_s in the scattered wave. The latter is just $\partial\varphi_s/\partial r$, and hence

$$v_s = B\left(-\frac{1}{r^2} - \frac{ik}{r}\right)e^{i(\omega t - kr)} \tag{9}$$

Again we approximate when $r = a$ and see that, if we can safely neglect k^2a^2 compared with unity, (9) with (6) gives

$$\frac{B}{a^2} = \frac{i\omega aC}{3\gamma p_0} \tag{10}$$

If now we eliminate C between (8) and (10), the value of B in terms of A comes out to be

$$B = \frac{aA}{3\gamma p_0/\rho_0\omega^2a^2 - (1 - ika)} \tag{11}$$

Now the intensity of the incident wave is (Sec. 9.3)

$$I_i = \frac{\overline{p_{ir}^2}}{\rho_0 V} = \frac{\omega^2\rho_0}{2V}|A|^2 \tag{12}$$

where V is the wave velocity in the medium in which the bubble is immersed and p_{ir} is the real part of the excess pressure in the incident wave, whereas the intensity of the scattered wave at $r = a$ is

$$I_s = \frac{\overline{p_{sr}^2}}{\rho_0 V} = \frac{\omega^2\rho_0}{2Va^2}|B|^2 \tag{13}$$

The ratio of scattered to incident intensity is therefore

$$\frac{I_s}{I_i} = \frac{|B|^2}{a^2|A|^2} = \frac{1}{(3\gamma p_0/\rho_0\omega^2a^2 - 1)^2 + k^2a^2} \tag{14}$$

The condition that this be a maximum yields the cubic equation

$$(ka)^6 = \frac{18\gamma^2 p_0^2}{\rho_0^2 V^4} - \frac{6\gamma p_0}{V^2\rho_0}(ka)^2 \tag{15}$$

In view of the smallness of ka compared with unity, the first (and good) approximation to the solution is

$$ka = \frac{1}{V}\sqrt{\frac{3\gamma p_0}{\rho_0}}$$

leading to the angular frequency

$$\omega_r = \frac{1}{a} \sqrt{\frac{3\gamma p_0}{\rho_0}} \tag{16}$$

We may call this the angular resonance frequency of the bubble. It may indeed be evaluated by a direct study of the vibrations of the bubble as a vibrating system. At this frequency the ratio of scattered to incident intensity becomes approximately

$$\left(\frac{I_s}{I_i}\right)_{\text{res}} \doteq \frac{\rho_0 V^2}{3\gamma p_0} \tag{17}$$

If p_0 is the standard atmospheric pressure, V the velocity in sea water at 20°C = 1.513 × 10⁵ cm/sec, and ρ_0 = density of sea water at 20°C = 1.021 g/cm³, the above ratio becomes

$$\left(\frac{I_s}{I_i}\right)_{\text{res}} \doteq 5.5 \times 10^3 \tag{18}$$

At first sight this may seem contradictory to the conservation of energy, until we reflect that the vibration of the bubble at resonance is acting to "load" the source of the sound and hence extract energy from it at a faster rate than would be the case at the same point in the medium if the bubble were not there.

Another way of looking at the scattering problem introduces the so-called scattering cross section σ of the bubble. This is defined so that

$$\sigma I_i = 4\pi a^2 I_s \tag{19}$$

which means that the average sound energy flowing per unit time through the area σ perpendicular to the incident sound beam is equal to the average sound energy scattered by the bubble in all directions. The result (18) means that at resonance the scattering cross section of the bubble is very much greater than its geometrical cross section.

Equation (16) may be used to compute the radius of the bubble for various resonance frequencies. Thus, using the data given above, for a resonance frequency of 20 kc ($\omega_r = 40\pi \times 10^3$ sec⁻¹) the bubble radius in sea water is 0.016 cm. As the pressure increases (e.g., with depth), the radius of the resonant bubble increases, other things being equal. The same result obviously obtains as the frequency is lowered.

The above discussion neglects the effect of damping, which will intervene in any actual case, principally because the vibrations of the bubble are not thermodynamically reversible; the rise in temperature of the gas in the bubble when it is compressed leads to heat conduction, which starts to take place before the bubble has ceased contracting. Thus the temperature and pressure get out of phase, and this leads to a kind of hysteresis cycle, which in Chap. 12 we shall call a *relaxation effect*. This corresponds to the irreversible transformation of the vibration into heat and thus damps the motion and reduces the scattering effect. Analysis shows that the introduction of this damping into the problem does not affect the general conclusion reached above. In fact, (14) maintains its form, though k^2a^2 in the denominator is now replaced by a larger term containing terms due to the damping. The value of the resonance frequency is not affected.

The extension of the foregoing theory to the case of sound scattering by a medium containing many bubbles has been carried out.[1] It involves, of course, the use of statistical considerations and will not be presented here.

9.6. Filtration of Sound

In Sec. 3.4 we investigated the transmission of a general harmonic wave through a structure possessing periodicity in its properties, such as density and sound velocity. We there found that the transmission is selective with respect to frequency and that, if the structure is extensive enough, genuine filtration with a succession of pass- and attenuation bands results. This analysis lends itself readily to the application to compressional or acoustic waves in fluids confined in geometrical structures of various kinds, leading to filtration of sound. We can look upon this, if we will, as a special aspect of the transmission of compressional wave energy through a medium possessing periodic nonhomogeneity of structure. As a matter of fact, any kind of nonhomogeneity will produce selective transmission for the appropriate form of radiation. We have already noted that the stretched string loaded with point masses acts like a filter for transverse waves along the string. Similarly, an electric transmission line consisting of an iterated combination of inductances, resistances, and capacitances is in general an electric wave filter, and a crystal metal lattice is a filter for the transmission of electron (De Broglie) waves (Sec. 6.6).

In this section we shall examine the transmission of sound waves in a confined fluid in which the confinement alters periodically. The fluid considered will in general be a gas, and the mode of confinement will include the presence of side attachments such as tubes and orifices. A simple illustration of what we are talking about is provided by a very long cylindrical tube (effectively infinite) containing a constriction or expansion. Figure 9.5 illustrates such a situation, with a plane harmonic wave coming in from the left in a tube of cross section S_1, encountering an expansion of cross section S_2, of length $2l$, and proceeding ultimately

[1] L. L. Foldy, *Phys. Rev.,* **67,** 107 (1945).

to the right through a tube of the original cross section S_1. It is assumed for simplicity that the tube at the right has no finite termination. It is of interest to observe that we can predict the transmission through such a structure in its broad outlines without going through the mathematical analysis. We can plausibly assume that the expansion acts like a cylindrical tube of length $2l$ effectively closed at both ends. From the discussion of stationary waves in a bounded one-dimensional medium in Sec. 1.5 we conclude that such a tube will resonate, that is, possess normal

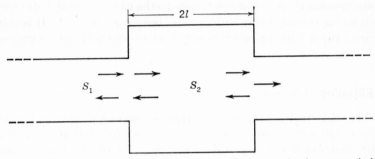

F<small>IG</small>. 9.5. Cylindrical tube with an expansion to illustrate selective transmission.

modes for those frequencies for which $\sin 2kl = 0$. We should therefore expect that the expanded tube would accept these frequencies most readily from the radiation coming from the left and transmit them strongly to the right. On the other hand, we expect that the expansion will reject most strongly those frequencies for which $\sin 2kl = 1$, since these are the antiresonant frequencies, and hence their transmission will be small. These expectations are borne out by the exact analysis, which indeed follows precisely the lines of the method set forth in Sec. 3.3 for the normal transmission through a plane parallel slab of fluid (or solid for that matter) embedded in a medium of different specific acoustic resistance. Inspection shows that formula (3.3-10) can apply to the case of the present section if we insert for r the ratio S_2/S_1. Hence the transmission coefficient, or, as it is often convenient to term it, the power transmission ratio P_r, becomes[1]

$$P_r = \frac{1}{1 - \dfrac{[(S_2/S_1)^2 - 1][(S_1/S_2)^2 - 1]}{4}\sin^2 2kl} \tag{1}$$

It is clear that this becomes unity when $\sin 2kl = 0$ and takes on a minimum value for $\sin 2kl = 1$. The plot of P_r vs. frequency then has the

---

[1] We use the symbol P_r for the power transmission ratio rather than the symbol T of Eq. (3.3-10). The latter strictly refers to the ratio of the transmitted to the incident *intensity*, whereas P_r in (1) denotes the ratio of the average transmitted *power* (total energy flow per unit time) to the average incident power.

general form shown in Fig. 3.4.   This justifies our plausibility consideration above.   Note that the result for a constriction is theoretically
identical to that for an expansion.

In Sec. 3.4 we discussed the transmission through an infinite structure
composed of alternating plane parallel layers of two different media
(different ρV values) and found that the structure acts like an ideal radiation filter.   Precisely the same type of analysis indicates that an air
tube consisting of an alternation of constrictions and expansions (cross
sections S_1 and S_2, respectively, and lengths $2l_1$ and $2l_2$, respectively)
constitutes an acoustic filter.   In the ideal infinite case the transmission
characteristics are given by a cos W function like that in (3.4-12, 15),
namely, the real function

$$\cos W = \cos 2kl_1 \cos 2kl_2 - \frac{1}{2}\left(\frac{S_2}{S_1} + \frac{S_1}{S_2}\right)\sin 2kl_1 \sin 2kl_2 \qquad (2)$$

This leads to a succession of alternating transmission and attenuation
bands.   Since $|\cos W| = 1$ for zero frequency, the first of these is a trans-
mission band and the filter may be termed "low-pass," though actually
it is of the bandpass type.   The main features of this filter follow from
the discussion in Sec. 3.4 and need not be repeated here.

It is clear that any periodic variation in the acoustic properties or
confinement of fluid in a tube will lead to filtration.   Let us consider the
simple cases of an orifice or a resonator in the side of a long tube.   These
constitute special cases of what may be called "branches" in an acoustic
line.   The transmission in the main line is affected by the nature and
dimensions of the branch.   The analytical problem can be worked out
in terms of a schematic representation (Fig. 9.6) in which MM (extend-

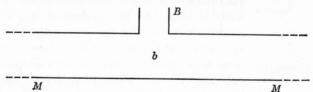

FIG. 9.6. Acoustic line with a branch to illustrate selective transmission.

ing from $-\infty$ on the left to $+\infty$ on the right) is the main acoustic line
and B is the branch, which will be characterized by its impedance at the
branch or junction point b (see Sec. 9.3).   What this means is simply
that if the excess acoustic pressure at b is p_b, the corresponding volume
current there, $\dot{X}_b$, will be

$$\dot{X}_b = \frac{p_b}{Z_b} \qquad (3)$$

where Z_b is the branch impedance at b.   No matter what the nature of the branch is, we can always obtain Z_b, and it will fully characterize the action of the branch on the acoustic transmission in the main line.

If we denote the incident excess pressure coming from the left, at b, as p_i and the corresponding volume current as $\dot{X}_i$, the corresponding reflected quantities as p_r and $\dot{X}_r$, respectively, and the transmitted quantities as p_t and $\dot{X}_t$, respectively, the boundary conditions at b take the form

$$
\begin{aligned}
p_i + p_r &= p_b = p_t \\
\dot{X}_i - \dot{X}_r &= \dot{X}_b + \dot{X}_t
\end{aligned}
\tag{4}
$$

If we assume that the main line has cross section S and that the specific acoustic resistance for a plane wave progressing through it is $\rho_0 V$, the ratio of p_t to p_i becomes

$$
\frac{p_t}{p_i} = \frac{1}{1 + \rho_0 V / 2 S Z_b}
\tag{5}
$$

Since Z_b is in general complex, we write

$$
Z_b = Z_{br} + i Z_{bi}
\tag{6}
$$

and from (5) get the general power transmission ratio past the branch in the form

$$
P_r = \frac{|Z_b|^2}{Z_{bi}^2 + (Z_{br} + \rho_0 V / 2 S)^2}
\tag{7}
$$

A simple illustration is provided by a Helmholtz resonator, which, as shown in Fig. 9.7, is a chamber communicating with the outside by an orifice, which may or may not have a neck. We let the volume of the resonator chamber be τ and the orifice have area of cross section S_b. If the resonator is excited by the production of a disturbance in the air in front of the orifice, the mass of air in the orifice will vibrate more or less as a whole in accordance with the equation of a simple linear oscillating system. Thus, if we denote the displacement from equilibrium of the vibrating "plug" of air by ξ, its mass by m, its stiffness by f, and its resistance coefficient by R, the equation of forced oscillations under harmonic external force F_e $(F_e = F_0 e^{i\omega t})$ becomes (Secs. 3.5 and 9.3)

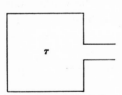

Fig. 9.7. Helmholtz resonator.

$$
m\ddot{\xi} + R\dot{\xi} + f\xi = F_e
\tag{8}
$$

To put this in the simplest form to obtain the equivalent acoustic impedance at the orifice, we write for the equivalent volume current

$$
\dot{X} = S_b \dot{\xi} = i\omega X = \frac{\ddot{X}}{i\omega}
\tag{9}
$$

so that the equation, written in terms of $\dot{X}$ and excess pressure $p_e = F_e/S_b$, becomes (S_b being the area of the neck)

$$\frac{i\omega m \dot{X}}{S_b{}^2} + \frac{R}{S_b{}^2}\dot{X} + \frac{f}{i\omega S_b{}^2}\dot{X} = p_e \tag{10}$$

The corresponding acoustic impedance is

$$\frac{p_e}{\dot{X}} = Z = \frac{R}{S_b{}^2} + \frac{i}{S_b{}^2}\left(\omega m - \frac{f}{\omega}\right) \tag{11}$$

For given impressed excess pressure amplitude the volume current is a maximum for the angular frequency

$$\omega_0 = \sqrt{\frac{f}{m}} \tag{12}$$

This is termed the angular *resonance* frequency of the system.

We can find the equivalent stiffness of the resonator by using the fundamental equation connecting excess pressure and condensation (see Sec. 9.1)

$$p_e = \rho_0 V^2 s \tag{13}$$

The change in volume of the resonator chamber $\Delta\tau$ associated with the volume displacement X is clearly $-X$ itself. Hence, since by definition of the condensation $s = -\Delta\tau/\tau$, we get, from (13),

$$p_e = \frac{\rho_0 V^2 X}{\tau}$$

and the equivalent stiffness becomes

$$f = \frac{p_e S_b{}^2}{X} = \frac{\rho_0 V^2 S_b{}^2}{\tau} \tag{14}$$

The mass m, which is obviously difficult to express for a simple orifice, can be most simply put in terms of the resonance frequency ω_0:[*]

$$m = \frac{\rho_0 V^2 S_b{}^2}{\tau \omega_0{}^2} \tag{15}$$

We therefore have for the *imaginary* part of the acoustic impedance at the mouth of the resonator used as a branch

$$Z_{bi} = \frac{\omega \rho_0 V^2}{\tau \omega_0{}^2} - \frac{\rho_0 V^2}{\tau \omega} \tag{16}$$

---

[*] In treatises on acoustics it is shown that m can be expressed in terms of the so-called "acoustic conductivity" of the orifice, generally denoted by c_0. This has the dimensions of a length and is ideally equal to S/l for an orifice which has a neck of length l and area of cross section S. However, if $l \to 0$, c_0 does not become infinite but, rather, approaches a value comparable to the diameter of the orifice if it is circular. See Rayleigh, "Theory of Sound," vol. 2, p. 176.

This vanishes at resonance, as it should. The *real* part of the impedance of a Helmholtz resonator is due to two physical characteristics: (1) the viscosity of the fluid in the orifice and (2) the radiation of sound from the orifice into the environment. It turns out that, except for very small orifices, the radiation impedance is by far the larger factor. Its value depends on the frequency and is indeed equal to[1]

$$\frac{R}{S^2} = \frac{\rho_0 \omega^2}{2\pi V} \tag{17}$$

Actually the radiation impedance of the resonator does not enter when the resonator is used as a branch, since it cannot radiate into the open air. Hence for the resonator as a branch (7) becomes effectively (neglecting viscous damping)

$$P_r = \frac{1}{1 + \rho_0^2 V^2 / 4 S^2 Z_{bi}^2}$$

$$= \frac{1}{1 + \omega^2 \omega_0^4 \tau^2 / 4 S^2 V^2 (\omega^2 - \omega_0^2)^2} \tag{18}$$

Clearly, for $\omega = 0$, $P_r = 1$, and as $\omega \to \infty$, $P_r \to 1$. For $\omega = \omega_0$, $P_r = 0$. Hence the plot of P_r as a function of ω looks somewhat as in Fig. 9.8. At the resonance frequency the energy of the incident wave in the main line merely excites the resonator and is then fed back into the line, allowing zero transmission down the line on the other side of the resonator.

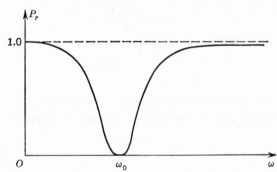

FIG. 9.8. Transmission through an acoustic line with a Helmholtz resonator as a branch.

The case of an orifice placed in the side of an acoustic line can be handled similarly (Fig. 9.6 can serve as a schematic representation). Here the real part of the impedance Z_b is primarily the radiation resistance [Eq. (17)], whereas the imaginary part is simply $m\omega/S_b^2$, where m is the mass of the plug of air moving in the orifice and S_b, as before, the

[1] G. W. Stewart and R. B. Lindsay, "Acoustics," p. 66, D. Van Nostrand Company, Inc., Princeton, N.J., 1930.

cross-sectional area of the orifice. We therefore have, neglecting the radiation impedance as too small for consideration,

$$P_r = \frac{1}{1 + \rho_0^2 V^2 S_b^2 / 4 S^2 m^2 \omega^2} \tag{19}$$

Even if we do not know the mass of the moving air in the orifice, we can see at once that the power transmission ratio is zero for $\omega = 0$ and rises monotonically to unity as ω increases to infinity. Thus the plot of P_r vs. ω appears as in Fig. 9.9. As a matter of fact, we can use the measured transmission to compute the effective mass m and hence the conductivity of the orifice.

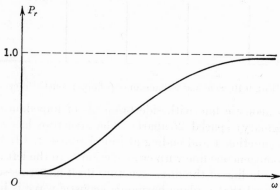

FIG. 9.9. Transmission through an acoustic line with an orifice as a branch.

It is reasonable to conclude that, if we have a branch consisting of a side tube of length l, the transmission in the main line will pass through a succession of minima at the resonance frequencies of the branch tube. This has been amply verified by experiment.[1]

The structures just considered are not precisely filters in the usual meaning of the term. However, we expect that, if we iterate the branch, a genuine filter will ensue. This is indeed the case. We need not follow the details here but merely refer to the literature.[2] For each iterated structure we obtain a $\cos W$ function similar to (2) and hence a succession of pass- and attenuation bands. Thus, in the general case of a structure with iterated branch lines each with impedance Z_b, the $\cos W$ expression takes the form

$$\cos W = \cos 2kl + \frac{iZ}{2Z_b} \sin 2kl \tag{20}$$

where $2l$ is the main-line distance between branches and $Z = \rho_0 V / S$ is the acoustic resistance of a plane wave progressing along the line (S being

[1] *Ibid.*, pp. 125ff.

[2] R. B. Lindsay, *J. Appl. Phys.*, **9**, 612 (1938); **10**, 680 (1939).

the area of cross section of the line, as usual). It is only proper to note that, if Z_b has a nonvanishing real component, cos W is complex and we no longer get complete transmission for any frequency. We can still use the present technique, however, to study the transmission.[1]

9.7. Finite Acoustic Filters

The discussion of the preceding section has been restricted to infinite acoustic lines. We now wish to treat a finite line which possesses filtration characteristics. Thus we imagine that Fig. 9.10 represents sche-

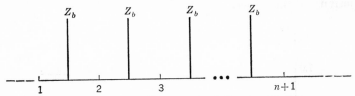

Fig. 9.10. Schematic diagram of a finite acoustic filter.

matically an acoustic line with side branches of impedance Z_b (treated as pure imaginary) spaced $2l$ apart. The structure has n "sections" beginning at junction 1 and ending at junction $n + 1$. It is inserted in an infinite homogeneous line with cross section S_i to the left and S_t to the right. The main line of the filter structure itself has cross-sectional area S. It is assumed that a plane harmonic acoustic wave is incident from the left at 1 and leaves the structure proceeding to the right at $n + 1$ and that there is no reflected wave from the right-hand part of the line. Using the notation of Sec. 3.4 (with cos W considered real) and employing mathematical induction, we can write for the excess pressure and volume current at $n + 1$

$$p_{n+1} = p_1 \cos nW - iZ\dot{X}_1 \sqrt{\frac{B}{C}} \sin nW$$

$$\dot{X}_{n+1} = \dot{X}_1 \cos nW - \frac{i}{Z} p_1 \sqrt{\frac{C}{B}} \sin nW$$

(1)

where

$$B = \sin 2kl + \frac{iZ}{Z_b} \sin^2 kl$$

$$C = \sin 2kl - \frac{iZ}{Z_b} \cos^2 kl$$

(2)

and $Z = \rho_0 V/S$, as in the previous section. Cos nW and sin nW are to be deduced from cos W in (9.6-20). Note that as in (3.4-14)

$$\cos^2 W + BC = 1$$

(3)

so that BC may be set equal to $\sin^2 W$.

[1] *Ibid.*, **10**, 680 (1939).

Taking p_0 as the excess pressure in the incident wave from the left at junction 1 (assumed for simplicity to be at $x = 0$) and noting that p_{n+1} is the excess pressure in the wave passing out of the finite structure into the acoustic line on the right, we have for the power transmission ratio of the structure

$$P_r = \frac{Z_i |p_{n+1}|^2}{Z_t |p_0|^2} \tag{4}$$

where $Z_i = \rho_0 V / S_i$ and $Z_t = \rho_0 V / S_t$. By the application of the boundary conditions in the usual way we finally obtain the general expression $P_r =$

$$\frac{4 Z_i / Z_t}{(1 + Z_i/Z_t)^2 \cos^2 nW + [(Z_i/Z) \sqrt{C/B} + (Z/Z_t) \sqrt{B/C}]^2 \sin^2 nW} \tag{5}$$

The simplest case is that in which $Z_i = Z_t = Z$, and for this (5) reduces to

$$P_r = \frac{1}{(1 + Z^2/|Z_b|^2)(\sin^2 nW)/(4 \sin^2 W)} \tag{6}$$

We can understand the significance of (6) by reflecting that, when $|\cos W| \leq 1$, W is real and both $|\sin nW|$ and $|\sin W|$ are less than or equal to unity. Moreover, in this case, examination of $\cos W$ (9.6-20) shows that $|Z_b|$ cannot be small compared with Z unless $\sin 2kl$ is also very small. We conclude that for ranges of frequency for which $|\cos W| \leq 1$, P_r in (6) can become close to unity. In fact it will become precisely unity for the frequencies for which $W = j\pi/n$ $(j = 1, 2, \ldots, n - 1)$. There will of course be minima in this same range, but by and large it will appear as a transmission band. On the other hand, when $|\cos W| > 1$, W is complex and equal to $W_r + iW_i$. Since, however, $\cos W$ is still real, $W_r = j\pi$, where j is integral. Hence in this case $\sin W = \pm i \sinh W_i$ and $\sin nW = \pm i \sinh nW_i$. As n increases, $\sin^2 nW / \sin^2 W$ will increase monotonically and P_r will become very small; this corresponds to an attenuation band. Actual experiments with finite filters bear out these theoretical conclusions.

It is of interest to observe that, if the branch lines are removed, so that Z_b becomes infinite, P_r automatically becomes unity for all frequencies; that is, the acoustic line is a tube of uniform cross section.

The analysis of this section is completely analogous to that of the transmission of transverse waves along a loaded string, as treated in Sec. 4.5. In particular, we can apply our method to the case of a *finite* tube with side branches. Let us suppose we have such a tube *open* at both ends, which will be taken to correspond to 1 and $n + 1$ in Fig. 9.10. For low frequencies the impedance at each end will be small (if the diameter of the tube is not too small). For a first approximation at any rate, let us call it zero. Then $p_1/\dot{X}_1$ in (1) vanishes as well as $p_{n+1}/\dot{X}_{n+1}$. This leads to

$$\sqrt{\frac{B}{C}} \tan nW = 0 \tag{7}$$

which in turn means effectively

$$\sin nW \sqrt{\frac{(2 + Z/Z_{bi}) \tan kl}{(2 - Z/Z_{bi}) \cot kl}} = 0 \tag{8}$$

It appears therefore that we can satisfy the required boundary conditions by either

$$\sin nW = 0 \tag{9}$$

or
$$\tan kl = -\frac{2Z_{bi}}{Z} \tag{10}$$

Let us take the very simple special case where the branches are not present, that is, $Z_{bi} = \infty$. If we go back to (2), we see that $BC = \sin^2 2kl$ and hence that

$$\cos W = \cos 2kl \tag{11}$$

Since $\sin nW = 0$, we get

$$nW = j\pi$$

where j is integral. Hence

$$nW = 2nkl + nn'\pi = j\pi$$

where n' is integral. We therefore have

$$kl = \frac{(j - nn')\pi}{2n} \tag{12}$$

Thus if $2nl$ is the length L of the structure, the boundary conditions are satisfied by

$$kL = p\pi \tag{13}$$

where p is any integer. This gives precisely the normal modes of a tube of length L open at both ends.

It is of interest to examine the case of the finite structure in which the side branches are equally spaced orifices in the side of the main line. Here then $Z_{bi} = m\omega/S_b{}^2$ (see Sec. 9.6). In terms of the acoustic conductivity c_0 of the orifice this becomes $Z_{bi} = \rho_0\omega/c_0$, where ρ_0 is the density of the air in the line. We then have, from (9.6-20),

$$\cos W = \cos 2kl + \frac{Vc_0}{2S\omega} \sin 2kl \tag{14}$$

The condition (10) has the form

$$\tan kl = -\frac{2\omega S}{Vc_0} \tag{15}$$

The detailed solution involves the solution of transcendental equations. We can at any rate investigate simply the extreme frequencies. For $\omega = 0$ or in the neighborhood thereof, $|\cos W| > 1$, corresponding to attenuation in the case of the equivalent finite filter. In the neighborhood of $\omega = 0$, it is impossible to satisfy (15), and hence the structure has no normal modes or does not resonate in this frequency range. On the other hand, if ω is very large the structure acts more or less as if the holes were not there at all.

A very good practical illustration of an acoustic filter of the kind discussed in this section is provided by a tube of varying cross section, that is, the usual horn (see Prob. 9.8).

9.8. Electromechanical Analogies

We have already had occasion, in Sec. 9.3, to introduce the concept of acoustic impedance in analogy with electric impedance. This procedure has proved of great value in the solution of many acoustical problems, particularly those which involve the coupling of mechanical sources of sound with electrical circuits, as is often done in practice.

The propagation of an elastic disturbance in a material medium presupposes the existence of the disturbance, that is, a source. In most cases of interest this is a device for altering the density of the medium at some point in periodic fashion. The case of the vibrating membrane comes at once to mind. We recall that, when vibrating in its lowest frequency mode (Sec. 5.3), it can be replaced by an equivalent piston vibrator with given mass, stiffness, and damping coefficient. The motion of such a system of one degree of freedom follows the usual second-order equation (see Secs. 3.5, 9.3, and 9.6)

$$m\ddot{\xi} + K\dot{\xi} + f\xi = F_0 e^{i\omega t} \tag{1}$$

where m, K, and f are here the effective mass, damping coefficient, and stiffness, respectively; ξ is the displacement; and $F_0 e^{i\omega t}$ is the applied harmonic force of angular frequency ω. The solution of (1) for the steady state (ignoring the transient vibration as being of little acoustical interest) has the well-known form

$$\xi = \frac{F_0 e^{i\omega t}}{K + i(m\omega - f/\omega)} \tag{2}$$

where the velocity $\dot{\xi}$ is usually a more interesting quantity from the dynamical point of view than the displacement ξ. The real part of $\dot{\xi}$ becomes

$$\dot{\xi}_r = \frac{F_0 \cos (\omega t - \alpha)}{\sqrt{K^2 + (m\omega - f/\omega)^2}} \tag{3}$$

where the phase angle α is given by

$$\alpha = \arctan \left[(m\omega^2 - f)/K\omega \right] \tag{4}$$

The basis for the idea of the electromechanical analogies is found in the fact that, when a harmonic electromotive force $E_0 e^{i\omega t}$ is applied to an electric circuit consisting of an inductance L, a resistance R, and a capacitance C in series (as in Fig. 9.11), the behavior of the electric current flowing through the circuit is given by the equation

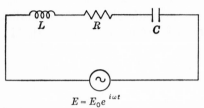

$E = E_0 e^{i\omega t}$

FIG. 9.11. Electrical series circuit.

$$L\ddot{q} + R\dot{q} + \frac{q}{C} = E_0 e^{i\omega t} = E \tag{5}$$

where $\dot{q}$ is the current, with real value

$$\dot{q}_r = \frac{E_0 \cos (\omega t - \beta)}{\sqrt{R^2 + (L\omega - 1/\omega C)^2}} \tag{6}$$

The differential equations (1) and (5) are of the same mathematical form, and so are the solutions (3) and (6), respectively. It is therefore customary to say that the displacement velocity $\dot{\xi}$ is analogous to the current $\dot{q}$, the mechanical force analogous to the electromotive force, etc. In particular, the definition of electrical impedance

$$Z = \frac{E_0 e^{i\omega t}}{\dot{q}} = R + i \left(L\omega - \frac{1}{\omega C} \right) \tag{7}$$

with absolute value

$$|Z| = \sqrt{R^2 + \left(L\omega - \frac{1}{\omega C} \right)^2} \tag{8}$$

suggests the desirability of defining and using an analogous mechanical impedance

$$Z_t = \frac{F_0 e^{i\omega t}}{\dot{\xi}} = K + i \left(m\omega - \frac{f}{\omega} \right) \tag{9}$$

with

$$|Z_t| = \sqrt{K^2 + \left(m\omega - \frac{f}{\omega} \right)^2} \tag{10}$$

Though it must be emphasized that the analogies just discussed are based on purely mathematical similarities and have nothing to do with any physically obvious resemblance between the mass of a vibrating particle and the inductance of a coil of wire, yet the careful use of such analogies can often enable one to reason from the known behavior of one kind of system to the behavior of the other. Since oscillating electrical circuits are now widely used as elastic radiation sources in the driving of mechanical systems and a great deal is known about the behavior of electrical circuits of considerable complexity, it is not surprising that there has grown up a tendency to treat the vibrations of mechanical systems in terms of the oscillations of the analogous electric circuits. Philosophically the analogy might just as well work the other way; the actual situation is historical.

The type of analogy we have just described is now usually referred to as the "classical analogy." It should be emphasized that it is not the only possible one. Let us go back to the series circuit considered and note that the total electromotive force is made up of the sum of the electromotive forces across the inductance, resistance, and capacitance, respectively. Thus

$$E_R = R\dot{q} = RI \qquad E_L = L\ddot{q} = L\dot{I} \qquad E_C = \frac{q}{C} = \int \frac{I\,dt}{C} \qquad (11)$$

if we express everything in terms of the current I rather than the charge q. But we can obviously express the current flowing through each element in terms of the emf across it. Thus

$$I_R = \frac{E_R}{R} \qquad I_L = \int \frac{E_L}{L}\,dt \qquad I_C = C\dot{E}_C \qquad (12)$$

Let us now imagine a circuit in which the electromotive force E' is maintained across a parallel arrangement of inductance L', resistance R', and capacitance C', as shown in Fig. 9.12. The current in the main circuit is the sum of the currents in the three branches. Hence

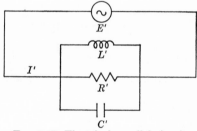

$$I' = C'\dot{E}' + \frac{E'}{R'} + \int \frac{E'\,dt}{L'} \qquad (13)$$

Compare this with the corresponding equation for the series circuit in

FIG. 9.12. Electrical parallel circuit.

Fig. 9.11, namely, (5), which may be written in terms of I and E as

$$L\dot{I} + RI + \int \frac{I\,dt}{C} = E \qquad (14)$$

We see that these have precisely the same form with E and I interchanged. In fact they become identical if we choose $C' = L$, $R' = 1/R$, $L' = C$ and interchange E with I' and E' with I. With this choice, the current depends at any moment on the emf in the series circuit in precisely the same way in which the emf depends on the current in the parallel circuit.

The two circuits discussed in the preceding paragraph are said to be *dual* to each other. The term *resistance reciprocal* is also used.[1]

To make clear the nature of the second type of electromechanical analogy and its relation to the classical analogy, we now draw the corresponding mechanical circuit diagrams. For this we use the symbolic notation in Fig. 9.13 to denote a mechanical compliance (or reciprocal stiffness of a spring), whereas we use Fig. 9.14 to denote a mechanical

FIG. 9.13. Symbolical notation for a mechanical compliance.   FIG. 9.14. Symbolical notation for a mechanical resistance.

resistance (dashpot). A mechanical parallel circuit then appears in the form shown in Fig. 9.15. At the left we indicate a rigid wall or, what amounts to the same thing, an infinite mass to which the moving mass m is connected through the compliance C_M and the mechanical resistance R_M in parallel. The physical meaning is that the ends of C_M and R_M have the same velocity at any instant and the total force on the system of mechanical elements is the sum of that acting on C_M, R_M, and m separately. The differential equation of the motion then becomes (with applied force F)

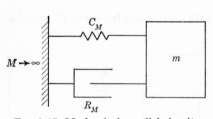

FIG. 9.15. Mechanical parallel circuit.

$$F = m\dot{v} + R_M v + \int \frac{v \, dt}{C_M} \quad (15)$$

It is to be emphasized that to render the analogy useful we must treat the force F as acting always between two points. This is consistent with the usual mechanical situation in which a force exerted on a mass always has to be exerted by another mass—there is no such thing as an isolated mass acted on by a force. In our diagram (Fig. 9.15) we have simplified by letting the second mass involved in the motion of m be infinite.

In a mechanical series circuit the elements are so arranged that the same force acts on all of them, and the resultant velocity is the sum of their respective velocities. Figure 9.16 exhibits schematically the series circuit, whose equation is

$$v' = C'_M \dot{F}' + \frac{F'}{R'_M} + \int \frac{F' \, dt}{m'} \quad (16)$$

[1] F. A. Fischer, "Fundamentals of Electroacoustics," chap. 1, Interscience Publishers, Inc., New York, 1955. Much of the discussion in this section is based on this source.

where F' is the common force, etc. The velocity v' is the resultant value at the point P. Just as in the electrical case, we can make the two circuits dual to each other, or resistance-reciprocal, by taking

$$m = C'_M \qquad R_M = \frac{1}{R'_M} \qquad C_M = m' \qquad (17)$$

and interchanging force and velocity.

In the electromechanical analogy of the first kind (the "classical" analogy), in which electromotive force is analogous to mechanical force, electric current to velocity, mass to inductance, compliance to capacitance, and mechanical resistance to electrical resistance, the electrical

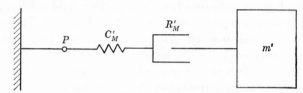

FIG. 9.16. Mechanical series circuit.

analogue of the mechanical parallel circuit is the electrical series circuit. On the other hand, in the electromechanical analogy of the second kind, sometimes called the "mobility" analogy, in which electromotive force is analogous to velocity, electric current to force, mass to capacitance, compliance to inductance, and mechanical resistance to the reciprocal of electrical resistance (conductance), the electrical analogue of the mechanical parallel circuit [as we see by comparing (13) and (14)] is still a parallel circuit (Fig. 9.12). In similar fashion it turns out that the classical electrical analogue of the mechanical series circuit (Fig. 9.16) is an electrical parallel circuit, whereas the mobility electrical analogue of the mechanical series circuit is still a series circuit.

A simple but important acoustic example of a mechanical parallel circuit is the Helmholtz resonator already discussed in Sec. 9.6. Here the equivalent mass m is that of the plug of air vibrating in the orifice of the resonator, the compliance is the reciprocal of the stiffness due to the elasticity of the resonator chamber, and the mechanical resistance is due to the viscosity of the air in the orifice as well as to the radiation of sound energy from the orifice (the latter being by far the more important). The analytical expressions in terms of the geometry of the resonator and the properties of the air are given in Sec. 9.6, together with the acoustic impedance, defined as the ratio of excess pressure to the total volume flow (area of cross section of the orifice multiplied by the flow velocity). The most practical electrical circuit analogue of the acoustic resonator is that of the first kind, with the series circuit of Fig. 9.11. As a matter of general practice the classical analogy is the one most commonly used in cases of acoustic devices involving the motion of fluids. The mobility analogy, so called because it uses in place of the impedance a quantity called the *mobility*, which is defined as the velocity divided by the force, turns out to be convenient in mechanical systems in which all vibrating parts are solid.[1]

9.9. Electroacoustics and Transducers

Since the theme of this book is mechanical wave propagation, we have not placed much emphasis on sources of elastic radiation. It is true that stationary wave systems in strings, rods, and membranes constitute disturbances leading to radiation into surrounding fluid media, and these we have discussed at some length in Chaps. 4, 5, and 7; however, we have not stressed their possible behavior as sources. In general we have assumed the source energy to be given and have been content to follow the fate of the radiation in the transmitting medium. In Sec. 3.5, to be sure, we gave an extensive treatment of the interaction between a pulsating sphere and the resulting radiation. This enabled us to introduce the important concept of radiation reaction. In Sec. 9.10 we shall apply this further to the more practical example of radiation from a vibrating piston source.

Standard texts in acoustics[2] describe in detail sound sources of all varieties. Without question, the most practical of all such sources now current use electrical energy in some way to produce mechanical vibration. This suggests some attention to the subject of electroacoustics, which concerns all ways of transforming electrical into mechanical energy and vice versa. The devices making possible this transformation are known as transducers, whether they transform electrical energy into mechanical (sources) or mechanical energy into electrical (receivers).

Electroacoustic transducers are of many kinds, which we shall briefly review. In the electromagnetic variety, an alternating current of the frequency desired for the radiated sound is passed through a coil which activates an electromagnet and thus produces a force of the same frequency on a diaphragm of some magnetic material (e.g., the standard telephone receiver). The electrodynamic type, which is more commonly used in loudspeakers, has the alternating current pass through a coil suspended in a permanent magnetic field; the coil experiences the usual reactive force, which then is communicated to a solid radiating surface.

---

[1] A thorough treatment of both types of analogies is found in F. A. Firestone, *J. Acoust. Soc. Am.*, **28**, 1117 (1956). Consult also H. F. Olson, "Dynamical Analogies," 2d ed., pp. 232ff., D. Van Nostrand Company, Inc., Princeton, N.J., 1958.

[2] Leo L. Beranek, "Acoustics," McGraw-Hill Book Company, Inc., New York, 1954.

The electrostatic, or condenser, transducer gives a uniform output over a wide range of frequency. In this instrument an oscillating electric field of large intensity is maintained between a fixed metal plate and a thin metal diaphragm separated from the plate by a very small distance. The diaphragm is set in motion by alternate attraction to and repulsion from the plate. The radiation efficiency of this transducer is relatively low, save at very high frequencies. It is most commonly used as a sound receiver or microphone.

For modern sound radiation and reception, particularly in the ultrasonic range, the most widely used electroacoustic transducers are those based on the magnetostrictive and piezoelectric effects, respectively. The former is the change in length of a rod of magnetizable material when the magnetizing field to which it is exposed varies in magnitude. An oscillating current passing through a coil surrounding such a rod will cause it to vibrate longitudinally with a frequency double that of the current if the rod was originally unmagnetized and with a frequency equal to that of the current if the rod was originally magnetized. When the frequency of the current in the latter case coincides with one of the normal modes of the rod, large oscillations of the rod ensue, and sound of this frequency is radiated.

We shall devote most of our attention in the rest of this section to piezoelectric transducers. Certain asymmetric crystals, like quartz, tourmaline, and rochelle salt, have electric charges of opposite sign appear on opposite faces when subjected to dilatational stress. This is the piezoelectric effect proper. Conversely, when such a crystal is made the dielectric in a capacitor subjected to an alternating electric field, it will oscillate with the frequency of the field and hence can serve as a source of sound. Piezoelectric crystals are used as transducers of both the emitting and receiving variety. The so-called "crystal microphone" in a public address, radio, or phonograph system is a piezoelectric transducer.

The complete treatment of the piezoelectric effect involves the expression of the charge per unit area or, alternatively, the electric polarization or electric field intensity on every crystal face in terms of the component stresses (direct effect) and the expression of the strain components in terms of the components of electric field intensity. We shall not go into generalities here but confine ourselves to a so-called "X-cut" quartz crystal, which is a plate whose sides are parallel to the optic axis. If we take the normal to the plate as the x axis and use the strain symbols of Chap. 6, we can write for the dilatational strain along the x axis

$$\delta_{xx} = d_{11}\mathcal{E}_x \tag{1}$$

where $\mathcal{E}_x$ is the electric field intensity perpendicular to the plate (i.e., the potential difference per unit thickness). If $\mathcal{E}_x$ is expressed in volts per centimeter, then for quartz $d_{11} = 2.12 \times 10^{-10}$ cm/volt, so that for a field of 1,000 volts/cm, the dilatational strain is 2.12×10^{-7}.

In the direct effect, if we denote the charge per unit area by q, then

$$q = d_{11}X_{xx} \tag{2}$$

where X_{xx} is the dilatational stress in the x direction. Since, from Hooke's law (Sec. 6.5),

$$X_{xx} = c_{11}\delta_{xx} \tag{3}$$

it follows that

$$q = d_{11}c_{11}\delta_{xx}$$

or the corresponding current is

$$I = d_{11}c_{11}\dot{\delta}_{xx} \tag{4}$$

There is some advantage in writing $\delta_{xx} = \xi/l$, where l is the thickness of the plate and ξ is the small change in thickness or the displacement at the surface. If F = total displacing force = SX_{xx}, where S is the area of cross section of the plate, we can express the ratio of the potential difference V ($= \mathcal{E}_x l$) to the piezoelectric current I by the equation

$$\frac{V}{I} = \frac{F}{\dot{\xi}(c_{11}d_{11}S/l)^2} \tag{5}$$

where we have indeed approximated by keeping l constant in the time differentiation of δ_{xx} ($= \xi/l$). It is customary to call the above ratio the *motional impedance* of the piezoelectric crystal and denote it by Z_m. We may compare it with the ordinary mechanical impedance of the vibrator Z_t, where

$$Z_t = \frac{F}{\dot{\xi}} \tag{6}$$

Hence

$$Z_m = \frac{Z_t}{(c_{11}d_{11}S/l)^2} \tag{7}$$

In the case of every type of electroacoustic transducer one can find a similar expression for the motional impedance in terms of the mechanical impedance.

The fundamental resonance frequency of the vibration being considered here (see Secs. 1.5 and 7.1) is

$$\nu = \frac{1}{2l}\sqrt{\frac{c_{11}}{\rho}} \tag{8}$$

since $\sqrt{c_{11}/\rho}$ is the dilatational wave velocity in the crystal plate. For quartz $c_{11} = 8.55 \times 10^{11}$ dynes/cm^2 and $\rho = 2.65$ g/cm^3. Hence

$$\nu \doteq \frac{5.8 \times 10^5}{2l} \quad \text{cycles/sec}$$

if l is in centimeters. A quartz plate 1 mm in thickness thus possesses a fundamental frequency of 2.9 megacycles. To get higher frequencies it is usually customary to work with harmonics.

The damping in quartz is very low, the logarithmic decrement (the natural logarithm of the ratio of successive amplitudes) being of the order of 10^{-4}. The corresponding quality factor Q, which is π divided by the decrement, is therefore very high. This means a very sharp and high resonance peak.

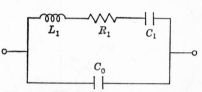

Rochelle salt (double tartrate of potassium and sodium) is much more strongly piezoelectric than quartz, though its activity is restricted to a narrower temperature range. Information about this and other newer piezoelectric materials, like the ceramic barium titanate, can be found in the professional literature.[1]

FIG. 9.17. Equivalent electric circuit for a piezoelectric crystal. [*Reprinted with permission from W. P. Mason, "Piezoelectric Crystals and Their Application to Ultrasonics," D. Van Nostrand Company, Inc., Princeton, N.J., 1950.*]

The action of a piezoelectric crystal can be represented by an equivalent electric circuit, as shown in Fig. 9.17. The various elements can be expressed in terms of the piezoelectric parameters.[2]

9.10. Radiation from a Piston Source

It was pointed out in Secs. 5.3 and 7.4 that the motions of a bounded vibrating membrane or plate, though in general very complicated, can be simply approximated when the driving frequency is lower than the fundamental. In fact there is considerable value in replacing the membrane or diaphragm in these circumstances by an equivalent piston in which all points have the same displacement and velocity at the same instant. In this section we shall study the radiation from such a piston into a fluid medium with two aspects in mind: (1) the nature of the radiation field and (2) the reaction of the radiation field on the piston.

We shall take up the second problem first, recognizing, indeed, that the two are closely related. The method followed is a generalization of that used in Sec. 3.5 for the simpler case of a pulsating spherical shell. In Fig. 9.18 we consider the surface of the piston as a circle of radius a with center at O. Our problem is to calculate the force of reaction of

---

[1] W. G. Cady, "Piezoelectricity," McGraw-Hill Book Company, Inc., New York, 1946; also W. P. Mason, "Piezoelectric Crystals and Their Application to Ultrasonics," D. Van Nostrand Company, Inc., Princeton, N.J., 1950.

[2] For the details, see Mason, *op. cit.*, p. 67. For the alternative representation in terms of the mobility analogy, consult Beranek, "Acoustics," pp. 70ff.

the radiation on the piston. If we can determine the velocity potential at an arbitrary point P distant r from O, the pressure there is at once given, and hence the required force can be obtained by integration over the whole surface. We treat each point on the piston as a point source of hemispherical waves. Thus, if we denote by A the velocity potential amplitude produced by unit area of surface at unit distance from this unit area (considered for simplicity as a point), the velocity potential at P due to element dS at P', which is distant r' from P, is (for a harmonic source of angular frequency ω at P')

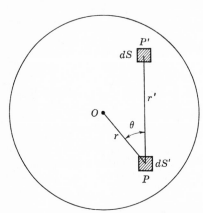

FIG. 9.18. Surface of vibrating piston.

$$\frac{A\,dS}{r'}\,e^{i(\omega t - kr')}$$

The total velocity potential at P then becomes

$$\varphi_P = A e^{i\omega t} \int \frac{e^{-kr'}}{r'}\,dS \tag{1}$$

where the integration is taken over the whole surface of the piston. The coefficient A can be evaluated in terms of the amplitude of the displacement velocity $\dot{\xi}_0$ of the piston as follows.

Let us consider a hemisphere of radius r_0 about point P' as center and treat this as a source of hemispherical waves. The velocity potential due to this source at a point distant r from P' is

$$\varphi = \frac{2\pi r_0{}^2 A}{r}\,e^{i[\omega t - k(r - r_0)]}$$

since in this case dS reduces to $2\pi r_0{}^2$, the area of the hemisphere. The flow velocity at the surface of the hemisphere is

$$\left(\frac{\partial \varphi}{\partial r}\right)_{r=r_0} = \dot{\xi}_{r_0} = -2\pi r_0{}^2 \left(\frac{1}{r_0} + ik\right)\frac{A}{r_0}\,e^{i\omega t} \tag{2}$$

But
$$\lim_{r_0 \to 0} \dot{\xi}_{r_0} = \dot{\xi}_0 e^{i\omega t}$$

by our original assumption. Hence we get from (2)

$$A = -\frac{\dot{\xi}_0}{2\pi} \tag{3}$$

which permits the calculation of the required pressure at P in terms of $\dot{\xi}_0$.

In fact, from $p = -\rho_0\dot{\varphi}$ and (1), we have

$$p_P = \frac{i\omega\rho_0\xi_0}{2\pi} e^{i\omega t} \int \frac{e^{-ikr'}}{r'} dS \tag{4}$$

To get the total force on the piston, we must integrate p_P over the whole surface. Thus, formally,

$$F = \frac{i\omega\rho_0\xi_0}{2\pi} e^{i\omega t} \int dS' \int \frac{e^{-ikr'}}{r'} dS \tag{5}$$

where dS' is the element of area at P. We employ the standard device for handling such a double surface integral; that is, for each point P and surface element dS', we integrate with respect to dS only over the portion of the surface *inside* the circle on which P is located. We then integrate the result with respect to dS over the whole area. Finally we multiply by two, since we are effectively taking each pair of area elements only once.

Let us consider first

$$Q = \int \frac{e^{-ikr'}}{r'} dS = \int_{-\pi/2}^{+\pi/2} \int_0^{2r \cos\theta} e^{-ikr'} dr' d\theta \tag{6}$$

(see Fig. 9.18 for the significance of θ). Carrying out the integration with respect to r', we have

$$Q = \frac{2i}{k} \int_0^{\pi/2} (e^{-2ikr \cos\theta} - 1) d\theta \tag{7}$$

Now $\qquad e^{-2ikr \cos\theta} = 1 - 2ikr \cos\theta - \dfrac{4k^2r^2 \cos^2\theta}{2!} \cdots$

and since

$$\int_0^{\pi/2} \cos^n\theta \, d\theta = \frac{1 \cdot 3 \cdot 5 \cdots (n-1)}{2 \cdot 4 \cdot 6 \cdots n} \frac{\pi}{2} \qquad n \text{ even}$$

$$= \frac{2 \cdot 4 \cdot 6 \cdots (n-1)}{1 \cdot 3 \cdot 5 \cdots n} \qquad n \text{ odd}$$

we can write

$$Q = \frac{\pi}{ik} + \frac{2i}{k} \left\{ \frac{\pi}{2} \left[1 - \frac{1}{2 \cdot 2!} (2kr)^2 + \frac{1 \cdot 3}{2 \cdot 4 \cdot 4!} (2kr)^4 \cdots \right] \right.$$
$$\left. - i \left[2kr - \frac{2}{3 \cdot 3!} (2kr)^3 + \cdots \right] \right\} \tag{8}$$

Now $\quad 1 - \dfrac{1}{2 \cdot 2!} (2kr)^2 + \dfrac{1 \cdot 3}{2 \cdot 4 \cdot 4!} (2kr)^4 + \cdots$

$$= 1 - \frac{1}{2^2} (2kr)^2 + \frac{(2kr)^4}{2^2 4^2} \cdots = J_0(2kr) \tag{9}$$

(see Sec. 5.3). At the same time, Rayleigh[1] defined the function

$$K(2kr) = \frac{2}{\pi}\left[2kr - \frac{(2kr)^3}{1^2 \cdot 3^2} + \cdots \right] \tag{10}$$

which is the term in the second set of brackets in (8), save for the multiplicative factor.[2] Hence we can set

$$Q = \frac{\pi}{k}\{K(2kr) - i[1 - J_0(2kr)]\} \tag{11}$$

We must now calculate

$$\int Q\,ds = \int_0^a Q\,2\pi r\,dr$$

and get

$$F = \frac{i\omega\rho_0\xi_0}{k}e^{i\omega t}\int_0^a 2\pi r\{K(2kr) - i[1 - J_0(2kr)]\}\,dr \tag{12}$$

Now

$$\int_0^b J_0(x)x\,dx = xJ_1(x)\Big]_0^b$$
$$\int_0^b K(x)x\,dx = K_1(x)\Big]_0^b \tag{13}$$

where

$$K_1(x) = \frac{2}{\pi}\left(\frac{x^3}{3} - \frac{x^6}{3^2 \cdot 5} + \frac{x^7}{3^2 \cdot 5^2 \cdot 7}\cdots\right) \tag{14}$$

The result of the integration gives finally for the radiation reaction force

$$F = \pi a^2\rho_0 V\xi_0 e^{i\omega t}\left[1 - \frac{J_1(2ka)}{ka}\right] + \frac{i\omega\pi\rho_0}{2k^3}\xi_0 e^{i\omega t}K_1(2ka) \tag{15}$$

It is attractive to interpret this result in terms of the acoustic impedance notation developed in earlier sections (e.g., Secs. 3.5 and 9.3). The specific acoustic impedance of the radiation at the piston is

$$Z_s = \frac{F}{\pi a^2\xi_0 e^{i\omega t}} = \rho_0 V\left[1 - \frac{J_1(2ka)}{ka}\right] + \frac{i\omega\rho_0}{2a^2k^3}K_1(2ka) \tag{16}$$

The real part of Z_s is the specific acoustic resistance Z_{s1} and the imaginary part the specific acoustic reactance Z_{s2}. The effect of the radiation is thus to alter the mechanical impedance of the vibrating piston by the above quantities. The physical significance is best grasped if we consider the limiting cases of low and high frequencies, respectively. Low frequency here evidently means $ka \ll 1$, that is, the wavelength λ much greater than the radius of the piston. Now from the properties of Bessel functions, as discussed in Sec. 3.6,

$$J_1(2ka) = \frac{2ka}{2}\left[1 - \frac{(2ka)^2}{2 \cdot 2^2} + \cdots\right]$$

---

[1] "Theory of Sound," vol. 2, pp. 162ff.
[2] Note that $K(2kr)$ is not to be confused with a Bessel function.

Hence, for $ka \ll 1$,

$$1 - \frac{J_1(2ka)}{ka} \doteq \frac{k^2a^2}{2}$$

so that the specific radiation resistance is

$$Z_{s1} = \frac{\rho_0 V k^2 a^2}{2} \tag{17}$$

which is much smaller than that for a plane wave. For small values of ka, $K_1(2ka)$ becomes

$$K_1(2ka) \doteq \frac{16}{3\pi} k^3 a^3$$

and the specific radiation reactance is

$$Z_{s2} = \frac{8}{3\pi} \omega \rho_0 a \tag{18}$$

The interpretation of this is clearer if we go back to the expression for the total radiation reaction force on the piston and write it

$$F = Z_{s1}S\dot{\xi} + iZ_{s2}S\dot{\xi}$$
$$= Z_{s1}S\dot{\xi} + \frac{Z_{s2}S}{\omega} \ddot{\xi} \tag{19}$$

where $\dot{\xi} = \dot{\xi}_0 e^{i\omega t}$ is the displacement velocity of the piston. This means that part of the reaction force is proportional to the velocity of the piston and hence corresponds to a dissipative effect, whereas the other part is proportional to the acceleration and hence corresponds to an inertial effect. Thus the presence of the radiation effectively increases the mechanical attenuation of the piston by the additional damping coefficient $Z_{s1}S$ and increases the ordinary mass of the piston by what may be called the radiation inertia $Z_{s2}S/\omega$, it being assumed that Z_{s2} is positive. If it were negative, it would figure as a stiffness or reciprocal capacitance. If the effective mass of the piston neglecting radiation is m (see Secs. 5.3 and 7.4), its mechanical damping coefficient (i.e., that due to internal friction, etc.) is R, and its mechanical stiffness is f, the equation of motion of the piston as a simple harmonic oscillator subject to its own radiation reaction is

$$\left(m + \frac{Z_{s2}S}{\omega}\right)\ddot{\xi} + (R + Z_{s1}S)\dot{\xi} + f\xi = \text{driving force} \tag{20}$$

Now in the low-frequency limit the radiation inertia is, from what we have just seen above,

$$\frac{Z_{s2}S}{\omega} \doteq \frac{8}{3}\rho_0 a^3 \tag{21}$$

or $2/\pi$ times the mass of a sphere of the density of the medium having the same radius as the plate. Similarly, the radiation resistance coefficient under the same conditions is

$$Z_{s1}S = \frac{\pi\rho_0 Vk^2a^4}{2} \tag{22}$$

The effective increase in mass associated with the radiation lowers the resonance frequency of the piston. If the radiation mass equals the mechanical mass, the frequency is lowered to $1/\sqrt{2}$ of its value when vibrating in a vacuum.

Passing now to the high-frequency case for which $ka \gg 1$ or $\lambda \ll a$, we have

$$Z_{s1}S \doteq \rho_0 VS \tag{23}$$

The radiation damping for a given piston reaches its maximum and becomes a constant independent of frequency. The radiation resistance indeed is then that of a plane wave with wavefront equal to the area of the piston. Since the rate of radiation from the piston (for given ξ) is directly proportional to $Z_{s1}S$, it is clear that the piston as a radiator reaches its maximum efficiency at high frequencies. For $ka \gg 1$, it can be shown that

$$K_1(2ka) \doteq \frac{2}{\pi}(2ka)$$

Hence the radiation inertia at high frequency becomes

$$\frac{SZ_{s2}}{\omega} \doteq \frac{2\rho_0 a^3}{k^2a^2} \tag{24}$$

which will be small unless a is very large.

We ought to note in connection with the radiation reaction on the piston source the important role of the density ρ_0 of the medium. For given piston area, frequency, and displacement velocity, as the density of the medium is lowered, the average rate of radiation into the medium is lowered proportionally. Other things being equal, radiation into water is thus more efficient than into air. And if the pressure of the air is lowered, the radiation efficiency is correspondingly reduced. This is the explanation of the famous demonstration experiment in which a bell ringing in an evacuated bell jar fails to be heard. We may also note the analogy with the problem of getting radiation to pass an interface separating two media (Sec. 3.3). We recall that this reaches maximum efficiency when the $\rho_0 V$ values are the same for both media, or, as one says, the acoustic impedances are matched. The present case is not strictly analogous, since the piston is treated as a vibrator of one degree of freedom and not as a medium. Nevertheless there is an interesting physical connection.

The considerations of this section have a bearing on practical sound sources, since many of the latter consist of vibrating diaphragms which can be considered as pistons.   However, to carry matters further in the direction of practice, it is necessary to say something about the radiation itself, that is, the pattern of intensity distribution in the radiation field. This we now proceed to examine.

In Fig. 9.19 the piston surface is denoted by S with center at O.   We wish first to determine the intensity of the radiation at the point P on

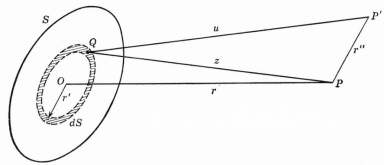

FIG. 9.19. To illustrate calculation of radiation field due to a vibrating piston.

the axis of the piston distant r from O.   To apply formula (1) to this case we must pick the element dS.   This will be chosen as the annular ring around O as center and with mean radius r'.   It is distant z from P. Hence we can write

$$\varphi_P = -\frac{\dot{\xi}_0 e^{i\omega t}}{2\pi} \int_0^a \frac{e^{-ikz}}{z} 2\pi r'\, dr' \tag{25}$$

Since $r' = \sqrt{z^2 - r^2}$, this becomes

$$\varphi_P = \frac{-i\dot{\xi}_0 e^{i\omega t}}{k} \left(e^{-ik\sqrt{a^2+r^2}} - e^{-ikr}\right) \tag{26}$$

The corresponding excess pressure at P is

$$p_P = -\rho_0 V \dot{\xi}_0 e^{i\omega t}\left(e^{-ik\sqrt{a^2+r^2}} - e^{-ikr}\right)$$

which has the real part

$$p_{Pr} = -\rho_0 V \xi_0[(\cos k \sqrt{r^2 + a^2} - \cos kr)\cos \omega t \\ - (\sin k \sqrt{r^2 + a^2} - \sin kr)\sin \omega t]$$

Using the usual identities for $\cos a - \cos b$, etc., and squaring, we finally get the intensity at P

$$I_P = \frac{\overline{p_{Pr}^2}}{\rho_0 V} = 2\rho_0 V \xi_0^2 \sin^2 \frac{k}{2}\left(\sqrt{r^2 + a^2} - r\right) \tag{27}$$

If $r \gg a$, this reduces to

$$I_P = 2\rho_0 c \dot{\xi}_0{}^2 \sin^2 \frac{ka^2}{4r} \tag{28}$$

For $a < r < ka^2/2\pi$, the intensity runs through a succession of maxima and minima corresponding to $ka^2/4r = (2n + 1)\pi/2$ and $n\pi$, where $n > 1$. For $r \geqq ka^2/2\pi$, the intensity falls off continuously. Hence the graph of

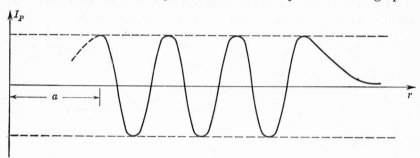

FIG. 9.20. Intensity in the radiation field due to a vibrating piston on the axis as a function of distance from the center of the piston.

its behavior looks like Fig. 9.20. For $r \gg ka^2/2\pi$, we have, to an increasingly good approximation,

$$I_P = \frac{\rho_0 V \dot{\xi}_0{}^2 k^2 a^4}{8r^2} \tag{29}$$

Under these conditions the radiation behaves like a spherical wave. Since the intensity is oscillatory with constant amplitude $2\rho_0 V \dot{\xi}_0{}^2$ out to $r = ka^2/2\pi$, it is customary to think of the radiation in this region as "beamlike." This is not strictly justified until one has investigated the behavior of the intensity at points off the axis. But in so far as the approximation can be maintained, it is clear that for a diaphragm of given size the beamlike character improves as the frequency increases. This might indeed have been qualitatively predicted from the analogous situation in light and in fact is closely connected with the discussion on diffraction of radiation in Sec. 2.4.

To examine the off-axis radiation intensity, we again consult Fig. 9.19 and let the coordinates of any point Q on the piston distant r' from O be x, y and the coordinates of any point P' on the plane through P parallel to the piston face (distant r'' from P) be x_0, y_0. We denote the distance from Q to P' by u. Then the fundamental formula (25) gives

$$\varphi_{P'} = -\frac{\dot{\xi}_0 e^{i\omega t}}{2\pi} \int_{-a}^{+a} \int_{-\sqrt{a^2-x^2}}^{+\sqrt{a^2-x^2}} \frac{e^{-iku}}{u} \, dx \, dy \tag{30}$$

From Fig. 9.19 we see that

$$u = \sqrt{r^2 + (x - x_0)^2 + (y - y_0)^2} \tag{31}$$

If we transform to polar coordinates ρ, θ,

$$x - x_0 = \rho \cos \theta \qquad y - y_0 = \rho \sin \theta$$

The integral takes the form[1]

$$\varphi_{P'} = - \frac{\xi_0 e^{i\omega t}}{2} \int_{\theta_1}^{\theta_2} \int_{\rho_1(\theta)}^{\rho_2(\theta)} \frac{e^{-ik\sqrt{\rho^2+r^2}}}{\sqrt{\rho^2 + r^2}} \rho \, d\rho \, d\theta \tag{32}$$

where the limits for ρ and θ depend on the relative magnitudes of r'' and a. For simplicity, we first confine attention to the special case $r'' = a$. Then $\rho_1(\theta) = 0$ and $\rho_2(\theta) = 2a \cos \theta$, whereas $\theta_1 = -\pi/2$, $\theta_2 = \pi/2$. Transferring back to u and θ, we get

$$\varphi_{P'} = - \frac{\xi_0 e^{i\omega t}}{\pi} \int_0^{\pi/2} \int_r^{\sqrt{r^2+4a^2\cos^2\theta}} e^{-iku} \, du \, d\theta \tag{33}$$

Now, if we assume that $r \gg 2a$,

$$\int_r^{\sqrt{r^2+4a^2\cos^2\theta}} e^{-iku} \, du = \frac{i}{k} \left[\cos k \left(r + \frac{2a^2}{r} \cos^2 \theta \right) - \cos kr \right.$$

$$+ i \sin k \left(r + \frac{2a^2}{r} \cos^2 \theta \right) - \left. i \sin kr \right]$$

$$= \frac{i}{k} \left[\cos kr \cos \left(\frac{2a^2 k}{r} \cos^2 \theta \right) \right.$$

$$- \sin kr \sin \left(\frac{2a^2 k}{r} \cos^2 \theta \right) - \cos kr$$

$$+ i \sin kr \cos \left(\frac{2a^2 k}{r} \cos^2 \theta \right) + i \cos kr \sin \left(\frac{2a^2 k}{r} \cos^2 \theta \right) - \left. i \sin kr \right]$$

But

$$\int_0^{\pi/2} \cos \left(\frac{2a^2 k}{r} \cos^2 \theta \right) d\theta = \int_0^{\pi/2} \cos \left(\frac{a^2 k}{r} + \frac{a^2 k}{r} \cos 2\theta \right) d\theta$$

$$= \cos \frac{a^2 k}{r} \int_0^{\pi/2} \cos \left(\frac{a^2 k}{r} \cos 2\theta \right) d\theta - \sin \frac{a^2 k}{r} \int_0^{\pi/2} \sin \left(\frac{a^2 k}{r} \cos 2\theta \right) d\theta$$

which by the substitution $\psi = \pi/2 - 2\theta$ gives

$$\frac{1}{2} \cos \frac{a^2 k}{r} \int_{-\pi/2}^{\pi/2} \cos \left(\frac{a^2 k}{r} \sin \psi \right) d\psi - \frac{1}{2} \sin \frac{a^2 k}{r} \int_{-\pi/2}^{\pi/2} \sin \left(\frac{a^2 k}{r} \sin \psi \right) d\psi$$

Since the sine is an odd function, the second integral vanishes. For the first we have[2]

$$\int_{-\pi/2}^{\pi/2} \cos \left(\frac{a^2 k}{r} \sin \psi \right) d\psi = \pi J_0 \left(\frac{a^2 k}{r} \right) \tag{34}$$

---

[1] Do not confuse ρ in this expression with density.

[2] H. Margenau and G. M. Murphy, "The Mathematics of Physics and Chemistry," p. 113, D. Van Nostrand Company, Inc., Princeton, N.J., 1943.

Similarly, it turns out that

$$\int_0^{\pi/2} \sin\left(\frac{2a^2 k}{r} \cos^2\theta\right) d\theta = \frac{\pi}{2}\sin\frac{a^2 k}{r} J_0\left(\frac{a^2 k}{r}\right) \tag{35}$$

Hence we get

$$\varphi_{P'} = -\frac{i\xi_0 e^{i\omega t}}{\pi k}\frac{\pi}{2}\left[\cos kr \cos\frac{a^2 k}{r} J_0\left(\frac{a^2 k}{r}\right) - \sin kr \sin\frac{a^2 k}{r} J_0\left(\frac{a^2 k}{r}\right)\right.$$
$$+ i\sin kr \cos\frac{a^2 k}{r} J_0\left(\frac{a^2 k}{r}\right) + i\cos kr \sin\frac{a^2 k}{r} J_0\left(\frac{a^2 k}{r}\right)$$
$$\left. - \frac{2}{\pi}\cos kr - \frac{2i}{\pi}\sin kr\right]$$

Moreover, the real part of the excess pressure at P' is

$$p_{P'r} = -\frac{1}{2}\rho_0 V\xi_0\left\{\cos\omega t\left[J_0\left(\frac{a^2 k}{r}\right)\cos k\left(r + \frac{a^2}{r}\right) - \cos kr\right]\right.$$
$$\left. + \sin\omega t\left[J_0\left(\frac{a^2 k}{r}\right)\sin k\left(r + \frac{a^2}{r}\right) - \sin kr\right]\right\} \tag{36}$$

Finally, the intensity at P' (given by $\overline{p_{P'}^2}/\rho_0 V$) becomes

$$I_{P'} = \frac{\rho_0 V\xi_0^2}{8}\left[1 - 2J_0\left(\frac{a^2 k}{r}\right)\cos\frac{a^2 k}{r} + \left[J_0\left(\frac{a^2 k}{r}\right)\right]^2\right] \tag{37}$$

The only value of $a^2 k/r$ for which $I_{P'} = 0$ is zero, corresponding to $r = \infty$. Hence there can actually be no parallel beam of sound of cross section equal to the area of the piston. However, it turns out that most of the sound is confined to a conical region extending outward, with its apex at the center of the piston. For if we seek the value of $a^2 k/r$ for which, for example,

$$\frac{I_{P'}}{I_P} = \frac{1}{10}$$

we find from tables of Bessel functions that this is true (see Fig. 9.21)

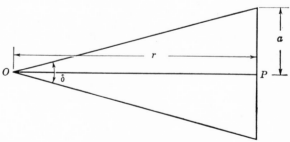

Fig. 9.21. Lateral spread of radiation from a vibrating piston.

for the central angle

$$\delta = 2 \arctan \frac{a}{r} = 2 \arctan \frac{0.45\lambda}{a} \tag{38}$$

which gives a measure of the lateral spread of the outgoing radiation. The corresponding solid angle at O is

$$\frac{\pi(0.45\lambda)^2}{a^2} \tag{39}$$

Hence most of the radiation is confined in a cone of solid angle given by this expression. Thus, for a piston of radius 10 cm radiating at 50 kc ($\lambda = 2.92$ cm in water), $\delta = 15°$.

The standard diffraction theory taken over from optics gives for the solid angle corresponding to the first bright spot on the distant screen the value

$$\frac{\pi(0.61\lambda)^2}{a^2} \tag{40}$$

This is based on the approximation[1] that r is very large compared with a and that the same is true for r''.

Recent work has endeavored to improve the approximations discussed above so as to evaluate the intensity more accurately in the region $0 < r'' < a$. For details and a bibliography, see the paper by Carter and Williams.[2]

9.11. Acoustic Radiation in a Viscous Fluid Medium.   Absorption and Dispersion of Sound

The basic equation for the propagation of a small compressional disturbance in a fluid medium as we have used it so far in this chapter is (9.1-5):

$$\nabla^2 \varphi = \frac{\ddot{\varphi}}{V^2} \tag{1}$$

where φ is the velocity potential and V is the wave velocity. We recall that a similar equation is satisfied by the excess pressure p_e and the excess density ρ_e. A wave satisfying this equation propagates without loss in intensity, save that due to geometrical spreading, as in the case of nonplane radiation. Now we know that in any actual fluid a compressional wave does suffer attenuation, and we must consider the reasons why this should be so and endeavor to modify the former theory so as to predict this attenuation successfully. This will serve to specialize the very general discussion of wave damping in Sec. 1.9.

[1] R. B. Lindsay, *Phys. Rev.*, **32**, 55 (1928).
[2] A. H. Carter and A. O. Williams, Jr., *J. Acoust. Soc. Am.*, **23**, 179 (1951).

For the sake of simplicity we confine our attention to plane waves proceeding in the x direction. This will permit us to use the actual fluid flow displacement from equilibrium ξ as the measure of the disturbance and the dependent variable in the analysis. We shall therefore write the hydrodynamic equation of motion in the absence of body forces in the form [a special case of (3.5-7)]

$$\rho_0 \ddot{\xi} = -\frac{\partial p_e}{\partial x} \tag{2}$$

where p_e is, as usual, the excess pressure and ρ_0 the mean equilibrium density. The equation of continuity becomes

$$\rho_0 \frac{\partial \xi}{\partial x} = -\dot{\rho}_e \tag{3}$$

and if we combine this with what amounts to the static equation of state

$$p_e = V^2 \rho_e \tag{4}$$

the result of (2), (3), (4) is, of course,

$$\ddot{\xi} = V^2 \frac{\partial^2 \xi}{\partial x^2} \tag{5}$$

or the wave equation for the propagation of ξ with velocity V, which we have already seen has the form (9.2-7)

$$V = \sqrt{\frac{B_{ad}}{\rho_0}} \tag{6}$$

where B_{ad} is the adiabatic bulk modulus of the fluid.

Equation (4) demands some scrutiny. It presumes that, at any instant when the excess pressure is p_e, the excess density is ρ_e, directly proportional to p_e. But this ignores the well-known physical observation that the alteration of density by the imposition of pressure is not an instantaneous phenomenon and that a finite time is needed to achieve a finite change. This is often referred to as a *relaxation* phenomenon. It suggests that a more meaningful equation of state should involve a time derivative of the excess density. The simplest version of this would have the form

$$p_e = V^2 \rho_e + R\dot{\rho}_e \tag{7}$$

in which R appears as a constant descriptive of the relaxation process. To see its significance further, let us imagine the special case in which a *constant* excess pressure p_{e0} is impressed. Then the solution of (7) is

$$\rho_e = \frac{p_{e0}}{V^2} \left(1 - e^{-V^2 t/R}\right) \tag{8}$$

This says that, as t increases, ρ_e approaches p_{e0}/V^2 as a limit, having started at zero for $t = 0$. In time $t = R/V^2$, the excess density is the fraction $1 - 1/e$ of its limiting value. This time is called the *relaxation time* of the process in question, usually represented by the symbol τ. It is a measure of the tendency of the system to relax into its steady state.

Relaxation phenomena are encountered throughout physics and indeed in every case in which a disturbed system strives to achieve a steady state. Another simple example is provided by the charging of a condenser by a constant source of electromotive force; what is commonly referred to as the time constant of the circuit containing the condenser is really the relaxation time.

We have now to see the effect of using the dynamic equation of state (7) on the equation for the propagation of a disturbance in a fluid. Since

$$\rho_e = -\rho_0 \frac{\partial \xi}{\partial x} \tag{9}$$

by definition, we can at once rewrite (7) in the form

$$\rho_e = -\rho_0 V^2 \frac{\partial \xi}{\partial x} - R\rho_0 \frac{\partial \dot{\xi}}{\partial x} \tag{10}$$

whence the equation of motion (2) is now replaced by

$$\ddot{\xi} = V^2 \frac{\partial^2 \xi}{\partial x^2} + R \frac{\partial^2 \dot{\xi}}{\partial x^2} \tag{11}$$

differing from the simple wave equation (5) by the addition of the correction term $R\, \partial^2 \dot{\xi}/\partial x^2$, which vanishes if the relaxation time

$$\tau = \frac{R}{V^2} \tag{12}$$

is equal to zero.

We find that we can satisfy (11) by a damped plane harmonic wave in which ξ is given by

$$\xi = \xi_0 e^{-\alpha x} e^{i(\omega t - kx)} \tag{13}$$

In fact substitution indicates (see Sec. 1.9) that this is a solution, provided that

$$k^2 - \alpha^2 = \frac{\omega^2}{V^2(1 + \omega^2\tau^2)} \tag{14}$$

and

$$2\alpha k = \frac{\omega^3 \tau}{V^2(1 + \omega^2 \tau^2)} \tag{15}$$

By elimination of k between these two equations we readily show that

$$\alpha = \frac{\omega^2 \tau V_p}{2V^2(1 + \omega^2 \tau^2)} \tag{16}$$

where $$V_p = \frac{\sqrt{2V}}{\omega\tau} \left[(1 + \omega^2\tau^2)(\sqrt{1 + \omega^2\tau^2} - 1)\right]^{\frac{1}{2}} \qquad (17)$$

Here $V_p = \omega/k$ is the new phase velocity of the wave. The dependence of the velocity on the frequency indicates that the relaxation behavior is associated with dispersion. To be sure, if the relaxation time is very short compared with the period of the sound wave, that is, if $\omega\tau \ll 1$, (17) becomes

$$V_p = V(1 + \omega^2\tau^2/2 + \cdots) \qquad (18)$$

and the dispersion is a second-order effect. On the other hand, if $\omega\tau \gg 1$, that is, a very long relative relaxation time, we have

$$V_p = V\sqrt{2\omega\tau} \qquad (19)$$

and the phase velocity increases with the square root of the frequency. A long relative relaxation time obviously is associated with considerable damping, as is clear from (16). The more normal situation to be expected is $\omega\tau \ll 1$. Then

$$\alpha \doteq \frac{\omega^2\tau}{2V} \qquad (20)$$

and the attenuation coefficient varies as the square of the frequency.

The value of τ and hence that of α depend on the type of relaxation mechanism assumed. Let us examine the special case in which the dissipation is due to the viscosity of the fluid. We recall that, whereas an ideal fluid does not support a shearing stress, in an actual fluid in motion adjacent layers tend to check each other's relative motion and hence provide a shearing effect. For many fluids (the so-called Newtonian ones) the shearing stress with which adjacent layers act on each other is found to be proportional to the gradient of the flow velocity taken in the direction perpendicular to the layers. The constant ratio of stress to gradient is called the *viscosity*, or sometimes, more specifically, the *shear viscosity coefficient* of the fluid. For a Newtonian fluid we may therefore assume that the stress is a linear function of the rate of change of the strains (instead of the strains themselves, as in an elastic solid). This permits us to utilize for the description of this type of fluid a simple modification of the Hooke's-law relations for an elastic solid, that is, (6.2-5). With the same definitions of the stresses X and the strains δ, we may now write in place of (6.2-5)

$$\begin{aligned}
X_{xx} &= \lambda'\dot{\Theta} + 2\eta\dot{\delta}_{xx} - p \\
X_{yy} &= \lambda'\dot{\Theta} + 2\eta\dot{\delta}_{yy} - p \\
X_{zz} &= \lambda'\dot{\Theta} + 2\eta\dot{\delta}_{zz} - p
\end{aligned} \qquad (21)$$

where λ' denotes a new and, at first, unknown constant in place of λ

(which is equal to $B - 2\mu/3$, the Lamé coefficient for the elastic solid) and η is the shear viscosity. The total static pressure p has also been inserted to make the stress the resultant one and not merely that due to the flow alone.

If we add the three equations in (21), the result is

$$\frac{X_{xx} + X_{yy} + X_{zz}}{3} = -p + \left(\lambda' + \frac{2\eta}{3}\right)\dot{\Theta} \qquad (22)$$

Maxwell and Stokes thought it reasonable to make the assumption that

$$\lambda' = -\frac{2\eta}{3} \qquad (23)$$

which is equivalent to the physical hypothesis that the average dilatational stress in a moving fluid is still equal to the negative of static pressure. This is further equivalent to the assumption that the fluid possesses no *bulk*, or volume, viscosity. Bulk viscosity is exhibited by a fluid in which there is a dilatational stress proportional to the time rate of change of the total dilatation, that is, $\dot{\Theta}$. Thus

$$\lambda' + \frac{2\eta}{3} = \eta' \qquad (24)$$

where η' is the bulk viscosity coefficient. As we shall see in Chap. 12, there is reason to believe that certain fluids, notably liquids, possess nonvanishing bulk viscosity. However, in the present case we shall follow the classical hypothesis and use (23).

If we further confine our attention, as usual, to motion in the x direction and take $\delta_{yy} = \delta_{zz} = 0$, we can then write the first equation in (21) in the form

$$X_{xx} = -(p_0 + p_e) + \frac{4\eta}{3}\frac{\partial \dot{\xi}}{\partial x} \qquad (25)$$

where we have written $p = p_0 + p_e$ in order to get the static excess pressure p_e into the picture. The dynamic excess pressure is now $-(X_{xx} + p_0)$, and the static excess pressure is still given by $-\rho_0 V^2 \partial \xi/\partial x$. Hence comparison of (25) with (10) reveals that the relaxation constant R for the case of viscous dissipation has the form

$$R = \frac{4\eta}{3\rho_0} \qquad (26)$$

corresponding to a relaxation time

$$\tau = \frac{4\eta}{3\rho_0 V^2} \qquad (27)$$

Using air as an illustration, we find that, at 20°C, $\eta = 1.8 \times 10^{-4}$ dyne-sec/cm^2 and $\rho_0 V^2 = \gamma p$, which at standard atmospheric pressure is approximately 1.5×10^6 dynes/cm^2. Hence $\tau = 1.6 \times 10^{-10}$ sec. For frequencies less than 10^7 cycles/sec, it is clear that $\omega\tau \ll 1$ and hence (20) will apply, with

$$\alpha = \frac{2\omega^2\eta}{3\rho_0 V^3} \tag{28}$$

for the attenuation coefficient. Since frequencies of the order of 10^9 cycles/sec are now becoming possible experimentally, we cannot expect to apply (28) in all cases. However, in the higher-frequency ranges for most fluids, viscosity actually fails to provide an adequate explanation of acoustic attenuation, and other relaxation processes must be sought.

9.12. Heat Conduction as a Source of Acoustic Attenuation

In the previous section we examined the concept of a relaxation mechanism as an explanation of the absorption and dispersion of sound in a fluid and gave viscosity as one illustration. Another is provided by the conduction of heat. In the compression of the fluid in the passage of the sound, the temperature is raised and a temperature gradient is locally established. This leads to a flow of heat by conduction, which can be significant before the subsequent rarefaction can be accomplished. Our task now is to estimate the relaxation time associated with this process.

The ensuing analysis is based on the assumption that the compressional disturbance in a fluid is a quasi-static process, so that the principles of equilibrium thermodynamics can be applied. This is admittedly a somewhat shaky hypothesis, though closer investigation indicates that it is probably a justifiable first approximation. We begin by applying the first law of thermodynamics to express the rate at which heat is transferred in the fluid:

$$\dot{Q} = \dot{U} + p\dot{v} \tag{1}$$

where Q represents quantity of heat, U the internal energy, and v the volume. For convenience we apply this equation to one mole of fluid. Now, if the heat flow is associated with a temperature gradient, the usual equation of heat conduction gives for flow in the x direction[1]

$$\dot{Q} = \frac{M\kappa}{\rho_0} \frac{\partial^2 T}{\partial x^2} \tag{2}$$

where T is, as usual, the absolute temperature, M the molecular weight, and κ the thermal conductivity. If we expand the differential of the

[1] For a derivation of the heat-conduction equation, see J. M. Cork, "Heat," pp. 114ff., John Wiley & Sons, Inc., New York, 1942.

internal energy U into a linear combination of differentials of p and v, we can write

$$dU = \left(\frac{\partial U}{\partial p}\right)_v dp + \left(\frac{\partial U}{\partial v}\right)_p dv \tag{3}$$

Transforming the coefficient of dp, we have

$$\left(\frac{\partial U}{\partial p}\right)_v = \frac{C_v}{(\partial p/\partial T)_v} \tag{4}$$

where C_v is the molar heat at constant volume. Moreover, by the use of a fundamental thermodynamic transformation,[1]

$$\left(\frac{\partial p}{\partial T}\right)_v = -v\left(\frac{\partial p}{\partial v}\right)_T \frac{1}{v}\left(\frac{\partial v}{\partial T}\right)_p = K\beta \tag{5}$$

where K is the isothermal bulk modulus and β the thermal coefficient of volume expansion. Finally, therefore,

$$\left(\frac{\partial U}{\partial p}\right)_v = \frac{C_v}{K\beta} \tag{6}$$

We handle $(\partial U/\partial v)_p$ similarly, recalling that, if C_p is the molar heat at constant pressure,

$$\left(\frac{\partial U}{\partial T}\right)_p = C_p - p\left(\frac{\partial v}{\partial T}\right)_p$$

Hence (1) finally becomes

$$\frac{M\kappa}{\rho_0}\frac{\partial^2 T}{\partial x^2} = \frac{1}{\beta}\left(\frac{C_v \dot{p}}{K} + \frac{C_p \dot{v}}{v}\right) \tag{7}$$

which can further be rewritten in the form

$$\dot{p} - \frac{K_s \dot{p}}{\rho_0} = \frac{M\kappa\beta K}{\rho_0 C_v}\frac{\partial^2 T}{\partial x^2} \tag{8}$$

where K_s = adiabatic bulk modulus = $(C_p/C_v)K$. This serves as the dynamic equation of state when heat conduction is considered. It is advisable to eliminate T so as to obtain an equation containing only p and ρ. For this it is necessary to express dT in terms of dp and dV, or

$$dT = \frac{dp}{K\beta} + \frac{dv}{\beta v}$$

with

$$\frac{\partial T}{\partial x} = \frac{1}{K\beta}\frac{\partial p}{\partial x} - \frac{1}{\beta\rho}\frac{\partial \rho}{\partial x}$$

and

$$\frac{\partial^2 T}{\partial x^2} = \frac{1}{K\beta}\frac{\partial^2 p}{\partial x^2} - \frac{1}{\beta\rho_0}\frac{\partial^2 \rho}{\partial x^2} \tag{9}$$

[1] M. W. Zemansky, "Heat and Thermodynamics," 2d ed., p. 28, McGraw-Hill Book Company, Inc., New York, 1943.

where we have discarded the nonlinear term in $(\partial\rho/\partial x)^2$, since we are confining our attention to small-amplitude disturbances. Therefore (8) ultimately becomes

$$\dot{p}_e - \frac{K_s\dot{\rho}_e}{\rho_0} = \frac{M\kappa}{\rho_0 C_v}\left(\frac{\partial^2 p_e}{\partial x^2} - \frac{K}{\rho_0}\frac{\partial^2 \rho_e}{\partial x^2}\right) \tag{10}$$

where the replacement of p and ρ by p_e and ρ_e, respectively, is self-explanatory. This is the equation which replaces (9.11-7). To use it for the evaluation of an equivalent sound attenuation coefficient, we can proceed as we did in that section. More simply, we can substitute into the equation of motion (9.11-2), the equation of continuity (9.11-3), and the equation of state (10) the assumed solutions for a plane harmonic wave

$$\begin{aligned}\xi &= \xi_0 e^{i(\omega t - kx)}\\ p_e &= p_{e0} e^{i(\omega t - kx)}\\ \rho_e &= \rho_{e0} e^{i(\omega t - kx)}\end{aligned} \tag{11}$$

where k is complex and given by

$$k = k_r - i\alpha \tag{12}$$

The substitution of the solution into (9.11-2), (9.11-3), and (10) gives, respectively,

$$\begin{aligned}\rho_0\omega^2\xi_0 + ikp_{e0} &= 0\\ \rho_0\omega k\xi_0 + i\omega\rho_{e0} &= 0\\ \left(i\omega + \frac{k^2 M\kappa}{\rho_0 C_v}\right)p_{e0} - \left(\frac{i\omega K_s}{\rho_0} + \frac{M\kappa K k^2}{\rho_0^2 C_v}\right)\rho_{e0} &= 0\end{aligned} \tag{13}$$

The elimination of p_{e0}, ρ_{e0}, and ξ_0 from these three equations gives the following relation connecting ω and k:

$$k^2\left(\frac{i\omega K_s}{\rho_0} + \frac{M\kappa K k^2}{\rho_0^2 C_v}\right) - \omega^2\left(i\omega + \frac{k^2 M\kappa}{\rho_0 C_v}\right) = 0 \tag{14}$$

or

$$k^2 = \frac{\omega^2(1 - ik^2 M\kappa/\omega\rho_0 C_v)}{K_s/\rho_0 - iM\kappa K k^2/\omega\rho_0^2 C_v} \tag{15}$$

Effectively this reduces to a quadratic in k^2 (a complex quantity). The general solution is somewhat involved but can be simplified by the assumption (justified by later inspection) that $k_r \gg \alpha$ in (12). Hence on the right-hand side we can safely replace k^2 by $k_r^2 = \omega^2/V_p^2$, where V_p is, as usual, the phase velocity at angular frequency ω. Similarly, we shall write for k^2 on the left-hand side $k_r^2 - 2ik_r\alpha$. By equating real and imaginary parts separately on the two sides of the equation, we finally arrive at the value of the attenuation coefficient

$$\alpha = \frac{V_p}{2V^2}(\gamma - 1)\frac{\omega_c\omega^2}{\omega_c^2 + \omega^2} \tag{16}$$

where
$$\omega_c = \frac{C_p \rho_0 V_p{}^2}{M \kappa} \tag{17}$$

Since ω_c is the reciprocal of a time, we may denote this time as the relaxation time for the process and rewrite (16) in the form

$$\alpha = \frac{V_p(\gamma - 1)}{2V^2} \frac{\omega^2 \tau}{1 + \omega^2 \tau^2} \tag{18}$$

The similarity in form between this and the value of the attenuation coefficient associated with the general relaxation mechanism discussed in Sec. 9.11 [Eq. (9.11-16)] should be noted. Of course the values of τ and V_p are different from what they would be for viscosity as the mechanism. As in the case of viscous attenuation, the relaxation time associated with heat conduction is usually so small that $\omega \tau \ll 1$ in general. Hence we can safely approximate (18) for not too high frequencies by

$$\alpha \doteq \frac{\gamma - 1}{\gamma} \frac{M \kappa \omega^2}{2 \rho_0 V^3 C_v} \tag{19}$$

We have here introduced the additional approximation $V_p \doteq V$, though the actual dispersion formula is

$$V_p = V \sqrt{\frac{1 + \omega^2 \tau^2}{1 + \gamma \omega^2 \tau^2}} \tag{20}$$

Substitution of appropriate values indicates that for gases the magnitude of α, from (19), is somewhat less than that for viscous attenuation at the same frequency but of the same order. For liquids, on the other hand, the heat conduction α is very much less as a rule than that due to viscosity.

It is usually assumed that the attenuation coefficient due to viscosity may be added to that due to heat conduction in order to find the resultant coefficient. This is presumably allowable when the effect of each is small and proportional to the square of the frequency multiplied by the appropriate relaxation time. Though the predicted dependence on the frequency is confirmed experimentally over fairly wide ranges for both gases and liquids, the order of magnitude of the measured values is in most cases in excess (often by a large factor) of that theoretically calculated in this and the previous section, except for the rare gases and liquid mercury. This has suggested the consideration of other types of relaxation processes supplementary to viscosity and heat conduction.[1] These are discussed in Chap. 12.

---

[1] For an interesting historical and analytical study of viscosity and heat conduction as mechanisms for sound absorption and dispersion, see C. Truesdell, *J. Rational Mech. Analysis*, **2**, 643 (1953).

9.13. High-intensity Sound.   Macrosonics

In setting up the fundamental equation for sound propagation in fluids in Sec. 3.5, we invoked the condition that the magnitude of the ratio ρ_e/ρ_0 or the condensation $|s| \ll 1$, that is, that the propagated disturbance consist of a volume strain whose magnitude is much smaller than unity. This at once puts a restriction on the intensity of the corresponding waves, as is seen from (9.3-7), which can be rewritten in terms of the condensation as

$$I = \rho_0 V^3 \overline{s^2} \tag{1}$$

A sound wave in air is easily audible if the root-mean-square value of s at the ear is 1.4×10^{-10}, corresponding to an intensity of about 10^{-16} watt/cm^2. The same value of s in a liquid will of course correspond to a much larger value of the intensity.   However, modern techniques can produce much larger sound disturbances than this and, in fact, excess pressures corresponding to s approaching unity in magnitude.   It is clear that in such cases (now often referred to as *macrosonics*) the standard propagation equations break down.   We have already commented briefly on this situation in Sec. 1.2.

Let us now discuss disturbances in a fluid without introducing any restriction on the size of the condensation.   For the sake of simplicity we shall limit ourselves at first to plane waves in the x direction.   As in Sec. 3.5, we write the equations of continuity and motion for fluid flow, but we make no use of the assumption that $|s| \ll 1$. The equation of continuity (3.5-2) becomes for the one-dimensional case

$$\dot{\rho} + v\frac{\partial \rho}{\partial x} + \rho\frac{\partial v}{\partial x} = 0 \tag{2}$$

and the equation of motion (3.5-6)

$$\rho\left(\dot{v} + v\frac{\partial v}{\partial x}\right) + \frac{\partial p}{\partial x} = 0 \tag{3}$$

where the flow velocity in the x direction is v (a scalar now, since there is no other flow, by assumption) and the other symbols have the same meaning as in previous sections.

The above equations are usually referred to as the equations of hydrodynamics for one-dimensional flow in the Eulerian form.   It will be recalled that x and t are here independent variables and that attention is concentrated on what happens at particular points of space as the fluid flows past them.   Our development of small-amplitude acoustics has been based on the use of the Euler equations as modified by the assumption of the smallness of s.

For some purposes it is convenient to adopt another point of view:[1] instead of concentrating on what happens at the point with coordinate x at time t, we may follow the fate of a particle of fluid which was at the *particular* point $x = a$ at time $t = 0$ and has reached any other point x at time t. Now x becomes a function of a and t, which are the independent variables. The velocity v of the particle which was at $x = a$ at time $t = 0$ is $v = \dot{x}$ at time t, and its acceleration at the same time is $\ddot{x}$. But this acceleration is due to the pressure gradient $\partial p/\partial x$, and hence we can write the equation of motion in the so-called Lagrangian form

$$\ddot{x} = -\frac{1}{\rho}\frac{\partial p}{\partial x} \tag{4}$$

We now need the corresponding form of the equation of continuity. If the original length of an element of fluid in the x direction with center at $x = a$ is δa, the corresponding length when x has changed from a to any other arbitrary x is [recalling $x = x(a,t)$]

$$\delta x = \frac{\partial x}{\partial a}\,\delta a \tag{5}$$

If we take the uniform cross section of this element as A, the conservation of mass, which is the basis of the equation of continuity, demands that

$$A\rho\,\delta x = A\rho_0\,\delta a \tag{6}$$

where ρ_0 is the original equilibrium density and ρ the density after the deformation of the fluid. Hence the equation of continuity in the Lagrangian form is

$$\rho_0 = \rho\,\frac{\partial x}{\partial a} \tag{7}$$

Incidentally, it may be worthwhile to point out that the general form of the continuity equation in three dimensions is[2]

$$\rho_0 = \rho\,\frac{\partial(x,y,z)}{\partial(a,b,c)} \tag{8}$$

where the factor multiplying ρ on the right is the Jacobian of the transformation from a, b, c to x, y, z.

We now assume, as usual, that the sound disturbance, no matter how intense, is still adiabatic in character. We further restrict our attention to an ideal gas for which the adiabatic relation between pressure and

---

[1] R. Courant and K. O. Friedrichs, "Supersonic Flow and Shock Waves," pp. 12ff., Interscience Publishers, Inc., New York, 1948; also H. Lamb, "Hydrodynamics," 6th ed., pp. 12ff., Dover Publications, New York, 1945.

[2] Lamb, *op. cit.*, p. 14.

density is

$$\frac{p}{\rho^\gamma} = \frac{p_0}{\rho_0{}^\gamma} = \text{const} \tag{9}$$

where γ has the usual significance (Sec. 9.2).

We now multiply (4) through by $\partial x/\partial a$ and utilize (7). The result is

$$\ddot{x} = -\frac{1}{\rho_0}\frac{\partial p}{\partial a} \tag{10}$$

But from the equation of continuity (7) and the adiabatic condition (9) we can write

$$\frac{\partial p}{\partial a} = -\frac{\gamma p_0}{(\partial x/\partial a)^{\gamma+1}}\frac{\partial^2 x}{\partial a^2} \tag{11}$$

whence (10) becomes

$$\ddot{x} = \frac{\gamma p_0}{\rho_0}\frac{1}{(\partial x/\partial a)^{\gamma+1}}\frac{\partial^2 x}{\partial a^2} \tag{12}$$

Now the small-amplitude theory gives $\gamma p_0/\rho_0 = V^2$, where V is the effective small-amplitude sound velocity in the gas. Hence (12) becomes

$$\ddot{x} = \frac{V^2}{(\partial x/\partial a)^{\gamma+1}}\frac{\partial^2 x}{\partial a^2} \tag{13}$$

It is usual to write

$$x = a + \xi \tag{14}$$

where ξ appears as the displacement of the fluid particle from its equilibrium position. In this notation, (13) takes the form

$$\ddot{\xi} = \frac{V^2}{(1 + \partial\xi/\partial a)^{\gamma+1}}\frac{\partial^2 \xi}{\partial a^2} \tag{15}$$

It is immediately recognized that, from the standpoint of the Lagrangian notation, $\partial\xi/\partial a$ measures the condensation in the disturbance. If this is small in magnitude compared with unity, (15) reduces to the standard small-amplitude form of the wave equation for plane waves.

There is no need to restrict the treatment to gases. For liquids, however, (9) has no meaning. If we first assume that the bulk modulus of a liquid is constant, or, what amounts to the same thing, that the excess pressure in the liquid is directly proportional to the excess density,

$$\frac{\partial p}{\partial a} = \frac{\gamma K}{\rho_0}\frac{\partial \rho}{\partial a} \tag{16}$$

where the derivatives are taken adiabatically, K is the isothermal bulk modulus, and γ, as usual, the ratio of specific heats, so that γK is the equivalent adiabatic bulk modulus. Calculating $\partial\rho/\partial a$ from the equation of continuity yields for the equation of motion, in place of (13),

$$\ddot{x} = \frac{V^2}{(\partial x/\partial a)^2} \frac{\partial^2 x}{\partial a^2} \tag{17}$$

where now $V^2 = \gamma K/\rho_0$. This corresponds to (13) for the special case $\gamma = 1$. As a matter of fact, for many liquids this is approximately correct. However, it is also a fact that for liquids in general it is not possible to represent the change in density as directly proportional to the change in pressure. A more realistic assumption is the quadratic expression

$$p - p_0 = P \frac{\rho - \rho_0}{\rho_0} + \frac{Q}{2} \left(\frac{\rho - \rho_0}{\rho_0} \right)^2 \tag{18}$$

where P and Q are constants corresponding to an adiabatic change. Then

$$\frac{\partial p}{\partial a} = \left[\frac{P}{\rho_0} + \frac{Q(\rho - \rho_0)}{\rho_0^2} \right] \frac{\partial \rho}{\partial a} \tag{19}$$

or

$$\frac{\partial p}{\partial a} = - \left[\frac{P}{\rho_0} + \frac{Q}{\rho_0} \left(1 - \frac{1}{\partial x/\partial a} \right) \right] \frac{\rho_0}{(\partial x/\partial a)^2} \frac{\partial^2 x}{\partial a^2} \tag{20}$$

so that the equation of motion becomes

$$\ddot{x} = \frac{P}{\rho_0} \left[1 + \frac{Q}{P} \left(1 - \frac{1}{\partial x/\partial a} \right) \right] \frac{1}{(\partial x/\partial a)^2} \frac{\partial^2 x}{\partial a^2} \tag{21}$$

It is clear that $P = \rho_0 V^2$, where V is the usual small-amplitude wave velocity. Then the equation takes the form (using $x = a + \xi$)

$$\ddot{\xi} = V^2 \left[\frac{1 + Q/P}{(1 + \partial\xi/\partial a)^2} - \frac{Q/P}{(1 + \partial\xi/\partial a)^3} \right] \frac{\partial^2 \xi}{\partial a^2} \tag{22}$$

For $\left| \dfrac{\partial \xi}{\partial a} \right| < 1$ and of such a magnitude that we can write

$$\frac{1}{(1 + \partial\xi/\partial a)^n} = 1 - n \frac{\partial \xi}{\partial a}$$

to a reasonably good approximation, (22) can be expressed in the approximate form

$$\ddot{\xi} = \frac{V^2}{(1 + \partial\xi/\partial a)^{Q/P-2}} \frac{\partial^2 \xi}{\partial a^2} \tag{23}$$

so that, for liquids following (18), $Q/P - 2$ takes the place of $\gamma + 1$ in the case of the ideal gas.

A rather more general method of derivation of the equation of large-amplitude compressional disturbances in a fluid is provided by a fundamental change in independent variable.[1] Instead of choosing a as the

---

[1] Courant and Friedrichs, "Supersonic Flow and Shock Waves," p. 30.

variable on which (together with t) x depends in the Lagrangian treatment, let us choose a quantity m defined by the expression

$$m = \int_{x(0,t)}^{x(m,t)} \rho \, dx \tag{24}$$

In words, m is the mass of the fluid in a tube of unit cross section extending from an arbitrary zero plane section for which m is taken to be zero to any other plane section. To each plane cross section of fluid there thus corresponds a value of m with respect to which we can measure the coordinate x attained by a given particle of fluid at time t. The density ρ, like x, is now considered to be a function of m and t.

If we differentiate (24) with respect to m on both sides, the result is

$$\frac{\partial x(m,t)}{\partial m} = \frac{1}{\rho(m,t)} = T(m,t) \tag{25}$$

where T is a new function defined as the reciprocal of ρ. This result comes from the following considerations. If we denote the indefinite integral $\int \rho \, dx$ by $f(x)$, then

$$m = \int_{x(0,t)}^{x(m,t)} \rho \, dx = f[x(m,t)] - f[x(0,t)] \tag{26}$$

Differentiating both sides of this equation with respect to m gives

$$1 = \frac{\partial f[x(m,t)]}{\partial m}$$

But
$$\rho(m,t) = \frac{df}{dx}$$

Now, therefore,

$$\frac{\partial f[x(m,t)]}{\partial m} = \frac{df}{dx} \frac{\partial x}{\partial m} = \rho(m,t) \frac{\partial x}{\partial m} = 1 \tag{27}$$

If $\partial x/\partial m$ is denoted by $T(m,t)$, (25) results. This same equation can also serve as the equation of continuity since it represents the conservation of mass (i.e., if the volume associated with given m increases, the density must decrease in the same proportion). We can also rewrite the Lagrangian equation of motion in terms of the parameter m. Thus from (4) we have

$$\ddot{x} = -\frac{1}{\rho} \frac{\partial p}{\partial x} = -\frac{1}{\rho} \frac{\partial p/\partial m}{\partial x/\partial m} = -\frac{\partial p}{\partial m} \tag{28}$$

We note indeed the close relation between (27) and (7).

We may now express the adiabatic condition in general thermodynamic fashion by introducing the entropy S of a particle of fluid and imposing the condition

$$\dot{S} = 0 \tag{29}$$

The equation of state will also be expressed in terms of the entropy instead of temperature:

$$p = f(\rho,S) = \varphi(T,S) \tag{30}$$

From (29) it is clear that S is a function of m only. Let us try to get the equation of motion in terms of x as the only dependent variable. We write

$$\frac{\partial p}{\partial m} = \frac{\partial \varphi}{\partial m} = \frac{\partial \varphi}{\partial T}\frac{\partial T}{\partial m} + \frac{\partial \varphi}{\partial S}\frac{\partial S}{\partial m} = \frac{\partial \varphi}{\partial T}\frac{\partial^2 x}{\partial m^2} + \frac{\partial \varphi}{\partial S}\frac{\partial S}{\partial m} \tag{31}$$

If we assume not merely that S does not vary with time but that it remains constant throughout the medium, a state of affairs to which the term isentropic (in addition to adiabatic) may be attached, the second term on the right of (31) disappears, and the equation of motion becomes

$$\ddot{x} = -\frac{\partial \varphi}{\partial T}\frac{\partial^2 x}{\partial m^2} \tag{32}$$

This can be further modified by writing

$$\frac{\partial \varphi}{\partial T} = -\rho^2 \frac{\partial p}{\partial \rho} = -\rho^2 V^2$$

since $\partial p/\partial \rho$ here is already adiabatic. Hence (32) takes the form

$$\ddot{x} = \rho^2 V^2 \frac{\partial^2 x}{\partial m^2} \tag{33}$$

If we take $v = \partial x/\partial t$ (the flow velocity) and T as the dependent variables, with t and m as the independent ones, we can replace the second-order equation of motion with two first-order equations, namely,

$$\dot{v} = \rho^2 V^2 \frac{\partial T}{\partial m}$$
$$\frac{\partial v}{\partial m} = \frac{\partial T}{\partial t} \tag{34}$$

since $\partial x/\partial m = T$ and the order of differentiation with respect to m and t is interchangeable.

It is of some interest and value to apply the preceding considerations to spherical waves in which the disturbance depends, in addition to the time, only on the radial distance from some fixed origin. Here we take a again as the initial distance from the origin of a particle of fluid which attains the distance r at time t. It then appears that the equation of continuity becomes

$$\rho_0 = \frac{r^2}{a^2}\frac{\partial r}{\partial a}\rho \tag{35}$$

Moreover, the equation of motion is then

$$\ddot{r} = -\frac{1}{\rho}\frac{\partial p/\partial a}{\partial r/\partial a} = -\frac{r^2}{\rho_0 a^2}\frac{\partial p}{\partial a} \tag{36}$$

If once more we confine our attention to an ideal gas and combine the adiabatic equation (9) with (35), the result is

$$p = p_0\left(\frac{a}{r}\right)^{2\gamma}\left(\frac{\partial r}{\partial a}\right)^{-\gamma} \tag{37}$$

with

$$\frac{\partial p}{\partial a} = 2\gamma p_0\left(\frac{a}{r}\right)^{2\gamma}\left(\frac{\partial r}{\partial a}\right)^{-\gamma}\left[\frac{1}{a} - \frac{1}{r}\frac{\partial r}{\partial a} - \frac{1}{r}\left(\frac{\partial r}{\partial a}\right)^{-1}\frac{\partial^2 r}{\partial a^2}\right] \tag{38}$$

With the assumption

$$r = a + \xi$$

and substitution into (36), the equation of motion finally becomes, after algebraic manipulation,

$$\left(1 + \frac{\xi}{a}\right)^{2(\gamma-1)}\left(1 + \frac{\partial\xi}{\partial a}\right)^{\gamma+1}\frac{\ddot{\xi}}{V^2} = \frac{\partial^2\xi}{\partial a^2} + \frac{2(1 + \partial\xi/\partial a)}{a(1 + \xi/a)}\left(\frac{\partial\xi}{\partial a} - \frac{\xi}{a}\right) \tag{39}$$

The treatment of spherical waves can be greatly simplified by the use of the same type of transformation of variables employed for plane waves. Thus we let $4\pi m$ be the mass of fluid inside a sphere of radius $r(m,t)$ with center at the origin of the waves.   Then

$$4\pi m = 4\pi\int_0^{r(m,t)}\rho r^2\,dr \tag{40}$$

The equation of continuity is obtained by differentiation with respect to m, whence

$$\rho(m,t) = \frac{1}{T(m,t)} = \frac{1}{r^2\,\partial r/\partial m} \tag{41}$$

The Lagrangian equation of motion, with the use of the equation of continuity, becomes

$$\ddot{r} = -r^2\frac{\partial p}{\partial m} \tag{42}$$

But since we can write [as in (30)]

$$p = \varphi(T,S)$$

it follows that

$$\frac{\partial p}{\partial m} = \frac{\partial p}{\partial T}\frac{\partial}{\partial m}\left(r^2\frac{\partial r}{\partial m}\right) + \frac{\partial p}{\partial S}\frac{\partial S}{\partial m} \tag{43}$$

If the flow is isentropic as well as adiabatic, we have $\partial S/\partial m = 0$, and the equation for the dependence of r on m and t finally becomes[1]

$$\ddot{r} = \rho^2 V^2 r^2 \frac{\partial}{\partial m} \left(r^2 \frac{\partial r}{\partial m} \right) \tag{44}$$

9.14. Waveform for Macrosonic Waves

Several methods have been devised for the solution of the macrosonic plane wave equation derived in the preceding section

$$\ddot{\xi} = \frac{V^2}{(1 + \partial \xi / \partial a)^{\gamma+1}} \frac{\partial^2 \xi}{\partial a^2} \tag{1}$$

We present here the analytical treatment due to Earnshaw.[2] If we go back to $x = a + \xi$, the equation takes the form

$$\ddot{x} = \frac{V^2}{(\partial x / \partial a)^{\gamma+1}} \frac{\partial^2 x}{\partial a^2} \tag{2}$$

Earnshaw observed that an equation of this type can be satisfied by taking $\dot{x}$ as a function of $\partial x / \partial a$, that is,

$$\dot{x} = f\left(\frac{\partial x}{\partial a}\right) = u \tag{3}$$

(where we shall find it convenient to use u for particle, or flow, velocity) since this implies

$$\ddot{x} = \frac{df}{d(\partial x/\partial a)} \frac{\partial \dot{x}}{\partial a} = \left[\frac{df}{d(\partial x/\partial a)} \right]^2 \frac{\partial^2 x}{\partial a^2} \tag{4}$$

and this is in the same form as (2) if

$$\frac{df}{d(\partial x/\partial a)} = \pm \frac{V}{(\partial x/\partial a)^{(\gamma+1)/2}} \tag{5}$$

or
$$f = \pm \frac{2V}{1 - \gamma} \left(\frac{\partial x}{\partial a}\right)^{(1-\gamma)/2} + K \tag{6}$$

as long as $\gamma \neq 1$. For $\gamma = 1$ we have on the contrary

$$f = \pm V \ln \frac{\partial x}{\partial a} + K \tag{7}$$

where K is in each case a constant of integration. We shall carry on with the general case of $\gamma \neq 1$. We proceed to evaluate K by assuming

[1] For the corresponding equations for cylindrical waves, see Prob. 18. For practical applications of this analysis, see N. McLachlan, "Loud Speakers," pp. 198ff., Oxford University Press, London, 1939.

[2] S. Earnshaw, *Phil. Trans. Roy. Soc. London*, **150**, 133 (1860). See also Rayleigh, "Theory of Sound," vol. 2, p. 37.

that the particle velocity $u = f = 0$ for $\partial x/\partial a = 1$ or $\partial \xi/\partial a = 0$. From the equation of continuity (9.13-7)

$$\rho_0 = \rho \frac{\partial x}{\partial a}$$

whence
$$K = \pm \frac{2V}{1 - \gamma}$$

and the solution is

$$u = f = \pm \frac{2V}{1 - \gamma}\left[\left(\frac{\partial x}{\partial a}\right)^{(1-\gamma)/2} - 1\right] \tag{8}$$

Now the value of u which holds for the particle at a at time t will be transmitted to the particle at $a + da$ at time $t + dt$ if

$$\dot{u}\, dt = -\frac{\partial u}{\partial a}\, da$$

or
$$\ddot{x}\, dt + \frac{\partial \dot{x}}{\partial a}\, da = 0 \tag{9}$$

By use of (4) this yields

$$da + \frac{df}{d(\partial x/\partial a)}\, dt = 0 \tag{10}$$

This means that the velocity u is effectively propagated at the rate

$$\pm \frac{V}{(\partial x/\partial a)^{(\gamma+1)/2}} = \pm V\left(\frac{\rho}{\rho_0}\right)^{(\gamma+1)/2} \tag{11}$$

It follows from (8) that ρ is also propagated at the same rate. But since ξ is a function of a and t, we can write

$$d\xi = \frac{\partial \xi}{\partial a}\, da + \dot{\xi}\, dt \tag{12}$$

Let us introduce the quantity β defined so that

$$\beta = 1 + \frac{\partial \xi}{\partial a} = \frac{\partial x}{\partial a} \tag{13}$$

whence $u = f(\beta)$. Therefore

$$d\xi = (\beta - 1)\, da + f(\beta)\, dt$$

which can be integrated to

$$\xi = (\beta - 1)a + f(\beta)t + \varphi(\beta) \tag{14}$$

provided that

$$a + t\frac{df}{d\beta} + \frac{d\varphi}{d\beta} = 0 \tag{15}$$

If we multiply (15) through by β and combine with (14), the result is

$$\xi + a = \left(u - \beta \frac{df}{d\beta} \right) t + \varphi(\beta) - \beta \frac{d\varphi}{d\beta}$$

or if we use $df/d\beta$ from (5) (with the minus sign), ultimately

$$\xi + a - \left(u \frac{1 + \gamma}{2} + V \right) t = \varphi(\beta) - \beta \frac{d\varphi}{d\beta} \tag{16}$$

Now $\varphi(\beta) - \beta \, d\varphi/d\beta$ is a function of β alone and hence, from (8), an arbitrary function of u itself. Thus it follows that u is an arbitrary function of $\xi + a - [u(1 + \gamma)/2 + V]t$, and we can therefore write

$$u = F\left[\xi + a - \left(u \frac{1 + \gamma}{2} + V \right) t \right] \tag{17}$$

which is then the general solution of (1) satisfying the assumed initial condition. It is interesting to observe that for the special case of $\gamma = 1$, it reduces to

$$u = F[\xi + a - (u + V)t] \tag{18}$$

which indeed would follow directly from the special assumption (7).

This type of solution leads to the physical situation in which an initially sinusoidal waveform for u will not maintain its shape as it travels. In fact the crests will tend to overtake the troughs, since for them the "effective" wave velocity $u + V$ is greater. A solution of the form (18) cannot hold for all a and t, since ultimately the function becomes multiple-valued, and the only physical significance of this would be the "breaking" of the wave. It follows that it is not possible to find a solution of (1) which represents a waveform that remains stable indefinitely. Since we know from experience that it *is* possible to produce a stable macrosonic waveform, the consequence is that (1) cannot be the correct equation for this type of radiation, though it may be a fair representation for the early stages of a wave in which $|\partial \xi / \partial a|$ is not too large. From a physical standpoint it is clear that we must introduce into (1) some stabilizing influence. It seems more or less obvious that a viscous force dependent on particle velocity might serve this purpose. We shall discuss efforts in this direction in the next section.

9.15. Macrosonics in a Viscous Fluid. Stable Waveform

We shall follow the general methods of Sec. 9.13 in setting up the fundamental equation for a large-amplitude plane wave disturbance in a viscous fluid. The Eulerian equation of motion in such a fluid (from

Sec. 9.11) is

$$\rho\left(\dot{u} + u\frac{\partial u}{\partial x}\right) = -\frac{\partial p_e}{\partial x} + \frac{4}{3}\frac{\partial}{\partial x}\left(\eta\frac{\partial u}{\partial x}\right) \tag{1}$$

where η is the shear viscosity and u the flow, or particle, velocity. On the Lagrangian scheme this equation becomes

$$\ddot{x} = -\frac{1}{\rho}\frac{\partial p_e}{\partial x} + \frac{4}{3\rho}\frac{\partial}{\partial x}\left(\eta\frac{\partial u}{\partial x}\right) \tag{2}$$

If we multiply both sides by $\partial x/\partial a$, where a has the same significance as in Secs. 9.13 and 9.14, we obtain

$$\ddot{x}\frac{\partial x}{\partial a} = -\frac{1}{\rho}\frac{\partial p_e}{\partial a} + \frac{4}{3\rho}\left(\eta\frac{\partial^2 u}{\partial x^2}\frac{\partial x}{\partial a} + \frac{\partial \eta}{\partial x}\frac{\partial u}{\partial x}\frac{\partial x}{\partial a}\right) \tag{3}$$

We now observe that

$$\frac{\partial u}{\partial x} = \frac{\partial u}{\partial a}\Big/\frac{\partial x}{\partial a} \qquad \frac{\partial^2 u}{\partial x^2} = \frac{\dfrac{\partial^2 u}{\partial a^2}}{\left(\dfrac{\partial x}{\partial a}\right)^2} - \frac{\dfrac{\partial u}{\partial a}}{\left(\dfrac{\partial x}{\partial a}\right)^3}\frac{\partial^2 x}{\partial a^2}$$

By the use of these relations, the equation of continuity (9.13-7), and the expression for $\partial p/\partial a$ given in (9.13-11), the equation (3) takes the form

$$\ddot{x} = \frac{\gamma p_0}{\rho_0}\frac{1}{(\partial x/\partial a)^{\gamma+1}}\frac{\partial^2 x}{\partial a^2} - \frac{4\eta}{3\rho_0}\frac{\rho}{\rho_0}\frac{\partial \dot{x}}{\partial a}\frac{\partial^2 x}{\partial a^2}\Big/\frac{\partial x}{\partial a}$$
$$+ \frac{4\eta}{3\rho_0}\frac{\rho}{\rho_0}\frac{\partial^2 \dot{x}}{\partial a^2} + \frac{4}{3\rho_0}\frac{\rho}{\rho_0}\frac{\partial \eta}{\partial a}\frac{\partial \dot{x}}{\partial a} \tag{4}$$

It will be noted that we are here not assuming that η is constant but are including $\partial \eta/\partial a$ to take account of the fact that η may vary from point to point in the medium.

Going over to ξ in analogy with the preceding sections, we write in place of (4)

$$\ddot{\xi} = \frac{\partial^2 \xi}{\partial a^2}\left[\frac{V^2}{(1 + \partial \xi/\partial a)^{\gamma+1}} - \frac{4\eta}{3\rho_0}\frac{1}{(1 + \partial \xi/\partial a)^2}\frac{\partial \dot{\xi}}{\partial a}\right]$$
$$+ \frac{4\eta}{3\rho_0}\frac{1}{(1 + \partial \xi/\partial a)}\frac{\partial^2 \dot{\xi}}{\partial a^2} + \frac{4}{3\rho_0}\frac{1}{(1 + \partial \xi/\partial a)}\frac{\partial \eta}{\partial a}\frac{\partial \dot{\xi}}{\partial a} \tag{5}$$

The term $\partial \eta/\partial a$ can be expressed in terms of the temperature dependence of viscosity for an ideal gas.[1] Thus

$$\frac{\eta}{\eta_0} = \sqrt{\frac{T}{T_0}} \tag{6}$$

[1] This was suggested by P. J. Westervelt [master's thesis (physics), Massachusetts Institute of Technology, Cambridge, Mass., 1949].

if T is the absolute temperature. Hence, in view of the adiabatic dependence

$$\frac{T}{T_0} = \left(\frac{\rho}{\rho_0}\right)^{\gamma-1}$$

this leads to

$$\frac{\eta}{\eta_0} = \left(1 + \frac{\partial \xi}{\partial a}\right)^{(1-\gamma)/2}$$

and

$$\frac{\partial \eta}{\partial a} = \eta_0 \frac{1 - \gamma}{2}\left(1 + \frac{\partial \xi}{\partial a}\right)^{-(1+\gamma)/2} \frac{\partial^2 \xi}{\partial a^2} \tag{7}$$

With this substitution and the combining of terms, the equation of motion (5) takes the form

$$\ddot{\xi} = \frac{\partial^2 \xi}{\partial a^2}\left[\frac{V^2}{(1 + \partial\xi/\partial a)^{\gamma+1}} - \frac{\gamma + 1}{2}\frac{4\eta_0}{3\rho_0}\left(1 + \frac{\partial \xi}{\partial a}\right)^{-(3+\gamma)/2} \frac{\partial \dot{\xi}}{\partial a}\right] + \frac{4\eta_0}{3\rho_0}\left(1 + \frac{\partial \xi}{\partial a}\right)^{-(1+\gamma)/2} \frac{\partial^2 \dot{\xi}}{\partial a^2} \tag{8}$$

This is a formidable nonlinear equation, and Fay[1] thought it safe to neglect the second term in the brackets compared with the first and to simplify the last term on the right, taking finally

$$V^2 \frac{\partial^2 \xi}{\partial a^2} = \left(1 + \frac{\partial \xi}{\partial a}\right)^{\gamma+1}\left(\ddot{\xi} - \frac{4\eta_0}{3\rho_0}\frac{\partial^2 \dot{\xi}}{\partial a^2}\right) \tag{9}$$

The second term in the brackets in (8) is sufficiently small so that the indicated approximation is probably justified. In any event, a complete solution of neither (8) nor (9) has ever been obtained. Fay expressed the excess pressure in terms of an expansion in powers of $\partial\xi/\partial a$ and proceeded to expand $\partial\xi/\partial a$ as a Fourier series in the time with spatially dependent coefficients modulated by series of exponential functions of a (decay factors). The details of the analysis are elaborate and tedious and will not be presented here. It is sufficient for our purposes to note the final result, which expresses the excess pressure p_{ex} as a function of x:

$$p_{ex} = -A\alpha_v \sum_{n=1}^{\infty} \frac{\sin nkx}{\sinh n\alpha_v(x_0 + x)} \tag{10}$$

The various quantities have the following meaning:

$$A = \frac{4V\gamma p_0}{(\gamma + 1)\omega} \qquad \alpha_v = \frac{2}{3}\frac{\eta\omega^2}{\rho_0 V^3}$$

$$k = \frac{\omega}{V} \qquad V = \sqrt{\frac{\gamma p_0}{\rho_0}} \tag{11}$$

p_0 = standard atmospheric pressure ρ_0 = corresponding density

[1] R. D. Fay, *J. Acoust. Soc. Am.*, **3**, 222 (1931).

The fundamental angular frequency of the macrosonic wave is ω. Physically the solution means that the large-amplitude wave disturbance is split up into a series of harmonic components, each of which decays in amplitude in accordance with the denominator term in (10). The quantity x_0 is an arbitrary constant to be evaluated by initial conditions.

Let us assume that $\alpha_v(x_0 + x)$ will be considerably less than unity except at very high frequencies and large x, where we expect the attenuation to be great. Hence we may approximate and write

$$\sinh n\alpha_v(x_0 + x) \doteq n\alpha_v(x_0 + x)$$

so that

$$p_{ex} = -\frac{A}{x_0 + x} \sum_{n=1}^{\infty} \frac{\sin nkx}{n} \tag{12}$$

If $0 < kx < 2\pi$ the evaluation of the sum yields[1]

$$p_{ex} = -\frac{A}{x_0 + x} \frac{\pi - kx}{2} \tag{13}$$

As kx goes through the range 0 to 2π, the term $(\pi - kx)/2$ runs linearly from $\pi/2$ to $-\pi/2$ through zero. This course is repeated as kx runs from 2π to 4π, etc. The result is a saw-tooth curve with discontinuities at multiples of 2π and modulated by the term $1/(x_0 + x)$, as in Fig. 9.22. The peak values of p_{ex}, denoted by p_{e0} and attained at $P_1, P_2, P_3, \ldots$ in the liquid, are thus given by

$$p_{e0} = \frac{A\pi}{2(x_0 + x)} = \frac{\gamma}{\gamma + 1} p_0 \lambda \frac{1}{x_0 + x} \tag{14}$$

where λ is the wavelength of the fundamental. Without the use of the approximation leading from (10) to (13) we may still expect to find a curve which is similar to that in Fig. 9.22 but in which the periodic discontinuities are smoothed over, without, however, changing the essential characteristics of a slowly rising rear part of the profile and a sharply falling front.

As an actual macrosonic wave approaches the saw-tooth character exhibited in Fig. 9.22, it is said to become a *shock* wave, characterized by a relatively large change in excess pressure across a very small region of space. Such waves arise in explosions and other rapid compressional disturbances in a fluid. In the next section we shall consider some of their properties and incidentally indicate how they lead independently to an equation of form (14).

[1] L. B. W. Jolley, "Summation of Series," p. 186, Chapman and Hall, Ltd., London, 1925.

It is interesting to observe that the attenuation represented by (14) is not exponential in x, nor does it appear to have anything to do with the viscosity which entered the original equation of motion. The reason for this is inherent in the method of expansion in terms of Fourier components. Clearly the significance of (10) is that the energy in the fundamental of the macrosonic wave is ultimately distributed among the higher modes. But each of the higher-frequency modes is itself attenuated by viscous dissipation; hence the over-all effect is a loss in intensity much greater than could be expected from the action of viscosity on the fundamental itself.

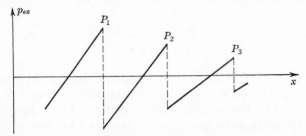

FIG. 9.22. Excess pressure as a function of distance from the source in a macrosonic wave.

Though the macrosonic attenuation is not exponential, it is of interest to try to represent it as such and to find the equivalent absorption coefficient when p_{e0} is expressed in the form

$$p_{e0} = Ce^{-\alpha x} \tag{15}$$

It is clear that α must now be a function of x. Since for any small change in x, say Δx, for which the above representation is possible, we have

$$\frac{x_0 + x + \Delta x}{x_0 + x} = e^{\alpha \Delta x}$$

it follows that

$$\alpha = \frac{1}{x_0 + x} \tag{16}$$

From (14) it follows that α increases with the peak excess pressure in the macrosonic wave and hence with the intensity. This is confirmed by observations on the absorption of macrosonic radiation in both gases and liquids.[1] We recall that the parameter x_0 depends on the initial conditions and hence on the excess pressure at a given point (e.g., the source

[1] For gases, see G. C. Werth and L. P. Delsasso, *J. Acoust. Soc. Am.*, **26**, 59 (1954); and I. Rudnick, *J. Acoust. Soc. Am.*, **25**, 1012 (1953). For liquids, consult F. E. Fox and W. A. Wallace, *J. Acoust. Soc. Am.*, **26**, 994 (1954); and D. M. Towle and R. B. Lindsay, *J. Acoust. Soc. Am.*, **27**, 530 (1955).

of the sound or some suitably chosen nearby point). If x_0 is large, α will not vary appreciably over a considerable range of x.

In the experiments of Werth and Delsasso[1] the attenuation in a "stable" saw-tooth wave in air of the kind that Fay's theory purports to represent was measured in a tube 9 ft long and 1.5 in. in diameter. The wave was actually produced as a repeated shock wave in which the ratio of peak-to-trough excess pressure ($2p_{e0}$ in the theory) to standard atmospheric pressure (p_0) varied from 0.06 to 0.10. The fundamental frequency in a typical run was 1,130 cycles/sec. The attenuation was measured over a range in x of about five wavelengths, and it was found that $2p_{e0}/p_0$ could be rather accurately represented by an expression of the form

$$\frac{2p_{e0}}{p_0} = \frac{K\lambda}{x_0 + x} \tag{17}$$

with $x_0 = 14\lambda$ and $K = 1.3$. It is seen that this is of the same form as (14) and disagrees with it only in the fact that the constant K should be $2\gamma/(\gamma + 1) = 1.17$ theoretically instead of 1.3. The nature of the discrepancy may perhaps be more clearly expressed by writing (17) in the form

$$\frac{\alpha/\nu^2}{2p_{e0}/p_0} = \frac{1}{KV\nu} \tag{18}$$

where ν is the frequency of the fundamental and K is still $2\gamma/(\gamma + 1)$ in the theory. This emphasizes the frequency dependence of α. As we have already noted in Sec. 9.11, viscosity and heat conduction lead to an attenuation coefficient which varies directly as the square of the frequency, or α/ν^2 is constant in frequency. This is not true for macrosonic radiation, as (18) emphasizes. The theory evidently predicts at given fundamental frequency a larger attenuation than was measured by Werth and Delsasso. In their measurements they varied the frequency from 402 to 1,130 cycles/sec and found that K stayed nearly constant at 1.30, thus verifying the theoretical prediction of the inverse frequency dependence of $(\alpha/\nu^2)/(2p_{e0}/p_0)$.

Macrosonic radiation in liquids is particularly important because of the many practical applications of high-intensity sound in acoustic processing in liquid media. Illustrations are provided by the production of emulsions, the cleaning of metal parts, and ultrasonic action on living organisms. Many of these effects are associated with cavitation, or the production of visible bubbles in either normal or degassed liquids. The transmission of macrosonics in a liquid is complicated by the presence of

[1] *Loc. cit.*

the cavitation it brings about. In particular, the cavitation bubbles scatter the sound and therefore lead to effective attenuation, in addition to the standard mechanisms at work. However, the intensity level at which cavitation appears increases with the frequency.[1] Hence for ultrasonic radiation (i.e., megacycle or higher) cavitation may not appear even for intensities that are definitely macrosonic.

There is no reason why the analysis of this section should not be applicable to liquids. Examination discloses that all one needs to do is to replace γp_0 wherever it occurs by $\rho_0 V^2$, where V is the velocity of low-amplitude sound in the liquid, and to replace $\gamma + 1$ by the quantity $Q/P - 2$ as presented in (9.13-18, 23). This is a number which can range from 2 to 10 depending on the liquid. Moreover, the approximation $\alpha_v(x_0 + x) \ll 1$, employed in the gas case, should also hold for liquids as well, save for very high frequencies. The experimental tests of the success of this application are still not wholly conclusive. In the measurements of Fox and Wallace and Towle and Lindsay,[2] there is order-of-magnitude agreement with the theory, though the theory here fails to predict all the attenuation which is observed at all frequencies studied. Recent work by Narasimhan and Beyer,[3] however, confirms the frequency dependence of α/ν^2 as given in (18).

The question might still be raised whether it is at all possible for a macrosonic wave to travel without change in waveform in a medium without dissipation. This was investigated by W. J. M. Rankine,[4] who showed that this could indeed take place, but only in a medium in which the following relation exists between pressure and density:

$$p + \frac{m^2}{\rho} = \text{const} \tag{19}$$

where m is the "mass swept past in unit time by a plane moving with the wave," to quote Lamb. This is a highly artificial and scarcely realizable relation. It seems essential, as indeed the Fay treatment of the problem in this section suggests, that some dissipative influence be at work in any actual physical medium in order to preserve the waveform of a finite-amplitude wave. Rayleigh[5] found that viscosity alone can maintain a stable waveform, though his method is more indirect than that of Fay.

---

[1] L. Bergmann, "Der Ultraschall," 6th ed., p. 847, S. Hirzel Verlag, Leipzig, 1956.
[2] *Loc. cit.*
[3] V. Narasimhan and R. T. Beyer, *J. Acoust. Soc. Am.*, **28**, 1233 (1956).
[4] H. Lamb, "Hydrodynamics," 6th ed., pp. 484f., Dover Publications, New York, 1945.
[5] *Ibid.*, pp. 650f.

9.16. Shock Waves

In the previous two sections we have commented on the fact that in a macrosonic wave the effect of the nonlinear denominator term $1 + \dfrac{\partial \xi}{\partial a}$ [Eq. (9.14-1)] is to produce a steepening of the wave profile. This process is opposed by the various attenuation mechanisms in the fluid, with the result that a saw-tooth curve (Fig. 9.22) is approached. When such a profile with a sharply defined front is formed, the result is called a *shock* wave. In an ideal shock there is consequently a discontinuity in pressure, density, and particle velocity which is propagated through the fluid with an effective velocity which is an average of the values of $V + u$ behind and ahead of the discontinuity, or shock front (recall Earnshaw's solution, Sec. 9.14). Such shocks can result from explosions, such as the rupture of a membrane separating a region of high pressure from a region of low pressure in a tube. The detonation of an explosive charge under water provides another illustration. Still another is the bow wave of a projectile traveling faster than the velocity of small-amplitude sound in still air. In any actual shock there is no mathematical discontinuity but only a very small transition region between the rear and forward values of pressure and density.

Since the literature on shock waves is now extensive,[1] we shall content ourselves here with an indication of some of the more important equations governing their propagation in one direction.

In Fig. 9.23 we depict a tube of unit cross section through which a shock front or transition region $F_1 F_2$ is being propagated in the x direc-

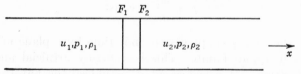

$$F_1 \quad F_2$$

$$u_1, p_1, \rho_1 \qquad u_2, p_2, \rho_2 \qquad \longrightarrow x$$

Fig. 9.23. Propagation of a shock front through a tube.

tion. It is assumed that behind the front the particle velocity in the fluid, the pressure, and the density are constant and equal to u_1, p_1, ρ_1, respectively, whereas ahead of the front their corresponding constant values are u_2, p_2, ρ_2, respectively. These quantities are measured for convenience with respect to a set of reference axes in which the front appears at rest. In other words, the coordinate system used here moves with the front.

[1] R. Courant and K. O. Friedrichs, "Supersonic Flow and Shock Waves," Interscience Publishers, Inc., New York, 1948; and M. J. Lighthill, Viscosity Effects in Sound Waves of Finite Amplitude, in G. K. Batchelor and R. M. Davies (eds.), "Surveys of Mechanics," pp. 250–351, Cambridge University Press, London, 1956.

Conservation of mass dictates that the rate of mass flow into the front equals that out of it [equation of continuity (Sec. 9.13)]. This yields

$$\rho_1 u_1 = \rho_2 u_2 \tag{1}$$

The conservation of momentum in the shock front, equivalent to the equation of motion of the fluid contained in $F_1 F_2$, yields

$$\rho_1 u_1 (u_2 - u_1) = p_1 - p_2 \tag{2}$$

since the left-hand term is the time rate of change of momentum of the fluid entering the front and the right-hand term is the net force acting on it. By the use of the equation of continuity, (2) can be rewritten as

$$\rho_1 u_1{}^2 + p_1 = \rho_2 u_2{}^2 + p_2 \tag{3}$$

We can also apply the conservation of energy in the form

$$p_1 u_1 - p_2 u_2 = \rho_1 u_1 [\tfrac{1}{2}(u_2{}^2 - u_1{}^2) + \Delta E] \tag{4}$$

where the left-hand side is the net rate at which work is being done per unit time on the fluid in the transition zone or shock front. The right-hand side is the rate of change of kinetic energy of the fluid in the front plus the rate of change of internal energy. ΔE is the change in internal energy per unit mass and $\rho_1 u_1$ is the rate at which mass of fluid enters the transition zone.

From (3) combined with (1) we obtain

$$u_1 = \frac{1}{\rho_1} \sqrt{\frac{p_1 - p_2}{1/\rho_2 - 1/\rho_1}} \tag{5}$$

or

$$u_2 = \frac{1}{\rho_2} \sqrt{\frac{p_1 - p_2}{1/\rho_2 - 1/\rho_1}} \tag{6}$$

It is of interest to note that since u_2 is the velocity in the region ahead of the shock front when the front is assumed to be stationary, it represents the velocity of the front itself through the otherwise undisturbed fluid. From (4) we obtain

$$\Delta E = \frac{1}{2}(p_2 + p_1)\left(\frac{1}{\rho_1} - \frac{1}{\rho_2}\right) \tag{7}$$

From this it is possible to obtain the change in enthalpy H per gram across the shock front. For by definition[1]

$$H = E + \frac{p}{\rho} \tag{8}$$

Hence

$$\Delta H = \frac{1}{2}(p_2 - p_1)\left(\frac{1}{\rho_1} + \frac{1}{\rho_2}\right) \tag{9}$$

[1] Zemansky, "Heat and Thermodynamics," p. 190.

Equations (5), (6), (7), and (9) are known as the Rankine-Hugoniot relations for the shock front.

They may be supplemented by the further relation, derivable from the conservation laws,

$$u_2{}^2 - u_1{}^2 = (p_1 - p_2)\left(\frac{1}{\rho_1} + \frac{1}{\rho_2}\right) \tag{10}$$

from which we can also deduce

$$u_2 - u_1 = \sqrt{(p_2 - p_1)\left(\frac{1}{\rho_1} - \frac{1}{\rho_2}\right)} \tag{11}$$

The latter gives the relative flow velocity on the two sides of the front.

It is of interest to note that, if $p_1 - p_2$ and $\rho_1 - \rho_2$ are very small compared with p_1 and ρ_1, respectively, we can write approximately

$$u_1 = \sqrt{\frac{\Delta p}{\Delta \rho}} = u_2$$

and both velocities reduce to the normal velocity of sound in the medium. In this limit, shock wave theory reduces to ordinary small-amplitude sound-propagation theory.

The above equations are straightforward deductions from hydrodynamics and thermodynamics and are therefore of general application to fluids of any kind. Further detailed use depends on the equation of state of the fluid. If the fluid is an ideal polytropic gas in which the internal energy is a function of temperature alone and, indeed, directly proportional to T, we have

$$\frac{p}{\rho} = RT \tag{12}$$

and
$$E = c_v T \tag{13}$$

where c_v is the specific heat at constant volume. From the general expression for R, the gas constant per gram, namely,

$$c_p - c_v = R = c_v(\gamma - 1) \tag{14}$$

where γ, as usual, is the ratio of specific heats, we obtain from (13)

$$E = \frac{1}{\gamma - 1} \frac{p}{\rho} \tag{15}$$

From this we get

$$\Delta E = \frac{1}{\gamma - 1}\left(\frac{p_2}{\rho_2} - \frac{p_1}{\rho_1}\right) \tag{16}$$

and if we substitute this into (4) and employ (10), we finally have

$$\frac{p_2}{p_1} = \frac{\rho_2(\gamma + 1) - \rho_1(\gamma - 1)}{\rho_1(\gamma + 1) - \rho_2(\gamma - 1)} \tag{17}$$

$$\frac{\rho_2}{\rho_1} = \frac{p_2(\gamma + 1) + p_1(\gamma - 1)}{p_1(\gamma + 1) + p_2(\gamma - 1)} \tag{18}$$

At the same time, the temperatures T_1 and T_2, behind and ahead of the shock front, respectively, have the ratio

$$\frac{T_2}{T_1} = \frac{p_2\rho_1}{p_1\rho_2} = \frac{V_2{}^2}{V_1{}^2} \tag{19}$$

where $V_1 = \sqrt{\gamma p_1/\rho_1}$, etc.

It is often valuable to express the above results in terms of the *Mach number* M_1. This is the ratio of the particle velocity to the local sound velocity V. Thus for the incident shock, or region behind the shock front,

$$M_1 = \frac{u_1}{V_1} \tag{20}$$

Equations (17) and (18) then become

$$\frac{p_2}{p_1} = \frac{\gamma(2M_1{}^2 - 1) + 1}{\gamma + 1} \tag{21}$$

$$\frac{\rho_2}{\rho_1} = \frac{M_1{}^2(\gamma + 1)}{M_1{}^2(\gamma - 1) + 2} \tag{22}$$

This brings out the fact that, if $M_1 = 1$, $p_1 = p_2$ and $\rho_1 = \rho_2$. In this case there is no shock wave at all but merely propagation of the disturbance with the normal sound velocity. If $M_1 > 1$, $p_2 > p_1$, from (21). In other words, the pressure rises as one goes across a shock front in the direction of its propagation. If we use the equation of continuity in (16), we see that, for $p_2 > p_1$, $u_1 > u_2$. Hence, if $u_1 > V_1$, $u_2 < V_1$, and flow at supersonic velocity on passage through a shock wave must become subsonic. It can also be shown, from (19), that the temperature across the shock increases in the direction of flow.

The final relation of importance in shock wave propagation is the entropy change across the front. From the first law of thermodynamics for unit mass of gas

$$T \, dS = dE + p \, d\left(\frac{1}{\rho}\right) \tag{23}$$

For a polytropic gas we may immediately write

$$dS = c_v \frac{dT}{T} + \frac{p}{T} d\left(\frac{1}{\rho}\right) \tag{24}$$

Since we are dealing with an ideal gas, we may use (12) with $R = c_p - c_v$. It follows from this that

$$\rho \, d \left(\frac{1}{\rho}\right) + \frac{dp}{p} = \frac{dT}{T}$$

whence (24) becomes

$$dS = c_v \frac{dp}{p} + c_p \rho \, d \left(\frac{1}{\rho}\right) \tag{25}$$

or, on integration,

$$S = c_v \ln p + c_p \ln \frac{1}{\rho} + \text{const} \tag{26}$$

Hence, across the shock front we expect a change in entropy equal to

$$\Delta S = c_v \ln \frac{p_2}{p_1} - c_p \ln \frac{\rho_2}{\rho_1} \tag{27}$$

which is an increase. In evaluating this expression it is convenient to introduce the quantity

$$\delta = \frac{p_2 - p_1}{p_1} \tag{28}$$

as the fractional change in pressure across the front. Then

$$\Delta S = c_v \left[\ln (1 + \delta) - \gamma \ln \frac{2\gamma + (\gamma + 1)\delta}{2\gamma + (\gamma - 1)\delta} \right] \tag{29}$$

If we expand the logarithms by means of the series

$$\ln (1 + \delta) = \delta - \frac{\delta^2}{2} + \frac{\delta^3}{3} + \cdots$$

valid for $|\delta| < 1$, we obtain for a not too strong shock, out to terms in δ^3,

$$\Delta S = c_v \frac{\gamma^2 - 1}{12\gamma^2} \delta^3 \tag{30}$$

It is noteworthy that the entropy change depends on the *third* power of the fractional pressure change across the shock.

We can now employ the expression (30) to derive an equation of the form (9.15-14) for the saw-tooth wave to which Fay's solution reduces. For each shock front the rate of increase of entropy per unit area of front is[1]

$$\dot{S}_a = \rho_0 V_0 \Delta S = \frac{\rho_0 V_0 c_v (\gamma^2 - 1)}{12\gamma^2} \delta^3 \tag{31}$$

since ΔS is the entropy increase per unit mass. Here V_0 is the ordinary velocity of sound at the average temperature in the wave. We know from our previous discussion that for weak shocks this is a good approxi-

[1] I. Rudnick, *J. Acoust. Soc. Am.*, **25**, 1012 (1953).

mation to the velocity of the shock front. The average density of the gas is ρ_0. The increase in entropy must come from somewhere. Let us make the reasonable assumption that it takes place at the expense of the energy W represented by the saw-tooth wave. Thus we get

$$\dot{S}_a = -\frac{\dot{W}}{T_0} \tag{32}$$

where, to be specific, W is the energy per unit cross section of shock wavefront included in a distance of one wavelength and T_0 is the average absolute temperature in the wave.

Now we can compute the energy in one wavelength of the saw-tooth wave by applying the methods outlined in Sec. 1.10, that is, either by calculating the average rate at which work is done on the medium or by computing directly the average total energy in one wavelength by utilizing the fact that in a plane wave of any form the total energy is precisely twice the potential energy. Since we assume that the shock is not strong, we can still approximate the potential energy density by

$$w_p = \frac{\rho_0 V_0^2 s^2}{2} \tag{33}$$

where s is, as usual, the condensation (Sec. 9.1). By integrating this over a wavelength we can show that

$$W = \frac{p_0 \lambda \delta^2}{12\gamma} \tag{34}$$

where p_0 is the average pressure in the shock wave. We further have

$$\dot{W} = V_0 \frac{dW}{dx} = \frac{p_0 V_0 \lambda \delta}{6\gamma} \frac{d\delta}{dx} \tag{35}$$

assuming once more that the effective velocity of the shock wave is approximately V_0. Hence, equating $\dot{W}$ in (35) to the same quantity in (32) and using (30), we obtain, finally,

$$\frac{1}{\delta^2} \frac{d\delta}{dx} = -\frac{\gamma + 1}{2\gamma\lambda} \tag{36}$$

This involves use of the ideal gas equation of state:

$$\frac{p_0}{\rho_0} = RT_0 = c_v(\gamma - 1)T_0$$

Integration of (36) results in

$$\frac{1}{\delta} - \frac{1}{\delta_0} = \frac{\gamma + 1}{2\gamma\lambda}(x - x_0) \tag{37}$$

If we solve this for δ and assume that it is always small compared with δ_0, this equation has the form (9.15-14) resulting from Fay's theory, with the one exception of the factor 2. The presence of this factor in the present discussion is due to the fact that $p_1 - p_2$ here means the total drop in pressure from peak to trough in the saw-tooth profile, whereas in the treatment of Sec. 9.15 p_{e0} refers to the drop from peak to average level.

The considerations of this section assume that the saw-tooth profile has already been formed. It was suggested in Sec. 9.15 that, in order to assure this, it was necessary to invoke some attenuation mechanism acting on the macrosonic wave. Obviously the formation of any shock wave demands the same sort of procedure.[1]

9.17. Radiation Pressure

The nonlinearity of the equations of hydrodynamics, which leads to the phenomena of macrosonics discussed in the preceding sections, also has other consequences which are worthy of investigation. One of these is the so-called *radiation pressure*.

In the linear theory of sound propagation, in which the condensation is treated as always very small in magnitude compared with unity, we derived the following relation connecting the excess pressure p_e and the condensation s:

$$p_e = \rho_0 V^2 s \tag{1}$$

In doing this, however, we assumed that the density remains essentially unchanged at its equilibrium value ρ_0 as the pressure increases. For small disturbances, this is a good approximation, but a somewhat better one would be obtained by letting ρ_0 in (1) be the *new* density prevailing *after* the pressure is increased. A somewhat better approximation to p_e would then be obtained in replacing (1) by

$$p_e = \rho_0(1 + s)V^2 s \tag{2}$$

Let us suppose that we have a plane harmonic wave for the condensation s, or

$$s = s_0 \cos (\omega t - kx) \tag{3}$$

On substitution into (2) we get

$$p_e = \rho_0 V^2 s_0 \cos (\omega t - kx) + \rho_0 V^2 s_0^2 \cos^2 (\omega t - kx) \tag{4}$$

Here p_e is represented as the sum of two terms; the one in $\cos (\omega t - kx)$

---

[1] For discussion of the various ways in which shocks may be formed, consult the references given at the beginning of the section, particularly Courant and Friedrichs, "Supersonic Flow and Shock Waves." This also contains much interesting material on the reflection and refraction of shock waves.

is a first-order term, and the term in $\cos^2(\omega t - kx)$ is clearly a second-order term and much smaller (because in general $|s| \ll 1$). However, it has the interesting property that, when averaged over time, it does not vanish like the term in $\cos(\omega t - kx)$. Rather we have

$$\bar{p}_e = \frac{\rho_0 V^2 s_0^2}{2} \tag{5}$$

This is then a static excess pressure, and its value in terms of the acoustic intensity is simply [see (9.3-7)]

$$\bar{p}_e = \frac{I}{V} \tag{6}$$

This is the so-called radiation pressure, which we shall denote by Π. In this approximate analysis, it turns out to be equal to the average energy density. It is similar to the pressure of light radiation[1] (the so-called Hull-Lebedev effect). There is an obvious connection with the flow of momentum associated with the radiation. From (6.3-23) we have the following connection between the condensation and the fluid particle displacement Δ:

$$s = -\nabla \cdot \Delta \tag{7}$$

which for a plane wave in the x direction becomes

$$s = -\frac{\partial \xi}{\partial x} \tag{8}$$

Hence the radiation pressure can be expressed in terms of the maximum flow velocity $\dot{\xi}_0 = v_0$ as

$$\Pi = \frac{\rho_0 v_0^2}{2} \tag{9}$$

But the average rate of flow of momentum per unit area is

$$\frac{d(mv)}{dt} = m\frac{dv}{dt} + v\frac{dm}{dt}$$

if m is the mass per unit area. The time average of the first term vanishes, since it has the form $\sin(\omega t - kx)$. However,

$$\frac{dm}{dt} = \rho_0 v$$

since it is the rate of change of mass due to the flow of the fluid per unit area. Hence

$$\overline{\frac{d(mv)}{dt}} = \frac{\rho_0 v_0^2}{2} \tag{10}$$

---

[1] P. Lebedev, *Ann. Physik*, **6**, 433 (1901); and E. F. Nichols and G. F. Hull, *Ann. Physik*, **12**, 225 (1903).

which is precisely II.   Hence the radiation pressure is the average rate of
flow of momentum per unit area in the wave transmission.

Objection may be leveled at the considerations leading to (6) on the
ground that the correction to (1) should not be really of the form (2)
but should use the exact equation of state.   For an ideal gas subject to
the adiabatic condition

$$\frac{p}{\rho^\gamma} = \text{const} \tag{11}$$

we get for the instantaneous pressure p in terms of the constant mean
static pressure p_0 in the gas

$$p = \frac{p_0}{(1 + \partial\xi/\partial x)^\gamma} \tag{12}$$

In this connection the reader should recall the discussion on macrosonics
in Sec. 9.13.   If we expand (12) in powers of $\partial\xi/\partial x$, the result is

$$p = p_0 \left[1 - \gamma \frac{\partial\xi}{\partial x} + \frac{\gamma(\gamma + 1)}{2} \left(\frac{\partial\xi}{\partial x}\right)^2 + \cdots \right] \tag{13}$$

Keeping only the first two terms in the bracket yields (1).   However, if
we keep the nonlinear term as well and substitute the harmonic plane
wave displacement

$$\xi = \xi_0 \sin (\omega t - kx) \tag{14}$$

the excess pressure becomes

$$p_e = p_0\gamma k\xi_0 \cos (\omega t - kx) + \tfrac{1}{2}p_0\gamma(\gamma + 1)\xi_0^2 k^2 \cos^2 (\omega t - kx) \tag{15}$$

whence

$$\bar{p}_e = \tfrac{1}{2}p_0\gamma(\gamma + 1)\xi_0^2 k^2 \tag{16}$$

Employing the same definition as above for the intensity of the wave,
we arrive at

$$\bar{p}_e = \frac{\gamma + 1}{2} \frac{I}{V} \tag{17}$$

which differs from (6) and presumably should replace it in the case of
ideal gases.   This suggests that the problem of radiation pressure is not
a simple one.   More careful study indicates that we must be careful
precisely how the radiation pressure is defined.   The pressure we have
calculated in (17) is the so-called Rayleigh radiation pressure, which is
defined to be the difference between the time averages of the pressure at
any point of a fluid traversed by a compressional wave and the pressure
which would have existed in a fluid of the same mean density at rest.
It is not difficult to show that, since in a perfectly elastic liquid the mean
density remains constant and (13) contains only the linear term (γ here
has a different meaning, namely, $\rho_0 V^2/p_0$, where $V = \sqrt{B_{ad}/\rho_0}$ and B_{ad} is

the adiabatic bulk modulus), the Rayleigh radiation pressure for such a
liquid is precisely zero. This is unrealistic, however, since such a liquid
does not exist.

More practical from the experimental point of view is the Langevin
radiation pressure, defined to be the difference between the pressure at
a wall on which a compressional wave is incident and the pressure in the
medium behind the wall assumed to be at rest. The wall here may be
either perfectly reflecting or perfectly absorbing. In this case calculation
shows[1] that no matter what the equation of state of the medium may be,
that is, whether the medium is a liquid or a gas, the radiation pressure
comes out in the form (6). Experimental observations appear to indicate
that this is the actual radiation pressure measured in practice.

The importance of the radiation pressure is obvious as a method of
measuring the intensity I of an acoustic wave. It is the basis of the
so-called "balance" method for determining the attenuation of sound in
liquids,[2] in which the decrease in radiation pressure with distance from
the source is "weighed" on a balance. Here the difference between (6)
and (17) is of no consequence, since they both say that the radiation
pressure is proportional directly to I. Thus, if ΔI is the change in intensity associated with a distance Δx in a medium with sound energy attenuation coefficient 2α, we have [Eq. (1.10-22)]

$$2\alpha = -\frac{1}{I}\frac{\Delta I}{\Delta x} = -\frac{1}{\Pi}\frac{\Delta \Pi}{\Delta x}$$

[1] G. Hertz and H. Mende, Z. Physik, **114**, 359 (1939); also R. T. Beyer, *Am. J.
Phys.*, **18**, 25 (1950).
[2] E. Hsu, *J. Acoust. Soc. Am.*, **17**, 127 (1945).

CHAPTER 10

ELASTIC WAVES IN THE ATMOSPHERE, THE SEA, AND THE EARTH

10.1. Elastic Radiation in a Nonhomogeneous Moving Medium

In the wave motion treated in the previous chapters the disturbed medium has been assumed to have no large-scale continuous motion as a whole with respect to a primary inertial system (e.g., the ground). It is true that in Sec. 1.2 we commented on the importance of the overall motion of a material medium for the elastic wave passing through it. This is particularly evident in the atmosphere with the effect of the winds on sound propagation and in the sea with its currents. If we are to handle such cases, we must study wave propagation in moving media. Since these are usually nonhomogeneous as well, because of temperature gradients and the like, we shall make the treatment rather general by not assuming constant sound velocity.

There are two possible approaches. The more general is to set up the fundamental equation of motion of the medium including both the overall motion relative to the primary inertial system and the disturbance from equilibrium. In the case of a stationary medium, however, we have seen (Sec. 1.12) that, if the properties of the medium do not change too rapidly over a distance of the order of magnitude of the wavelength λ, we may use rays in place of wavefronts in describing the propagation of harmonic waves. This effectively reduces the wave problem to one in kinematics. For reasonably short wave or high frequency radiation, the ray method offers advantages in simplicity, which are particularly apparent in atmospheric and underwater acoustics. We shall begin, therefore, by examining ray propagation in a nonhomogeneous moving medium in steady motion with vector velocity $\mathbf{u}$, a function of the coordinates x, y, z.

The velocity of the compressional disturbance in the equivalent stationary medium will, as usual, be denoted by $V(x,y,z)$. Figure 10.1 shows schematically the plane wavefront ABC. The position vector at point P in the wavefront is $\mathbf{r}$, and the normal to the wavefront at P is $\mathbf{n}$. Since the medium at P is supposed to have the steady equilibrium velocity $\mathbf{u}$, the motion of the point on the wavefront which coincides with P at time t is given by

$$\dot{\mathbf{r}} = V\mathbf{n} + \mathbf{u} \tag{1}$$

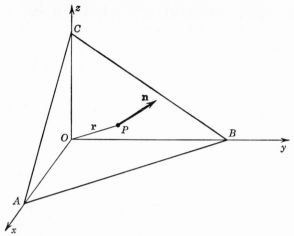

FIG. 10.1. Plane wavefront in sound propagation.

If we use $\delta\mathbf{r}$ to denote the change in position vector from one point to another on the same wavefront, then

$$\delta\mathbf{r} \cdot \mathbf{n} = 0 \tag{2}$$

which, on differentiation with respect to the time, yields

$$\dot{\mathbf{n}} \cdot \delta\mathbf{r} + n \cdot \delta\dot{\mathbf{r}} = 0 \tag{3}$$

Since by definition

$$\delta\dot{\mathbf{r}} = (\delta\mathbf{r} \cdot \nabla)\dot{\mathbf{r}} \tag{4}$$

we get from (3), with the help of (1),

$$\delta\mathbf{r} \cdot [\dot{\mathbf{n}} + \nabla(V + \mathbf{n} \cdot \mathbf{u})] = 0 \tag{5}$$

Here we must recall that the components of $\mathbf{n}$ are simply the direction cosines α, β, γ of the normal, with $\alpha^2 + \beta^2 + \gamma^2 = 1$ and

$$\alpha \, d\alpha + \beta \, d\beta + \gamma \, d\gamma = 0$$

We note, moreover, that $\mathbf{n}$ is not operated on by ∇. If for simplicity we put

$$c = V + \mathbf{n} \cdot \mathbf{u} \tag{6}$$

the conditions (2) and (5) ultimately lead to

$$\dot{\mathbf{n}} = (\mathbf{n} \cdot \nabla c)\mathbf{n} - \nabla c \tag{7}$$

The two relations giving $\dot{\mathbf{r}}$ and $\dot{\mathbf{n}}$ determine the motion normal to the wavefront and hence give the acoustical ray.

The simplest illustration of the foregoing analysis is found in a stratified medium, that is, one in which the only variation in properties is in one direction, which we may conveniently take to be the z axis. Hence $u_z = 0$, and u_x and u_y, as well as V, are functions of z only. Equation (1) reduces to the equations

$$\dot{x} = \alpha V + u_x \qquad \dot{y} = \beta V + u_y \qquad \dot{z} = \gamma V \qquad (8)$$

and (7), similarly, reduces to

$$\dot{\alpha} = \alpha\gamma \frac{dc}{dz} \qquad \dot{\beta} = \beta\gamma \frac{dc}{dz} \qquad \dot{\gamma} = (\gamma^2 - 1)\frac{dc}{dz} \qquad (9)$$

From the first two equations in (9) there results

$$\frac{\beta}{\alpha} = \text{const} \qquad (10)$$

If we fix our attention on a given ray and think of the wavefronts as drawn at every point of this ray, the projections of these normals on the xy plane will therefore all have the same direction. This also means that the normals to the successive wavefronts corresponding to a given ray will remain parallel to some fixed plane through the z axis. For a particular ray we may, without loss of generality, choose this plane as the xz plane. Then $\beta = 0$. Moreover, since

$$\frac{dc}{dz} = \frac{dV}{dz} + \alpha \frac{du_x}{dz} \qquad (11)$$

we get from (8) and (9)

$$\dot{z} = \gamma V$$

$$\dot{\alpha} = \gamma\alpha\left(\frac{dV}{dz} + \alpha\frac{du_x}{dz}\right) \qquad (12)$$

From this we can establish

$$\frac{d(V/\alpha)}{dz} = -\frac{du_x}{dz} \qquad (13)$$

which is integrated at once to

$$\frac{V}{\alpha} - \frac{V_0}{\alpha_0} = u_{x0} - u_x \qquad (14)$$

the zero subscripts referring to boundary values. Recalling that

$$\alpha = \cos\theta$$

where θ is the instantaneous angle which the ray makes with the x axis, we can rewrite (14) as

$$V \sec\theta - V_0 \sec\theta_0 = u_{x0} - u_x \qquad (15)$$

This is the general law of refraction in a medium stratified in the z direction for a ray in the xz plane. We see that, if the motion of the medium as a whole vanishes, (15) reduces to the familiar Snell law of refraction

[Eq. (2.1-16)]. On the other hand, if V remains constant, that is, if the medium is homogeneous, we have

$$\sec \theta - \sec \theta_0 = \frac{u_{x0} - u_x}{V} \tag{16}$$

which gives the refraction of the sound ray due to the motion of the medium and hence may be called the law of *convective* refraction. It can, of course, be derived very simply and directly in this special case.[1] Its practical importance in sound propagation in a windy atmosphere is obvious: elevated sound sources are decidedly advantageous in transmitting to windward.

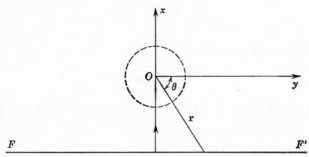

Fig. 10.2. A simple linear vortex.

Another special case of somewhat greater complexity but of possible practical value in atmospheric propagation is the transmission of a plane sound wave through a simple linear vortex. Figure 10.2 represents a linear vortex with axis directed along the z axis in terms of its projection on the xy plane (the dashed circle with O as center). In accordance with the usual hydrodynamic definition,[2] the peripheral velocity of the fluid at distance r from the axis is

$$v_t = \frac{a^2 \omega}{2r} = \frac{M}{r} \tag{17}$$

where M is the strength of the vortex. This type of motion is irrotational for $r > a$, though the so-called "circulation" is nonvanishing. The circulation is defined as $\int \mathbf{u} \cdot d\mathbf{s}$, where $\mathbf{u}$ is, as usual, the equilibrium flow velocity of the medium, $d\mathbf{s}$ is the element of arc in the direction of flow, and the integral is taken around any closed path. The reader may verify the nonvanishing of the circulation by an examination of (17).

In Fig. 10.2 FF' denotes the trace of a wavefront originally plane and parallel to the yz plane and advancing in the x direction, that is, for r

[1] G. W. Stewart and R. B. Lindsay, "Acoustics," pp. 11f., D. Van Nostrand Company, Inc., Princeton, N.J., 1930.

[2] L. M. Milne-Thomson, "Theoretical Hydrodynamics," 3d ed., pp. 336f., Macmillan & Co., Ltd., London, 1955.

very great.   We wish to find the change in form of the wavefront due to the vortex.   The stationary medium compressional wave velocity V is assumed to be constant.

The vector velocity of the medium in this situation is

$$\mathbf{u} = -\frac{\mathbf{i}My}{r^2} + \frac{\mathbf{j}Mx}{r^2} \tag{18}$$

with $r^2 = x^2 + y^2$.   The normal to the wavefront makes the angle $\pi/2$ with the y axis initially, that is, when r is infinitely great.   For finite r the corresponding angle is φ.   Then

$$\mathbf{n} = \mathbf{i} \sin \varphi + \mathbf{j} \cos \varphi \tag{19}$$

The combination of (6) and (7) for V constant gives

$$\dot{\mathbf{n}} = [\mathbf{n} \cdot \nabla(\mathbf{n} \cdot \mathbf{u})]\mathbf{n} - \nabla(\mathbf{n} \cdot \mathbf{u}) \tag{20}$$

Forming $\dot{\mathbf{n}} \cdot \dot{\mathbf{n}}$, which from (19) is $\dot{\varphi}^2$, and utilizing the fact that $\mathbf{n} \cdot \dot{\mathbf{n}} = 0$, we are led ultimately to

$$\dot{\varphi} = -\frac{M}{r^4} [2xy \sin 2\varphi + (y^2 - x^2) \cos 2\varphi] \tag{21}$$

We must add to this the form of (1) appropriate to this special case, namely,

$$\begin{aligned} \dot{x} &= V \sin \varphi - \frac{My}{r^2} \\ \dot{y} &= V \cos \varphi + \frac{Mx}{r^2} \end{aligned} \tag{22}$$

But it is simpler to rewrite these equations in terms of polar coordinates r, θ in the xy plane, thus confining our attention to the traces of the wavefronts and rays in this plane.   Using $x = r \sin \theta$ and $y = r \cos \theta$, we get for (21)

$$\dot{\varphi} = -\frac{M}{r^2} \cos 2(\theta - \varphi) \tag{23}$$

and in place of (22)

$$\begin{aligned} \dot{r} &= V \cos (\theta - \varphi) \\ \dot{\theta} &= -\frac{V}{r} \sin (\theta - \varphi) - \frac{M}{r^2} \end{aligned} \tag{24}$$

The three equations (1), (23), and (24) are the fundamental differential equations for the propagation through the vortex.   It is apparent that, in the limiting case in which $M = 0$, these reduce to plane wave propagation in a homogeneous medium at rest.   For then

$$\varphi = \text{const} = \varphi_0$$
$$\dot{r} = V \cos (\theta - \varphi_0)$$
$$\dot{\theta} = -\frac{V}{r} \sin (\theta - \varphi_0) \tag{25}$$

Combining the equations for $\dot{r}$ and $\dot{\theta}$ in (25) yields

$$\cos (\theta - \varphi_0)\, dr - \sin (\theta - \varphi_0) r\, d\theta = V\, dt \tag{26}$$

which is integrable to

$$r \cos (\theta - \varphi_0) = Vt + K \tag{27}$$

with K as the constant of integration, evaluated by assigning the initial values of θ and r.   Choosing $\varphi_0 = \pi/2$, we have

$$r \sin \theta = Vt + K \tag{28}$$

As soon as K has been chosen, this is the equation of a straight line in the xy plane parallel to the y axis for each value of the time t.   The corresponding wavefronts are all parallel to the xz plane and advance along the x direction with velocity V.   Since the rays are the normal trajectories of the wavefronts, the differential equation for them is [from (26)]

$$\cos (\theta - \varphi_0) r\, d\theta + \sin (\theta - \varphi_0)\, dr = 0 \tag{29}$$

with solution

$$r \cos \theta = K' \tag{30}$$

if again we take $\varphi_0 = \pi/2$.   The rays then are all straight lines parallel to the x axis.   The analysis thus is confirmed for this special case.

Passing now to the general case where $M \neq 0$, we find it convenient to set $\theta - \varphi = \psi$.   Then the difference between $\dot{\theta}$ and $\dot{\varphi}$ in the general equations results in

$$\dot{\psi} = -\frac{\sin \psi}{r} \left(V + \frac{2M}{r} \sin \psi \right) \tag{31}$$

The combination of this with the $\dot{r}$ equation (24) gives

$$\frac{dr}{d\psi} = -\frac{r \cos \psi}{(\sin \psi)[1 + (2M/Vr) \sin \psi]} \tag{32}$$

which integrates at once to

$$M \sin \psi + Vr = Gr^2 V \sin \psi \tag{33}$$

where G is the constant of integration.   Similarly, the $\dot{r}$ and $\dot{\theta}$ equations, when divided, lead to

$$\frac{dr}{d\theta} = -\frac{r \cos \psi}{M/rV + \sin \psi} \tag{34}$$

The elimination of ψ between (33) and (34) yields

$$\frac{dr}{d\theta} = -\frac{\sqrt{(Gr^2V - M + rV)(Gr^2V - M - rV)}}{V + M(Gr^2V - M)/r^2V} \tag{35}$$

which is the differential equation of the family of rays in the presence of the vortex. Somewhat more interesting, actually, is the equation giving the change in r with t along the rays. This we obtain by eliminating ψ between (33) and the equation for $\dot{r}$ in (24). The result is

$$\frac{(Gr^2V - M)\,dr}{\sqrt{(Gr^2V - M + rV)(Gr^2V - M - rV)}} = V\,dt \tag{36}$$

The integration of (35) and (36) involves elliptic functions. However, we can reach some physical results of interest by simple but plausible approximations. Let us assume that the vortex is weak enough so that

$$\frac{M}{G^2rV} \ll 1$$

and also that $M/GV \ll 1$. Then (35) takes the approximate form

$$\frac{dr}{r\sqrt{G^2r^2 - 1}} = -d\theta \tag{37}$$

which integrates to

$$r\cos\theta = -\frac{1}{G} \tag{38}$$

Similarly, (36) becomes approximately

$$\frac{Gr\,dr}{\sqrt{G^2r^2 - 1}} - \frac{M}{rV\sqrt{G^2r^2 - 1}} = V\,dt \tag{39}$$

which, from (37) and (38), integrates to

$$r\sin\theta + \frac{M\theta}{V} = Vt + K' \tag{40}$$

with K' as the new constant of integration; this indicates how the original plane wavefront (28) is modified to a first approximation by a weak vortex of strength M.

A satisfactory practical way of representing the effect of the vortex is to determine the difference in the times of arrival of a particular wavefront at two points P_1 and P_2 on a line parallel to the original position of the front. In the absence of the vortex this difference would be zero, and its deviation from zero is a measure of the influence of the vortex on the wave propagation. From (40) we have for the time difference in question

$$\Delta t = \frac{M}{V^2} (\theta_1 - \theta_2) \tag{41}$$

since $r_1 \sin \theta_1 - r_2 \sin \theta_2 = 0$, because of the choice of P_1 and P_2 on a line parallel to the original wavefront (see Fig. 10.2). Let us suppose, for example, that the line joining P_1 and P_2 passes through O, the center of the vortex. Then $\theta_1 = 2\pi$, $\theta_2 = \pi$, and (41) reduces to

$$\Delta t = \frac{\pi M}{V^2} \tag{42}$$

For $M = 10^5$ cm²/sec, the peripheral velocity of the medium v_t at 5 m from the center of the vortex is 2 m/sec, or 7.2 km/hr. If this holds in air at 20°C, the value of Δt is

$$\Delta t = 2.7 \times 10^{-4} \text{ sec}$$

If the wave is a harmonic one with frequency 200 cycles/sec, the corresponding phase difference is

$$\omega \Delta t = 0.34 \text{ radian} \doteq 19.5°$$

If O is halfway between the points P_1 and P_2, this would be the phase difference experienced at a separation of 10 m. Phase fluctuations of this order are commonly observed in sound propagation in air with the wind blowing and are of considerable importance in sound ranging.[1]

The indication is that the passage of such vortices as are considered in this section across a sound field may account theoretically for the observed phase differences at different points in the field. Naturally the problem is very complicated, and it is likely that other mechanisms are also at work; whatever their nature, however, they almost certainly involve some sort of motion of the medium.

10.2. Wave Theory of Propagation in a Moving, Compressible, Viscous, Thermally Conducting Fluid

In the previous section we considered the propagation of sound through a moving fluid medium in terms of the ray theory. For a stationary medium the latter is certainly an adequate approximation for harmonic waves satisfying the conditions laid down in Sec. 1.12 and, in general, for waves of sufficiently small wavelength. For long-wavelength radiation, however, we know that the ray theory analysis breaks down and that it is essential to use the solution of the wave equation rather than the eikonal equation. It is of interest to note the form which the equa-

---

[1] For further details of other cases to which (41) may be applied, see R. B. Lindsay, *J. Acoust. Soc. Am.*, **20**, 89 (1948).

tions of wave propagation take for a moving medium. We may at once surmise that they will display a considerably increased complexity, due essentially to the nonlinear character of the motions involved. It is, moreover, readily apparent that the large-scale motion of the medium itself can give rise to the production of sound which is wholly different from the propagation of independently produced sound through the moving medium.

We proceed to rewrite in most general form the equations governing the motion of a compressible, viscous fluid subject to the conduction of heat.[1] The velocity of the fluid relative to some chosen inertial system will be denoted by **v**. If the density is ρ, the equation of continuity, the old standby (3.5-2), is

$$\dot{\rho} + \nabla \cdot (\rho \mathbf{v}) = 0 \tag{1}$$

In the equation of motion we wish to include the effect of viscosity, assuming that the fluid is a Newtonian one, so that the relation between dilatational stress and rate of strain is given by (9.11-21), with the corresponding equations for the shears, namely,

$$
\begin{aligned}
X_{xy} &= \eta \left(\frac{\partial \dot{\xi}}{\partial y} + \frac{\partial \dot{\eta}}{\partial x} \right) \\
X_{xz} &= \eta \left(\frac{\partial \dot{\zeta}}{\partial x} + \frac{\partial \dot{\xi}}{\partial z} \right) \\
X_{yz} &= \eta \left(\frac{\partial \dot{\zeta}}{\partial y} + \frac{\partial \dot{\eta}}{\partial z} \right)
\end{aligned}
\tag{2}
$$

where η is the shear viscosity [to be distinguished, of course, from the y component of fluid displacement, which appears in (2) only as the velocity $\dot{\eta}$]. Setting up the equations of motion by the method of Sec. 6.3, we have at once (making no approximation with respect to the magnitude of **v**)

$$\rho[\dot{\mathbf{v}} + (\mathbf{v} \cdot \nabla)\mathbf{v}] = -\nabla p + \frac{4\eta}{3} \nabla \nabla \cdot \mathbf{v} - \eta \nabla \times \nabla \times \mathbf{v} \tag{3}$$

where p is the pressure. If we were to disregard the terms in the viscosity, (3) would reduce to (3.5-6). By use of the well-known vector identity

$$\nabla(\mathbf{A} \cdot \mathbf{B}) = \mathbf{A} \cdot \nabla\mathbf{B} + \mathbf{B} \cdot \nabla\mathbf{A} - (\nabla \times \mathbf{B}) \times \mathbf{A} - (\nabla \times \mathbf{A}) \times \mathbf{B} \tag{4}$$

we can rewrite the left-hand side and obtain ultimately

$$\rho \left[\dot{\mathbf{v}} + (\nabla \times \mathbf{v}) \times \mathbf{v} + \nabla \left(\frac{\mathbf{v} \cdot \mathbf{v}}{2} \right) \right] = -\nabla p + \eta \nabla^2 \mathbf{v} + \frac{\eta}{3} \nabla \nabla \cdot \mathbf{v} \tag{5}$$

[1] The discussion in this section owes much to D. Blokhintzev, *J. Acoust. Soc. Am.*, **18**, 322 (1946).

If we wish to include the fact that the fluid is subject to gravity, we must add ρg to the right-hand side. Our next step is to express the conservation of energy for the fluid. If we denote the *internal* energy per gram of the fluid by U, the total energy per cubic centimeter of the flowing fluid will be

$$\rho \frac{v^2}{2} + \rho U \qquad (6)$$

This internal energy is to be taken in the thermodynamic sense, as in Sec. 9.12, where U refers to the internal energy per mole of gas. If we consider an elementary volume of fluid, conservation of energy for this implies that the instantaneous time rate of change of the total energy in the volume plus the rate of flow of energy across its boundary plus the rate at which work is done by the stresses on the surface must equal zero. We need to remember, indeed, that in the flow of energy across the boundary we must include the flow of heat, as given by the generalized form of (9.12-2). Let us call the heat-flow vector $\mathbf{H}$, that is, the vector whose magnitude is the flow of heat per second per unit area. The rate of flow of total mechanical energy across the boundary is ($\mathbf{n}$ being the unit normal to the boundary)

$$\int \left(\rho \frac{v^2}{2} + \rho U \right) \mathbf{v} \cdot \mathbf{n} \, dS \qquad (7)$$

whereas for the corresponding rate of flow of heat we have

$$\int \mathbf{H} \cdot \mathbf{n} \, dS \qquad (8)$$

Finally, the rate at which work is done at the surface by the stresses is

$$\int [\mathbf{i} v_x (X_{xx} + X_{xy} + X_{xz}) \\ + \mathbf{j} v_y (X_{yx} + X_{yy} + X_{yz}) \\ + \mathbf{k} v_z (X_{zx} + X_{zy} + X_{zz})] \cdot \mathbf{n} \, dS \qquad (9)$$

If we change the surface integrals to volume integrals by the use of the divergence theorem and combine into a single volume integral, we finally arrive at the differential equation

$$\frac{\partial}{\partial t} \left(\frac{\rho v^2}{2} + \rho U \right) + \nabla \cdot \left[\left(\frac{\rho v^2}{2} + \rho U \right) \mathbf{v} + \mathbf{H} \right] + \nabla \cdot \mathbf{R} = 0 \qquad (10)$$

where $\mathbf{R}$ is the bracket in the integral in (9). From the continuity equation we see that

$$\frac{\partial}{\partial t} \left(\frac{\rho v^2}{2} \right) + \nabla \cdot \left(\frac{\rho v^2}{2} \mathbf{v} \right) = \frac{\rho}{2} \frac{\partial}{\partial t} (v^2) + \frac{\rho}{2} \mathbf{v} \cdot \nabla v^2 \qquad (11)$$

Moreover, for the same reason

$$\frac{\partial}{\partial t} (\rho U) + \nabla \cdot (\rho U \mathbf{v}) = \rho \frac{\partial U}{\partial t} + \rho \mathbf{v} \cdot \nabla U = \rho \frac{dU}{dt} \qquad (12)$$

where dU/dt is, as usual, the total rate of change of the internal energy, taking into account the motion of the fluid. Consequently, (10) takes the form

$$\frac{\rho}{2} \frac{\partial v^2}{\partial t} + \frac{\rho}{2} (\mathbf{v} \cdot \nabla v^2) + \rho \frac{dU}{dt} + \nabla \cdot \mathbf{H} + \nabla \cdot \mathbf{R} = 0 \qquad (13)$$

Now it turns out that we can combine part of $\nabla \cdot \mathbf{R}$ with the first two terms to yield zero if we write the rest as

$$-p\nabla \cdot \mathbf{v} + \eta \sum_{i,h=1}^{3} \left(\frac{\partial v_i}{\partial v_k} + \frac{\partial v_k}{\partial x_i} \right)^2 \qquad (14)$$

where $v_1 = v_x$, $v_2 = v_y$, $v_3 = v_z$, $x_1 = x$, etc. It is customary to call the second term in (14) the dissipation function D. To arrive at (14) we need to use the equation of motion (5) again. We now set

$$\nabla \cdot \mathbf{H} = -\kappa \nabla^2 T \qquad (15)$$

where κ is the thermal conductivity and T the absolute temperature. The conservation of energy finally reduces to

$$\rho \frac{dU}{dt} = \kappa \nabla^2 T + D - p\nabla \cdot \mathbf{v} \qquad (16)$$

Physically, $\kappa \nabla^2 T$ represents the transfer of energy accompanying the flow of heat into the element, D the rate of addition of heat due to the action of the shear viscosity, and $-p\nabla \cdot \mathbf{v}$ the loss due to the pressure work (squeezing, etc.).

It is often convenient to write this equation in terms of the entropy S. From the first law of thermodynamics

$$T \, dS = dU + p \, d\tau \qquad (17)$$

where τ is the specific volume. We readily get

$$\frac{dU}{dt} = T \frac{dS}{dt} - \frac{p}{\rho} \nabla \cdot \mathbf{v} \qquad (18)$$

since $d\rho/dt = \partial\rho/\partial t + (\mathbf{v} \cdot \nabla)\rho = -\rho\nabla \cdot \mathbf{v}$. Hence (16) takes the form

$$T \frac{dS}{dt} = \frac{\kappa}{\rho} \nabla^2 T + \frac{D}{\rho} \qquad (19)$$

The left-hand side is the rate at which heat is added to unit mass of the gas. It turns out to be entirely due to the flow of heat into the gas by the existence of temperature gradients and the heat produced by viscous forces. If, to a first approximation, we were to neglect both heat conduction and viscosity, we should have

$$\frac{dS}{dt} = \frac{\partial S}{\partial t} + (\mathbf{v} \cdot \nabla)S = 0 \tag{20}$$

or, in words, the motion is *adiabatic;* that is, a given particle of fluid moves in such a way that no heat enters or leaves it. Note that in this case we can still have $\partial S/\partial t \neq 0$. If also $\partial S/\partial t = 0$, we call the motion *isentropic*. In a certain sense we might feel justified in setting up (19) on purely intuitive physical grounds.

Equations (1), (5), and (19) constitute the general equations of motion of a viscous, compressible fluid, taking into account the flow of heat. To use them for the study of sound propagation we need, as previously, the equation of state. Here, for convenience, we shall at first limit ourselves to the case of an ideal gas, for which

$$\frac{p}{\rho} = R_m T \tag{21}$$

R_m being the gas constant per gram. We wish to eliminate T and write p in terms of ρ and the entropy S. For this purpose we write the first law of thermodynamics in the form

$$T\, dS = dU + p\, d\tau = dU - \frac{p\, d\rho}{\rho^2} \tag{22}$$

But for an ideal gas the internal energy U is

$$U = c_v T \tag{23}$$

where c_v is the specific heat at constant volume. Using (21) in (22) then yields

$$dS = c_v \frac{dT}{T} - R_m \frac{d\rho}{\rho} \tag{24}$$

But $R_m = c_p - c_v = (\gamma - 1)c_v$, where γ here is the ratio c_p/c_v. Hence, if we substitute into (24) and express dT/T in terms of a linear function of dp and $d\rho$, we finally have

$$dS = c_v \frac{dp}{p} - \gamma c_v \frac{d\rho}{\rho} \tag{25}$$

which integrates at once to

$$S = S_0 + c_v \ln \frac{p}{p_0} - \gamma c_v \ln \frac{\rho}{\rho_0}$$

Hence

$$p = \frac{\rho^\gamma p_0}{\rho_0^\gamma} e^{(S-S_0)/c_v} \tag{26}$$

is the required state equation, where p_0 and ρ_0 are equilibrium pressure and density, respectively.

Since we are interested in wave motion, we naturally write

$$p = p_0 + p_e \tag{27}$$

where p_e is the excess pressure associated with a small disturbance in the gas. Similarly, we put

$$S = S_0 + S_e \qquad \rho = \rho_0 + \rho_e \tag{28}$$

Substitution into (26) with the assumptions $p_e/p_0 \ll 1$, $\rho_e/\rho_0 \ll 1$, $S_e/c_v \ll 1$ yields

$$p_e = V^2 p_e + \frac{p_0}{c_v} S_e \tag{29}$$

where

$$V = \sqrt{\frac{\gamma p_0}{\rho_0}} \tag{30}$$

The term $p_0 S_e / c_v$ is a correction term. We now apply the same technique to the fundamental equations (1), (5), and (19) and, in the process of substituting, discard terms of degree higher than the first in p_e, ρ_e, S_e, and $\dot{\xi}$, where

$$\mathbf{v} = \mathbf{v}_0 + \dot{\xi} \tag{31}$$

We also, for simplicity, neglect the terms containing κ and η. The result is the set of equations in the excess quantities

$$\ddot{\xi} + (\nabla \times \mathbf{v}_0) \times \dot{\xi} + (\nabla \times \dot{\xi}) \times \mathbf{v}_0 + \nabla(\mathbf{v}_0 \cdot \dot{\xi}) = -\frac{\nabla p_e}{\rho_0} + \frac{\nabla p}{\rho_0^2} \rho_e \tag{32}$$

$$\dot{\rho}_e + \mathbf{v}_0 \cdot \nabla \rho_e + \dot{\xi} \cdot \nabla \rho_0 + \rho_0 \nabla \cdot \dot{\xi} + \rho_e \nabla \cdot \mathbf{v}_0 = 0 \tag{33}$$

$$\dot{S}_e + \mathbf{v}_0 \cdot \nabla S_e + \dot{\xi} \cdot \nabla S_0 = 0 \tag{34}$$

Note that, because of the nonhomogeneity, $\mathbf{v}_0$, p_0, ρ_0, and S_0 are still functions of space.

Equations (29), (32), (33), and (34) are then the equations governing elastic wave propagation through the nonhomogeneous moving medium. By virtue of (34) the motion is assumed to be adiabatic since the κ and D terms in (19) are disregarded. It is, however, still nonisentropic, since we do not in general assume $\dot{S}_e = 0$.

It must be admitted that these equations are sufficiently formidable. However, let us assume for a simple special case, which, indeed, can correspond to reality in many important cases, that the motion is irrotational (nonvortical). Then

$$\nabla \times \mathbf{v}_0 = 0 \tag{35}$$

We also assume that

$$\nabla S_0 = 0 \tag{36}$$

or that the variation in entropy from place to place in the medium in equilibrium vanishes. This entails, from (34), that

$$\frac{dS_e}{dt} = 0 \tag{37}$$

or
$$S_e = \text{const} \tag{38}$$

We may as well put this constant equal to zero, since we are interested only in quantities which vary in both space and time. It now follows from (29) that

$$p_e = V^2 \rho_e \tag{39}$$

Now, since the motion is irrotational, a velocity potential φ must exist, and we write

$$\dot{\xi} = \nabla\varphi \tag{40}$$

We may then write (32) in the form

$$\nabla\dot{\varphi} + \nabla(\mathbf{v}_0 \cdot \nabla\varphi) = -\nabla\left(\frac{p_e}{\rho}\right)$$

or
$$\dot{\varphi} + \mathbf{v}_0 \cdot \nabla\varphi = \frac{d\varphi}{dt} = -\frac{p_e}{\rho} \tag{41}$$

If now we look back at (33), we see that it can take the form

$$\frac{d\rho_e}{dt} = -\dot{\xi} \cdot \nabla\rho_0 - \rho_0 \nabla \cdot \dot{\xi} - \rho_e \nabla \cdot \mathbf{v}_0$$

But from $\dot{\xi} = \nabla\varphi$ and $p_e = V^2 \rho_e$, etc., this can be rewritten

$$\frac{V^2}{\rho_0} \frac{d\rho_e}{dt} = -\nabla\varphi \cdot \frac{\nabla p_0}{\rho_0} - V^2 \nabla^2 \varphi - \frac{p_e}{\rho_0} \nabla \cdot \mathbf{v}_0 \tag{42}$$

Hence, employing (41), we have

$$\frac{d^2\varphi}{dt^2} = \nabla\varphi \cdot \frac{\nabla p_0}{\rho_0} + V^2 \nabla^2 \varphi + \frac{d\varphi}{dt} \nabla \cdot \mathbf{v}_0 \tag{43}$$

For a homogeneous medium in which the flow is constant we can set $\nabla p_0 = 0$ and $\nabla \cdot \mathbf{v}_0 = 0$, whence (43) becomes

$$\frac{d^2\varphi}{dt^2} = \left(\frac{\partial}{\partial t} + \mathbf{v}_0 \cdot \nabla\right)\left(\frac{\partial\varphi}{\partial t} + \mathbf{v}_0 \cdot \nabla\varphi\right) = V^2 \nabla^2 \varphi \tag{44}$$

Expanded, this becomes

$$\nabla^2\varphi - \frac{\ddot{\varphi}}{V^2} - \frac{2\mathbf{v}_0}{V^2} \cdot \nabla\dot{\varphi} - \frac{(\mathbf{v}_0 \cdot \nabla)(\mathbf{v}_0 \cdot \nabla\varphi)}{V^2} = 0 \tag{45}$$

This is most simply handled by supposing the steady-flow velocity $\mathbf{v}_0$ to be directed along the x axis with magnitude still called v_0, whence

$$\left(1 - \frac{v_0{}^2}{V^2}\right)\frac{\partial^2\varphi}{\partial x^2} + \frac{\partial^2\varphi}{\partial y^2} + \frac{\partial^2\varphi}{\partial z^2} - \frac{\ddot{\varphi}}{V^2} - \frac{2v_0}{V^2}\frac{\partial\dot{\varphi}}{\partial x} = 0 \qquad (46)$$

It is interesting to observe that, if we introduce a new set of coordinates x', y', z' such that

$$x' = x - v_0 t \qquad y' = y \qquad z' = z \qquad (47)$$

the above equation takes the form

$$\nabla'^2\varphi - \frac{\ddot{\varphi}}{V^2} = 0 \qquad (48)$$

where the prime on the ∇' indicates that in the Laplacian the derivatives are now with respect to the primed coordinates. It is scarcely surprising that in these coordinates, which move with speed v_0 along the common x axis, the equation of the disturbance in the moving medium reduces to the standard wave equation.

The plane harmonic wave with angular frequency ω' in the primed coordinates, for which the velocity potential is

$$\varphi(x',y',z',t) = A \exp\left\{i\left[\omega't - \frac{\omega'}{V}(\alpha x' + \beta y' + \gamma z')\right]\right\} \qquad (49)$$

with the direction cosines of the direction of propagation obeying the usual rule

$$\alpha^2 + \beta^2 + \gamma^2 = 1$$

satisfies (48). Consequently

$$\varphi(x,y,z,t) = A \exp\left\{i\left[\omega t - \frac{\omega}{V}(\alpha x + \beta y + \gamma z)\right]\right\} \qquad (50)$$

where now $\qquad \omega = \omega'\left(1 + \frac{v_0}{V}\alpha\right) \qquad (51)$

satisfies (46). This means that the frequency of the harmonic wave in the coordinate system which moves with the flow (i.e., stays at rest with respect to the medium) is different from the frequency of the same wave as observed by one with respect to whom the medium is moving. This is the Doppler effect for a moving wave source, since in this case the source of sound is carried along by the moving medium.

By an elaboration of the above method, one can develop the general formula of the Doppler effect for both source and observer in motion relative to a primary inertial system. However, the analysis is rather involved, and it is much simpler to use purely kinematic analysis based on the ray concept.

10.3. Kinematic Theory of the Doppler Effect

In the previous section we discussed the wave theory of propagation in a moving medium and derived the Doppler formula for the change in frequency due to the motion of a source of sound with the medium. It is advantageous to look at the same problem from the purely kinematic point of view. In Fig. 10.3, we shall let O denote a fixed observer and S a harmonic source of sound moving along the x axis (whose perpendicular distance from O is l) with velocity v.

Ignoring any disturbing effect of the motion of S on the medium (an approximation which we do not have to make on the strict wave theory), we may assume that the velocity of the wave emitted from S is constant and equal to V. If the distance SO from source to observer were to remain constant, the wavelength observed at O would be $\lambda = V/\nu$, where ν is the frequency of the emitted harmonic wave, as measured at the source (i.e., in a system of coordinates moving with the source). However, since S as it moves toward D is effectively approaching O with the speed $v \cos \theta$, the result is an apparent wavelength λ' at O equal to

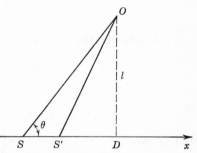

Fig. 10.3. Doppler effect for a moving source.

$$\lambda' = \frac{V - v \cos \theta}{\nu} \tag{1}$$

whence the apparent frequency at O is

$$\nu' = \frac{V}{\lambda'} = \frac{\nu}{1 - (v/V) \cos \theta} \tag{2}$$

We may, if we wish, look at it another way. Let us suppose that the source moves from S to a nearby point S' in the time Δt. The time it takes for a given disturbance, say a wave crest, to travel from S to O is SO/V, and the corresponding time from S' to O is $S'O/V$. If a given wave crest starts from S and travels to O in time SO/V and if the next wave crest leaves the source when it is at S', the difference between the time of arrival at O of these two crests is clearly

$$\Delta t' = \Delta t + \frac{S'O}{V} - \frac{SO}{V}$$

$$= \Delta t - \frac{SS' \cos \theta}{V}$$

or

$$\Delta t' = \Delta t \left(1 - \frac{v \cos \theta}{V} \right) \tag{3}$$

Since the apparent frequency is $1/\Delta t' = \nu'$, whereas the actual frequency is $\nu = 1/\Delta t$, we again have (2).

Now let us suppose that O is a *fixed* source of sound and S is an observer moving with speed v along the x axis. A wave crest leaves O at time $t = 0$ and arrives at S at time OS/V. The next wave crest leaves O at time Δt, where $1/\Delta t = \nu$, the actual frequency of the harmonic source. It arrives at S' at time $\Delta t + OS'/V$. The time between arrival of two successive crests at the observer is therefore

$$\Delta t + \frac{OS'}{V} - \frac{OS}{V}$$

and this must be the apparent period of the wave as observed. Hence

$$\Delta t' = \Delta t - \Delta t' \frac{v \cos \theta}{V}$$

or

$$\Delta t' \left(1 + \frac{v \cos \theta}{V}\right) = \Delta t$$

and hence

$$\nu' = \nu \left(1 + \frac{v}{V} \cos \theta\right) \tag{4}$$

If v is positive, it is clear that both the motion of the source toward the fixed observer and the motion of the observer toward the fixed source lead to an *increase* in apparent frequency. However, it is significant that the formulas are not the same. If indeed $v \ll V$, the apparent frequency predicted by both (2) and (4) becomes approximately the same. Of course it must be noted that, after S passes through D and recedes from O, the sign before v in both (2) and (4) must be changed.

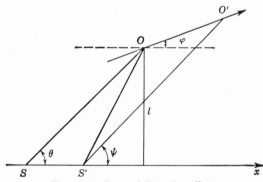

FIG. 10.4. General Doppler effect.

We can readily extend this analysis to the case in which both source and observer move relatively to the medium (assumed fixed). In Fig. 10.4 the source S still moves along the x axis with velocity v, whereas O, the observer, moves along the line OO' making angle φ with the x axis with velocity u. Here we assume for simplicity that O and S move in the same plane. We suppose, as before, that S moves to S' in the time Δt between the emission of successive crests, whereas O moves to O' in the time $\Delta t'$ between the receipt of successive crests. Then, as before, we can show that

$$\Delta t' = \frac{S'O' - SO}{V} + \Delta t \tag{5}$$

But from the geometry of Fig. 10.4

$$S'O' - S'O = u\,\Delta t' \cos(\psi - \varphi)$$
$$S'O = SO - SS' \cos \theta$$

Hence, ultimately,

$$\Delta t'\left[1 - \frac{u}{V}\cos(\psi - \varphi)\right] = \Delta t\left(1 - \frac{v}{V}\cos\theta\right)$$

or

$$\nu' = \frac{\nu[1 - (u/V)\cos(\psi - \varphi)]}{1 - (v/V)\cos\theta} \tag{6}$$

If $u = 0$, this reduces to (2). If $\varphi = 0$ and $v = 0$, it reduces essentially to (4). If $l = 0$, so that $\varphi = \psi = \theta = 0$, it reduces to

$$\nu' = \frac{\nu(1 - u/V)}{1 - v/V} \tag{7}$$

If the medium itself moves with respect to the primary inertial system, with velocity w, we see that (7) must be altered to

$$\nu' = \frac{\nu(1 - u/V + w/V)}{1 - v/V + w/V} \tag{8}$$

10.4. Sound Transmission in the Atmosphere

The considerations developed in Secs. 10.1 and 10.2 apply with particular appropriateness to sound transmission through the atmosphere. The latter is by no means a homogeneous fluid medium, because of the temperature gradients which prevail in it. Thus in the normal daytime condition the temperature decreases with height above the surface. On the other hand, early in the morning after a clear night, an inversion may take place, with temperature increasing upward to a certain height. Since the velocity of sound in an ideal gas varies as the square root of the absolute temperature (Sec. 9.2), it follows that refraction of sound is the rule in the atmosphere. Since the variation of velocity is usually rather gradual, it is adequate to treat the propagation in terms of rays (Sec. 1.12). We have already expressed Snell's law of refraction for a medium with continuously varying index of refraction (Sec. 10.1), and thus can readily understand that, when the temperature and, therefore, the velocity decrease with height in the atmosphere, rays of sound tend to bend upward. The result of this is to decrease the range from the value in an isothermal atmosphere. On the other hand, in a temperature inversion the sound rays are bent downward, and sound carries farther. We shall find a similar situation in sound transmission in the sea in Sec. 10.5 and shall develop the subject more elaborately there.

The atmosphere is in a more or less continuous state of motion because of the winds. Hence sound transmission through it demands consideration of a moving medium, as discussed in Secs. 10.1 and 10.2. We merely note here that, when sound is produced near the surface of the earth and the wind blows with velocity increasing upward, the analysis just referred to shows that rays of sound traveling with the wind are curved downward toward the earth, whereas those traveling against the wind are curved upward away from the earth. This means that, when trying to transmit sound against the wind, one should employ an elevated source rather than one on the ground.

Even in a perfectly homogeneous atmosphere there is sound attenuation, due both to the geometrical spreading and to irreversible absorption—for example, heat conduction and viscosity (see Secs. 9.11 and 9.12). In Sec. 12.1 we shall study still another mode of sound absorption in air, namely, molecular absorption. This helps to account for the fact that observed values of absorption in the atmosphere always exceed, and often considerably, those based on transport processes alone. Molecular absorption is much affected by the presence of water vapor, that is, humidity. For given humidity the molecular absorption coefficient is frequency-dependent and usually shows a maximum at some frequency. In general, the theoretical molecular absorption (see Sec. 12.1 for the relevant formulas), as well as the classical transport absorption, agrees better with experimental findings at low humidities than at high humidities. For high humidities the experimental values can be two or three times the theoretically predicted ones, particularly at frequencies below 10 kc. Better agreement at all humidities is generally found at the higher frequencies. It may be mentioned that, typically, the molecular value of the attenuation coefficient α at 1,000 cycles at 20°C and 60 per cent relative humidity is approximately 4.4×10^{-4} db/m, or 0.44 db/km. To this must be added the classical absorption coefficient, which under these conditions is about one-third of the above value. In general, the molecular absorption is considerably higher than the classical value. The full explanation for the excess of the absorption actually observed over that theoretically computed still remains to be found. Scattering due to local nonhomogeneities (i.e., "blobs" of heated air) as well as to turbulent regions (see Sec. 10.1) undoubtedly provides part of the answer. Sound propagation near the ground is also seriously affected by the nature of the terrain, but this is extremely complicated.

Fog and smoke particles produce a decided effect on sound propagation through the atmosphere. In the neighborhood of suspended particles in a fluid medium special viscous and heat-conduction processes take place in addition to those effective in the body of the fluid.[1] These lead to losses which increase rather more rapidly than the square of the frequency. At 100 cycles, for example, in a fog with 5.4×10^3 droplets/cm^3 of average radius 6.6×10^{-4} cm, the contribution to α from this source is about 0.95×10^{-2} db/m. In addition, there is a relaxation process[2] connected with the evaporation of the water in the fog droplet as affected by the passage of the sound wave. The normal equilibrium between the saturated vapor near the bubble and the surrounding air is upset by the sound wave, and there is a lag in its restoration (see Sec. 9.11). The details are complicated, but it turns out that, in general, this loss mechanism accounts for more of the observed attenuation than the viscous effects just mentioned. Thus, in the example quoted immediately above, at 100 cycles the contribution of the evaporation relaxation mechanism is 1.53×10^{-2} db/m. The total theoretically calculated attenuation $(2.48 \times 10^{-2}$ db/m) agrees fairly well with observations in this case.[3] This figure is greatly in excess of the predicted classical and molecular relaxation attenuation for the homogeneous atmosphere under the same conditions of temperature and for the same sound frequency.

The phase velocity of sound is always lowered in foggy air, though for temperatures less than 30°C its value never falls below $0.9V$, where V is the velocity in perfectly dry air.[4]

Many of the problems of atmospheric sound propagation are closely related to those of transmission in the sea, and reference should be made to Sec. 10.5 for further details.

10.5. Sound Transmission in the Sea

The sea, like the atmosphere, is a nonhomogeneous fluid medium. Though it is a liquid, and hence of low compressibility, the pressure and density increase with the depth. At the same time, the temperature varies with the depth and hence produces a change in the sound velocity independently of the density. Finally, the sea also manifests changes in

[1] P. S. Epstein and R. R. Carhart, *J. Acoust. Soc. Am.*, **25**, 553 (1953).

[2] K. L. Oswatitsch, *Physik. Z.*, **42**, 365 (1941).

[3] Based on a study of an artificial fog in an impedance tube by Y. T. Wei (doctoral thesis, University of California, Los Angeles, 1950).

[4] W. L. Nyborg and D. Mintzer, Review of Sound Propagation in the Lower Atmosphere, *Wright Air Development Center Tech. Rept.* 54-602, May, 1955. Much of the material in this section has come from this report.

salinity, which are most marked near the shore line. Thus, though sea water is a good medium for the transmission of compressional waves because of its relatively large density (making it a better match than air for the usual sound transducer), the actual propagation is complicated by the same factors that disturb atmospheric transmission. It is true that, relatively speaking, the motion of the sea is by no means the disturbing element that the wind is in the atmosphere. The temperature variation can be extremely complicated, since it is affected by absorption of solar radiation from the air, both directly and indirectly, and by the cooling of the surface by evaporation as well as by currents which bring deep water to the surface and vice versa.

In view of these considerations it is not surprising that sound transmission in the sea is not at all a simple phenomenon. As a matter of fact, even if we disregard the nonhomogeneous character of sea water as an acoustic medium, we find that the relatively sharp interface between water and air produces characteristic consequences, particularly for radiation emitted by sources relatively close to the surface, as indeed most practical underwater sound sources will be. The wave treatment of elastic radiation from a point source near such an interface is rather intricate.[1] It is therefore fortunate that in many problems of underwater acoustics we may safely employ ray acoustics, the basic ideas and limitations of which have already been set forth in Sec. 1.12.

Figure 10.5 represents the boundary surface between air and water as the line AB. A point source of sound is at S at depth h below the surface.

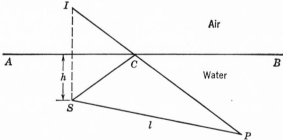

FIG. 10.5. Reflection of underwater sound from a water-air interface. Lloyd mirror effect.

The effect of the radiation at any point P in the water (treated here, for simplicity, as a homogeneous medium) depends not only on the sound which travels directly from S to P but also on the sound which reaches P after reflection from the surface. The sound ray SC, which after reflection from the surface at C ultimately reaches P, appears to come from the acoustic image I of the source in the surface, considered as a kind of

[1] I. Rudnick, *J. Acoust. Soc. Am.*, **19**, 348 (1947).

acoustic mirror. The total effect of the source at P, therefore, may be thought of as the superposition of the direct and reflected waves. We represent the excess pressure at P in the direct wave from S as p_1, where

$$p_1 = A_1 \cos (\omega t - \delta_1) \tag{1}$$

and we assume that the radiation is harmonic in character with angular frequency ω. The quantity δ_1 is the phase difference between the disturbance at the source S and the receiving point P. Strictly,

$$\delta_1 = \frac{2\pi l}{\lambda} = \frac{\omega l}{V} \tag{2}$$

where l is the distance SP, λ the wavelength, and V the velocity in the water. Similarly, the excess pressure at P due to the reflected wave is

$$p_2 = A_2 \cos (\omega t - \delta_2 - \pi) \tag{3}$$

where δ_2 is the corresponding phase angle for the distance IP and we take into account the fact (Sec. 3.2) that there is a phase change of π on reflection in going from water to air. The resultant excess pressure at P then is

$$p = p_1 + p_2 = (A_1 \cos \delta_1 - A_2 \cos \delta_2) \cos \omega t \\ + (A_1 \sin \delta_1 - A_2 \sin \delta_2) \sin \omega t \tag{4}$$

Using a method already exemplified in Sec. 1.5, we can write this

$$p = p_{\max} \cos (\omega t - \beta) \tag{5}$$

where

$$p_{\max} = \sqrt{A_1{}^2 + A_2{}^2 - 2A_1A_2 \cos (\delta_1 - \delta_2)} \tag{6}$$

and

$$\tan \beta = \frac{A_1 \sin \delta_1 - A_2 \sin \delta_2}{A_1 \cos \delta_1 - A_2 \cos \delta_2} \tag{7}$$

The intensity of the resultant radiation at P becomes

$$I_r = \frac{p_{\max}^2}{2\rho_0 V} = \frac{A_1{}^2 + A_2{}^2 - 2A_1A_2 \cos (\delta_1 - \delta_2)}{2\rho_0 V} \tag{8}$$

if ρ_0 is the mean density of the water. It is convenient to express this in terms of the intensity I_1, which is produced at P by the direct radiation from S. Then

$$I_r = I_1[1 + R^2 - 2R \cos (\delta_1 - \delta_2)] \tag{9}$$

where R is the ratio of the excess pressure due to the reflected wave to that due to the direct wave. It is clear from (9) that, as the point P is moved relatively to S, $\cos (\delta_1 - \delta_2)$ will oscillate between -1 and $+1$ and the resultant intensity I_2 will oscillate between $I_1(1 + R)^2$ and $I_1(1 - R)^2$. In particular, if the source is very close to the surface, R will approximate unity, and the intensity will fluctuate between zero and four times that due to the source by itself in the absence of the boundary. Thus we have an *interference* effect, which for certain source positions can lead to a decided loading of the source, that is, increased average emission of energy from the source. Of course, if S is very close to the surface, $\delta_1 - \delta_2$ remains effectively zero until P is very far from the source, unless h is comparable to the wavelength. The phenomenon involved here is usually known as the Lloyd mirror effect, after the corresponding interference effect in optics.[1]

The preceding discussion is idealized in that the sea is actually rarely homogeneous, as was emphasized in the first paragraph of this section. A fairly common temperature distribution encountered in deep sea water is illustrated in Fig. 10.6. From the surface (indicated by O) down to C,

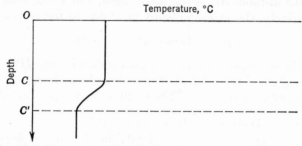

Fig. 10.6. Temperature distribution in sea water. Thermocline.

the temperature remains constant (isothermal water with more or less constant sound velocity, save for the slight increase with depth due to increase in hydrostatic pressure and density). From C to C' the temperature drops rapidly in a layer called the *thermocline*, whereas from C' on down, the rate of decrease is much slower and indeed eventually may turn into an increase.

In Sec. 1.12 we developed the analytical theory of wave propagation in terms of rays, which, we pointed out, is a good approximation if the change in wavelength over a distance of the order of one wavelength due to the change in velocity in the medium is a negligibly small fraction of the wavelength itself. Moreover, the wavefront must not curve too sharply, etc. Actually these conditions are met rather well in a medium in which the changes in temperature, etc., and therefore the changes in sound velocity, are gradual—and also, of course, if the frequency is rather high. For not too high ultrasonic transmission in sea water one may generally use ray analysis as a safe first approximation.

In Sec. 2.2 we worked out by ray analysis the case of transmission in a medium in which the variation in velocity takes place in one direction only (i.e., a stratified medium), and we showed that, if the velocity is a

[1] F. A. Jenkins and H. E. White, "Fundamentals of Optics," 2d ed., p. 238, McGraw-Hill Book Company, Inc., New York, 1950.

linear function of distance in this direction (e.g., the z axis measured vertically downward), the rays are arcs of circles with upward curvature if the velocity increases downward and with downward curvature in the opposite situation (see Fig. 2.4). Without going through elaborate analysis, we can readily see the general situation in sea water corresponding to the velocity distribution in Fig. 10.6. Suppose a point source S lies in the region OC. Since the sound velocity increases slightly with depth in this region, the rays from S will bend upward slightly. However, in the thermocline these rays will bend downward, since the effect of the temperature gradient outweighs that of the change in pressure. Hence the situation appears more or less as in Fig. 10.7, where we have

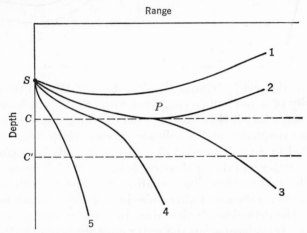

FIG. 10.7. Underwater sound rays. Shadow zone.

plotted the rays on a range-depth diagram. Ray 1 stays entirely in the isothermal layer. Ray 2 grazes the surface of the thermocline at P and splits, part going up and the other part going down (ray 3). This means that no direct ray from S penetrates into the region beyond P between rays 2 and 3. Hence this region can legitimately be called an acoustic *shadow zone*. Actually rays from S, after reflection from the surface, can penetrate the shadow zone, and hence we cannot expect the intensity there to drop to zero. We might anticipate that the more precise treatment of the diffraction of wavefronts would show some energy getting into the shadow zone, and this is indeed the case. However, the existence of such a low-intensity zone has been experimentally verified.

Another interesting example of the effect of reflection and refraction in sea water is the so-called sound *channel*. Figure 10.8 depicts on the left a velocity profile in which the velocity decreases from the surface down to C, where it reaches a minimum and thereafter increases. Consider a source S located between O and C. If we draw rays in the right-hand part of the figure following the rules we have discussed above, it is seen that they all lie within a region OD. Thus the sound from S is concentrated in a channel, and the normal loss in intensity due to spreading is considerably diminished. This type of velocity profile is responsible for long-distance transmission of sound in the sea.

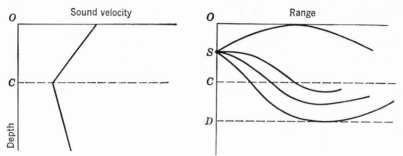

FIG. 10.8. Underwater sound-channeling effect.

In view of the relatively large density of sea water and the relatively large velocity of sound in it as compared with air, it is much easier to get radiation energy into it than into air from the same transducer vibrating at the same frequency and amplitude, a fact which was analytically demonstrated in Secs. 3.5 and 9.10. Moreover, this impedance match between sea water and the solid source is better at high frequencies than at low. This and the beamlike radiation produced by high frequencies have accounted for the use of ultrasonics in underwater depth finding and signaling. The detection of submarines by *sonar* is another application. In this case a transducer scans the water until the beam hits an obstacle and produces an echo, whose reception at the source can be made to give an indication of bearing and range of the obstacle.

A very definite limitation on this technique is the fall-off of intensity with distance, usually called the *transmission loss*. This is made up of two components: (1) spreading and (2) irreversible attenuation by the medium. The first we have already met on numerous occasions in earlier sections. It is geometrical in origin; an outgoing spherical wave, for example, decreases in intensity inversely as the square of the distance from the source. A cylindrical wave has its intensity decreased with the inverse first power of the distance. In Sec. 1.12 we pointed out how we can estimate transmission loss due to spherical spreading by plotting rays in the sound field in question and studying their divergence or convergence at the point where the intensity is to be estimated.[1]

The attenuation loss is that due to the properties of the medium itself. It results in part from the scattering of sound by obstacles such as bubbles

[1] For analytical details see J. W. Horton, "Fundamentals of Sonar," pp. 99ff., United States Naval Institute, Annapolis, 1957.

or small regions of turbulent water, but it is due also to the absorption by the transport processes of viscosity and heat conduction (primarily the former). These mechanisms have already been treated in Secs. 9.11 and 9.12. It turns out that they are not adequate to predict the whole attenuation in homogeneous still water. In Chap. 12 we shall show that the difference is believed to be due to molecular absorption. In the case of sea water, this is thought to have its origin in the magnesium sulfate in solution.

When sound passes from one medium to another of different properties, it suffers a change in intensity, as shown in Sec. 3.2. This also is effective in producing transmission loss in sea water, though the boundaries between such media are rarely sharp.

10.6. Seismic Waves

Elastic waves in the earth's crust, long known as earthquakes, provide an interesting illustration of the theoretical development in Chap. 6. There we saw that in an unbounded isotropic medium two types of elastic waves can be propagated: (1) the irrotational variety, for which the curl of the displacement vanishes and which may therefore be termed *dilatational*, and (2) the solenoidal kind, for which the divergence of the displacement vanishes and which may be termed *shear* waves. We showed that an irrotational plane wave is longitudinal and that a solenoidal plane wave is transverse. The velocity of an irrotational wave is

$$V = \sqrt{\frac{B + 4\mu/3}{\rho}} \tag{1}$$

where B is the bulk modulus, μ the shear modulus, and ρ the density. The velocity of a shear wave is

$$V = \sqrt{\frac{\mu}{\rho}} \tag{2}$$

Both types of waves have been observed in seismic research, in both natural and artificial earthquakes, that is, those produced by natural disturbances in the earth's crust and those set off by man-made explosions. In general, as might be expected, the values of both longitudinal and transverse wave velocities increase with depth below the surface. Thus at a depth of 100 km longitudinal waves have a velocity about 8 km/sec, a figure which increases first very slowly with depth and then more rapidly in the neighborhood of 100 km, until at 2,900 km it has reached a value of 13.7 km/sec. This corresponds to $B = 6.5 \times 10^{12}$ dynes/cm^2, $\mu = 3.1 \times 10^{12}$ dynes/cm^2, and $\rho = 5.7$ g/cm^3. The behavior of earthquake waves indicates the presence of a discontinuity in the constitution of the body of the earth at a depth of about 3,000 km, since there is a fairly sharp reflection of longitudinal waves from this vicinity. The records are consistent with the assumption that at this discontinuity the density jumps from about 5.7 to 10 g/cm³, whereas the bulk modulus decreases slightly. The corresponding longitudinal velocity drops back to 8 km/sec, though with a further increase in depth the velocity increases to 10 km/sec.*

The velocity of shear waves increases from 4.45 km/sec at the surface to about 7.3 km/sec at the discontinuity, below which, it is generally agreed, no shear waves are known. The results are used as a basis for the conclusion that, whereas the mantle of the earth (i.e., the shell down to a depth of 3,000 km) is solid, the core beneath this is a very dense liquid, or at any rate has an elastic behavior that one would associate with a liquid (with $\mu = 0$, effectively).

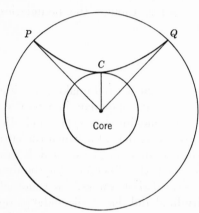

As in the case of atmospheric and underwater sound transmission, the study of earthquake waves is facilitated by the use of rays. Thus, Fig. 10.9 shows the path of a longitudinal ray from P to Q on the earth's surface after passing through the earth and being reflected from the core at C. The path of this ray can be computed from the type of analysis presented in Sec. 2.2.

FIG. 10.9. Path (PCQ) of longitudinal seismic ray.

In Sec. 7.5 we dealt with waves on the surface of an elastic solid, which were first investigated by Rayleigh and which were named after him. It might be expected that such waves would be important in seismology, particularly for disturbances originating at, or very near, the surface of the earth. Actually such surface waves are observed, with both horizontal and vertical components, and the theory of Rayleigh waves applies. However, other surface waves are observed which have no vertical displacement components. Love attributed these observations to waves in a relatively thin surface layer differing in physical properties from the medium beneath it and showed that one can have purely transverse waves existing in such a layer which penetrate only very little into the lower medium. The waves then act as if they were confined to the surface layer. This is a good place to consider Love's theo-

* B. Gutenberg, Seismological and Related Data in "American Institute of Physics Handbook," pp. 2–101ff., McGraw-Hill Book Company, Inc., New York, 1957.

retical deduction in some detail; it reminds us of the channeling phenomenon in underwater sound waves described in the previous section.

For convenience we shall assume a plane surface layer of thickness h parallel to the xy plane. The layer is to have density ρ and shear modulus μ. The interface between the layer and the medium below it (with density ρ' and shear modulus μ') is taken to be the plane $z = 0$, and the free surface of the layer is then the plane $z = h$. It is assumed that we have only transverse waves in the layer proceeding in the x direction, with the displacement in the y direction. This means that $\xi = \zeta = 0$ and only η is nonvanishing.[1] If we insert these conditions in (6.3-26), we have

$$\nabla^2 \eta = \frac{\rho}{\mu} \ddot{\eta} \tag{3}$$

or if we further specialize to harmonic waves with angular frequency ω,

$$\nabla^2 \eta + \frac{\omega^2}{V^2} \eta = 0 \tag{4}$$

where we use (2). From the symmetry of the situation we get the same equation governing the waves in the lower medium, with η replaced by η' and V by V', where

$$V' = \sqrt{\frac{\mu'}{\rho'}} \tag{5}$$

In the layer we try a solution of the form

$$\eta = (Ae^{mz} + Be^{-mz})e^{i(\omega t - kx)} \tag{6}$$

where, since there is assumed to be no attenuation in the z direction, m must be pure imaginary. In the lower medium we postulate a solution of similar form with primed constants:

$$\eta' = A'e^{m'z}e^{i(\omega t - k'x)} \tag{7}$$

where, since attenuation is assumed in the lower medium, k' is real and positive (recall that z is negative in the lower medium and that we cannot allow a term of the form $e^{-m'z}$).

If η in (6) is to satisfy (4), we must clearly have

$$m = \pm \sqrt{k^2 - \frac{\omega^2}{V^2}}$$

$$= \pm i \sqrt{\frac{\omega^2}{V^2} - k^2} = \pm iq \tag{8}$$

[1] Do not confuse η here with the viscosity in Sec. 10.2.

The requirement that m shall be pure imaginary entails that

$$\frac{\omega}{V} > k \tag{9}$$

in the layer.   On the other hand, in the lower medium

$$\frac{\omega}{V'} < k' \tag{10}$$

Notice that

$$m' = \sqrt{k'^2 - \frac{\omega^2}{V'^2}} \tag{11}$$

The solution in the layer therefore takes the form

$$\eta = (C \cos qz + D \sin qz)e^{i(\omega t - kx)} \tag{12}$$

We must now impose boundary conditions.   The tangential displacement at the interface must be continuous.   This means that

$$\eta = \eta' \qquad \text{at } z = 0 \tag{13}$$

and leads to

$$C = A' \qquad k = k' \tag{14}$$

Next, the tangential stress must be continuous across the interface. This means that

$$\mu \frac{\partial \eta}{\partial z} = \mu' \frac{\partial \eta'}{\partial z} \qquad \text{at } z = 0 \tag{15}$$

and leads to

$$\mu \, Dq = \mu' A' m' \tag{16}$$

Finally, the stress must vanish at the free surface where $z = h$.   This means that

$$\frac{\partial \eta}{\partial z} = 0 \qquad \text{for } z = h \tag{17}$$

or

$$\tan qh = \frac{D}{C} \tag{18}$$

Since $C = A'$, we get, from the use of (15),

$$\tan qh = \frac{\mu' m'}{\mu q} \tag{19}$$

Inserting the values of m' and q gives

$$\tan qh = \frac{\mu'}{\mu} \sqrt{\frac{k^2 - \omega^2/V'^2}{\omega^2/V^2 - k^2}}$$

$$= \frac{\mu'}{\mu} \sqrt{\frac{k^2}{q^2}\left(1 - \frac{V^2}{V'^2}\right) - \frac{V^2}{V'^2}} \tag{20}$$

From (9) and (10) it follows that we can satisfy the existence of the postulated waves only if

$$V' > V \tag{21}$$

This leads to $\tan qh$ being real and positive. Now the velocity of the Love waves is

$$V_L = \frac{\omega}{k}$$

From (20) it follows that

$$V' > V_L > V \tag{22}$$

If we express V_L in terms of $\tan qh$, it develops from (20) that, as the wavelength increases, the Love wave velocity increases and in the limit of very long wavelengths approaches V', whereas, as the wavelength decreases to zero, the Love wave velocity approaches V as a limit.

It is clear that the conditions for the existence of Love waves in the earth's mantle are satisfied. Waves of this type have been observed, but the phenomena are complicated by other factors not accounted for by the simple theory just given.

CHAPTER 11

ACOUSTIC RADIATION IN CLOSED SPACES

11.1. Reverberation in a Room

When a source of mechanical radiation is placed in a medium more or less completely surrounded by a reflecting boundary (i.e., a source of sound in a closed room), the resultant intensity of the radiation at any point inside the bounded space is due to the superposition of the disturbance resulting from repeated reflections at the boundary and that reaching the point directly from the source. If the reflections were complete, it is clear that the steady output of power by the source would lead to an indefinitely high intensity at certain points. Though there always is some absorption at the walls, leading to a steady state in the radiation field, the increased intensity over that for the same source in open and unbounded space is very marked. It has long been referred to as *reverberation*. Anyone who has ever clapped his hands or uttered a single loud vowel sound in a large hall with hard walls, floor, and ceiling will have noted the relatively long time it takes the sound to die down to inaudibility. This serves as the basis for the definition of a precise, if arbitrary, reverberation time, namely, the time it takes the original disturbance to decay to one-millionth of its intensity.

Since reflection at the boundaries leads to the production of standing waves, the radiation field in a closed space has in general a complicated pattern with nodes and loops. Any thorough study of reverberation will have to take this into account. However, we shall introduce the subject with rather simple considerations. Thus we shall assume that the average energy density in the space is uniform at any instant. As in Chap. 1 we denote it by $\bar{w}$. The fundamental physical idea at the basis of an evaluation of the reverberation time is that the average rate at which radiation energy is being produced in the space plus the average rate at which it is being absorbed at the boundary is equal to the power output of the source. This neglects, to be sure, the absorption in the medium, which under certain conditions may be important.

If the volume of the enclosed space is τ, the average rate at which the energy in the space builds up is

$$\tau \dot{\bar{w}} \tag{1}$$

To find the average rate at which absorption takes place at the boundary, we must first find the average rate at which radiation energy falls on unit area of the boundary. It is assumed that the disturbance in *any* volume element in the space will travel in all directions with constant velocity V. Consider the element of surface dS with center at O and normal ON, as in Fig. 11.1. At distance r is the volume element $d\tau$, con-

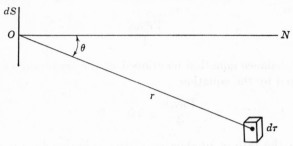

FIG. 11.1. Radiation falling on surface in a closed space.

taining, on the average, radiation energy $\bar{w}\,d\tau$. The fraction of this that will reach dS is that included in the solid angle

$$d\Omega = \frac{dS\cos\theta}{r^2}$$

But since the total solid angle about the volume element is 4π, the amount of energy in $d\tau$ which will ultimately reach dS is

$$\frac{\bar{w}\,d\tau\,dS\cos\theta}{4\pi r^2}$$

If r is equal to or less than the distance traveled by sound in 1 sec, this energy will reach dS in 1 sec or less. This will then be true of all volume elements within a hemisphere of radius V about dS as center. The volume element $d\tau$ is therefore most conveniently taken as the zone of a hemispherical shell bounded by r, $r + dr$, θ, $\theta + d\theta$. This volume is

$$d\tau = 2\pi r^2 \sin\theta\,d\theta\,dr$$

Hence the rate at which radiation energy falls on dS from all directions is

$$\frac{\bar{w}\,dS}{2}\int_0^V\int_0^{\pi/2}\sin\theta\cos\theta\,d\theta\,dr = \frac{\bar{w}V}{4}\,dS \tag{2}$$

and the rate at which it falls on unit area is

$$\frac{\bar{w}V}{4} \tag{3}$$

If the fraction of the total energy falling on unit area which is *not* reflected is α, then that for dS is $\alpha\, dS$. Hence the total energy not reflected for the entire boundary is

$$a = \int \alpha\, dS = \bar{\alpha} S \tag{4}$$

where the integration is carried out over the whole area of the boundary S, and $\bar{\alpha}$ is the *average* absorption coefficient (average absorbing power per unit area). The average rate at which energy is absorbed by the walls is then

$$\frac{V \bar{w} \bar{\alpha} S}{4} \tag{5}$$

The energy-balance equation mentioned at the beginning of the section is represented by the equation

$$\frac{V \bar{w} \bar{\alpha} S}{4} + \tau \dot{\bar{w}} = W \tag{6}$$

where W is the rate of production of the radiation by the source (the power output). The solution of this equation is

$$\bar{w} = \frac{4W}{V \bar{\alpha} S} \left(1 - e^{-(V \bar{\alpha} S / 4\tau)t}\right) \tag{7}$$

where it is assumed that $\bar{w} = 0$ at $t = 0$. There is then a maximum value of $\bar{w}$ given by

$$\bar{w}_{\max} = \frac{4W}{V \bar{\alpha} S} \tag{8}$$

and this is the steady-state value. Let us suppose that, after the steady state has been established, the source is stopped. We integrate (6) with $W = 0$ and get

$$\bar{w} = \bar{w}_{\max} e^{-(V \bar{\alpha} S / 4\tau)t} \tag{9}$$

an equation presumably first derived by W. S. Franklin[1] in 1903. From it we can immediately deduce the time taken for $\bar{w}/\bar{w}_{\max}$ to become 10^{-6}. For sound radiation in air at 20°C this is

$$T = \frac{0.161\tau}{\bar{\alpha} S} \tag{10}$$

if all linear dimensions are in meters and we use $V = 344$ m/sec, the velocity of sound in air at room temperature. T is then the reverberation time, as introduced by W. C. Sabine,[2] who obtained an equation of the same form as (10) by his experiments, though with the coefficient 0.164 in place of 0.161. Sabine's measurements referred to the decay of

[1] *Phys. Rev.*, **16**, 373 (1903).

[2] "Collected Papers on Acoustics," Harvard University Press, Cambridge, Mass., 1927.

sound intensity in a closed room. However, since the intensity is equal (see Sec. 1.10) to the product of the average energy density and the velocity of propagation (strictly the group velocity, but the distinction is unnecessary if the dispersion is small), the rate of decay of both quantities is the same. The relation (10), despite the approximate nature of its derivation, has been very useful in practical room acoustics when the absorption coefficient $\bar{\alpha}$ is much less than unity. This might well be considered surprising in view of the many factors neglected—the precise shape of the room, the interference due to phase differences in the sound arriving at any given point from various directions (i.e., the standing wave pattern effect), the difference in absorption associated with different angles of incidence at the boundaries, the absorption in the medium due to viscosity and other transport processes (see Secs. 9.11 and 12.1), and finally the fact that the reflections at the boundaries are not single but multiple, with the consequence that the associated absorption is really discontinuous. These neglected factors are of different weights. Perhaps the most important are the normal-mode patterns and the multiple reflections.

The importance of considering the absorption associated with multiple reflections in deriving the reverberation equation was first pointed out by C. F. Eyring.[1] A simplified version of his derivation has been suggested by R. F. Norris.[2] At each incidence of a wavefront on a boundary the fraction of the incident power per unit area $\bar{\alpha}$ is, on the average, absorbed, and the fraction $1 - \bar{\alpha}$ is reflected. If there are, on the average, n incidences per unit time on the walls and each one removes a fraction $\bar{\alpha}$ of the incident power, the rate at which the average energy density is decreased per unit time is clearly $n\bar{\alpha}\bar{w}$. Hence we have the approximate equation, which indeed assumes temporal continuity in what is really a discrete process

$$\dot{w} = -n\bar{\alpha}\bar{w} \tag{11}$$

Now, if we denote by l the average distance traveled by the sound between wall incidences, we have

$$n = \frac{V}{l} \tag{12}$$

We are now permitted to equate $\dot{w}$ in (11) to $\dot{w}$ in (6) (with W put equal to zero). This yields at once

$$l = \frac{4\tau}{S} \tag{13}$$

where S is the total wall area. The average number of reflections in

[1] J. Acoust. Soc. Am., 1, 217 (1930).

[2] V. O. Knudsen, "Architectural Acoustics," appendix II, John Wiley & Sons, Inc., New York, 1932.

time t then becomes

$$\frac{StV}{4\tau}$$

and the average energy density of the sound at time t is

$$\bar{w} = \bar{w}_{max}(1 - \bar{\alpha})^{VSt/4\tau}$$
$$= \bar{w}_{max}e^{[VS \ln (1-\bar{\alpha})/4\tau]t} \qquad (14)$$

This is to be compared with (9). If $\bar{\alpha} \ll 1$, $\ln (1 - \bar{\alpha}) \doteq -\bar{\alpha}$, and (14) reduces to (9). On the other hand, if $\bar{\alpha}$ is not small compared with unity, (14) gives a decidedly different reverberation time from the Sabine formula (10), namely,

$$T = \frac{0.161\tau}{-S \ln (1 - \bar{\alpha})} \qquad (15)$$

This associates a smaller $\bar{\alpha}$ with given T than (9) and indicates that for a so-called "dead" room (i.e., a room with very small reverberation) the amount of absorption necessary to achieve the desired value of T is less than that predicted by the Sabine formula. It is of interest to note that we could derive (14) from an energy-balance equation of the form

$$\tau\dot{\bar{w}} - \frac{\bar{w}SV \ln (1 - \bar{\alpha})}{4} = 0 \qquad (16)$$

in which $-\bar{w}SV \ln (1 - \bar{\alpha})/4$ appears as the average rate of energy absorption by the walls.

The Eyring formula can be modified to include the effect of absorption in the medium and then has the form

$$T = \frac{K\tau}{-S \ln (1 - \bar{\alpha}) + 4m\tau} \qquad (17)$$

where K is an appropriate constant factor and m is the energy attenuation coefficient for plane waves in the medium [corresponding to 2α in (9.11-13)].[1] The Eyring formula has been criticized by P. M. Morse and R. H. Bolt[2] on the grounds that the assumption of a uniform distribution of absorbing material at the boundaries is unrealistic and, more seriously still, that the reflected wave in general cannot be considered spherically symmetric and hence the assumption that the reflections are all alike and each leads to the same amount of absorption is fallacious. Nevertheless the formula (17) has been used in practice with considerable success.

The application of the reverberation-time equation to practical room acoustics involves the measurement of the average absorption coefficient

[1] V. O. Knudsen, *J. Acoust. Soc. Am.*, **2**, 126 (1931).
[2] *Revs. Mod. Phys.*, **16**, 69 (1944).

$\bar{a}$ or, ultimately, of the absorption coefficient of each different piece of absorbing surface in the room. This can, of course, be carried out by the measurement of the reverberation time itself, but this is commonly replaced by a method using (8) for the maximum energy density. The whole problem in its ramifications is now an important branch of acoustical engineering and is discussed at length in treatises on architectural acoustics.[1]

11.2. Normal Modes in a Room

From the basic scientific standpoint the most significant element in room acoustics, after reverberation, is the presence of normal modes in the standing wave pattern produced by the reflections at the boundaries. Since this situation was mentioned briefly in Sec. 1.5 and treated more extensively in Sec. 3.1, we can recall that for a rectangular enclosure of dimensions l_1, l_2, and l_3 in the x, y, z directions, respectively, the wave equation in rectangular coordinates and the boundary conditions can be satisfied by an excess pressure of the form

$$p_e = p_{e,\max} \sin k_1 x \sin k_2 y \sin k_3 z \, e^{i\omega t} \tag{1}$$

where the allowed values of the angular frequency ω are

$$\omega_{n_1,n_2,n_3} = \pi V \sqrt{\left(\frac{n_1}{l_1}\right)^2 + \left(\frac{n_2}{l_2}\right)^2 + \left(\frac{n_3}{l_3}\right)^2} \tag{2}$$

V being the velocity of the radiation and n_1, n_2, n_3 any trio of integers. The k parameters are given by

$$k_j = \frac{n_j \pi}{l_j} \qquad j = 1, 2, 3 \tag{3}$$

If the source of radiation in the room contains a frequency equal to one of those in (2), the room will resonate to it and the room response will be correspondingly accentuated. To evaluate the number of normal modes up to a given frequency from (2) is a rather complicated problem in the mathematical theory of numbers. We can see from inspection, at any rate, that in the low-frequency range the distribution of modes is rather discrete (i.e., relatively large frequency intervals between modes) but that, as the frequency increases, the distribution becomes more crowded. Since in actual practice the resonance peak associated with each resonant frequency is never infinitely sharp, because of the damping due to absorption (see Sec. 9.8), the room response becomes more nearly a continuous function of frequency as the frequency increases.

[1] V. O. Knudsen and C. M. Harris, "Acoustical Designing in Architecture," John Wiley & Sons, Inc., New York, 1950.

In Sec. 3.1 we calculated the number of modes in unit frequency interval for the rectangular room for which (2) holds, for the case of high frequency. This is given by (3.1-15) for a room of volume τ. If we could assume that this formula holds for all frequencies, we could calculate the total number of modes up to the maximum frequency ν_m by simple integration and obtain

$$N = \frac{4\pi}{3} \tau \left(\frac{\nu_m}{V}\right)^3 \tag{4}$$

But this confines attention to oblique waves in which all the n's in (2) are different from zero, and neglects the proper counting of axial waves for which two of the n's are zero and tangential waves for which one of the n's is zero. This classification of the modes has been given by P. M. Morse,[1] who shows that, if we take account of all classes, (4) will be replaced by the following approximate expression

$$N \doteq \frac{4\pi\tau}{3} \left(\frac{\nu_m}{V}\right)^3 + \frac{\pi A}{4} \left(\frac{\nu_m}{V}\right)^2 + \frac{L}{8} \left(\frac{\nu_m}{V}\right) \tag{5}$$

where A is the total wall area and L is the sum of the lengths of all the edges of the room, that is, $L = 4(l_1 + l_2 + l_3)$. As the frequency ν_m increases, the first term predominates over the rest. In fact, if $\nu_m \gg 3VA/16\tau$, the second and third terms can be neglected compared with the first. For example, if a rectangular room has dimensions 10 by 20 by 30 m with a total volume $\tau = 6 \times 10^3$ m^3, we may safely use (4) if the frequency is well above 20 cycles/sec.

The number of modes per unit frequency interval in the neighborhood of frequency ν for a rectangular room has the approximate form

$$dN \doteq \left(\frac{4\pi\tau\nu^2}{V^3} + \frac{\pi A\nu}{2V^2} + \frac{L}{8V}\right) d\nu \tag{6}$$

where again the first term predominates at high frequencies. Thus in the above example in the neighborhood of 100 cycles/sec there are about 18 modes per cycle; at around 1,000 cycles/sec this number rises to about 1,800 modes per cycle.

An interesting question is this: Will the formula (6) hold for rooms of nonrectangular shape? Morse has investigated this problem and finds that, though the formula as a whole breaks down for rooms with curved surfaces, such as cylinders and spheres, the first term in parentheses is independent of the shape of the room. This would indeed be suggested by the analysis of Sec. 3.1. It turns out, indeed, that the more symmetrical a room is for given size, the greater is the tendency for the

---

[1] "Vibration and Sound," 2d ed., pp. 391ff., McGraw-Hill Book Company, Inc., New York, 1948.

response to be irregular; that is, the normal modes tend to be spread more widely apart. This is due largely to the fact that in such a case there are more stationary wave patterns with different n values but with the same frequency. This situation is known as *degeneracy*. The suggestion is strong that the introduction of irregularities in a room can have a marked effect in smoothing the response. It is understood, of course, that such irregularities must be of the same order of magnitude as the wavelength corresponding to the resonant frequency. This type of treatment has been of great success in the acoustical design of rooms.

Basic for the significance of the reverberation time as a measure of room acoustics is the assumption of the complete diffusion of sound in the room. There have been many attempts by architectual acousticians to provide a meaningful measure of this diffusion, or *diffusivity*, as it is sometimes called.[1] The distribution of the normal modes would appear to provide one measure of this quantity, but E. Meyer has shown that this is not in general sufficient. He himself prefers to use the quantity

$$\psi = \frac{\Sigma(p_{max} - p_{min})}{n\,\Delta\nu} \tag{7}$$

where we sum the difference between the excess pressure maxima and minima (p_{max} and p_{min}, respectively) over the frequency interval $\Delta\nu$ covering the frequency range of greatest interest in the actual acoustic use of the room. The number n is the number of such maxima and associated minima in the interval in question. According to a theory developed by Schroeder in Meyer's Institute at Göttingen, ψ should be directly proportional to the reverberation time. The agreement between this result and experiment is rather good. Of course it must be recognized that every theoretical result of an assumption in architectual acoustics must be tested ultimately against the judgment of persons listening in the room in question, and this introduces an element of subjectivity into the whole problem.

[1] E. Meyer, *J. Acoust. Soc. Am.*, **26**, 630 (1954); also *Proc. Intern. Congr. Acoust.*, 2d *Congr.*, p. 59 (1957).

CHAPTER 12

MECHANICAL RADIATION
AND THE PROPERTIES OF MATTER

12.1. Molecular Theory of Absorption and Dispersion of Sound in Fluids

In Secs. 9.11 and 9.12 it was pointed out that the transmission of compressional radiation through a viscous, thermally conducting fluid is accompanied by attenuation and dispersion. The absorption coefficient associated with the first varies directly with the viscosity and the square of the frequency of the harmonic radiation; the dispersion is a second-order effect. It was also emphasized that the predicted absorption agrees with that experimentally observed for only a few fluids, notably the rare gases and liquid mercury. In general, the absorption coefficient due to viscosity and heat conduction falls far short of the measured values. It is therefore necessary to seek another source to account for the excess. This has been found in the internal energy states of the molecules composing the fluid.

It is well known that polyatomic molecules possess not only energy of translation but also energy of vibration of their constituent atoms and energy of rotation of these particles about each other. The latter are usually referred to as internal energy states. When molecules collide, a transition is likely to take place from one internal energy state to another, involving the transfer of energy from the external, or translational, form to the internal form, or vice versa. How does such an energy transfer affect the propagation of a sound wave? Such a wave involves a momentary compression of the fluid which, by increasing the density, also produces an increase in pressure or in mean kinetic energy of translation of the molecules. But the increase in pressure does not occur instantaneously, since some of the extra energy of translation is transferred to the internal molecular states. After the density has begun to decrease, the pressure keeps on increasing, as the energy is transferred back from the internal states to the translational form. Thus excess pressure and excess density get out of phase, and this (as in any hysteresis phenomenon) produces an effective transformation of acoustic energy into heat, corresponding to attenuation of the acoustic wave. It remains

334

to study this mode of absorption analytically.   This is a relaxation phenomenon like the effect of viscosity and heat conduction discussed in Secs. 9.11 and 9.12.

It will be simplest to confine our attention to the special case in which there are only two states of energy of each molecule: (1) that in which it possesses translational energy E_1 only and (2) that in which it possesses energy E_2 due to translation plus the excitation of an internal energy level.   Let us suppose that because of the collisions normally occurring in the fluid, here effectively treated as an ideal gas, there exist in a state of equilibrium n_{10} molecules per mole in state 1 and n_{20} molecules per mole in state 2, where

$$n_{10} + n_{20} = N \tag{1}$$

and N is Avogadro's number.   It will be assumed that the effect of the sound wave is to alter the numbers n_{10} and n_{20} to n_1 and n_2, respectively, though their sum still remains N.   Moreover, it is postulated that the average number of transitions per second per molecule from state 1 to state 2 is k_{12} and that the average number of transitions per second per molecule from state 2 to state 1 is k_{21}.   The equation giving the average rate of change of number of molecules in the excited state (2) with time is then[1]

$$\dot{n}_2 = n_1 k_{12} - n_2 k_{21} \tag{2}$$

where we make the natural assumption that the average number of transitions per second is proportional to the number of molecules in each initial state.   Equation (2) is a linear reaction-rate equation.   Under equilibrium conditions, that is, when the gas is unaffected by the sound radiation, $\dot{n}_2 = 0$ and hence

$$\frac{n_{20}}{n_{10}} = \frac{k_{12}^{\circ}}{k_{21}^{\circ}} \tag{3}$$

where the superscripts on the k's refer to the equilibrium case.   It is natural to introduce the assumption of classical statistical mechanics that the equilibrium distribution of the molecules follows the Boltzmann canonical law,[2] that is,

$$\frac{n_{20}}{n_{10}} = e^{-\epsilon/kT} \tag{4}$$

where $\epsilon = E_2 - E_1$.

Now the presence of sound radiation alters the relative numbers of molecules in the two states as well as the transition coefficients k_{12} and k_{21}.   Hence if we denote the alteration by the symbol Δ, the reaction-rate

---

[1] We are here following a method first applied to sound propagation by H. O. Kneser. See *J. Acoust. Soc. Am.*, **5**, 122 (1933).

[2] R. B. Lindsay, "Physical Statistics," pp. 53ff., John Wiley & Sons, Inc., New York, 1941.

equation (1) becomes

$$\Delta \dot{n}_2 = n_{10} \, \Delta k_{12} + k_{12}^{\circ} \, \Delta n_1 - n_{20} \, \Delta k_{21} - k_{21}^{\circ} \, \Delta n_2 \tag{5}$$

But, from (1), $\Delta n_1 = -\Delta n_2$. Using this and (4), we obtain

$$\Delta \dot{n}_2 = \frac{n_{20} k_{21}^{\circ} \epsilon \, \Delta T}{kT^2} - \Delta n_2 (k_{12}^{\circ} + k_{21}^{\circ}) \tag{6}$$

If the time rate of change is due to a periodic sound wave with angular frequency ω, we can replace $\Delta \dot{n}_2$ by $i\omega \, \Delta n_2$ and solve (6) for Δn_2, obtaining

$$\Delta n_2 = \frac{n_{20} k_{21}^{\circ} \epsilon \tau \, \Delta T / kT^2}{1 + i\omega\tau} \tag{7}$$

where we have put

$$\frac{1}{k_{12}^{\circ} + k_{21}^{\circ}} = \tau \tag{8}$$

which will be called the relaxation time for the process. This is justified by the physical significance of (6) (see Sec. 9.11). If we were to solve this equation for Δn_2 under the assumption of constant ΔT, treating $\Delta \dot{n}_2$ as $(d/dt)(\Delta n_2)$ in perfectly general fashion, we would obtain

$$\Delta n_2 = \frac{n_{20} k_{21}^{\circ} \epsilon \tau \, \Delta T}{kT^2} (1 - e^{-t/\tau}) \tag{9}$$

assuming also that the initial value of Δn_2 is zero. Then τ is the time in which Δn_2 reaches $(1 - 1/e)$th of its ultimate value $n_{20} k_{21}^{\circ} \epsilon \tau \, \Delta T / kT^2$.

We now revert to (7) and introduce some thermodynamics. According to the first law for a gas (see Sec. 9.12),

$$J \, \Delta Q = \Delta U + p \, \Delta v \tag{10}$$

where $J \, \Delta Q$ is the energy equivalent of the heat contributed to the thermodynamic system during any process, ΔU is the change in the internal energy, and $p \, \Delta v$ the work done by the system during the process (Δv is here the change in volume). J is of course the mechanical equivalent of heat (4.2 joules/cal). As has already been pointed out in Sec. 9.2, it is assumed that the compressions and rarefactions whose propagation constitutes the transmission of sound through a fluid take place adiabatically. Hence (10) becomes

$$\Delta U + p \, \Delta v = 0 \tag{11}$$

Since the system we are here considering is an ideal gas, the change in internal energy is due to change in temperature only and indeed $\Delta U = C_v \, \Delta T$, where C_v is the molar specific heat at constant volume. However, in the present case $C_v \, \Delta T$ is the sum of two parts: (1) the contribution $C_e \, \Delta T$ to the internal energy of the gas in the form of translational energy of the molecules (C_e being a kind of external specific heat) and (2) the contribution $\epsilon \, \Delta n_2$, which is the change in internal energy due to the transfer of energy to the excited state of the molecules.   The modified adiabatic condition becomes therefore

$$\left(\frac{\epsilon \, \Delta n_2}{\Delta T} + C_e\right) \Delta T + p \, \Delta v = 0 \tag{12}$$

in which we must substitute for $\Delta n_2 / \Delta T$ from (7).   We may appropriately refer to $\epsilon \, \Delta n_2 / \Delta T$ at zero frequency as the equivalent internal molar specific heat of the gas at constant volume, or the specific heat associated with the internal degree of freedom corresponding to the excited state. We shall call this C_i, that is,

$$C_i = \frac{n_{20} k_{21}^\circ \epsilon^2 \tau}{kT^2} \tag{13}$$

The adiabatic condition then takes the form

$$p \, \Delta v + \left(C_e + \frac{C_i}{1 + i\omega\tau}\right) \Delta T = 0 \tag{14}$$

If we combine this with the general expression for $p \, \Delta v$ given by the equation of state of the ideal gas, namely,

$$p \, \Delta v + v \, \Delta p = R \, \Delta T \tag{15}$$

where R is the gas constant per mole, we can calculate, by elimination of ΔT, the ratio $\Delta p / \Delta \rho$ and hence obtain the velocity of sound in the gas. Thus the general expression for V^2 is

$$V^2 = \frac{\Delta p}{\Delta \rho} = \frac{p}{\rho}\left[1 + \frac{R}{C_e + C_i/(1 + i\omega\tau)}\right] \tag{16}$$

It is of interest to note that, for $C_i = 0$, this reduces (because of the relation $R = C_p - C_v$) to the ideal form $V^2 = \gamma p/\rho$ already discussed in Sec. 9.2.   The general expression, however, makes V^2 a complex quantity, and we have seen in Sec. 1.9 that this corresponds (for a plane harmonic sound wave of the form $\xi = \xi_0 e^{i(\omega t - \omega x / V)}$) to absorption and dispersion.   In fact we showed that if

$$V = V_r + iV_i$$

the displacement in the wave takes the form

$$\xi = \xi_0 e^{-\alpha x} e^{i(\omega t - \omega x / V_p)} \tag{17}$$

where the attenuation coefficient is

$$\alpha = \frac{\omega V_i}{|V|^2} \tag{18}$$

and the phase velocity of the wave is

$$V_p = \frac{|V|^2}{V_r} \tag{19}$$

From (16) we therefore deduce

$$\frac{2\alpha}{\omega^2} = \frac{1}{V_0} \frac{RC_i}{C_e(C_e + R)} \frac{\tau}{1 + \omega^2\tau^2} \tag{20}$$

showing that the intensity attenuation coefficient (2α) varies directly as the square of the frequency, provided that $\omega\tau \ll 1$. In the foregoing expression, V_0 denotes the limiting phase velocity for zero frequency. We also obtain

$$V_p{}^2 = \frac{p}{\rho}\left[1 + R\frac{C_i + C_e(1 + \omega^2\tau^2)}{(C_e + C_i)^2 + C_e{}^2\omega^2\tau^2}\right] \tag{21}$$

for the general expression for the phase velocity as a function of frequency. The dispersion is thus a second-order effect.

If we plot $2\alpha/\omega$ as a function of ω, the result is a curve like that shown in Fig. 12.1. The function rises from zero to a maximum at $\omega = 1/\tau$ and

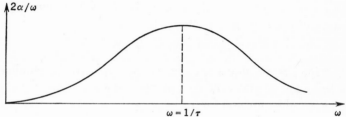

FIG. 12.1. Relaxation attenuation peak.

thereafter falls asymptotically to zero. The maximum reminds us indeed of a resonance peak, but we must be careful to recall that its physical significance is quite different, since it does not take place at one of the internal frequencies of motion of the molecular system but corresponds to the relaxation frequency or, more accurately, the reciprocal of the relaxation time. The relaxation frequency is related, as we have seen, to the average rate at which transitions to the excited molecular state occur.

The maximum value of $2\alpha/\omega$ is often of importance. We have

$$\left(\frac{2\alpha}{\omega}\right)_{max} = \frac{RC_i}{2V_0C_e(C_e + R)} \tag{22}$$

and hence (20) may be written

$$\frac{2\alpha}{\omega^2} = 2\left(\frac{2\alpha}{\omega}\right)_{max}\frac{\tau}{1 + \omega^2\tau^2} \tag{23}$$

The total specific heat at constant volume for very low frequencies (strictly in the limit of vanishing $\omega\tau$) is

$$C_v = C_e + C_i \tag{24}$$

Since $C_i \ll C_e$, we can, with sufficient accuracy, replace C_e by C_v in (22) and then use this equation to obtain C_i once $(2\alpha/\omega)_{max}$ is experimentally known.

Equation (23) is in excellent agreement with the results of experiments on diatomic ideal gases like oxygen, nitrogen, and hydrogen.[1]

12.2. Structural Relaxation in Liquids

In Sec. 12.1 we developed the general idea of a two-state relaxation process in which some translational energy of molecular motion is transferred on collision to internal molecular energy states (e.g., vibrational or rotational). Since it is simplest to refer to the energy exchange in this case in terms of external and internal specific heats, it has become usual to denote the process *thermal* relaxation. We saw that it is successful in accounting for the observed absorption of sound in gases in excess of that predicted by the classical transport mechanisms described in Chap. 9.

Thermal relaxation has also been applied successfully to certain liquids, specifically those of the nonpolar variety, such as benzene. It has not been so successful, however, in accounting for the excess absorption in polar liquids, such as water. This has suggested a search for other types of relaxation mechanisms. It is clear that the existence of any two or more kinds of energy states in a molecular aggregate between which there can take place a transfer, which in turn is affected by the passage of a compressional disturbance, will lead to a relaxation process, resulting in absorption and dispersion. One such theory, applied to water with some success by L. H. Hall,[2] has received the name *structural* relaxation, since it assumes that the liquid in question can exist in two different states of mutual molecular orientation and that the presence of sound radiation affects the average rate of transfer. Hall postulated specifically that water is a two-state liquid. The state of lower energy is the normal state, which is taken to be a somewhat loosened version of the structure of ice, shown by X-ray diffraction studies to have tetrahedral symmetry, with each water molecule surrounded by four nearest neighbors arranged at the corners of the regular tetrahedron, at the center of which the given one resides. The state of higher energy corresponds to a more closely packed structure in which the molecules have more or less the arrangement in a face-centered cubic crystal. In the ordinary undisturbed con-

---

[1] J. J. Markham, R. T. Beyer, and R. B. Lindsay, *Revs. Mod. Phys.*, **23**, 353 (1951).
[2] *Phys. Rev.*, **73**, 775 (1948).

dition there is an equilibrium between the two states, and there are, obviously, relatively few molecules in the second state. However, the passage of a compressional wave promotes the transfer of molecules from the more open state 1 to the more closely packed state 2, upsetting the equilibrium and leading to relaxational dissipation of wave energy.

Two interesting concomitants of Hall's theory for water may be mentioned briefly before we embark on the analytical details. The first is the existence for water of a *dynamical* compressibility, showing relaxation, in addition to the usual static compressibility of ordinary measurement (low- or zero-frequency case). The second is the existence of a bulk, or volume, viscosity in addition to the usual shear viscosity. The bulk viscosity is the ratio of the excess pressure in the compressional wave to the time rate of change of the density, as already mentioned in Sec. 9.11. There we saw that, in the standard fluid theories based on the usual transport properties, the bulk viscosity is set equal to zero [Stokes' relation, Eq. (9.11-23)]. However, it is basic in structural relaxation, and in Hall's theory its value for water is several times the shear viscosity.

As in Sec. 9.11, we begin the analytical treatment by setting up a dynamical equation of state. This might well be in the form of (9.11-7), in which the excess pressure is a linear function of the excess density and its time derivative. This makes the whole compression relaxational. It seems more satisfactory, however, to take the general point of view that only part of the compression is relaxational and the rest instantaneous. If we work with the condensation s $(= \rho_e/\rho_0)$, we can, for convenience, write such a combined dynamical and statical equation of state in the form

$$\dot{s} = \frac{\beta_0 p_e - s}{\eta \beta_0} + \beta_\infty \dot{p}_e \tag{1}$$

where β_∞ appears as the instantaneous compressibility and β_0 as the total adiabatic compressibility. The excess pressure is still denoted by p_e. That (1) satisfies the physical requirements adequately is clear from the fact that, if there were no relaxation, so that

$$s = \beta_0 p_e$$

β_0 would then be the same as β_∞. The equation clearly conforms to this special case. On the other hand, if the compression were entirely relaxational, so that $\beta_\infty = 0$, the equation would reduce to

$$p_e = \frac{s}{\beta_0} + \eta \dot{s} \tag{2}$$

or to the form of (9.11-7) (with s in place of ρ_e), β_0 appearing as the relaxational compressibility and η as the bulk viscosity.

We can treat (1) as a hypothesis. On the other hand, an equation of precisely this form has been derived by Meixner[1] from fundamental considerations of irreversible thermodynamics. Meixner introduces as a thermodynamical variable the concentration n of one of the components in the reaction equivalent to the change from one state to the other and puts its time rate of change directly proportional to the so-called thermodynamical *affinity*[2] $A(S,\rho,n)$, where S is the entropy. A is defined by the energy equation

$$dU = R\, dS - p\, dV - A\, dn \qquad (3)$$

If one denotes quantities in the equilibrium state in the absence of the disturbing sound field by the subscript zero, one can expand $d(n - n_0)/dt$ and $p - p_0$, respectively, in Taylor series with the initial parts (and the only ones that need be retained if the disturbance is considered small) equal to a sum of terms in $S - S_0$, $\rho - \rho_0$, and $n - n_0$. Elimination of $n - n_0$ between the two expansions leads at once to an equation of the form (1) if the adiabatic condition is invoked, that is, $S = S_0$ and $\dot{S} = 0$, and the condensation is used in place of excess density. The significant assumption in the derivation is, of course, the first-order reaction-rate equation for dn/dt. It will be recalled that a similar idea is inherent in the discussion in Sec. 12.1.

To continue with the application of (1) to a liquid, we investigate the result of supposing that p_e is harmonic in time, that is,

$$p_e = p_{e0}e^{i\omega t} \qquad (4)$$

Substitution of this into (1) yields, after a little algebra,

$$s = \left(\beta_\infty + \frac{\beta_r}{1 + i\omega\tau}\right)p_e \qquad (5)$$

where $\beta_r = \beta_0 - \beta_\infty$ and may be called the relaxational compressibility. The quantity τ is the equivalent relaxation time and is given by

$$\tau = \eta\beta_0 \qquad (6)$$

From the form of (5) we may refer to

$$\beta_\infty + \frac{\beta_r}{1 + i\omega\tau} \qquad (7)$$

as the "effective" compressibility for the liquid undergoing the relaxation process in the presence of a harmonically varying compressional

[1] J. Meixner, *Kolloid-Z.*, **134**, 3 (1953).

[2] I. Prigogine and R. Defay, "Chemical Thermodynamics," p. 38, Longmans, Green & Co., Ltd., London, 1954.

disturbance. Formally, this leads to a complex sound velocity c for which

$$V^2 = \frac{1}{\rho_0[\beta_\infty + \beta_r/(1 + i\omega\tau)]} \tag{8}$$

with

$$(V^2)_r = \frac{\beta_0 + \beta_\infty\omega^2\tau^2}{\rho_0(\beta_0{}^2 + \beta_\infty{}^2\omega^2\tau^2)} \tag{9}$$

$$(V^2)_i = \frac{\omega\tau(\beta_0 - \beta_\infty)}{\rho_0(\beta_0{}^2 + \beta_\infty{}^2\omega^2\tau^2)} \tag{10}$$

as the real and imaginary parts of V^2, respectively.

We now proceed to utilize the results of the general treatment of Sec. 1.9, where we showed that for a plane harmonic wave with complex sound velocity the attenuation coefficient in the displacement is

$$\alpha = \frac{V_i}{|V|^2} \tag{11}$$

This has already been used in the preceding section [Eq. (12.1-18)]. Since the relaxation effect is presumed to be small, that is, $\omega\tau \ll 1$, we can safely assume

$$V_i \ll V_r$$

and ultimately get

$$\alpha \doteq \frac{\omega}{2V_p} \frac{(V^2)_i}{(V^2)_r} \tag{12}$$

where V_p is, as usual, the resulting phase velocity, which in general is given by (12.1-19) but which may be replaced with sufficient accuracy in (12) by V_r and, indeed, by $V_0 = \sqrt{1/\rho_0\beta_0}$. We can therefore express the attenuation coefficient due to the relaxation process in the form

$$\frac{2\alpha}{\nu^2} = \frac{4\pi^2\tau}{V_p} \frac{\beta_0 - \beta_\infty}{\beta_0 + \beta_\infty\omega^2\tau^2} \tag{13}$$

with, of course, $\nu = \omega/2\pi$. This is a convenient general form for comparison with the classical expression for $2\alpha/\nu^2$. Since we have been led to assume that $\omega\tau \ll 1$, it seems clear that in (13) it is safe to neglect the term $\beta_\infty\omega^2\tau^2$ in comparison with β_0 and rewrite our result in the simpler form

$$\frac{2\alpha}{\nu^2} = \frac{4\pi^2\tau}{V_p}\left(1 - \frac{\beta_\infty}{\beta_0}\right) \tag{14}$$

The evaluation of the attenuation then depends on the ability to calculate the relaxation time τ and the instantaneous compressibility β_∞. The quantities V_p and β_0 may be taken directly from experimental measurements. It should be emphasized, of course, that 2α in (14) is the excess energy absorption coefficient due to the structural relaxation mechanism and must be added to the viscosity and heat-conduction absorption coefficient to get the total absorption.

The instantaneous compressibility β_∞ may be obtained by evaluating the potential energy of a water molecule due to four nearest neighbors, on the assumption that the normal structure of water has tetrahedral symmetry. We can show that, if E is the mutual potential energy of any two molecules,

$$\frac{1}{\beta_\infty} = v_m \frac{\partial^2 E}{\partial v_m{}^2} \tag{15}$$

where v_m is the volume per molecule ($= v/N$, where v is the total molar volume of the liquid and N is the number of molecules per mole). For if v_0 denotes the undisturbed molar volume and v that in the compressed state, we can expand the energy E in a Taylor's series in $v - v_0$:

$$E = E_0 + (v - v_0)\left(\frac{\partial E}{\partial v}\right)_{v_0} + \frac{1}{2}(v - v_0)^2 \left(\frac{\partial^2 E}{\partial v^2}\right)_{v_0} + \cdots \tag{16}$$

Now, since the potential energy must be a minimum for the equilibrium state, $(\partial E/\partial v)_{v_0} = 0$, and keeping only the next term yields

$$N(E - E_0) = \frac{1}{2} N(v - v_0)^2 \left(\frac{\partial^2 E}{\partial v^2}\right)_{v_0} \tag{17}$$

The term on the left is the total work done in compressing the liquid from volume v_0 to volume v. But by the definition of compressibility this is

$$-\int_{v_0}^{v} p \, dv = \frac{1}{\beta_\infty} \int_{v_0}^{v} \frac{v - v_0}{v_0} \, dv = \frac{1}{2\beta_\infty v_0}(v - v_0)^2 \tag{18}$$

Equating this result to the right-hand side of (17) at once yields (15). There are various ways of estimating E. One effective way is to use the Raman scattering at a frequency of 6×10^{12} sec^{-1}. This leads[1] to an E dependence on v of such a character that for water $\beta_\infty = 12 \times 10^{-12}$ cm^2/dyne. The total, or static, compressibility β_0 has experimental values ranging from 50.8×10^{-12} cm^2/dyne to 45.1×10^{-12} cm^2/dyne as the temperature runs from 0 to 80°C. Hence the relaxational compressibility β_r runs from 38.8 to 33.1 $\times 10^{-12}$ cm^2/dyne over the temperature range indicated. It is true that the estimates for β_∞ are not strictly definitive, since they depend on assumptions about the nature of intermolecular forces. Indeed, it is possible that once we are reasonably sure of the reliability of structural relaxation as a means of accounting for the excess sound absorption in a liquid like water, we can use the comparison with experiment as a means of checking independently on intermolecular forces. Here ultrasonics may ultimately prove to be an important tool in chemical physics.

[1] P. C. Cross, J. Burnham, and P. A. Leighton, *J. Am. Chem. Soc.*, **59**, 1134 (1937).

To obtain the relaxation time τ we evidently must return to the Kneser reaction-rate theory of Sec. 12.1 and in particular to (12.1-5). In the use of this to get (12.1-7) for Δn_2 it was assumed that ϵ, or the energy difference between the two states, is independent of temperature, whereas the change in k_{21} is due entirely to the temperature change involved in the passage of the sound wave. In the case of the liquid, however, Hall assumes that the important process taking place is the *isothermal* compression of the liquid lattice. Hence (12.1-7) must be rewritten as

$$\Delta n_2 = -\frac{k_{21}^{\circ} n_{20} \tau \Delta(\epsilon/kT)}{1 + i\omega\tau}$$

$$= \frac{-k_{21}^{\circ} n_{20} \tau (\partial\epsilon/\partial p)\,\Delta p}{kT(1 + i\omega\tau)} \tag{19}$$

where τ, as before, is put equal to $1/(k_{12}^{\circ} + k_{21}^{\circ})$. The Δp in (19) corresponds to the increase in pressure associated with the change of state from the more open to the more closely packed molecular arrangements.

We can rewrite (19) in the more useful form

$$\frac{\partial n_2}{\partial p} = -\frac{N\,\partial\epsilon/\partial p}{2kT[1 + \cosh\,(\epsilon/kT)]}\frac{1}{1 + i\omega\tau} \tag{20}$$

where N is Avogadro's number and ϵ means the energy difference *per molecule*. The complex relaxational compressibility then appears as

$$\beta' = -\frac{1}{v}\frac{\partial v}{\partial n_2}\frac{\partial n_2}{\partial p} = \frac{\beta_r}{1 + i\omega\tau} \tag{21}$$

where
$$\beta_r = \frac{1}{v}\frac{\partial v}{\partial n_2}\frac{N\,\partial\epsilon/\partial p}{2kT[1 + \cosh\,(\epsilon/kT)]} \tag{22}$$

The evaluation of the quantity $\partial\epsilon/\partial p$ requires the concept of the energy barrier between the two energy states. Figure 12.2 shows an

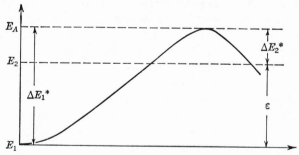

FIG. 12.2. Energy-level diagram for a two-state liquid.

energy-level diagram for the states in question. E_1 and E_2 are the respective energies whose difference $\epsilon = E_2 - E_1$ enters into the Kneser formulation being used here. But it is well known that in molecular configuration changes there is usually a potential barrier which must be surmounted before the change can take place.   This might correspond, for example, to the intermolecular bonds which must be broken in a transition between two states.   This is usually expressed by saying[1] that, in order to undergo a transition from state 1 to state 2, the system in question must get into an *activated state* and acquire an activation energy sufficient to take it from its original energy E_1 to the height of the barrier indicated in the figure as E_A.   Thus the activation energy is represented by

$$\Delta E_1^* = E_A - E_1 \tag{23}$$

Similarly, for the transition from state 2 to state 1 the activation energy is

$$\Delta E_2^* = E_A - E_2 \tag{24}$$

From the diagram it follows that

$$\Delta E^* = \Delta E_1^* - \Delta E_2^* = E_2 - E_1 = \Delta E = \epsilon \tag{25}$$

The energy E_1, which it is most convenient to treat thermodynamically as a free energy (Gibbs free energy), can be expressed as the sum of a pressure-independent part E_1' and a pressure-dependent part pv_{m1}, where v_{m1} is the volume per molecule in state 1.   Then

$$\epsilon = \Delta E = E_2 - E_1 = E_2' - E_1' + p(v_{m2} - v_{m1}) \tag{26}$$

where $$v_{m1} - v_{m2} = \Delta v_m \tag{27}$$

is the effective diminution in volume per molecule associated with the transition.   We then have, from (26),

$$\frac{\partial \epsilon}{\partial p} = -\Delta v_m = \frac{\partial v}{\partial n_2} \tag{28}$$

since $\partial v / \partial n_2$ is also the effective change in volume for each molecular transition from state 1 to state **2**.   Hence we write (22) as

$$\beta_r = \frac{N}{v} \frac{(\Delta v_m)^2}{2kT[1 + \cosh (\epsilon/kT)]} \tag{29}$$

But $N \Delta v_m = \Delta v$, the total volume change per mole, and $Nk = R = $ gas constant per mole; therefore

$$\beta_r = \frac{v(\Delta v/v)^2}{2RT[1 + \cosh (\epsilon/RT)]} \tag{30}$$

where ϵ is now the effective change of energy between states *per mole*.

The philosophy connected with (30) is simply that, if we can estimate $\Delta v/v$, our prior knowledge of β_r enables us to use the equation to compute

[1] S. Glasstone, K. J. Laidler, and H. Eyring, "The Theory of Rate Processes," p. 482, McGraw-Hill Book Company, Inc., New York, 1941.

ϵ as a function of temperature. This is the next step on the way to the calculation of the relaxation time τ.

Reverting to the special case of water, Δv represents the change in volume per mole in going from the open to the close-packed structure. If we take the open as the normal structure, we have the volume per mole of pure water as 18 cm^3 (since a mole of water has a mass of 18 g). If we assume that the close-packed state corresponds to a face-centered cubic (an arbitrary but not implausible hypothesis), the molar volume[1] is

$$v = 4 \sqrt{2} \, N a^3$$

where a is the radius of the water molecule (approximately 1.45×10^{-8} cm from X-ray studies). On this basis v comes out to be 10.4 cm^3, and therefore

$$\frac{\Delta v}{v} = 0.42$$

One can get variations on this depending on the specific crystal structure assumed. The order of magnitude, however, is not seriously affected.

The reaction-rate theory of Eyring[2] expresses k_{10} and k_{20} in terms of ΔE_1^* and ΔE_2^*, respectively. Thus

$$\begin{aligned} k_{12}^\circ &= \frac{kT}{h} \, e^{-\Delta E_1^*/RT} \\ k_{21}^\circ &= \frac{kT}{h} \, e^{-\Delta F_2^*/RT} \end{aligned} \tag{31}$$

where h is Planck's constant (6.55×10^{-27} erg-sec). Then

$$\tau = \frac{1}{k_{12}^\circ + k_{21}^\circ} = \frac{h}{kT} \frac{e^{\Delta E_1^*/RT}}{1 + e^{\epsilon/RT}} \tag{32}$$

Hall assumes that the activation energy barrier is the same for both compressive and shear viscous flow. Eyring's reaction-rate theory of shear viscosity yields the formula for the coefficient of shear viscosity η'

$$\eta' = \frac{hN}{v} \, e^{\Delta E_{\text{vis}}^*/RT} \tag{33}$$

From the assumption $\Delta E_1^* = \Delta E_{\text{vis}}^*$ we can substitute into (31) and obtain finally[3]

$$\tau = \frac{\eta' v}{RT} \frac{1}{1 + e^{\epsilon/RT}} \tag{34}$$

[1] W. P. Davey, "A Study of Crystal Structure and Its Applications," p. 409, McGraw-Hill Book Company, Inc., New York, 1934.

[2] Glasstone, Laidler, and Eyring, *op. cit.*, pp. 188ff.

[3] η' must be carefully distinguished from η, the bulk viscosity.

Knowledge of ϵ and η' as functions of T makes possible the calculation of τ as a function of T and hence the evaluation of $2\alpha/\nu^2$ in (14).

It must be confessed that the method just outlined is encumbered with numerous questionable assumptions. Nevertheless the predicted excess absorption agrees rather well with the measured values for water, particularly as regards the variation with temperature (a decrease) over the range from 10 to 80°C. It may be pointed out that the relaxation time τ is computed to vary from about 3.0×10^{-12} to 0.65×10^{-12} sec as the temperature runs through the range just indicated. The corresponding variation in the bulk viscosity $\eta = \tau/\beta_0$ is from 47 to 14 millipoises (10^{-3} dyne-sec/cm³), compared with values of shear viscosity η' of 13 to 3.5 millipoises. There has been a great deal of discussion concerning the physical meaning and validity of this very large bulk viscosity. There has been a tendency to look upon the excess absorption of sound in any fluid as due effectively to the existence of an equivalent bulk viscosity. This is questionable. It is unfortunate that as yet there is no simple method, other than sound attenuation, for confirming the existence of this viscosity.

12.3. Other Relaxation Mechanisms in Liquids

It is useful to summarize here the contents of the two previous sections with respect to the difference in emphasis involved in the nature of the relaxation mechanism. Section 12.1, though it introduced the general idea of relaxation between two energy states of the fluid particles, laid special emphasis on the dependence of the change in the number of particles in the higher energy state, brought about by the presence of the acoustic radiation, on the *temperature change* associated with the wave. We therefore referred to the process as *thermal* relaxation and expressed the concomitant absorption coefficient in terms of an equivalent specific heat connected with the transition from one energy state to another. In Hall's theory of absorption in liquids, on the other hand, the transition from one state to the other is thought of as associated with *pressure change* involved in the sound wave. Obviously we could associate an acoustically effective mechanism with the change in any thermodynamic variable, but for practical purposes it is probably sufficient to concentrate on pressure and temperature.

It was mentioned in Sec. 12.2 that thermal relaxation may explain the excess absorption in certain liquids, though it is certainly not competent to do so for water. We probably should note here the form the absorption coefficient 2α takes for thermal relaxation in a liquid; it is clear that (12.1-20) cannot apply directly, since there is no meaning to R for a liquid. (Our analysis in 12.1 was applied to an ideal gas with equation of state $pv = RT$.)   It is not difficult to generalize this equation.   Without going through the analysis, we shall state the result in the form

$$\frac{2\alpha}{\omega^2} = \frac{1}{V_0} \frac{C_i \Delta}{C_e(C_e + \Delta)} \frac{\tau}{1 + \omega^2 \tau^2} \tag{1}$$

where C_i and C_e have the same meaning as before but

$$\Delta = C_p - C_v \tag{2}$$

the actual difference between the total specific heats at constant pressure and constant volume.   This takes the place of R in the formula for the ideal gas.   For most liquids Δ is close to zero, and since C_i is small compared with the total specific heat at constant volume, the excess absorption will depend for its magnitude largely on τ.   It has been shown that one can use (1) for the excess absorption in the nonpolar liquid benzene, for example, with the choice of τ of the order of 10^{-10} sec, and this is consistent with the condition that $\omega^2 \tau^2 \ll 1$, needed to agree with the experimental constancy of $2\alpha/\omega^2$ over the experimental range studied.   This, of course, does not work for water, and this fact stimulated the search for another mechanism.

The structural relaxation excess absorption contribution [Eq. (12.2-13)] can be put into the form

$$\frac{2\alpha}{\omega^2} = \frac{\beta_r \tau}{\beta_0 V_0[1 + (\beta_\infty/\beta_0)\omega^2 \tau^2]} \tag{3}$$

which is rather similar to (1), particularly if $\beta_\infty/\beta_0 \to 1$ or β_r becomes very small.   [This is not true in Hall's theory, though the term $(\beta_\infty/\beta_0)\omega^2 \tau^2$ can be neglected compared with unity because of the smallness of τ.]

We should like to emphasize at this point that (3) is by no means restricted to structural relaxation as developed by Hall; it is more general than the treatment in Sec. 12.2 suggests.   It may be used for any mechanism involving transitions from one molecular state to another which is dependent on pressure.   Let us suppose, for example, that in the liquid in question a chemical reaction is proceeding in which the reaction rate is pressure-dependent.   Then (3) should apply.   If the reaction is also temperature-dependent, then, of course, (1) should also apply.   A possible application is found in electrolytes.   For example, sea water manifests a decided excess $2\alpha/\omega^2$ over that for pure water, which could hardly be handled by regular structural relaxation.   We would naturally refer to this as chemical relaxation.

R. W. Leonard[1] has studied absorption in sea water experimentally and has been able to show that the values of $2\alpha/\omega^2$ are consistent with the

[1] *J. Acoust. Soc. Am.*, **21**, 63 (1949).

assumption that the excess absorption over pure water is due almost entirely, not to the NaCl in sea water, but rather to $MgSO_4$. Indeed, in magnesium sulfate solutions he has shown that $2\alpha/\omega^2$ can be expressed in the form

$$\frac{2\alpha}{\omega^2} = \frac{A_1\tau}{1 + \omega^2\tau^2} + A_2 \tag{4}$$

For 0.02 M $MgSO_4$ at 25°C, Leonard's measurements yield

$$A_1 = 3.4 \times 10^{-10} \text{ sec/cm}$$

and $\tau = 1.1 \times 10^{-6}$ sec, a very much larger relaxation time than that for pure water (see Sec. 12.2). It corresponds to a relaxation frequency of about 1.43×10^5 cycles/sec with a peak in the $2\alpha/\omega$ curve at this point, well within the experimentally explorable range. Here again there is a definite contrast to pure water, for which no peak has ever been observed. Comparison of (4) with (3) indicates that $\beta_r/\beta_0 \doteq 0.5 \times 10^{-4}$, so that for the relaxation process responsible for absorption in $MgSO_4$ solutions the relaxation compressibility is a much smaller fraction of the total than in the case of structural relaxation in pure water.

L. Liebermann[1] has evaluated the relaxation compressibilities β_r associated with various types of chemical reactions, for example, the reaction

$$G \rightleftharpoons H \tag{5}$$

which is simply the reaction associated with the two-state model already discussed in the two previous sections. Hence for this the relaxation compressibility is simply given by β_r in (12.2-30). This may be rewritten in the form

$$\beta_r = \frac{v}{RT}\left(\frac{\Delta v}{v}\right)^2 \frac{n_{10}}{N}\frac{n_{20}}{N} \tag{6}$$

where N is the total number of molecules per mole (Avogadro's number). This should be clear from (12.1-4).

A somewhat similar expression results in the case of a dissociation reaction of the form

$$GH \rightleftharpoons G + H \tag{7}$$

If we denote the number of molecules dissociated by n_{20} and the number undissociated by n_{10}, we have[2] in place of (6)

$$\beta_r = \frac{v}{RT}\left(\frac{\Delta v}{v}\right)^2 \frac{n_{10}}{N}\frac{n_{20}}{N}\left(2 - \frac{n_{20}}{N}\right)^{-1} \tag{8}$$

An important test of the applicability of either of these types of chemical

[1] *Phys. Rev.*, **76**, 1520 (1949).

[2] R. Barthel, *J. Acoust. Soc. Am.*, **24**, 313 (1952).

relaxation is the dependence of $2\alpha/\omega^2$ on concentration of the solute in the electrolyte. This reduces [from (3)] to an examination of the concentration dependence of β_r and τ. Looking first at β_r, we note that we can further rewrite this as

$$\beta_r = \frac{(\Delta v)^2}{RTv} \frac{k_{21}^\circ k_{12}^\circ}{(k_{21}^\circ + k_{12}^\circ)^2} \tag{9}$$

from (12.1-3). We recall from (12.2-27) that

$$\Delta v = N \frac{\partial v}{\partial n_2}$$

It does not appear physically plausible that Δv should have much dependence on concentration.[1] On the other hand, v evidently varies inversely as the molar concentration m. The quantity $k_{21}^\circ k_{12}^\circ/(k_{12}^\circ + k_{21}^\circ)^2$ is clearly independent of concentration. It therefore results that for the unimolecular, two-state reaction (5) the relaxation compressibility should vary directly as the molar concentration. Since τ is simply $1/(k_{12}^\circ + k_{21}^\circ)$, it is independent of concentration. The total compressibility β_0 will vary only slightly with concentration. Hence the concentration dependence of $2\alpha/\omega^2$ depends almost wholly on that of β_r and should for the reaction indicated be approximately linear with m.

For the dissociation reaction (7) Barthel shows that

$$\beta_r \propto \frac{k_{21}^\circ}{k_{12}^\circ} \gamma_G \gamma_H m^2 \tag{10}$$

if the dissociation is almost complete and

$$\tau \doteq \frac{1}{k_{12}^\circ} \tag{11}$$

In (10) γ_G and γ_H are the so-called activity coefficients of the reaction.[2] If these are independent of m, it follows that for the dissociation reaction β_r is proportional to the square of the concentration. However, in a dissociation reaction like

$$MgSO_4 \rightleftharpoons Mg^{++} + SO_4^{=}$$

it has been shown that γ_G and γ_H each vary very nearly as $m^{-\frac{1}{2}}$, so that $\gamma_G \gamma_H m^2$ still varies approximately as m. The best experimental data indicate a linear dependence of A_1 in (4) on m and the independence of τ on concentration. Either type of reaction might then satisfy the demands of experiment. The unimolecular reaction (5) might in the case of magnesium sulfate solutions correspond to the transition between two different states of hydration of the $MgSO_4$ molecule in solution.

---

[1] *Ibid.*

[2] Glasstone, Laidler, and Eyring, "The Theory of Rate Processes," p. 403.

The above is only an introduction to the important role which sound-absorption measurements may ultimately play in elucidating theoretically the structure and chemical properties of liquids.

12.4. Shear Waves in Liquids.   Viscoelasticity

An ideal fluid cannot support a shear and hence possesses volume elasticity only.   Our discussion of wave propagation in fluids has therefore been limited to compressional waves which are irrotational in character and in general longitudinal, in contrast to the transverse character of shear waves in solids.   However, it was pointed out long ago by Stokes[1] that it is possible to produce a transverse wave in a viscous liquid without the presence of shear elasticity.   To see this, let us go back to the discussion in Sec. 9.11 and in particular to (9.11-21).   We limited ourselves there to dilatational stresses only.   Now let us write the equations for viscous fluid flow that correspond to (6.2-7) as well:

$$
\begin{aligned}
X_{xy} &= \eta' \left(\frac{\partial \xi}{\partial y} + \frac{\partial \dot{\eta}}{\partial x} \right) \\
X_{zz} &= \eta' \left(\frac{\partial \dot{\zeta}}{\partial x} + \frac{\partial \xi}{\partial z} \right) \\
X_{yz} &= \eta' \left(\frac{\partial \dot{\zeta}}{\partial y} + \frac{\partial \dot{\eta}}{\partial z} \right)
\end{aligned}
\tag{1}
$$

where we now denote the shear viscosity by η' to distinguish it from η, the y component of displacement of the fluid.   From (6.3-1) the x-component equation of motion now takes the form

$$
\begin{aligned}
\rho_0 \ddot{\xi} = \lambda' \frac{\partial}{\partial x} \left(\frac{\partial \xi}{\partial x} + \frac{\partial \dot{\eta}}{\partial y} + \frac{\partial \dot{\zeta}}{\partial z} \right) \\
+ \eta' \left(2\frac{\partial^2 \xi}{\partial x^2} + \frac{\partial^2 \xi}{\partial y^2} + \frac{\partial^2 \xi}{\partial z^2} + \frac{\partial^2 \dot{\eta}}{\partial x \, \partial y} + \frac{\partial^2 \dot{\zeta}}{\partial x \, \partial z} \right) - \frac{\partial p_e}{\partial x}
\end{aligned}
\tag{2}
$$

If we employ the Stokes relation (9.11-23), the above equation reduces to

$$
\rho_0 \ddot{\xi} = \eta' \nabla^2 \xi + \frac{\eta'}{3} \frac{\partial}{\partial x} \left(\frac{\partial \xi}{\partial x} + \frac{\partial \dot{\eta}}{\partial y} + \frac{\partial \dot{\zeta}}{\partial z} \right) - \frac{\partial p_e}{\partial x}
\tag{3}
$$

The corresponding y- and z-component equations become at once

$$
\rho_0 \ddot{\eta} = \eta' \nabla^2 \dot{\eta} + \frac{\eta'}{3} \frac{\partial}{\partial y} \left(\frac{\partial \xi}{\partial x} + \frac{\partial \dot{\eta}}{\partial y} + \frac{\partial \dot{\zeta}}{\partial z} \right) - \frac{\partial p_e}{\partial y}
\tag{4}
$$

$$
\rho_0 \ddot{\zeta} = \eta' \nabla^2 \dot{\zeta} + \frac{\eta'}{3} \frac{\partial}{\partial z} \left(\frac{\partial \xi}{\partial x} + \frac{\partial \dot{\eta}}{\partial y} + \frac{\partial \dot{\zeta}}{\partial z} \right) - \frac{\partial p_e}{\partial z}
\tag{5}
$$

[1] Lord Rayleigh, "Theory of Sound," 2d ed., vol. 2, p. 317, Dover Publications, New York, 1945.

Now let us assume that the fluid is disturbed by the motion of a plane parallel to the xy plane moving parallel to itself in the x direction. There is thus no motion of fluid in the y and z directions, so that $\dot{\eta}$ and $\dot{\zeta}$ vanish. At the same time, the variable quantities depend on z only. In (5), therefore, all terms vanish identically on both sides, save $\partial p_e/\partial z$. Hence, since p_e must depend on z only, it follows that p_e is constant in this motion. Equation (3) yields the whole motion, the equation for which becomes

$$\ddot{\xi} = \frac{\eta'}{\rho_0} \frac{\partial^2 \xi}{\partial z^2} \tag{6}$$

To take a relatively simple case, suppose that ξ is a harmonic function of the time with angular frequency ω. Then (6) becomes

$$\frac{\partial^2 \xi}{\partial z^2} = \frac{i\omega\rho_0}{\eta'} \xi \tag{7}$$

with the general solution

$$\xi = A \exp\left[\sqrt{\frac{\omega\rho_0}{2\eta'}} (1 + i)z \right] + B \exp\left[-\sqrt{\frac{\omega\rho_0}{2\eta'}} (1 + i)z \right] \tag{8}$$

We make the natural assumption that, for z very large positively, ξ must vanish. This means $A = 0$. Hence, incorporating the temporal dependence, we have for the physically realizable solution

$$\xi = B \exp\left(-\sqrt{\frac{\omega\rho_0}{2\eta'}} z \right) \exp\left[i\left(\omega t - \sqrt{\frac{\omega\rho_0}{2\eta'}} z \right) \right] \tag{9}$$

This corresponds to a damped harmonic wave progressing in the z direction (i.e., at right angles to the disturbance itself and therefore transverse) with phase velocity

$$V = \sqrt{\frac{2\omega\eta'}{\rho_0}} = \sqrt{2\omega\nu'} \tag{10}$$

where ν' is the kinematic viscosity ($= \eta'/\rho_0$). The attenuation coefficient is

$$\alpha = \sqrt{\frac{\omega}{2\nu'}} \tag{11}$$

which has the interesting property of being equal to the wave parameter k. Rayleigh[1] applied this analysis to the propagation of ordinary sound in air through a tube so narrow that the drag of the walls due to the viscosity is appreciable. Thus one can readily calculate the tangential force on the vibrating plane in the above example and assume that there is a similar drag on the walls of a tube. We shall not go into the details but

[1] *Ibid.*, paragraph 347.

shall merely note the result, which is that the effective attenuation coefficient for a circular cylindrical tube of radius a is

$$\alpha' = \frac{1}{2V} \sqrt{\frac{\omega \nu'}{2}} \qquad (12)$$

where V, as usual, is $\sqrt{\gamma p/\rho}$, ω the angular frequency of the sound wave, and ν' the kinematic viscosity of the air. It is also of some interest to note that the viscous drag on the walls has the additional effect of lowering the velocity of sound in the tube from V to V', where

$$V' = V\left(1 - \frac{1}{a}\sqrt{\frac{\nu'}{2\omega}}\right) \qquad (13)$$

In this section, however, we are more interested in the transverse shear waves in a viscous liquid. Examination of (11) discloses that for moderate frequency the attenuation of these waves is very high except in very viscous liquids. Thus for water with $\nu' = 10^{-2}$ poise/g-cm^3 at room temperature for a frequency of 10^3 cycles, $\alpha \doteq 800$ cm^{-1}, more commonly expressed as 800 nepers/cm. In the familiar decibel notation (see Sec. 1.10) for intensity attenuation, this corresponds to about 6.95×10^3 db/cm, a very large value indeed (recall that the decibels per centimeter corresponding to α in nepers per centimeter is $20\alpha \log_{10} e \doteq 8.69\alpha$). Even for a frequency as low as 20 cycles, α for water is in excess of 100 nepers/cm. It would therefore appear difficult to detect such waves by regular propagation techniques, since they are damped out in such a very short distance from the source. However, W. P. Mason[1] has been able to produce them by vibrating a piezoelectric crystal in a purely torsional mode, so that all the motion produced in a liquid in contact with the crystal is tangential to the surface. It then develops that the shear waves can be detected by their loading effect on the crystal (see Secs. 3.5 and 9.10). As a matter of fact, Mason has been able to use this effect as a means of measuring the viscosity of the liquid acoustically. Proceeding from the fact that the amplitude of the tangential stress on the crystal by the viscous fluid is

$$X = \sqrt{\omega \rho_0 \eta'} \qquad (14)$$

[readily obtained by differentiating $\dot{\xi}$ in (9) with respect to z] and equating this to the mechanical resistance per unit area R_M, Mason gets

$$\eta' = \frac{R_M{}^2}{\omega_R \rho_0} = \left(\frac{\Delta R_E}{K_1}\right)^2 \frac{1}{\omega_R \rho_0} \qquad (15)$$

---

[1] "Piezoelectric Crystals and Their Application to Ultrasonics," pp. 339ff., D. Van Nostrand Company, Inc., Princeton, N.J., 1950.

where ΔR_E is the increase in the electrical resistance of the crystal at resonance brought about by its radiation into the liquid and K_1 is a constant depending on the dimensions and equivalent capacitance of the crystal (see Sec. 9.9). The resonant angular frequency is ω_R. This acoustical method of measuring the viscosity of a liquid is apparently capable of considerable precision. So far the results obtained agree very well with viscosities measured with an ordinary capillary flow viscometer. There is a possibility, however, that the viscosity of some liquids may be a function of the frequency, and this would provide a very satisfactory way of ascertaining this.

Of considerable interest is the behavior of certain high-polymer liquids of very high viscosity. For these, Mason's measurements show that the attenuation α is no longer equal to the wave parameter k, as in the theory of Stokes set forth above. This behavior can be most readily explained by the assumption that the liquid exhibits shear *elasticity* as well as viscosity. Through the interpretation of the propagation properties of the liquid by means of an equivalent electric transmission line (see Secs. 9.6 and 9.9), Mason has been able to measure the equivalent shear elasticity. His book should be consulted for the details. But it is of interest to note that for polymerized castor oil the shear elasticity for frequencies in the neighborhood of 30 kc/sec is approximately 10^7 dynes/cm². This type of elasticity is found to increase with temperature. It should, of course, have an effect on the velocity of propagation, but this is difficult to detect because of the very high attenuation already emphasized.

Presumably the origin of the shear elasticity found in high polymers is associated with the long chain structure of the molecules. These chains are flexible and can exist in many configurations. In particular, in the normal unstressed state of the liquid they may be coiled up in helical shapes. The application of shearing strain may distort these shapes, and the removal of the stress may produce a corresponding transition back to the original form, with a time lag. This may be called configurational relaxation. The relaxation times tend to be rather longer than those encountered in compressional wave transmission through fluids, but in general they decrease with temperature. Thus, for a form of polyisobutylene at 50°C, Mason finds a configurational relaxation time of 3×10^{-5} sec.

12.5. Acoustic Streaming

It is a well-known fact that, associated with the periodic changes in pressure, density, and particle velocity characterizing the propagation of a harmonic compressional wave through a fluid, there are also one-directional flows, or streaming motions. Thus on the axis of a piezoelectric transducer radiating high-frequency sound into a fluid there is a steady motion of the fluid away from the transducer. In a closed vessel this is accompanied by a return current in the opposite direction along the sides of the vessel remote from the axis. A spectacular example of such a streaming motion is provided by the liquid fountain that results when a high-intensity beam of ultrasound is directed from the interior of a liquid at the free surface. Another illustration comes from the vortices which are associated with the formation of the dust piles at the nodes in a Kundt's-tube experiment for the measurement of the velocity of sound in air.

Acoustic streaming appears to be connected with the nonlinearity of the equations of fluid motion, usually neglected in wave propagation at small amplitude. We encountered in Sec. 9.17 an important consequence of this in the existence of a radiation pressure which, like the streaming motions, is a steady and nonoscillatory effect. The two phenomena are evidently closely associated. In this section we shall investigate streaming in a viscous fluid through which harmonic compressional waves pass, and establish the relation between the streaming velocity and the viscosity of the fluid, as well as the attenuation of the radiation.

In Secs. 9.11 and 12.4 we discussed the propagation of sound in a viscous fluid. We observed there that we were able to set up the fundamental propagation equations for such a medium by using a simple generalization of the relations between stress and strain in an elastic medium, as developed in Chap. 6. This generalization consists essentially in replacing the fluid displacement in the Hooke's-law relations by the flow velocity and replacing the elastic constants by appropriate coefficients, known as *viscosities*. In the treatment of the effect of viscosity on acoustic propagation we confined our attention to plane wave transmission in the x direction. We shall find it advantageous here to be more general and keep the equations in vector form. This enables us to utilize the general elastic equation (6.3-8) at once and merely rewrite it (retaining the complete acceleration term) for the viscous flow problem in the form

$$\rho[\ddot{\boldsymbol{\Delta}} + (\dot{\boldsymbol{\Delta}} \cdot \nabla)\dot{\boldsymbol{\Delta}}] = -\nabla p + \left(\eta + \frac{4\eta'}{3}\right) \nabla\nabla \cdot \dot{\boldsymbol{\Delta}} - \eta \nabla \times \nabla \times \dot{\boldsymbol{\Delta}} \quad (1)$$

where we have replaced $\boldsymbol{\Delta}$, the particle displacement vector, by $\dot{\boldsymbol{\Delta}}$, the velocity vector. The shear elastic constant μ becomes the shear viscosity η' and the bulk modulus B becomes the bulk viscosity η. We have included $-\nabla p$ on the right-hand side, since the motion of the fluid is subjected to a pressure gradient, and we have included the complete acceleration term on the right-hand side, since we are dealing with a fluid and not a solid. The justification of these steps has been fully explained in Secs.

9.11 and 12.4.   The resulting equation (1) is usually referred to as one form of the Stokes-Navier equation.

The meaning of bulk viscosity emerges clearly in (1).   If, for example, the shear viscosity were to vanish, the equation says that there is still a contribution to the net stress of the form

$$\eta \dot{\Theta}$$

since $\dot{\Theta} = \nabla \cdot \dot{\mathbf{\Delta}}$.   Hence η is the ratio of this stress to the time rate of change of the total dilatation; hence the name "bulk viscosity."

If we now make use of the equation of continuity and, for convenience, set $\dot{\mathbf{\Delta}} = \mathbf{v}$, (1) becomes

$$\frac{\partial(\rho\mathbf{v})}{\partial t} + \rho(\mathbf{v}\cdot\nabla)\mathbf{v} + \mathbf{v}\nabla\cdot(\rho\mathbf{v})$$

$$= -\nabla p + \left(\eta + \frac{4\eta'}{3}\right)\nabla\nabla\cdot\mathbf{v} - \eta'\nabla\times\nabla\times\mathbf{v} \quad (2)$$

We assume that the excess pressure p_e, the excess density ρ_e, and the flow velocity $\mathbf{v}$ can be expanded in terms of quantities of first and higher orders.   Thus

$$p_e = p_1 + p_2 + \cdots$$
$$\rho_e = \rho_1 + \rho_2 + \cdots \qquad (3)$$
$$\mathbf{v} = \mathbf{v}_1 + \mathbf{v}_2 + \cdots$$

In these expansions p_1, ρ_1, and $\mathbf{v}_1$ are first approximations to the solutions of the equations of motion and continuity and an assumed equation of state (relation between p_e and ρ_e) that vary harmonically with the time with angular frequency ω.   They are the standard small-amplitude harmonic solutions for compressional wave propagation in a viscous fluid, which we have already studied in Sec. 9.11.   The quantities p_2, ρ_2, and $\mathbf{v}_2$ are correction terms introduced by the fact that the equations we are now trying to solve are not reduced to linear form.   The complete correction term involves terms which are independent of time (see Sec. 9.17, Radiation Pressure) as well as terms which are oscillatory with angular frequency 2ω, characteristic of nonlinear behavior.   We shall confine our attention to the time-independent terms and assume that p_2, ρ_2, and $\mathbf{v}_2$ have this character.   The term $\mathbf{v}_2$ will then correspond to the streaming velocity.

Substituting (3) into (2) and averaging over the time (long compared with $2\pi/\omega$), we get

$$\rho_0\overline{[(\mathbf{v}_1\cdot\nabla)\mathbf{v}_1]} + \rho_0\overline{[\mathbf{v}_1(\nabla\cdot\mathbf{v}_1)]}$$

$$= -\nabla p_2 + \left(\eta + \frac{4\eta'}{3}\right)\nabla\nabla\cdot\mathbf{v}_2 - \eta'\nabla\times\nabla\times\mathbf{v}_2 \quad (4)$$

where the bars indicate time average and we are utilizing the fact that in the expansion of

$$\frac{\partial}{\partial t} \left[(\rho_0 + \rho_1 + \rho_2)(\mathbf{v}_1 + \mathbf{v}_2) \right]$$

we can write

$$\rho_0 \frac{\partial \mathbf{v}_1}{\partial t} = -\nabla p_1 + \left(\eta + \frac{4\eta'}{3} \right) \nabla \nabla \cdot \mathbf{v}_1 - \eta' \nabla \times \nabla \times \mathbf{v}_1$$

by virtue of the assumption that $\mathbf{v}_1$ and p_1 are first-order approximations. Also,

$$\overline{\frac{\partial}{\partial t} (p_0 \mathbf{v}_2)} = 0$$

since $\mathbf{v}_2$ is time-independent. Furthermore

$$\overline{\frac{\partial}{\partial t} (\rho_1 \mathbf{v}_1)} = 0$$

since both ρ_1 and $\mathbf{v}_1$ are harmonic functions of the time with the same frequency. It will be noted that the time derivative reduces to terms in the time of the form $\sin \omega t \cos \omega t$.

It seems physically plausible that the streaming velocity $\mathbf{v}_2$ will be a solenoidal vector.[1] Thus, (4) reduces to

$$\eta' \nabla^2 \mathbf{v}_2 = \nabla p_2 + \rho_0 \overline{(\mathbf{v}_1 \cdot \nabla \mathbf{v}_1)} + \rho_0 \overline{[\mathbf{v}_1 (\nabla \cdot \mathbf{v}_1)]} \tag{5}$$

It will be convenient to denote the sum of the two time averages in (5) by $\mathbf{F}$. If we take the curl of both sides of this equation in order to get rid of ∇p_2, the result is[2]

$$\eta' \nabla \times \nabla^2 \mathbf{v}_2 = \nabla \times \mathbf{F} \tag{6}$$

which is a linear, nonhomogeneous equation of the third order. If we use the usual vector identities governing the operation of the curl and assume that $\nabla \times \mathbf{v}_1$ is negligible (irrotational flow in the first approximation), (6) becomes

$$\eta' \nabla \times \nabla^2 \mathbf{v}_2 = \overline{\rho_0 [\nabla (\nabla \cdot \mathbf{v}_1) \times \mathbf{v}_1]} \tag{7}$$

This provides an equation for the determination of the streaming velocity, though for certain cases (5) is just as convenient (assuming that p_2 is known or can be readily determined). For the moment we proceed with (7). The solution demands a knowledge of $\mathbf{v}_1$. But since this is the

---

[1] P. J. Westervelt, *J. Acoust. Soc. Am.*, **25**, 60 (1953).

[2] This method is due essentially to Rayleigh, "Theory of Sound," vol. 2, p. 333. It has also been employed by C. Eckart, *Phys. Rev.*, **75**, 68 (1948). A good review with special applications is provided by W. L. Nyborg, *J. Acoust. Soc. Am.*, **25**, 68 (1953).

first-order solution by our original assumption, we have, from the approximate equation of motion,

$$\rho_0 \dot{\mathbf{v}}_1 = -\nabla p_1 + \left(\eta + \frac{4\eta'}{3} \right) \nabla \nabla \cdot \mathbf{v}_1 \qquad (8)$$

Similarly, the approximate equation of continuity is

$$\dot{\rho}_1 = -\rho_0 \nabla \cdot \mathbf{v}_1 \qquad (9)$$

and finally the dynamical equation of state is [see (9.11-7)]

$$p_1 = V_0^2 p_1 + R \dot{p}_1 \qquad (10)$$

where $V_0 = \sqrt{B/\rho_0}$ with B the adiabatic bulk modulus and R the relaxation constant. The use of the foregoing expressions for the first-order quantities leads to

$$\rho_0 \overline{[\nabla(\nabla \cdot \mathbf{v}_1) \times \mathbf{v}_1]} = -\overline{(\nabla \dot{\rho}_1 \times \mathbf{v}_1)}$$

By the use of the fact that

$$\overline{\dot{\rho}_1 \mathbf{v}_1} = -\overline{\dot{\mathbf{v}}_1 \rho_1}$$

and the vector formula for the curl of the product of a scalar and a vector (in this case $\dot{\rho}_1 \mathbf{v}_1$), there results

$$\overline{\rho_0[\nabla(\nabla \cdot \mathbf{v}_1) \times \mathbf{v}_1]} = \frac{1}{\rho_0} \overline{\left\{ \nabla \rho_1 \times \left[-\nabla p_1 + \left(\eta + \frac{4\eta'}{3} \right) \nabla \nabla \cdot \mathbf{v}_1 \right] \right\}}$$

and finally (7) becomes

$$\nabla \times \nabla^2 \mathbf{v}_2 = -\frac{\beta}{\rho_0^2} \nabla \rho_1 \times \nabla \dot{\rho}_1 \qquad (11)$$

where

$$\beta = \frac{\rho_0 R + \eta + \dfrac{4\eta'}{3}}{\eta'} \qquad (12)$$

It is clear that the quantity β will enter into the expression for the streaming velocity $\mathbf{v}_2$. But β is also involved in the attenuation coefficient of a plane compressional wave in the viscous fluid subject to a further relaxation mechanism with relaxation constant equal to R. In fact from Sec. 9.11 we recall [Eqs. (9.11-12) and (9.11-16)] that the total attenuation due to shear viscosity, bulk viscosity, and an additional relaxation mechanism characterized by the constant R is given by

$$\alpha = \frac{\omega^2 \beta \eta'}{2\rho_0 V_0^3} \qquad (13)$$

to the approximation that neglects $\omega^2 R^2 / V_0^4$ compared with unity. Hence there is a definite connection between the acoustic streaming velocity and the acoustic attenuation.

As a special case,[1] let us consider fluid in a tube in the form of a rectangular parallelepiped of unit width (in the z direction) and $2a$ in depth, that is, bounded by plane surfaces at $y = \pm a$. Its axis lies along the x direction. For simplicity, the bounding surfaces are not rigid but rather are considered to be films separating regions of the same acoustic properties. The reason for their existence is to provide a barrier to the streaming. It is assumed that an attenuated plane wave travels in the positive x direction. The approximate flow velocity $\mathbf{v}_1$ will then have only the component v_{1x}, which will be in the form

$$v_{1x} = v_0 e^{-\alpha x} e^{i(\omega t - kx)} \tag{14}$$

No assumption is made here as to the precise mechanism leading to the attenuation coefficient α, though it will be taken to be in the form (13), with β given by (12).

To obtain the streaming velocity we shall here employ (5) and calculate the right-hand side $\mathbf{F}$ by substitution from (14). Thus $\mathbf{F}$ has only one component, namely, F_x, which becomes

$$F_x = \overline{2v_{1x} \frac{\partial v_{1x}}{\partial x}} = -\rho_0 \alpha v_0^2 e^{-2\alpha x} \tag{15}$$

In obtaining this, we recall that we must take the real part of each factor in the product before multiplying and taking the time average. The streaming velocity $\mathbf{v}_2$ is assumed to be not only time-independent and directed along the x axis but also steady, in the sense that it is independent of x and a function of y only. For (5) we then get

$$\eta' \frac{\partial^2 v_{2x}}{\partial y^2} = \frac{\partial p_2}{\partial x} - \rho_0 \alpha v_0^2 e^{-2\alpha x} \tag{16}$$

where we have made the additional plausible assumption that p_2 is a function of x only, since the wave is assumed to travel in this direction.

The solution of (16) which satisfies the boundary conditions

$$u_2(x,a) = u_2(x,-a) = 0$$

is

$$u_{2x} = \frac{y^2 - a^2}{2\eta'} \left(\frac{\partial p_2}{\partial x} - \rho_0 \alpha v_0^2 e^{-2\alpha x} \right) \tag{17}$$

The sum in the parentheses must be independent of x and, indeed, must be a constant. If we denote the change in pressure between two points in the x axis, x_0 and x_1, by Δp_2, we can write

$$\frac{\partial p_2}{\partial x} - \rho_0 \alpha v_0^2 e^{-2\alpha x} = \frac{1}{x_1 - x_0} \left(\Delta p_2 + \int_{x_0}^{x_1} \rho_0 \alpha v_0^2 e^{-2\alpha x} \, dx \right)$$

[1] Nyborg, *loc. cit.*

Hence knowledge of Δp_2 at once yields v_{2x} in the form

$$v_{2x} = \frac{a^2 - y^2}{2\eta'(x_1 - x_0)} \left\{ \frac{\rho_0 v_0^2}{2} [1 - e^{-2\alpha(x_1 - x_0)}] - \Delta p_2 \right\} \tag{18}$$

To get an idea of the magnitudes involved, we shall take the special case in which Δp_2 is negligible compared with the other term in the braces. If the absorption is small, we can approximate the bracket term by expanding the exponential and keeping only the first two terms. The streaming velocity along the axis ($y = 0$) then has the form

$$v_{2x} = \frac{\rho_0 a^2 v_0^2 \alpha}{2\eta'} = \frac{\omega^2 a^2 \beta v_0^2}{4 V_0^3} \tag{19}$$

If we take water as an example and assume that the only attenuating mechanism is shear viscosity (actually this is not true; see Sec. 12.2), we have $\beta = \frac{4}{3}$. Suppose the intensity of 1 megacycle radiation is 1 watt/cm^2. Then v_0 is about 11.5 cm/sec. If a is taken as 1 cm, v_{2x} comes out to be around 0.4 cm/sec. The actual experimental values are higher, since β is greater than the figure just cited. Equation (19) has been used to measure β and hence the over-all attenuation coefficient for the fluid through observation of the streaming velocity.[1]

12.6. Cavitation in Liquids

In the previous section we commented on the fountain produced by an ultrasonic beam incident on the surface of a liquid from the interior. Equally striking is the effect resulting when a vessel containing a small amount of a volatile liquid like benzene is partly immersed in an oil bath in which it is irradiated by an intense ultrasonic beam; the liquid is rapidly vaporized, and the vessel fills with fog. This is believed to be due to the *cavitation* produced in the benzene by the sound, namely, the production of bubbles. Cavitation, of course, can be produced by many agencies and, in fact, by anything that causes large local changes in pressure in the liquid (e.g., propeller cavitation in ship propulsion). Ultrasonic cavitation is of two kinds: (1) if the irradiated liquid contains dissolved air or other gases, the large and rapid changes of pressure due to the sound cause the gas to come out of solution in the form of bubbles—a reaction that is often called "pseudocavitation" or "gassy cavitation"; (2) genuine cavitation, in which bubbles are still found in a thoroughly degassed liquid if the pressure changes are sufficient to overcome the tensile strength of the liquid. It seems clear that the inception of cavitation depends on the presence of nuclei on which the bubbles can form. It is at present not clear what these nuclei are. One theory assumes that

[1] H. Medwin, *J. Acoust. Soc. Am.*, **26**, 332 (1954).

in the case of liquids containing dissolved gases the nuclei are very small solid particles of foreign matter to which the gas may adhere. Another theory assumes that the nuclei are genuine gas (usually air) bubbles, too small to be seen, whose persistence despite surface tension is due to the protection of a monomolecular organic layer or skin. In the latter view the existence of a cavitation intensity threshold, well attested by experiment, is due to the fact that it takes a certain radiation intensity to break the skin so that air or other gases may diffuse into the bubble and cause it to grow. It is an interesting fact that the excess acoustic pressure amplitude necessary to produce genuine cavitation increases with the viscosity of the liquid, ranging from about 1.5 atm for liquids of very low viscosity (like carbon tetrachloride) to about 4 atm for very viscous liquids like castor oil. But the cavitation threshold for a given liquid also depends on the frequency, as seems plausible; the higher the frequency, the higher the threshold. Some experimental results[1] for ordinary tap water indicate that, whereas for a frequency of 15 kc the threshold is around 1 atm, for 0.5 megacycle it has increased to 15 or 20 atm. This suggests that one can prevent the appearance of obvious cavitation even at very great sound intensities if the frequency is high enough. This was mentioned earlier in connection with macrosonic radiation in liquids, in Sec. 9.18, where it was also recalled that cavitation plays an important role in the attenuation of sound in liquids. The scattering and effective absorption of sound by a liquid containing bubbles were treated in detail in Sec. 9.5.

Ultrasonically produced cavitation in liquids has numerous interesting consequences. At low powers, not far from the threshold, the bubbles tend to collect at the pressure nodes of a standing wave pattern and hence can be used to determine the wavelength and velocity of the radiation. At high intensity, cavitation can bring about the complete mixing of otherwise immiscible liquids, such as water and mercury, into a rather stable emulsion. This is thought to be due to the rather large forces released in the collapse of the bubbles with excess pressures of the order of magnitude of some thousands of atmospheres. Hydrodynamic streaming (Sec. 12.5) is also particularly rapid in the neighborhood of cavitation bubbles, and this also may contribute to the emulsifying action of high-intensity ultrasonics.

Certain liquids become luminescent when exposed to ultrasonic radiation, the intensity of the light being proportional to the product of the viscosity and the electric dipole moment. There are at present two competing theories for this effect. The first considers that the luminescence is due to electrical discharge through a large potential difference set up by charges produced by friction between the bubbles and the surround-

[1] L. Bergmann, "Der Ultraschall," 6th ed., p. 847, S. Hirzel Verlag, Leipzig, 1954.

ing liquid. The other treats the luminescence as essentially of chemical origin. Thus, in the collapse of a cavitation bubble, very high local temperatures can be produced, and these may be sufficient to cause ionization, with resultant emission of radiation. This theory ties in well with the fact that certain types of chemical reactions are greatly accelerated by ultrasonic radiation—for example, the formation of hydrogen peroxide in water containing dissolved oxygen or the production of free chlorine in the reaction of water with carbon tetrachloride in the presence of dissolved gases. These reactions appear to be best explained as gas phase reactions in the cavitation bubbles.

Many biological effects of ultrasound are attributed to cavitation, such as the destruction of protozoa and red blood corpuscles and the killing of small fish. The destructive action on bacteria has been applied industrially in the ultrasonic sterilization of milk.[1]

12.7. Optical Diffraction and Scattering by Sound

An interesting example of the interaction of two physical phenomena is the diffraction of light by a medium traversed by sound waves. The possibility of this is suggested by the fact that light is scattered when passing through a medium containing obstacles, that is, objects in which the velocity of light differs from its value in the medium itself. A material medium traversed by a sound wave experiences alterations in density from point to point and instant to instant, and such density fluctuations should, in principle, diffract light. It might indeed be objected that the continual variation in density at every point associated with a progressive sound wave would wash out the diffraction effect, so to speak, and that one might have to employ stationary waves with fixed nodes and loops in order to observe the phenomenon. As a matter of fact, the effect has been detected experimentally for both kinds of sound waves.[2]

In the usual experimental arrangement, intense monochromatic light from a slit is made parallel and is incident on the plane parallel walls of the container of the liquid being irradiated by the sound. The light beam is usually normal to the direction of the sound beam. After emergence from the sound cell, the light is focused by a lens on a screen and appears in the form of a series of diffraction bands or diffracted images of the slit. If we denote by θ_j the diffraction angle (in the usual optical

---

[1] The theoretical study of acoustically produced cavitation is beset with great difficulties. For recent work in this field, see F. E. Fox and K. F. Herzfeld, *J. Acoust. Soc. Am.*, **26**, 989 (1954); S. Takagi, *J. Appl. Phys.*, **24**, 1453 (1953); H. J. Naake, K. Tamm, P. Dämmig, and H. W. Helberg, *Acoustica*, **8**, 142 (1958).

[2] P. Debye and F. W. Sears, *Proc. Natl. Acad. Sci. U.S.*, **18**, 409 (1932); also R. Lucas and P. Biquard, *J. phys. radium*, **3**, 464 (1932).

sense) of the jth image from the central undeviated one, it is found that the usual diffraction law holds,[1] namely,

$$\lambda_s \sin \theta_j = j\lambda_l \qquad (1)$$

where λ_s is the wavelength of the sound and λ_l the wavelength of the light. If the frequency of the sound is known accurately, the above equation provides a precise measure of the velocity of sound in the liquid.

The sound field acts like a grating moving at right angles to the light beam with the velocity of sound. Since the latter is so much smaller than the velocity of light, it is clear that there should, after all, be no

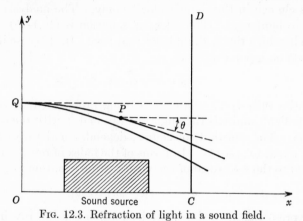

Fig. 12.3. Refraction of light in a sound field.

difficulty associated with optical diffraction by a progressive sound wave. However, it turns out that the intensity variation in the light in the various bands does not follow the same rule as for an ordinary ruled grating. Hence it will be worthwhile to summarize the treatment of Lucas and Biquard for the passage of a light ray through the sound field. In Fig. 12.3 the trace of the sound cell on the xy plane is represented by the y axis and the line CD. The light beam comes in from the left along the x axis, and the sound wave moves along the y axis. Since we expect that the optical refractive index n will vary with the excess pressure in the sound wave, we may write

$$n = n_0 + b \cos (\omega t - ky) \qquad (2)$$

Here n_0 is the index of refraction in the absence of the sound field. The parameter b is proportional to the excess pressure amplitude of the sound wave whose angular frequency is ω. Of course $k = 2\pi/\lambda_s = \omega/V$, where V is the sound velocity.

[1] F. A. Jenkins and H. E. White, "Fundamentals of Optics," 2d ed., p. 326, McGraw-Hill Book Company, Inc., New York, 1950.

Let us consider a light ray entering the cell at Q (where $OQ = y_0$). P will denote any point on the ray, which is curved in passing through the cell because of the variation in index of refraction. Since even for very high sound frequency the time taken by the light to pass through the cell is very small compared with $2\pi/\omega$, the period of the sound wave, we may approximate (2) by

$$n = n_0 + b \cos ky \tag{3}$$

Now we have already derived in Sec. 10.1 the general law of refraction for sound rays passing through a stratified medium in which there is a continuous change in the sound velocity only. The analysis is equally applicable to light rays. The relevant equation is (10.1-15) specialized to the case in which the medium itself is at rest. In this case it becomes, for all points on a particular ray,

$$c \sec \theta = \text{const} \tag{4}$$

where c is the velocity of whatever is being propagated, in the present instance the light, and θ is the angle the ray makes with the direction of propagation. The constant, of course, depends on the ray chosen and can be put equal to $c_1 \sec \theta_1$. In terms of the index of refraction, which is proportional to the reciprocal of the velocity, the equation takes the form

$$n \cos \theta = \text{const} = n_1 \cos \theta_1 \tag{5}$$

We can express this as a differential equation for the ray in terms of x and y by using (3) and the fact that

$$\cos \theta = \left[1 + \left(\frac{dy}{dx} \right)^2 \right]^{-\frac{1}{2}} \tag{6}$$

The result is

$$\left(\frac{n_0 + b \cos ky}{n_0 + b \cos ky_0} \right)^2 = \frac{1 + (dy/dx)^2}{1 + (dy/dx)_0^2} \tag{7}$$

where

$$n_1 \cos \theta_1 = (n_0 + b \cos ky_0) \left[1 + \left(\frac{dy}{dx} \right)_0^2 \right]^{-\frac{1}{2}} \tag{8}$$

Let us suppose that the incident ray is directed parallel to the x axis at Q. Hence $(dy/dx)_0^2$ is zero, and (7) becomes

$$\left(\frac{n_0 + b \cos ky}{n_0 + b \cos ky_0} \right)^2 = 1 + \left(\frac{dy}{dx} \right)^2 \tag{9}$$

Since we expect in practice that the term $b \cos ky$ will be much smaller than n_0, we can safely approximate (9) to

$$\left(\frac{dy}{dx} \right)^2 = \frac{2b}{n_0} (\cos ky - \cos ky_0) \tag{10}$$

which is the differential equation of the family of light rays. The solution depends on the quadrature

$$x = \int_{y_0}^{y} \frac{dy}{\sqrt{(2b/n_0)(\cos ky - \cos ky_0)}} \qquad (11)$$

The integral can be put into the form of the sum of two elliptic integrals[1] and, by the use of tables, y can be plotted as a function of x for each ray satisfying a given boundary condition. Plotting of a number of rays reveals that rays for which ky is initially small tend to curve in such a way that they combine to cluster around the x axis. On the other hand, rays for which ky is initially close to π tend to curve in such a way that they converge for values of ky close to $-\pi$ at a value of $kx \sqrt{b/n_0}$ equal to 6 and again at appropriately larger values. Similarly, rays for which ky has the initial value $-\pi$ converge for $ky = +\pi$. The result is that when the light is focused on a screen at some distance from the sound cell, it appears to come from sources spaced λ_s apart. If λ_s is sufficiently small, the waves from these sources interfere with each other to produce diffraction bands obeying the usual diffraction grating rule (1). The light-intensity distribution in the various bands can be calculated from the ray plot, since where many rays converge, the intensity is relatively high, etc., but the details are complicated.[2]

Although the diffraction of light by sound waves has found its principal use in the accurate measurement of the velocity of sound in liquids, it has also been adapted, with somewhat less success, to the measurement of sound absorption. The method here is based on the fact that the intensity of the light in the diffraction bands is proportional to the intensity of the sound field in the region from which the diffracted light comes.

It is of interest to note that the fact that the equivalent sound wave grating, in the case of a progressive wave, moves at right angles to the light beam with the velocity of sound V leads to the existence of a Doppler shift in the frequency of the diffracted light. Thus the source of the diffracted light in the jth order effectively moves with a component velocity $\pm V \sin \theta_j$, and hence the apparent frequency of the diffracted light will be (see Sec. 10.3)

$$\nu_j = \frac{c\nu_0}{c \mp V \sin \theta_j} \qquad (12)$$

where ν_0 is the actual frequency of the incident light. Since, from (1),

$$\frac{\nu_j V \sin \theta_j}{c} = j\nu_s \qquad (13)$$

---

[1] P. Vigoureux, "Ultrasonics," p. 62, Chapman & Hall, Ltd., London, 1950.
[2] For more details and approximate evaluation, see Bergmann, "Der Ultraschall," pp. 263ff.

where ν_s is the sound frequency, we can rewrite (12) in the form

$$\nu_j = \nu_0 \pm j\nu_s \tag{14}$$

The plus sign, corresponding to an increase in apparent frequency, prevails when the direction of sound propagation makes an acute angle with the direction of the diffracted light ray. There is a corresponding decrease in the frequency when the corresponding angle is obtuse. This Doppler shift, though small, has been experimentally observed.[1]

The diffraction of light by a single progressive sound wave naturally suggests the study of the corresponding problem when three mutually perpendicular sound beams are used. Here we should expect diffraction effects similar to those observed when X rays are diffracted by a crystal (a three-dimensional grating). This has been realized by actual experiment, and spot patterns similar to the well-known Laue spot patterns have been observed. Bergmann's book should be consulted for details.

Though the discussion in this section has been confined to fluids, there appears to be no reason why light diffraction should not take place in transparent solids through which sound radiation is passing. This has indeed been observed and has been made the basis for a very precise method of determining the elastic constants of such solids, both crystalline and amorphous. Full details will be found in the book by Bergmann, who has himself been responsible for much of the work in this field.

12.8. Ultrasonic Attenuation in Solids at Low Temperatures. Superconductivity

In Sec. 7.6 we called attention to the irreversible attenuation of elastic waves in solids, though we paid little or no attention to the detailed mechanisms which have been proposed. There is considerable interest in this problem when the solid is at very low temperature (e.g., that of liquid helium, close to 0°K), since here the attenuation in metals in particular may shed some light on the relation between the free electrons and the atomic lattice.

We recall first that the propagation of sound in the metal is ultimately due to the vibrations of the atomic lattice or, rather, to the changes produced in these vibrations by the change in equilibrium density, which in turn alters the separation distance of the atoms in the lattice. Since the metal contains a free electron gas in addition to the atomic lattice, the question naturally arises, What influence does this have on sound propagation? Certainly energy is continually passed back and forth between the electrons and the lattice, because of collisions. At ordinary temperatures (and higher) the mean free path of the electrons is so short that

[1] *Ibid.*, p. 268.

collisions are very frequent. Hence the energy transferred from the atoms to the electrons is passed back to the atoms with very little lag. We therefore expect that the interaction of electrons with the lattice will produce little noticeable effect on the absorption of sound by the metal at ordinary temperatures. However, at very low temperatures the mean free path of the electrons becomes so long that energy transfer may be expected to show a relaxation effect similar to that encountered in gases in the transfer of translational energy of molecules to internal energy states. The relaxation time will be directly proportional to the electron mean free path; and since for all kinds of relaxation processes the attenuation coefficient divided by ω^2 is in the form of a quotient in which the first power of the relaxation time τ appears in the numerator and $1 + \omega^2\tau^2$ appears in the denominator [see, for example, (12.1-20) and also (9.11-16) for the special case of viscosity], if the wavelength of the sound is large compared with the mean free path, $\omega^2\tau^2 \ll 1$, and the attenuation coefficient will be directly proportional to the square of the angular frequency ω. This suggests that the electron-lattice relaxation effect might become noticeable at high frequencies and very low temperatures, and observation appears to confirm this conjecture.

We shall follow essentially the analysis developed by Mason,[1] which treats the relaxation as associated with the viscosity of the electron gas. The kinetic theory of an ideal gas gives the viscosity in terms of the mean free path $\bar{l}$ by the formula[2]

$$\eta = \frac{nmv_m\bar{l}}{3} \tag{1}$$

where m is the mass of the molecule, n the number of molecules per unit volume, and v_m the root-mean-square molecular velocity. In the above formula the coefficient $\frac{1}{3}$ results from an approximate analysis but turns out to be more or less independent of the precise kind of distribution law for the molecules. Now, quantum statistics indicates that for temperatures up to 10,000°K the electron gas in a metal is degenerate and obeys the Fermi distribution law.[3] This leads to the following expression for the average kinetic energy per electron in the electron gas:

$$E = \frac{1}{2}mv_m^2 = \frac{3}{10}\frac{h^2}{m}\left(\frac{3n}{8\pi}\right)^{\frac{2}{3}}\left[1 + \frac{5\pi^2mk^2}{3h^4}\left(\frac{3n}{8\pi}\right)^{-\frac{4}{3}}T^2 + \cdots\right] \tag{2}$$

where h is Planck's quantum constant (6.55×10^{-27} erg-sec) and k is Boltzmann's gas constant (1.37×10^{-16} erg/°K). The second term in

[1] W. P. Mason, "Physical Acoustics and the Properties of Solids," pp. 323ff., D. Van Nostrand Company, Inc., Princeton, N.J., 1958.

[2] R. B. Lindsay, "Physical Statistics," p. 83, John Wiley & Sons, Inc., New York, 1941.

[3] Ibid., pp. 188ff. and 213ff.

the brackets is small compared with unity unless the absolute temperature T is very high. For low temperatures, such as we are considering here, it is negligible, and we content ourselves with the part outside the brackets.

The quantum statistical theory of metals leads to the following relation between the electron mean free path and the electrical conductivity:[1]

$$l = \sqrt{\frac{5}{3}} \, \frac{3h}{8\pi^2 e^2} \left(\frac{8\pi}{3n}\right)^{\frac{2}{3}} \qquad \sigma = \frac{\sigma m v_m}{ne^2} \tag{3}$$

If we combine (1), (2), and (3), the result for the viscosity is

$$\eta = \frac{h^2 \sigma}{20\pi^2 e^2} \, (3\pi^2 n)^{\frac{2}{3}} \tag{4}$$

We can at once apply (9.11-28) to write the attenuation coefficient for a plane dilatational wave in the form

$$\alpha = \frac{2\omega^2}{3\rho_0 V^3} \, \frac{h^2 \sigma}{20\pi^2 e^2} \, (3\pi^2 n)^{\frac{2}{3}} \tag{5}$$

This assumes still that $\omega^2 \tau^2 \ll 1$ for the viscosity relaxation process. It also assumes that we can neglect any presumptive bulk viscosity η. If the latter is taken into account, our previous analysis in Chap. 9 and Sec. 12.2 indicates that we must write in place of (5)

$$\alpha = \frac{\omega^2}{\rho_0 V^3} \left[\frac{h^2 \sigma}{15\pi^2 e^2} \, (3\pi^2 n)^{\frac{2}{3}} + \eta \right] \tag{6}$$

Here V is, of course, the velocity of a dilatational wave in the solid (see Sec. 6.3). For a pure shear wave in the electron gas, (6) must be still further modified to read

$$\alpha = \frac{\omega^2}{2\rho_0 V_s^3} \, \frac{h^2 \sigma}{20\pi^2 e^2} \, (3\pi^2 n)^{\frac{2}{3}} \tag{7}$$

This follows from a revamping of the analysis of Sec. 9.11 to apply to shear waves.

The interesting thing about the above expressions for the attenuation coefficient is that α is a linear function of the electrical conductivity σ, and its dependence on temperature in the low-temperature range will thus follow that of σ (the temperature dependence of the density and wave velocity is very slight in the region contemplated). Since the conductivity increases rapidly at low temperatures—and, indeed, for very pure metals increases proportionally to the fifth power of T, according to the theory of Debye—the elastic wave attenuation should follow suit.

---

[1] *Ibid.*, p. 253. Note that the factor $\sqrt{\frac{5}{3}}$ in (3) is needed to normalize l to the rms velocity v_m.

Behavior of this kind has indeed been observed in metals like lead, tin, copper, and indium, though the precise agreement between theory and experiment is much affected by impurities in the metals. Moreover, there is usually uncertainty as to the value of n, the number of free electrons per unit volume. Actually, if the theory is accepted, a combination of precise measurements of α and σ as a function of T in the low-temperature range could provide information on n, thus indicating a direct use of ultrasonic measurements for the evaluation of electronic solid-state parameters.

Perhaps the greatest interest in the electron-lattice relaxation theory of ultrasonic attenuation at low temperatures centers around the behavior of superconductors, that is, those metals whose electrical resistance appears to become vanishingly small at some finite temperature above $0°K$ (the so-called transition temperature). Although there is no completely accepted theory of this effect, it is evidently connected with the relation between the free electrons and the lattice. One plausible theory assumes that two varieties of electrons exist in the superconducting state: (1) normal electrons which exchange momentum and energy with the lattice and (2) superconducting electrons which move freely and exchange no momentum and energy with the lattice. It is supposed that, as the temperature falls below the transition temperature, the number of superconducting electrons increases relatively to the number of normal electrons. It follows from this theory that in the superconducting state the type of ultrasonic dissipation due to the interaction of electrons with the lattice and discussed above will be largely inhibited, and hence in this state the attenuation should follow the temperature-dependence characteristic of temperatures above the superconducting transition and fall as the temperature is lowered. This has been experimentally verified. It is interesting that both types of attenuation can be studied for the same superconducting specimen over the superconducting range, since the imposition of a suitable temperature-dependent magnetic field destroys superconductivity and restores normal conducting behavior. Thus it is found that, if in the superconducting range such a field is imposed on the specimen being studied, the ultrasonic attenuation immediately rises again to its relaxational value. This is shown in Fig. 12.4, which plots the measured α for dilatational waves as a function of T for lead (a superconductor) in the range from 0 to $14°K$. The frequency is 26.5 megacycles. From P down to the lowest temperature at which measurements were made, the agreement between theory and experiment was excellent. T_s is the superconducting transition temperature. The discontinuity in slope at T_s is rather sharp. In fact in certain recent measurements[1] there appears to be a discontinuity of value as well as slope for very pure indium

[1] R. W. Morse, P. Tamarkin, and H. Bohm, *Phys. Rev.*, **101**, 1610 (1956).

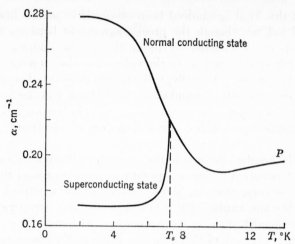

Fig. 12.4. Variation of acoustic attenuation with temperature for a superconductor. [*Reprinted with permission from R. W. Morse, Phys. Rev.*, **97**, 1716 (1955), *with certain changes.*]

at the transition temperature. The theory of this effect is not at present clear, but the relation of the phenomenon to the behavior of liquid helium II should be noted (see Sec. 12.10).

12.9. Hypersound and the Thermal Properties of Matter

In considering the transmission of elastic waves through matter and their effect on the general properties of the medium, we have had occasion to note that it is in the ultrasonic range that the most interesting effects take place. On purely physical grounds we should expect this, since at the high ultrasonic frequencies the wavelength grows small and closer to the distances separating the constituent particles of the matter; at the same time the period becomes more comparable with times (e.g., relaxation times) characteristic of molecular energy changes (recall Sec. 12.1). It is interesting to note what may be expected to be the shortest elastic waves we can expect to deal with. On any reasonable theory of elastic wave propagation we obviously cannot expect a wavelength shorter than the average distance between atoms. In fact the lower limit will really have to be double this, since if the wavelength were precisely the average interatomic distance, the atoms would all have to move in phase; but this could not correspond to the propagation of density and pressure changes. The atoms must move out of phase, and the smallest wavelength for which this can happen has its half value equal to the interatomic distance.

If we take the interatomic distance in a metal crystal,[1] for example, as

---

[1] "American Institute of Physics Handbook," pp. 2–48, McGraw-Hill Book Company, Inc., New York, 1957.

of the order of 2×10^{-8} cm and use 5×10^5 cm/sec as the order of magnitude of the velocity of a longitudinal wave in a metal, we obtain as the highest frequency of a harmonic elastic wave to be expected from these considerations

$$\nu = 1.25 \times 10^{13} \text{ cycles/sec}$$

This is of course far above any ultrasonic frequency which it has been possible to produce by any laboratory transducer.

The question arises whether there is any way either to produce practically or to detect the existence of elastic waves of this limiting frequency, which we may call *hypersound*. One immediately thinks of the higher harmonics of vibrating piezoelectric crystals. Thus the twenty-first harmonic of a 10-megacycle quartz crystal (already very thin) would put one close to the frequency stated above. But it is customarily not feasible to work above the tenth harmonic with a crystal of such a high fundamental. A basic difficulty is that, in attempting to produce elastic waves of such high frequency, one is really trying to induce ordered motion of the constituent atoms in competition with their random motion, which we call thermal agitation and which is supposed to be the origin of the thermal energy of the material. One obvious plan would be to drive the piezoelectric crystal at a very low temperature, as close to absolute zero as possible. Early in 1959, E. H. Jacobsen of the General Electric Research Laboratory in Schenectady, New York, was able to produce ultrasonic radiation of frequency 20,000 megacycles (2×10^{10} cycles/sec) in a quartz rod by employing essentially a method suggested by H. E. Bömmel and K. Dransfeld.[1] In this scheme the piezoelectric rod is placed between two reentrant microwave cavities tuned to the driving frequency and is kept at a temperature around 4°K. Practically usable ultrasonic radiation at ordinary temperatures is limited to about 1,000 megacycles.

The next question is: Can one detect the presence in a material medium of ultrasonic radiation of very high frequency by any other physical effect? The answer is yes, and we shall consider two methods: (1) the modern theory of the specific heats of solids and (2) light scattering in liquids.

The theory of specific heats of crystalline solids developed by Debye assumes that the random thermal motion of the atoms is equivalent to a set of stationary harmonic elastic waves in an equivalent continuous elastic medium. We have already seen (Sec. 3.1) that in a cube of side l at the walls of which the disturbance vanishes the normal modes have frequencies given by [Eq. (3.1-8)]

$$\nu_n = \frac{V}{2l} \sqrt{n_1{}^2 + n_2{}^2 + n_3{}^2} \tag{1}$$

[1] *Phys. Rev. Letters*, **1**, 234 (1958); **2**, 298 (1959).

where n_1, n_2, n_3 are any three integers and V is the velocity of the radiation. In Sec. 3.1 we also solved the problem of finding the number of normal modes lying in the frequency interval ν and $\nu + d\nu$. If we assume that these are continuously distributed, the result is [Eq. (3.1-15)]

$$N(\nu) \, d\nu = \frac{4\pi l^3 \nu^2 \, d\nu}{V^3} \tag{2}$$

Of course the actual distribution of normal modes is discrete and not continuous, so that (2) is only an approximation. However, Debye assumed that it would be a good starting point, at any rate. Now the total number of allowed modes is fixed by the number of particles or atoms in the cube, which we designate by N. In fact the number of modes[1] is $3N$. Hence there must be a maximum frequency ν_{max} such that if we integrate (2) from $\nu = 0$ to $\nu = \nu_{max}$, paying due regard to the fact that both longitudinal and transverse modes are present in the cube and that in any given direction two transverse modes and one longitudinal mode exist, we get $3N$. Thus

$$4\pi l^3 \left(\frac{2}{V_t^3} + \frac{1}{V_l^3} \right) \int_0^{\nu_{max}} \nu^2 \, d\nu = 3N \tag{3}$$

where V_l denotes the velocity of longitudinal waves and V_t that of transverse waves. The result of the integration is

$$\nu_{max}^3 = \frac{9N}{4\pi l^3 (1/V_l^3 + 2/V_t^3)} \tag{4}$$

This suggests at once a check on the order-of-magnitude value obtained at the beginning of this section. Let us take, for example, a cube of copper containing 1 g molecule, or mole (1 gram atom in this case, since copper is monatomic). The number N is then the Avogadro number 6.03×10^{23}. The atomic weight and density of copper are, respectively, 63.5 and 8.95 g/cm^3. The bulk and shear moduli are, respectively, 20×10^{11} and 4.3×10^{11} dynes/cm^2. Hence $V_l = 5.3 \times 10^5$ cm/sec, and $V_t = 2.19 \times 10^5$ cm/sec. Moreover, $l^3 = 7.1$ cm^3. If we insert these data into (4), the result is

$$\nu_{max} \doteq 6.75 \times 10^{12} \text{ cycles/sec}$$

in good order-of-magnitude agreement with our previous result.

We can use (4) to write the appropriately revised $N(\nu)$ in the form

$$N(\nu) = \frac{9N\nu^2}{\nu_{max}^3} \tag{5}$$

[1] This is a simple generalization of the number of modes of oscillation of a loaded string (see Sec. 4.5).

In order to use this to evaluate the specific heat at constant volume of the solid, it is necessary to calculate the total internal energy of the collection of vibrating atoms as a function of temperature. This is a problem in quantum statistical mechanics.[1]   Only the result will be given here for the specific heat at constant volume C_v, namely,

$$C_v = \frac{k}{Nm} \sum_{j=1}^{3N} \frac{(h\nu_j/kT)^2 e^{h\nu_j/kT}}{(e^{h\nu_j/kT} - 1)^2} \tag{6}$$

where ν_j is the frequency for the jth normal mode; k is here Boltzmann's gas constant, 1.67×10^{-16} erg/°K (see Sec. 12.2); and h is Planck's constant, 6.55×10^{-27} erg-sec.   The mass of the atom concerned is m.   The absolute, or Kelvin, temperature is represented by T.   Note that (6) expresses C_v as a sum over contributions from the discrete normal modes. In using (5), it is therefore necessary to replace the sum by an equivalent integral and write

$$C_v = \frac{9k}{m\nu_{max}^3} \int_0^{\nu_{max}} \frac{(h\nu/kT)^2 e^{h\nu/kT}}{(e^{h\nu/kT} - 1)^2} \nu^2 \, d\nu \tag{7}$$

If we set, for convenience, $w = h\nu/kT$, the above expression becomes

$$C_v = \frac{9k}{mw_{max}^3} \int_0^{w_{max}} \frac{w^4 e^w}{(e^w - 1)^2} \, dw \tag{8}$$

Debye introduced a so-called *characteristic temperature* Θ_D, where

$$\Theta_D = \frac{h\nu_{max}}{k} \tag{9}$$

whence
$$w_{max} = \frac{\Theta_D}{T}$$

Then (8) expresses C_v as a function of Θ_D/T or T/Θ_D.   The integration must be conducted numerically.   When it is and C_v is plotted as a function of T/Θ_D, one gets the universal curve shown in Fig. 12.5.   It may be applied to any particular crystalline solid by evaluating Θ_D.   The variation of C_v with temperature, shown in the curve, is fairly well substantiated experimentally.   In particular we can see that at very low temperature C_v would vary approximately as T^3, since under these conditions w_{max} is very large and we can approximate the integral in (8) by setting $w_{max} = \infty$ and get for its value $4\pi^4/15$.

The success of the Debye theory is a good indication, then, of the existence in a solid of high-frequency elastic waves corresponding to the

---

[1] F. Seitz, "The Modern Theory of Solids," p. 102, McGraw-Hill Book Company, Inc., New York, 1940.

actual vibratory motions of the constituent atoms. More recently, improvements have been made in this theory by calculation of the actual frequency spectrum of the crystalline solid; this has led to better agreement with observation.[1]

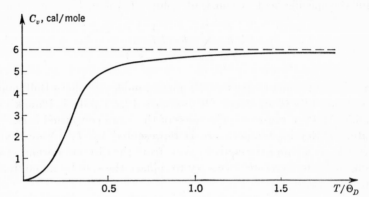

Fig. 12.5. Variation of specific heat with temperature on the Debye theory.

It is well known that light is scattered by liquids and gases. This is largely explained through the diffraction by actual suspended particles or even by collections of molecules. It has been observed, however, that a spectral line, already broadened by the Doppler effect, shows an even stronger Doppler broadening after passage through a liquid. This has been attributed[2] to the presence in the liquid of elastic waves corresponding to the propagation of density fluctuations associated with thermal motion of the molecules. We should therefore expect a change in frequency of a spectral line of the same kind as that experienced in the optical diffraction by an externally produced sound wave passing through the liquid, as discussed in Sec. 12.7. At any particular point, we can expect along any line two hypersound waves traveling in opposite directions. Hence from (12.7-13, 14) the Doppler change in frequency becomes

$$\Delta \nu = \pm 2\nu \frac{V}{c} \sin \theta \qquad (10)$$

where now θ indicates the angle of light scattering. This equation may be used to calculate the velocity V of the hypersound waves. Observations by Rao in carbon tetrachloride indicate V as some 15 per cent higher than the velocity of the normal externally produced ultrasonic radiation, whereas in acetone the figure was about 20 per cent lower. These effects are still being studied in an attempt to reach an under-

[1] N. F. Mott and H. Jones, "The Theory of the Properties of Metals and Alloys," pp. 6ff., Oxford University Press, London, 1936.

[2] L. Bergmann, "Der Ultraschall," p. 437.

standing of the difference. It seems clear, however, that we have here another indication of the existence of sound waves of frequencies of the order of 10^{12} cycles/sec.

12.10. Sound Propagation in Liquid Helium. Second Sound

In Sec. 12.8 we discussed the propagation of sound at very low temperatures. This related primarily to solids, the practically universal state of matter near absolute zero, at temperatures made possible largely by the relative ease of production of liquid helium. It is perhaps not surprising that sound propagation through liquid helium itself is of considerable interest. It is an unusual liquid which fails to solidify even at absolute zero, except under an applied pressure of 25 atm. Moreover, it undergoes a remarkable second-order phase transition at 2.18°K (the so-called λ point), where the specific heat has a discontinuity, rising abnormally high and falling off abruptly on either side. The phases above and below the point are termed, respectively, helium I and helium II. If the viscosity of helium II is observed with a capillary flow viscometer, it is found to be practically zero—for example, less than 10^{-11} poise (as compared with 10^{-5} poise for helium I). Helium II is therefore often called a superfluid. Actually, if the viscosity is measured with an oscillating disk, the value for helium II is practically the same as that for helium I. This anomalous behavior has been attributed by L. Tisza[1] to the presence in helium II of two components, a normal component like helium I and a superfluid component which can flow relative to the normal component without friction. If this view is correct, it should have an important bearing on the propagation of sound in helium II. When such a liquid is disturbed mechanically, if the two components move in phase with each other, we expect fluctuations in density and pressure, accompanied by the transmission of a compressional wave, or a sound wave in the usual sense. However, it should also be possible for the two components to move out of phase with each other by 180°. In this case, though the density and pressure will remain constant, the temperature will fluctuate, and the change will be propagated as a temperature wave, now usually referred to as "second" sound.

The details of second-sound propagation were worked out by L. Tisza,[2] but we shall present here a simplified treatment due to D. V. Gogate and P. D. Pathak.[3] The total density of helium II is thought of as made up of a contribution of the normal component ρ_n and a contribution of the

[1] C. E. Chase, *Am. J. Phys.*, **24**, 136 (1956). Much of the material of this section is taken from this source. It has an excellent bibliography.

[2] *Phys. Rev.*, **72**, 838 (1947).

[3] *Proc. Phys. Soc. London*, **59**, 457 (1947).

superfluid component ρ_s. If we call the velocity of the normal component $\mathbf{v}_n$ and that of the superfluid component $\mathbf{v}_s$, the total rate of mass flow per unit area is

$$\rho_n\mathbf{v}_n + \rho_s\mathbf{v}_s \tag{1}$$

For normal compressional waves this is different from zero; for the temperature waves that constitute second sound it is equal to zero. The kinetic energy density of the liquid is

$$K = \tfrac{1}{2}(\rho_n\mathbf{v}_n \cdot \mathbf{v}_n + \rho_s\mathbf{v}_s \cdot \mathbf{v}_s)$$
$$= \frac{(\rho_n\mathbf{v}_n + \rho_s\mathbf{v}_s) \cdot (\rho_n\mathbf{v}_n + \rho_s\mathbf{v}_s)}{2(\rho_n + \rho_s)} + \frac{\rho_n\rho_s(\mathbf{v}_n - \mathbf{v}_s) \cdot (\mathbf{v}_n - \mathbf{v}_s)}{2(\rho_n + \rho_s)} \tag{2}$$

For the case in which we are interested the mass flow per unit area vanishes, and hence K reduces to

$$K = \frac{(\rho_n + \rho_s)\rho_n}{2\rho_s} v_n{}^2 \tag{3}$$

(where $v_n{}^2 = \mathbf{v}_n \cdot \mathbf{v}_n$). The time rate of change of the kinetic energy density is

$$\dot{K} = \frac{(\rho_n + \rho_s)\rho_n}{\rho_s} \mathbf{v}_n \cdot \dot{\mathbf{v}}_n \tag{4}$$

Another expression for this quantity can be obtained by considering the transfer of heat through a layer of unit area and thickness dx. Recalling that it is only the normal fluid which carries the entropy, we have from thermodynamics

$$\dot{K} = -(\rho_n + \rho_s)S\mathbf{v}_n \cdot \nabla T \tag{5}$$

where S is the entropy per gram. Hence we can write from (4) and (5)

$$\dot{\mathbf{v}}_n + \frac{\rho_s}{\rho_n} S \nabla T = 0 \tag{6}$$

We now assume that the entropy per unit volume obeys the equation of continuity, that is,

$$\frac{\partial}{\partial t} (\rho S) + \nabla \cdot (\rho S\mathbf{v}_n) = 0 \tag{7}$$

If we eliminate $\mathbf{v}_n$ between (6) and (7), we obtain

$$\ddot{S} - \frac{\rho_s}{\rho_n} S^2 \nabla^2 T = 0 \tag{8}$$

But if the specific heat at constant pressure is C,

$$\ddot{S} = C\ddot{T} \tag{9}$$

and hence (8) becomes the wave equation in T

$$\ddot{T} = \frac{\rho_s}{\rho_n} \frac{S^2}{C} \nabla^2 T \tag{10}$$

corresponding to a temperature wave propagating with velocity

$$c = \sqrt{\frac{\rho_s}{\rho_n} \frac{S^2}{C}} = \sqrt{-\frac{\rho_s}{\rho_n} \frac{dT}{d(1/S)}} \tag{11}$$

The experimental test of this formula is still somewhat uncertain, though the general evidence so far favors it.

The velocity of normal sound in liquid helium rises from a value of about 180 m/sec at the normal boiling point (4.2°K) to a maximum of

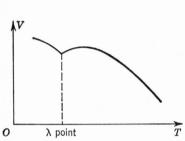

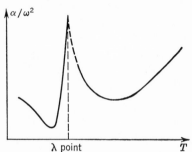

FIG. 12.6. Variation of velocity of sound in liquid helium with temperature near the λ point.

FIG. 12.7. Attenuation of sound in liquid helium near the λ point.

about 220 m/sec at 2.5°K. It then falls sharply to about 216 m/sec at the λ point and thereafter rises again as the temperature is lowered. Experimentally it seems to level off at about 239 m/sec as absolute zero is approached. The general shape of the curve is shown in Fig. 12.6. These plotted values are based largely on experimental measurements of sound of frequency in the neighborhood of 15 megacycles.

The attenuation of normal sound in liquid helium well above the λ point is completely explainable in terms of the classical transport processes of viscosity and heat conduction (Secs. 9.11 and 9.12). However, as the λ point is approached, the absorption coefficient rises sharply and a maximum is attained at the λ point. Figure 12.7 gives a rough picture of the plot of α/ω^2 as a function of temperature. The dashed part of the curve on the upper side of the λ point is not known experimentally with any accuracy. On the lower side of the λ point a minimum is reached at about 2°K, but thereafter the curve rises steeply, though it shows some signs of leveling off below 1°K. Actually, in this lowest range α/ω^2 is not independent of frequency but decreases as the frequency is raised. This suggests the presence of a relaxation mechanism. In any case, in the whole temperature range below the λ point the values of α/ω^2 are much in excess of those predicted by viscosity and heat conduction.

Several theories have been advanced for the behavior of liquid helium II. We have already noted the theory due to Landau and Tisza, which predicts the existence of second sound. The most sophisticated theory is due to Landau.[1] It is a kind of quantum hydrodynamics, in which the two principal types of motion of a liquid are quantized. Thus the motions for which a velocity potential exists and which correspond to ordinary compressional waves are quantized to *phonons*. These are the elementary quantized longitudinal waves of the Debye theory of the specific heats of solids (Sec. 12.9) closely associated with the normal modes of the mechanical radiation in a fluid in a closed space. On the other hand, Landau also visualizes in helium II the existence of quantized vortex motions, which he calls *rotons*. When helium II is disturbed, both types of motions are imagined as being excited, but only with certain allowed energy values, depending on the momentum. Thus, if the momentum of a phonon is p, the energy is given by the usual quantum relation

$$\epsilon = Vp$$

where V is the velocity of ordinary sound. For the roton the corresponding dependence of ϵ on p was chosen by Landau as

$$\epsilon = \Delta + \frac{(p - p_0)^2}{2\mu}$$

where Δ, p_0, and μ are constant parameters, whose values have been chosen to provide the best fit with measured second-sound velocity values.

[1] C. E. Chase, *Am. J. Phys.*, **24**, 136 (1956).

APPENDIX A

General Solution of the Wave Equation

The solutions of the three-dimensional wave equation by means of separation of variables as discussed in Sec. 1.8 are rather specialized, and it is therefore worthwhile to devote a little attention to a more general treatment, in which we no longer assume a solution in the form (1.8-1) but approach the problem differently.[1] We begin by expressing (1.7-14) in terms of spherical coordinates r, θ, and φ, obtaining[2] (see page 132)

$$\frac{1}{r^2}\frac{\partial}{\partial r}\left(r^2\frac{\partial f}{\partial r}\right) + \frac{1}{r^2\sin\theta}\frac{\partial}{\partial\theta}\left(\sin\theta\frac{\partial f}{\partial\theta}\right) + \frac{1}{r^2}\frac{\partial^2 f}{\partial\varphi^2} = \frac{\ddot{f}}{V^2} \tag{1}$$

Multiplying both sides of the equation by $\sin\theta\,d\theta\,d\varphi$, we integrate over the surface of a sphere of radius r about the origin as center.

The integral of the second term on the left becomes

$$\frac{1}{r^2}\int_0^\pi\int_0^{2\pi}\frac{\partial}{\partial\theta}\left(\sin\theta\frac{\partial f}{\partial\theta}\right)d\theta\,d\varphi \tag{2}$$

and this vanishes as long as $\partial f/\partial\theta$ remains everywhere finite. Similarly, the integral of the third term on the left vanishes as long as $\partial f/\partial\varphi$ is a single-valued function of φ. If we introduce the notation

$$X = \int_0^\pi\int_0^{2\pi} f\sin\theta\,d\theta\,d\varphi \tag{3}$$

which is a function of r only, (1) then gives

$$\frac{1}{r^2}\frac{\partial}{\partial r}\left(r^2\frac{\partial X}{\partial r}\right) = \frac{\ddot{X}}{V^2} \tag{4}$$

which can be rewritten in the form

$$\frac{\partial^2}{\partial r^2}(rX) = \frac{1}{V^2}\frac{\partial^2(rX)}{\partial t^2} \tag{5}$$

---

[1] The method is essentially that due to Liouville and presented in J. H. Jeans, "Electricity and Magnetism," 4th ed., pp. 521f., Cambridge University Press, New York, 1923.

[2] H. Margenau and G. M. Murphy, "Mathematics of Physics and Chemistry," p. 217, D. Van Nostrand Company, Inc., Princeton, N.J., 1943.

which is in the same form as (1.7-7) and therefore has the solution

$$X = \frac{1}{r} [g_1(Vt - r) + g_2(Vt + r)] \tag{6}$$

where g_1 and g_2 are mathematically well-behaved functions, but otherwise arbitrary.

We shall assume that X is finite at $r = 0$ for all t. Then we must have

$$g_1(Vt) + g_2(Vt) = 0 \tag{7}$$

Hence g_2 is identically the negative of g_1. If we expand the bracket term in (6) in a Taylor series about $r = 0$ and utilize (7), the result is

$$X_0 = -2 \frac{dg_1(Vt)}{d(Vt)} \tag{8}$$

where the subscript denotes that X is taken at $r = 0$. But from (3) it follows that

$$X_0 = 4\pi f_0 = -2 \frac{dg_1(Vt)}{d(Vt)} \tag{9}$$

where f_0 is the value of f at $r = 0$. Our aim now is to determine the value of f_0 at any arbitrary time t in terms of the values of f and $\dot{f}$ at time $t = 0$ on some surface surrounding the origin—for example, a sphere with the origin as center. To accomplish this, we put $g_2 = -g_1$ in (6) and differentiate rX with respect to r, getting

$$\frac{\partial}{\partial r} (rX) = -\frac{dg_1}{d(Vt - r)} - \frac{dg_1}{d(Vt + r)} \tag{10}$$

If next we differentiate rX with respect to t, we obtain

$$\frac{1}{V} \frac{\partial}{\partial t} (rX) = \frac{dg_1}{d(Vt - r)} - \frac{dg_1}{d(Vt + r)} \tag{11}$$

Adding the two preceding equations yields

$$-2 \frac{dg_1}{d(Vt + r)} = \frac{\partial}{\partial r} (rX) + \frac{1}{V} \frac{\partial}{\partial t} (rX) \tag{12}$$

which is true for all r and t. For the special case of $t = 0$ it becomes

$$-2 \frac{dg_1}{dr} = \frac{\partial}{\partial r} (rX_{t=0}) + \frac{r}{V} \dot{X}_{t=0} \tag{13}$$

which holds for all values of r. Hence it is true for $r = Vt$, so that we can further write

$$-2 \frac{dg_1}{d(Vt)} = \frac{\partial}{\partial t} (tX_{t=0}) + t\dot{X}_{t=0} \tag{14}$$

which from (9) yields

$$4\pi f_0 = \frac{\partial}{\partial t} (tX_{t=0}) + t\dot{X}_{t=0} \tag{15}$$

or

$$f_0 = \frac{1}{4\pi} \left(\frac{\partial}{\partial t} t \int_0^\pi \int_0^{2\pi} f_{t=0} \sin \theta \, d\theta \, d\varphi + t \int_0^\pi \int_0^{2\pi} \dot{f}_{t=0} \sin \theta \, d\theta \, d\varphi \right) \tag{16}$$

This means that the value of f at the point $r = 0$ (which, of course, can be any arbitrary point) at the instant t is determined solely by the *average* values of f and $\dot{f}$ at $t = 0$ on the surface of the sphere of radius Vt surrounding this point.   In other words a disturbance on the surface of the sphere at time $t = 0$ may be said to lead to a disturbance at the center of the sphere distant Vt from the surface at the later time t.   This justifies us in concluding that something has been propagated from the surface to the center with velocity V.   The disturbance which reaches the center at time t may not be precisely the disturbance which was on the surface at time $t = 0$ and, indeed, in general will not be so.   But we shall still find it convenient to call the process wave motion, just as in the case of a so-called spherical wave [Eq. (1.3-3)], and this provides a further justification for referring to (1.7-14) as a differential equation of wave motion in three dimensions.

   It should be emphasized again that, if the above results are to apply meaningfully to disturbances in a compressible fluid, the quantity f must be of the nature of a velocity potential, excess pressure, or excess density (see Sec. 9.1).   This presentation of the solution of the wave equation should be compared with that discussed in Sec. 2.4 in connection with Huygens' principle and diffraction.

APPENDIX B

Matrix Techniques in Filter Analysis

It will be recalled that the conclusions reached in Sec. 9.7 concerning finite acoustic filters were based entirely on the relations (9.7-1), which were said to be verifiable by mathematical induction. These relations can be deduced by the application of a matrix method which has considerable utility for wave-transmission problems.

We can write, following the notation of Secs. 9.6 and 9.7, for the type of filter discussed in Sec. 9.7

$$p_{j+1} = p_j \cos W - iZ\dot{X}_j \sqrt{\frac{B}{C}} \sin W$$

$$\dot{X}_{j+1} = \dot{X}_j \cos W - \frac{i}{Z} p_j \sqrt{\frac{C}{B}} \sin W$$

(1)

where B and C are given in (9.7-2), so that

$$B = \sqrt{\frac{B}{C}} \sin W$$

$$C = \sqrt{\frac{C}{B}} \sin W$$

(2)

The index j is an integer referring to the mid-point of the jth section. The content of (1) can be expressed in matrix form as follows:

$$\left\| \begin{matrix} p_{j+1} \\ \dot{X}_{j+1} \end{matrix} \right\| = \left\| \begin{matrix} \cos W & -iZB \\ -(i/Z)C & \cos W \end{matrix} \right\| \cdot \left\| \begin{matrix} p_j \\ \dot{X}_j \end{matrix} \right\|$$

(3)

This is based on the definition of matrix multiplication, which says that the product of two matrices α and β, where

$$\alpha = \left\| \begin{matrix} \alpha_{11} & \alpha_{12} & \alpha_{13} & \cdots & \alpha_{1n} \\ \alpha_{21} & \alpha_{22} & & & \\ \alpha_{31} & & & & \\ \cdot & & & & \\ \cdot & & & & \\ \cdot & & & & \\ \alpha_{n1} & & & & \alpha_{nn} \end{matrix} \right\|$$

(4)

and
$$\beta = \begin{Vmatrix} \beta_{11} & \beta_{12} & \beta_{13} & \cdots & \beta_{1n} \\ \beta_{21} & \beta_{22} & & & \\ & & & & \\ \cdot & & & & \\ \cdot & & & & \\ \beta_{n1} & & & & \beta_{nn} \end{Vmatrix} \tag{5}$$

is
$$\gamma = \alpha\beta \tag{6}$$

if
$$\gamma_{ij} = \sum_{k=1}^{n} \alpha_{ik}\beta_{kj} \tag{7}$$

In (3) the matrices $\begin{Vmatrix} p_j \\ \dot{X}_j \end{Vmatrix}$ and $\begin{Vmatrix} p_{j+1} \\ \dot{X}_{j+1} \end{Vmatrix}$ are called column matrices and the matrix containing cos W is a square matrix.[1]

Since j is *any* integer, it follows from repeated application of (3) that

$$\begin{Vmatrix} p_{n+1} \\ \dot{X}_{n+1} \end{Vmatrix} = \left\{ \begin{Vmatrix} \cos W & -iZB \\ (-i/Z)C & \cos W \end{Vmatrix} \right\}^{n} \cdot \begin{Vmatrix} p_1 \\ \dot{X}_1 \end{Vmatrix} \tag{8}$$

The deduction of (9.7-1) therefore depends on the ability to find the nth power of the square matrix. This might well be considered a tedious task. However, suppose we have a column matrix **M** and can find a square matrix **K** such that

$$\mathbf{KM} = \lambda\mathbf{M} \tag{9}$$

where λ is an ordinary number. In this case λ is called an *eigenvalue* of the matrix **K**, and the corresponding matrices **M** are called *eigenmatrices*—or, more usually, *eigenvectors*, since a vector can be represented in matrix notation as a column matrix. Since

$$\mathbf{K}(\mathbf{KM}) = \mathbf{K}\lambda\mathbf{M} = \lambda\mathbf{KM} = \lambda^2\mathbf{M}$$

and so on for higher powers, it follows that

$$\mathbf{K}^n\mathbf{M} = \lambda^n\mathbf{M} \tag{10}$$

and the process of finding the nth power of the matrix **K** is reduced to that of finding the nth powers of its eigenvalues.

We are able to rewrite (9) in the form

$$\begin{Vmatrix} \mathbf{K} - \lambda \begin{Vmatrix} 1 & 0 \\ 0 & 1 \end{Vmatrix} \end{Vmatrix} \cdot \mathbf{M} = 0 \tag{11}$$

where $\begin{Vmatrix} 1 & 0 \\ 0 & 1 \end{Vmatrix}$ is the so-called "unit" matrix; it is the *diagonal* matrix

[1] For an adequate introduction to matrix algebra, consult H. Margenau and G. M. Murphy, "The Mathematics of Physics and Chemistry," pp. 287ff., D. Van Nostrand Company, Inc., Princeton, N.J., 1943.

with unit values along the diagonal. Since our interest is confined to square matrices with four elements only (2 × 2), we may at once specialize $\mathbf{K}$ to

$$\mathbf{K} = \left\| \begin{matrix} a & b \\ c & d \end{matrix} \right\| \tag{12}$$

whence (11) reduces to

$$\left\| \begin{matrix} a - \lambda & b \\ c & d - \lambda \end{matrix} \right\| \cdot \left\| \begin{matrix} M_1 \\ M_2 \end{matrix} \right\| = 0 \tag{13}$$

where

$$\mathbf{M} = \left\| \begin{matrix} M_1 \\ M_2 \end{matrix} \right\| \tag{14}$$

Equation (13) in turn is equivalent to the two linear equations

$$\begin{aligned} (a - \lambda)M_1 + bM_2 &= 0 \\ cM_1 + (d - \lambda)M_2 &= 0 \end{aligned} \tag{15}$$

The condition that these be satisfied for M_1 and M_2 not both equal to zero is that

$$\left| \begin{matrix} a - \lambda & b \\ c & d - \lambda \end{matrix} \right| = 0 \tag{16}$$

The values of λ which satisfy this equation, that is, the quadratic

$$\lambda^2 - \lambda(a + d) + ad - bc = 0 \tag{17}$$

are the eigenvalues of the matrix $\mathbf{K}$. We thus have

$$\begin{aligned} \lambda_\alpha &= \frac{a + d}{2} + \sqrt{\left(\frac{a + d}{2}\right)^2 - (ad - bc)} \\ \lambda_\beta &= \frac{a + d}{2} - \sqrt{\left(\frac{a + d}{2}\right)^2 - (ad - bc)} \end{aligned} \tag{18}$$

Associated with λ_α is the eigenvector $\mathbf{M}_\alpha = \left\| \begin{matrix} M_{\alpha 1} \\ M_{\alpha 2} \end{matrix} \right\|$, where

$$\begin{aligned} M_{\alpha 1}(a - \lambda_\alpha) + M_{\alpha 2}b &= 0 \\ M_{\alpha 1}c + M_{\alpha 2}(d - \lambda_\alpha) &= 0 \end{aligned} \tag{19}$$

The equations for the eigenvector $\mathbf{M}_\beta$ associated with λ_β are written similarly.

We can now specialize these results to the case of the filter represented by the matrix equation (8). We have in fact

$$\begin{aligned} \lambda_\alpha &= \cos W + \sqrt{\cos^2 W - 1} = e^{iW} \\ \lambda_\beta &= \cos W - \sqrt{\cos^2 W - 1} = e^{-iW} \end{aligned} \tag{20}$$

Now in general the matrix $\mathbf{M}$ which in our case [from (8)] has the form

$$\left\|\begin{matrix} p_1 \\ \dot{X}_1 \end{matrix}\right\|$$

can be written as a linear combination of the eigenmatrices $\mathbf{M}_\alpha$ and $\mathbf{M}_\beta$. Thus

$$\left\|\begin{matrix} p_1 \\ \dot{X}_1 \end{matrix}\right\| = \alpha \left\|\begin{matrix} M_{\alpha 1} \\ M_{\alpha 2} \end{matrix}\right\| + \beta \left\|\begin{matrix} M_{\beta 1} \\ M_{\beta 2} \end{matrix}\right\| \tag{21}$$

where therefore

$$\alpha = \frac{\left|\begin{matrix} p_1 & M_{\beta 1} \\ \dot{X}_1 & M_{\beta 2} \end{matrix}\right|}{\Delta} \qquad \beta = \frac{\left|\begin{matrix} M_{\alpha 1} & p_1 \\ M_{\alpha 2} & \dot{X}_1 \end{matrix}\right|}{\Delta} \tag{22}$$

with
$$\Delta = M_{\alpha 1} M_{\beta 2} - M_{\alpha 2} M_{\beta 1} \tag{23}$$

Hence from (8) and (10) we can write

$$\left\|\begin{matrix} p_{n+1} \\ \dot{X}_{n+1} \end{matrix}\right\| = \alpha \lambda_\alpha{}^n \left\|\begin{matrix} M_{\alpha 1} \\ M_{\alpha 2} \end{matrix}\right\| + \beta \lambda_\beta{}^n \left\|\begin{matrix} M_{\beta 1} \\ M_{\beta 2} \end{matrix}\right\| \tag{24}$$

This leads to the pair of equations

$$\begin{aligned} p_{n+1} &= \alpha \lambda_\alpha{}^n M_{\alpha 1} + \beta \lambda_\beta{}^n M_{\beta 1} \\ \dot{X}_{n+1} &= \alpha \lambda_\alpha{}^n M_{\alpha 2} + \beta \lambda_\beta{}^n M_{\beta 2} \end{aligned} \tag{25}$$

which by use of (22) become

$$p_{n+1} = p_1 \frac{\lambda_\alpha{}^n M_{\beta 2} M_{\alpha 1} - \lambda_\beta{}^n M_{\alpha 2} M_{\beta 1}}{\Delta}$$
$$+ \dot{X}_1 \frac{\lambda_\beta{}^n M_{\alpha 1} M_{\beta 1} - \lambda_\alpha{}^n M_{\alpha 1} M_{\beta 1}}{\Delta}$$
$$\dot{X}_{n+1} = \dot{X}_1 \frac{\lambda_\beta{}^n M_{\alpha 1} M_{\beta 2} - \lambda_\alpha{}^n M_{\beta 1} M_{\alpha 2}}{\Delta}$$
$$+ p_1 \frac{\lambda_\alpha{}^n M_{\alpha 2} M_{\beta 2} - \lambda_\beta{}^n M_{\alpha 2} M_{\beta 2}}{\Delta} \tag{26}$$

It is now necessary to evaluate the M_α and M_β terms. The first equation in (19) becomes
$$M_{\alpha 1}(-i \sin W) + M_{\alpha 2}(-iZB) = 0$$

or
$$M_{\alpha 2} = -M_{\alpha 1} \frac{\sin W}{ZB} \tag{27}$$

Similarly,
$$M_{\beta 2} = M_{\beta 1} \frac{\sin W}{ZB} \tag{28}$$

Since the fundamental equation (9) remains true if $\mathbf{M}$ is multiplied by any constant, it is proper to take $M_{\alpha 1} = M_{\beta 1}$. Then, from (23),

$$\Delta = \frac{2 \sin W}{ZB} = \frac{2}{Z} \sqrt{\frac{C}{B}} \tag{29}$$

Finally, with the appropriate substitutions, Eqs. (26) yield

$$p_{n+1} = p_1 \cos nW - i\dot{X}_1 Z \sqrt{\frac{B}{C}} \sin nW$$

$$\dot{X}_{n+1} = \dot{X}_1 \cos nW - \frac{i}{Z} p_1 \sqrt{\frac{C}{B}} \sin nW \tag{30}$$

which is precisely equivalent to (9.7-1) and thus serves as the basis for the further development of the finite filter analysis.

PROBLEMS

Chapter 1

1. Suppose that in a linear medium directed along the x axis there are waves of velocity V traveling back and forth in both positive and negative directions, so that the resulting disturbance as a function of space and time has the form

$$\xi = f_1(x - Vt) + f_2(x + Vt)$$

where at first f_1 and f_2 do not need to be of the same functional form. Now assume that the disturbance is confined to the portion of the medium between $x = 0$ and $x = l$, so that $\xi = 0$ at $x = 0, l$. Show that both f_1 and f_2 are periodic functions of time with period equal to $2l/V$. To what physical phenomenon taking place at $x = 0, l$ does this correspond?

2. The equation of a moving plane wavefront can be written in the form

$$\alpha x + \beta y + \gamma z - Vt = C$$

Find the equation of the family of rays corresponding to this wavefront. Do the same for a diverging spherical wavefront.

3. Discuss the superposition of two plane harmonic waves $\xi_1 = A_1 \cos(\omega_1 t - k_1 x)$ and $\xi_2 = A_2 \cos(\omega_2 t + k_2 x)$ proceeding in opposite directions along the x axis. Treat in particular the special case in which ω_1 and ω_2 are very close together.

4. A harmonic source is located at $x = 0$ and drives a linear medium distributed along the x axis. The displacement of the source is given by $\xi = A e^{i\omega t}$. At $x = l$, there is a rigid barrier so that $\xi = 0$ there. Find the expression for the displacement at any point in the medium at any time.

Suppose the medium is the elastic solid rod discussed in Sec. 1.10 and that the rigid barrier is replaced by a boundary from which the incident wave is reflected with a reflection coefficient R (ratio of reflected to incident intensity). Find the condition for the maximum average transmission of wave energy along the rod.

5. A plane harmonic elastic wave progresses along a long, thin solid rod for which Young's modulus is Y, the density is ρ_0, and the wave velocity is V. The excess stress in the rod is X and is given by

$$X = A \cos(\omega t - kx)$$

What is the instantaneous displacement ξ from equilibrium at any point? If the area of cross section of the rod is S, at what average rate is energy transmitted by the wave?

6. Derive the relation

$$\alpha\lambda = \omega_i T$$

connecting the spatial and temporal attenuation coefficients α and ω_i, respectively, with the wavelength λ and the period T of a damped harmonic wave.

Show that in spatial attenuation the attenuation in a distance of one wavelength is

387

given by

$$\alpha\lambda = \frac{2\pi V_i}{V_r}$$

7. The unit for the intensity attenuation coefficient 2α in

$$w = w_0 e^{-2\alpha x}$$

is nepers per centimeter. Express the attenuation in decibels per centimeter.

8. Calculate the time averages of $\dot{f}_n{}^2$ and $\dot{f}_r\dot{f}_s$ in (1.10-37) over the time interval $2l/V$ and comment on their behavior.

9. Prove that the differential equations of the rays in a medium of index of refraction n, namely, (1.12-29), can be written as a single vector equation

$$\frac{1}{n}(l_1 \cdot \nabla)l_1 = \left[l_1 \cdot \nabla\left(\frac{1}{n}\right)\right]l_1 - \nabla\left(\frac{1}{n}\right)$$

Examine this for the special cases in which n is, respectively, a constant and a linear function of one coordinate, say x.

Show that the same results ensue by finding a complete integral of the eikonal equation (1.12-12).

10. In the establishment of the eikonal equation, examine the physical significance of the inequality

$$\frac{\nabla^2 A}{A} \ll k^2|\nabla\psi|^2$$

11. Write the eikonal equation (1.12-12) in cylindrical and spherical coordinates and discuss the solution in some special cases.

Chapter 2

1. A plane wave is incident from medium I (see Fig. P2-1) at the angle 30° and passes into medium II, for which the wave velocity is three-fourths that in I. The

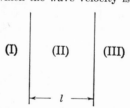

Fig. P2-1. Transmission of a plane wave through three linear media.

thickness of medium II is l. The wave then passes out of II into III, in which the wave velocity is two-thirds that in II. What is the angle of emergence into III?

How would the velocity in III have to be related to that in II so that the wavefront emerging into III would be parallel to the incident wavefront in I? Trace the corresponding rays in this case.

2. Prove by the use of Fermat's principle that the incident and reflected rays on reflection from a plane surface lie in the same plane.

3. Find the equation of the family of rays in a stratified medium in which the index of refraction obeys the law

$$n(z) = \frac{1}{\sin a(z + z_0)}$$

where a and z_0 are constants. Plot a typical ray path in the xz plane.

4. Referring to the approximate discussion in Sec. 2.3, compute the diameter of the circular orifice that will produce the first maximum effect at a distance of 2 m from O on the axis if the frequency is 1,000 cycles/sec. Also find the diameters for the first minimum and second maximum, respectively.

5. Show that the approximate argument in Sec. 2.3 can apply equally well if the orifice is replaced by a flat circular reflector of radiation. Suppose a source of harmonic radiation is located at the point P on the axis 1 m from the reflector. Calculate the diameter of the circular disk which will give the first maximum intensity at its center. Take the frequency as 1,000 cycles/sec.

6. Apply the analysis of Sec. 2.4 to the diffraction of a plane wave by a circular aperture in an infinite plane screen. This involves specialization of Fig. 2.8 to a surface consisting of the circular aperture, the infinite plane, and an infinite hemisphere enclosing the point P at which the effect of the diffracted wave is to be calculated. Moreover, (2.4-21) must be modified to correspond to a plane wave incident normally on the orifice. Show that the following integrals enter into the problem:

$$S = \iint \sin{(px + qy)}\, dx\, dy$$
$$C = \iint \cos{(px + qy)}\, dx\, dy$$

and further show that for the case of the circular orifice these lead to expressions in terms of Bessel functions. Find the radii of the first few diffraction rings.

7. Show that, if the point P in Fig. 2.7 lies outside the surface S_1, the integral over S_1 in (2.4-13) vanishes. What physical meaning does this have?

8. Prove that any plane polarized wave may be thought of as compounded of two circularly polarized waves whose amplitudes, phases, and velocities of propagation are equal. How do the two circularly polarized waves differ?

Chapter 3

1. In a linear finite medium in which wave propagation takes place subject to the condition that the disturbance $f = 0$ for $x = 0$ and $x = l$, find the expression for the disturbance at any x and t if $f_0(x) = ax + bx^2$ and $\dot{f}_0(x) = 0$. What relation must exist between a and b? Compare the average energy density in the fundamental mode and the second harmonic.

2. The medium described in Prob. 1 has zero displacement for all x at $t = 0$ but is given a velocity v at the point $x = l/2$. Find the expression for the disturbance as a function of x and t.

Hint: The imposition of velocity v at $x = l/2$ only necessitates the use of the Dirac delta function $\delta(x)$, which has a nonvanishing value at only one point on the x axis and is zero everywhere else. It is normalized in such a fashion that

$$\int_{-\infty}^{+\infty} \delta(x)\, dx = 1 \tag{1}$$

In this problem we use the property

$$\int_{-\infty}^{+\infty} \delta(x)F(x)\, dx = F(0) \tag{2}$$

where $F(x)$ is a suitably behaved mathematical function, and $\delta(x)$ has its nonvanishing value at the origin.

If the reader chooses not to use the delta function, the same results may be obtained by the use of the function

$$\frac{a}{\sqrt{\pi}}\, e^{-a^2 x^2}$$

which, when integrated over x from $-\infty$ to $+\infty$, yields unity just as $\delta(x)$ does in (1). For a sufficiently large value of a, (2) also follows.

3. Find the number of normal-mode frequencies in a cubical space of side a for which the frequency is equal to or less than $\sqrt{\frac{7}{2}}\frac{V}{a}$, where V is the velocity of the radiation. Use the reciprocal lattice as shown in Fig. 3.1. Find the nodal planes corresponding to each mode.

4. In the cubical space of Prob. 3, the medium is disturbed at point $(a/2, a/2, a/2)$ only, with a disturbance of magnitude D. The initial velocity of the disturbance is zero. Find the disturbance for any point (x,y,z) at time t. *Hint:* Use the delta function or equivalent.

5. We wish to reflect 50 per cent of the intensity of a plane wave incident normally on the boundary separating a medium I and medium II. The plane wave specific acoustic resistance for medium I is 3.9×10^{-2} g/cm²-sec. What must be the specific acoustic resistance for medium II? Try to find an actual substance which approximates this value.

6. Obtain the intensity reflection coefficient for a plane wave incident normally on the interface separating two solid elastic media in which the plane wave specific acoustic resistances are $\rho_1 V_1$ and $\rho_2 V_2$, respectively, and the attenuation coefficients are α_1 and α_2, respectively. Assume that the attenuation in the incident medium is so small as to be negligible and evaluate α_2 in terms of the reflection coefficient. Comment on the suitability of this as a means of evaluating attenuation coefficients.

7. Derive the expression for the intensity transmission coefficient through a series of three media in which I is the incident medium, II is the inserted medium (of length l), and III is the medium into which transmission takes place. The specific acoustic resistances are $\rho_1 V_1$, $\rho_2 V_2$, and $\rho_3 V_3$, respectively. Use the notation of Sec. 3.3.

Under what conditions is the transmission coefficient independent of the properties of the second medium? Under what conditions is the transmission coefficient equal to unity?

8. Apply the analysis of Sec. 3.4 to the study of a layered-medium elastic wave filter in which $l_1 = l_2 = 10$ cm and the two media are, respectively, steel and aluminum. Find in particular the frequencies ν_1 and ν_2 (Fig. 3.6).

9. Generalize the treatment of Sec. 3.4 to the case in which (for solid media) the areas of cross section of the alternate layers are not the same but are equal to S_1 and S_2, respectively. Show that in this case, the characteristic transmission function becomes

$$\cos W = \cos 2k_1 l_1 \cos 2k_2 l_2 - \frac{1}{2}\left[\left(\frac{S_2}{S_1}\right)^2 \frac{Z_2}{Z_1} + \left(\frac{S_1}{S_2}\right)^2 \frac{Z_1}{Z_2}\right] \sin 2k_1 l_1 \sin 2k_2 l_2$$

where $Z_1 = \rho_1 V_1/S_1$, $Z_2 = \rho_2 V_2/S_2$. Examine the effect of the magnitude of S_2/S_1 on the cutoff frequencies and the width of the bands.

10. A pulsating sphere (Sec. 3.5) of radius a radiates into a fluid medium of density ρ and compressional wave velocity V. Find the expression for the ratio of the average radiated power to the average mechanical power that must be delivered to the radiator to drive it without radiation at the same average velocity. Show that as the frequency increases without limit this ratio approaches the specific acoustic resistance for a plane wave divided by the mechanical resistance of the vibrating sphere per unit area of its surface. Comment on the significance of resistance matching for maximum radiation output. Apply to the case of a source of sound in a medium of low density.

11. Verify (3.6-40), (3.6-41), and (3.6-42).

12. Apply the analysis of Sec. 3.7 to a square wave pulse, as defined in (3.7-1).

13. Examine the wave pulse in a dispersive medium

$$f(x,t) = \int_{-\infty}^{+\infty} A(k) \cos(kx - \omega t)\, dk$$

where

$$A(k) = Ae^{-\beta(k-k_0)^2}$$

corresponding to a Gaussian wave packet. The quantities A and β are constants. Evaluate the integrals in (3.8-4) so as to find $R(x,t)$ and $\alpha(x,t)$ in (3.8-6). Plot the profile of the wave pulse.

Chapter 4

1. A flexible horizontal string 100 cm long with a mass of 5 g is stretched with a tension of 10^8 dynes. Find the first four harmonic frequencies of transverse stationary wave motion of the string.

The string is pulled aside at a point 25 cm from one end a distance of 0.5 cm and released. Find the amplitudes of the first four harmonics of the resulting stationary wave pattern.

Find the time average total energy of the string in each of the first four normal modes.

2. The string in Prob. 1 is struck at the point 25 cm from the end so as to give it an initial velocity there of 10 cm/sec. Answer the same questions asked in Prob. 1.

3. Prove that the total average energy for a plucked finite stretched string is the sum of the average energies associated with the individual modes.

4. A horizontal string 40 cm long of negligible mass is stretched with tension equal to the weight of 2,500 g. Three particles, each of mass 50 g, are placed at equal intervals along the string. Find the characteristic vibration frequencies of the system. Show that they agree with those given in (4.5-34). Find the normal coordinates in terms of the actual displacements of the particles.

5. A very long string stretched with a tension of 10^8 dynes and having a line density of 0.05 g/cm has inserted in it a section 100 cm long loaded with five particles, each of mass 50 g, spaced 20 cm apart. Figure P4-5 shows the situation schematically.

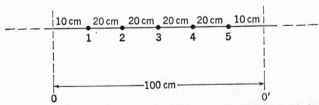

FIG. P4-5. Transmission of a harmonic wave through a finite loaded string.

A harmonic wave enters the finite filter going from left to right at O and leaves it at O'. Use the analysis of Sec. 4.5 to calculate the power transmission through the structure as a function of frequency. Plot this in terms of frequency over a sufficient range to indicate some transmission and attenuation bands.

6. Two flexible strings of length 50 cm, but having line densities of 0.1 g/cm and 0.2 g/cm, respectively, are joined together. The opposite ends are then fastened so that the resulting composite string is stretched horizontally with a tension of 10^8 dynes. Find an expression for the harmonics of this stretched string.

If the string is pulled aside a distance of 0.25 cm from its horizontal position at the junction point of the two separate strings and then let go, find the amplitudes of the first two harmonics of the resulting stationary wave pattern.

Chapter 5

1. A square membrane with surface density 0.2 g/cm² and stretched with a tension of 10^6 dynes/cm is 10 cm on a side. Find the first four normal-mode frequencies. How many normal modes lie below 700 cycles/sec?

2. A flexible circular membrane of radius a with surface density σ and stretched by fastening at the periphery with surface tension T is subject to a dissipative force $R\xi$ per unit area. Write the equation of motion for the membrane under these conditions and solve it for the case of harmonic motion. In particular, find the effect of the dissipation on the normal modes.

3. Assume that the membrane in Prob. 2 is driven by a harmonic force per unit area $F_0 e^{i\omega t}$. Find the steady-state solution in the form of $\xi(r)$ as a function of t and r. Discuss the behavior of $\xi(r)$ as the driving frequency is varied.

4. Apply the Rayleigh-Ritz method to the determination of the fundamental frequency of a circular membrane by choosing the approximation [see (5.3-32)]

$$\xi = \cos\frac{\pi r}{2a} + c\cos\frac{3\pi r}{2a} + c'\cos\frac{5\pi r}{2a}$$

where c and c' are constants.

5. In Fig. P5-5 LL' is an infinite cylindrical solid rod of radius R_1 and cross-sectional area S. It lies at the center of a rigidly mounted right circular cylinder CC' of inside

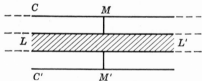

Fig. P5-5. Transmission of a harmonic compressional wave through a solid rod with a membrane as a branch.

radius R_2. MM' is a flexible circular membrane annulus, fastened along its outer edge to the cylinder and along its inner edge to the rod. The membrane is stretched with uniform surface tension T.

A plane progressive harmonic compressional wave moves along the rod LL'. Assume that this sets up in the membrane a symmetric harmonic transverse wave. Find the transmission coefficient for radiation energy in the rod across the membrane.

How could the above device be extended to provide a filter for compressional waves along the rod? What kind of filter would it be?

6. Referring to Fig. P5-5, assume that torsional waves travel along the solid rod (consult Sec. 7.3). These will give rise to a radial torsional wave in the membrane with tangential displacement η. Show that the equation of motion for such a wave in the membrane, if it is harmonic, is

$$\frac{d^2\eta}{dr^2} + \frac{1}{r}\frac{d\eta}{dr} + \left(k'^2 - \frac{1}{r^2}\right)\eta = 0 \tag{1}$$

where $k' = \omega/V'$ and $V' = \sqrt{\mu'/\rho_0'}$ and is the velocity of torsional waves in an elastic medium of shear modulus μ' and mean density ρ_0'.

Show that a solution of (1) for harmonic waves can be had in the form

$$\eta = [AJ_1(k'r) + BN_1(k'r)]e^{i\omega t}$$

where the J's and N's are the usual Bessel functions (Sec. 5.3).

Discuss the transmission of a torsional wave in the rod across the membrane.

Chapter 6

1. In a certain homogeneous, isotropic elastic medium, ξ is a function of x only, η a function of y only, and ζ a function of z only. Show that the strain matrix is the diagonal matrix D'. Also show that each deformation component is propagated as a dilatational wave with velocity $\sqrt{(B + 4\mu/3)/\rho}$.

2. Discuss the conditions under which a solenoidal spherical wave can be transverse.

3. Derive (6.3-30). Solve to find Δ_r, Δ_θ, and Δ_ϕ and discuss the significance of the fact that these components do not themselves satisfy the simple wave equation (1.7-7).

4. Prove that a plane electromagnetic wave in free space is a transverse wave.

5. Set up the equation for electromagnetic radiation in an electrically conducting medium and show that it leads to absorption. Find the absorption coefficient in terms of the conductivity.

6. Prove that for a general elastic medium the total instantaneous rate of flow of energy per unit area in the elastic radiation field is

$$[-Cs\dot{\Delta} + \mu\Delta \cdot \nabla\Delta] \cdot \mathbf{n}$$

where the notation is that of Sec. 6.4. Specialize this to the cases of a plane dilatational wave and a plane transverse shear wave, respectively.

7. Show that for a cubic crystal the three independent nonvanishing elastic constants s_{11}, s_{12}, and s_{44} are given in terms of the corresponding elastic coefficients c_{11}, c_{12}, and c_{44} by the following equations:

$$s_{11} = \frac{c_{11} + c_{12}}{(c_{11} - c_{12})(c_{11} + 2c_{12})}$$

$$s_{12} = -\frac{c_{12}}{(c_{11} - c_{12})(c_{11} + 2c_{12})}$$

$$s_{44} = \frac{1}{c_{44}}$$

8. Extend the analysis of Sec. 6.6 to a linear lattice composed of equally spaced particles alternating in mass from m_1 to m_2, as shown in Fig. P6-8. Assume that

FIG. P6-8. Linear lattice.

each particle, when disturbed from its equilibrium position, is subject to a harmonic restoring force due to its nearest neighbors only. Find the dispersion law corresponding to (6.6-9). To what sort of physical situation might this apply?

Chapter 7

1. A thin solid rod of length l with density ρ and Young's modulus Y is supported so as to be free at both ends. What are the normal-mode frequencies of the rod? How will these be altered if a particle of mass M is attached to the middle of the rod?

Hint: First solve by using the wave method to determine the longitudinal displacement for harmonic radiation in the rod on both sides of the mass M (using appropriate boundary conditions at the mass; see Sec. 4.5). Then apply the usual boundary conditions at the ends of the rod.

Solve also by estimating the increase in the effective mass of the rod as a vibrator. This may be done in the fashion of Lord Rayleigh,[1] in which the mass vibrates with the velocity corresponding to the particular normal mode. Hence calculate the total kinetic energy for a particular mode as modified by the presence of the mass M and compare with the original kinetic energy in the absence of M. This will lead to an estimate of the change in the effective mass and, since the frequency of an oscillating system is inversely proportional to the square root of its effective mass, will also lead to an estimate of the alteration in the frequency of each mode due to the presence of the mass M.

Compare the two methods.

2. Lord Rayleigh applied the second method mentioned in Prob. 1 to an estimation of the effect of the lateral motion of a rod on the natural frequencies of longitudinal vibration. Work out the details by calculating the approximate kinetic energy of lateral motion for a rod with Poisson's ratio σ, when the rod is free at both ends. Show that the effect essentially leads to a decrease in the wave velocity (as estimated from $V = \lambda\nu$) and compare with the results of the wave treatment in Sec. 7.1.

3. A thin solid rod has density ρ and Young's modulus Y, which are continuously variable. Set up the equation for dilatational wave motion in such a rod. Show that, if the variation in ρ and Y is small, the solution of the equation for harmonic displacement ξ from equilibrium can be written in the approximate form

$$\xi = \frac{A}{\sqrt{k}} \exp\left(-i \int_0^x k \, dx\right) + \frac{B}{\sqrt{k}} \exp\left(i \int_0^x k \, dx\right)$$

where $k = \omega/V$ and V is the variable wave velocity. Discuss the solution for a special case.

4. Find the group velocity associated with the dispersion relation (7.2-14) and compare it with (7.2-13).

5. Use the variation method described in Sec. 1.11 to derive the equation for flexural waves in a solid rod [Eq. (7.2-9)].

6. Derive the expression for the total energy of a circular plate vibrating in its fundamental flexural mode. Compare the average kinetic and potential energies, respectively.

7. Use (7.5-24) to find the velocity of Rayleigh waves in a copper plate.

8. Examine from tables the nature of the product of the logarithmic decrement of a solid rod and Young's modulus for a number of materials. Find the dependence of the dissipation coefficient α on the frequency for such materials.

Chapter 8

1. Show that even in nonirrotational steady flow of a fluid, Bernoulli's theorem holds along any particular streamline.

[1] "Theory of Sound," 2d ed., vol. 1, p. 249, Dover Publications, 1945.

2. Evaluate $C(t)$ in (8.1-11) for the special case of a diverging harmonic spherical wave for which φ has the form

$$\varphi = \frac{A}{r} \cos (\omega t - kr)$$

3. Find the group velocity corresponding to the general dispersion relation (8.2-17).

4. When a ship moves through the water and creates the commonly observed train of gravity waves in its wake, the radiation exerts a resistance on the ship. Show that the average resisting force R is given by

$$R = \frac{k\rho A^2}{8} \left(1 - \frac{2kh}{\sinh 2kh} \right) \sinh 2kh$$

where A is the amplitude constant in the expression (8.2-16) for the velocity potential and the other symbols are those used in Chap. 8.

What happens when the speed of the ship exceeds $\sqrt{gh}$?

5. Assume that a gravity wave in water starts out with a sine wave profile of the form

$$\eta = A \sin (\omega t - kx)$$

Trace graphically and in some detail the effect on this of a velocity dependence on η as given in (8.3-3).

6. Examine magnetohydrodynamic waves for their solenoidal or irrotational character. Calculate their velocity in water for a steady magnetic field intensity of 10^4 oersteds.

Chapter 9

1. A plane harmonic acoustic wave in the x direction has flow velocity in the form

$$\xi = A \cos (\omega t - kx)$$

Find the expressions for the velocity potential φ, the condensation s, and the excess pressure p_e. If the frequency is 1,000 cycles/sec and the wave is in air at 20°C, find A if the excess pressure amplitude is 10^{-1} dyne/cm^2. Also find the condensation amplitude.

2. Using the data supplied and computed in Prob. 1, calculate the magnitude of the term $\mathbf{v} \cdot \nabla \mathbf{v}$ neglected in the use of the hydrodynamical equation of motion in the derivation of the wave equation. Find the percentage error involved in the neglect.

3. The Beattie-Bridgeman equation of state for gases has the following form:

$$pv^2 = RT \left(1 - \frac{c}{vT^3} \right) \left(v + B_0 - \frac{bB_0}{v} \right) - A_0 \left(1 - \frac{a}{v} \right)$$

where A_0, B_0, a, b, and c are constants for a given gas; v is the molar volume; and R is the gas constant per mole. The pressure is given in atmospheres.

Derive the expression for the velocity of sound in such a gas. Evaluate it numerically for the case of ammonia, for which

$$A_0 = 2.393 \qquad a = 0.1703 \qquad B_0 = 0.0342 \qquad b = 0.0191 \qquad c \times 10^{-4} = 476.87$$

4. An approximate equation of state for liquids can be put in the form[1]

$$pv^3 = F(S)$$

[1] J. O. Hirschfelder, C. F. Curtiss, and R. B. Bird, "Molecular Theory of Gases and Liquids," p. 262, John Wiley & Sons, Inc., New York, 1959.

where S is the entropy per mole and

$$F(S) = A(S)[v(0,S)]^3$$

Here $A(S)$ is the Helmholtz free energy as a function of entropy and $v(0,S)$ is the molar volume at very low pressure, also as a function of entropy. Recalling the assumed adiabatic character of sound propagation, derive the expression for the velocity of sound in a liquid with this equation of state and show that it is directly proportional to the pressure.

5. A plane harmonic progressive sound wave of frequency 1,000 cycles/sec passes through air. If the maximum excess pressure is 10^{-1} dyne/cm², calculate the intensity of the wave. What is the average energy density? What is the decibel value of the intensity with respect to the audible threshold, corresponding to a maximum excess pressure of 7×10^{-4} dyne/cm² at this frequency? If the wave is confined to a tube of diameter 5 cm, what is the acoustic impedance?

6. A spherical harmonic wave of frequency 500 cycles/sec diverging from a point source in air has a velocity potential amplitude of 1 cm²/sec at 1 cm from the source. Find the excess pressure amplitude 10 cm from the source. Also find the specific acoustic resistance and the specific acoustic reactance at 10 cm and 100 cm from the source, respectively. Comment on the physical significance of the results. What is the intensity of the wave 100 cm from the source? What is the total power output of the source in watts?

7. In Prob. 6, find the decibel difference between the intensities at 10 cm and 100 cm from the source. How far from the source will the intensity be reduced to the minimum audible (neglecting dissipative absorption)?

8. A plane sound wave passes from left to right through a cylindrical tube whose area of cross section varies from S_1 to S_2 to S_3, as indicated in Fig. P9-8. Find the

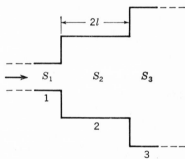

Fig. P9-8. Transmission of sound through a series of cylindrical tubes of increasing cross section.

expression for the acoustic impedance at 3 (neglecting any orifice effect) in terms of the impedance at 1. By the use of appropriate boundary conditions, determine the normal modes of the structure. In what sense does the structure behave like a horn?

9. A plane wave of sound in dry air is incident on a fog bank in which the mean equilibrium density is 1 per cent less than that of dry air. Calculate the critical angle. If the angle of incidence is 60°, calculate the ratio of the reflected intensity to the incident intensity.

10. A horizontal layer of water of thickness l lies on the surface of mercury (sound velocity = 1,407 m/sec, and density = 13.6 g/cm³) with its top surface exposed to air.

Compute the power transmission P_r for plane harmonic sound waves progressing from mercury to air through the water layer at normal incidence.

Work the same problem for a sound wavefront incident at an angle of 30° to the mercury-water interface.

11. Show by a direct analysis of the radial vibrations of a spherical bubble of gas of equilibrium radius a in a liquid of mean density ρ_0 that the resonance frequency of the bubble is

$$\nu = \frac{1}{2\pi a} \sqrt{\frac{3\gamma p_0}{\rho_0}}$$

where p_0 is the mean equilibrium pressure and γ the specific-heat ratio of the gas inside the bubble.

12. A low-pass acoustic filter has a main line with cross-sectional area $= 9\pi/16$ cm^2. The branches are Helmholtz resonators separated by equal intervals of 1.67 cm. The volume of each resonator chamber is 4.36 cm^3, and the acoustic conductivity of the opening to each resonator is 2.26 cm. Plot the cos W curve for the equivalent infinite filter from 0 to 10,000 cycles. In particular, find by direct calculation the frequency limits of the first attenuation region.

13. If the filter in Prob. 12 is finite and consists of 4 sections inserted in an infinite conduit of area of cross section $9\pi/16$ cm^2, find the frequencies in the first transmission band for which P_r is unity. Calculate the transmission ratio P_r for 4,000 cycles and comment on the significance of the result.

14. Plot the specific radiation resistance and the specific radiation reactance as a function of frequency for a flat circular plate of radius 10 cm vibrating as an equivalent piston in water. Plot for every 1,000 cycles/sec from zero to 10,000 cycles/sec and for every 5,000 cycles/sec from 10,000 to 50,000 cycles/sec. If the maximum displacement velocity at the surface of the plate is 10^{-1} cm/sec, calculate the maximum excess pressure there due to the radiation at frequencies of 1,000 and 20,000 cycles/sec, respectively. What is the intensity of the radiation on a line perpendicular to the plate through its center and 10 m from the center?

15. A plane harmonic wave of frequency 1,000 cycles traverses water. How far will it travel before its amplitude is diminished in the ratio 1 to e, assuming viscous damping only? Work the same problem if the frequency is 20,000 cycles. How will the results change if the medium is air?

16. Calculate the relaxation times due to heat conduction for sound absorption in air and water, respectively. Compare with the corresponding values due to viscosity. What conclusion can you draw?

17. From tables of the properties of water, evaluate P and Q in (9.13-18) for water. Hence estimate the departure from linear conditions in the transmission of high-intensity sound in water for which $|\partial\xi/\partial a|$ is of the order of 10^{-2}.

18. Extend the treatment in Sec. 9.13 to high-intensity cylindrical waves. Specifically, find the cylindrical wave equation corresponding to the spherical wave equation (9.13-43). Go over to the standard Lagrangian form and find the cylindrical wave equation corresponding to (9.13-38).

Chapter 10

1. In an isothermal atmosphere, the wind velocity is parallel to the ground and has the constant velocity 1.5 m/sec up to a height of 10 m. Thereafter it increases at the constant rate of 0.1 m/sec-m to a height of 100 m. Find the equation of a sound ray that begins at a source on the ground and makes an initial angle of 60° with the horizontal.

2. In a still atmosphere a temperature inversion exists; that is, the temperature first increases at a constant rate up to height h, stays constant from h_1 to h_2, and thereafter decreases. Sketch the path of a ray of sound that is emitted initially in the vertical direction.

3. Discuss the solution of (10.1-35) by means of elliptic functions.

4. A vertical vortex like that discussed in Sec. 10.1 and having a strength of 10^5 cm^2/sec has a center O which moves parallel to the line joining two microphones 5 m apart and separated from this line by 10 m. The velocity of the center is 1 m/sec. The air is at 20°C. Trace the change in the phase at the microphones for a harmonic sound wavefront (frequency = 200 cycles/sec) originally parallel to the line joining the microphones, as brought about by the motion of O as it moves in from the extreme left and moves off to the extreme right.

5. How will the fundamental Doppler shift (10.2-51) be modified to a first approximation when viscosity and heat conduction are considered?

6. It is desired to determine the height above the ground and the speed (assumed constant) of a sound-producing object by an observation of the Doppler effect at a single station on the ground. Can this be done? If so, how?

7. A point source of sound with a frequency of 500 cycles and an acoustical power output of 1 watt is placed 5 m below the surface of sea water. Find the maximum excess pressure and the intensity at a point 50 m below the surface. At what frequency would this intensity be doubled? (Dissipative effects are disregarded.)

8. A point source of sound lies in water at a distance below the surface much smaller than the wavelength of the emitted sound, which corresponds to a frequency of 15 kc. If the acoustical output of the source is 5 watts, find the resultant intensity at a point which lies 100 cm below the surface and whose horizontal distance from the source is 400 cm.

Suppose the same source is now displaced to a point 100 cm below the surface. Find the resultant intensity at the receiving point indicated above. Plot the variation in intensity with depth at the horizontal distance of 400 cm from the source and that with horizontal distance at the depth of 100 cm.

9. Find the wavelength (as a function of frequency) for which the Love wave velocity (Sec. 10.6) is the arithmetical mean of the velocities V and V'.

Chapter 11

1. Solve (11.1-10) and (11.1-15) for $\bar{a}$ as a function of T and verify the statement made in Sec. 11.1 concerning the difference between the Sabine and the Eyring formulas.

2. The absorption of sound at the surfaces of a room can profitably be discussed in terms of the specific acoustic impedance of the radiation at the surfaces (Sec. 9.3), commonly termed the specific acoustic impedance of the surface. Denoted by Z_s, this was previously defined as the ratio of the excess pressure at the surface to the flow velocity in the radiation normal to the surface and directed into it. As noted in Sec. 9.3, it is usually a complex quantity.

Show that, when a plane wave is incident at angle θ on a plane surface with specific impedance Z_s, the ratio of the reflected to the incident intensity is

$$\frac{I_r}{I_i} = \left| \frac{\rho_0 V - Z_s \cos \theta}{\rho_0 V + Z_s \cos \theta} \right|^2$$

In terms of this ratio, what is the fraction $\alpha(\theta)$ of incident intensity at angle θ lost on reflection by the wall? Assuming uniform distribution of the sound energy density throughout the room, calculate the average of $\alpha(\theta)$ over all angles of incidence and over all azimuths ϕ. Hence express α, the effective sound absorption coefficient, as used in Sec. 11.1, in terms of Z_s, the specific impedance of the absorbing surface.

3. Equation (11.1-8) can be used as the basis for the estimation of the absorption $\bar{\alpha}$ in a room. The maximum average energy density $\bar{w}_{max}$ is first measured in the room as it stands. Then it is measured again after the introduction of a known amount of absorption $a' = \bar{\alpha}'S$. Derive the equation for $a = \bar{\alpha}S$ in terms of a' and illustrate by a numerical example.

4. A cubical room 3 m on a side has absorbing material placed in it such that $\bar{\alpha} = \frac{1}{2}$. It is first filled with oxygen under standard conditions, and the reverberation time T_1 is measured. It is then filled with argon under standard conditions, and the reverberation time T_2 is measured. Find the theoretically predicted ratio T_1/T_2, and hence estimate the percentage change in the reverberation time produced by the change in the gas in the room.

5. Find the approximate number of normal-mode frequencies in the frequency band 100 cycles/sec at the mean frequency 500 cycles/sec for a cubical room of volume 1,000 m³.

Chapter 12

1. Apply the molecular theory of absorption of sound to oxygen in which the vibrational energy per mole is 4,420 cal/mole. (This is $n_{10}\epsilon$, where n_{10} is Avogadro's number.) Find n_{20} in terms of n_{10}, and hence show that $k^\circ_{12} \ll k^\circ_{21}$. Use this fact to evaluate C_i in (12.1-13) at 20°C. Treating C_e as approximately equivalent to the ordinary molar specific heat at constant volume, evaluate the maximum value of $2\alpha\lambda$, or intensity absorption in one wavelength. If $2\alpha\lambda$ is a maximum at 6,000 cycles/sec, calculate the relaxation time τ. Then evaluate $2\alpha/\omega$ as a function of frequency up to 15,000 cycles/sec. Compare $2\alpha/\omega$ obtained in this way with the corresponding values calculated from viscosity and heat conduction.

2. Calculate and plot the relaxational compressibility of water from (12.2-30) as a function of temperature over the range from 0 to 100°C. Do the same for the relaxation time τ from (12.2-34). Evaluate the bulk viscosity for water on the structural relaxation theory. Finally plot $2\alpha/\nu^2$ as a function of temperature for water from 0 to 100°C.

3. Derive (12.3-1) for thermal relaxational absorption in a liquid.

4. Evaluate the group velocity for shear waves in a viscoelastic medium in which the dispersion relation is given by (12.4-10). Do the same for the dispersion relation (12.4-13) for compressional waves in narrow tubes. Apply numerically to argon and to glycerine.

5. Carry out the analysis leading to (12.4-12) and (12.4-13) for the absorption coefficient and velocity, respectively, for compressional waves in narrow tubes. What limitation is placed on the radius of the tube in order that the results may be valid?

6. Calculate the value of α/ω^2 from (12.8-5) for copper in the range from the superconducting transition temperature up to 50°K.

7. A solid rod is exposed to a stress X which rises from zero at t_0 abruptly to X_0, maintains this value until t_1, and then falls abruptly to zero again.

  a. Sketch the time variation of stress in this problem.

  b. On the assumption that the solid is elastic and obeys Hooke's law, sketch the time variation of the linear strain (δ).

  c. On the assumption that the solid is a simple viscous medium in which the stress is a linear function of the rate of strain, sketch the time variation of the linear strain.

d. On the assumption that the stress-strain relation has the form (Sec. **12.2**)

$$\delta + a\dot{\delta} = cX + g\dot{X}$$

sketch the time variation of the linear strain and comment on the physical meaning of the constants a, c, and g.

8. Discuss graphically the relaxation process in a gas in which translational energy is partially transformed into internal energy of the molecules. To be specific, plot as a function of time a square wave variation of specific volume, associated with a corresponding sound wave. Adjacent to this, plot the corresponding time variation in the excess pressure in the gas. Do this for both the nonrelaxation and the relaxation cases. Plot a complete cycle in the pV plane for both cases. Show that in the relaxation case the cycle is an open one (a hysteresis loop), corresponding to dissipation of translational energy into heat.

9. The resonance frequency of oscillation of a spherical bubble in a liquid medium of mean density ρ_0 is given by (9.5-16), in which p_0 is the mean static pressure in the gas in the bubble. If the hydrostatic pressure is very small, practically the whole contribution to the pressure comes from the effect of surface tension, being given by $2T/a$, where T is the surface tension and a is the radius of the bubble. On this basis, what is the radius of an air bubble in water with a resonance frequency of 100 kc? According to experiment, the radius of the smallest bubble which can be stable in water is about 5×10^{-5} cm. What is the resonance frequency? What bearing does this have on the frequency dependence of the acoustic production of cavitation in water?

10. Carry through the evaluation of the integral in (12.7-11).

11. In liquid mercury, shear viscosity accounts for nearly the whole sound attenuation. Calculate the streaming velocity associated with 1 megacycle radiation of intensity 100 watts/cm² in a tube 2 cm in radius.

INDEX